Howard Wellman

THE AMERICAN FORESTRY SERIES

WALTER MULFORD, Consulting Editor

TEXTBOOK OF WOOD TECHNOLOGY

Volume I

Structure, Identification, Defects, and Uses of the

Commercial Woods of the United States

THE AMERICAN FORESTRY SERIES

WALTER MULFORD, Consulting Editor

Allen—
AN INTRODUCTION TO AMERICAN FORESTRY

Baker—
THE THEORY AND PRACTICE OF SILVICULTURE

Boyce—
FOREST PATHOLOGY

Brown, Panshin, and Forsaith—
TEXTBOOK OF WOOD TECHNOLOGY, VOLUME I

Bruce and Schumacher—
FOREST MENSURATION

Chapman and Meyer—
FOREST VALUATION

Doane, Van Dyke, Chamberlin, and Burke—
FOREST INSECTS

Guise—
THE MANAGEMENT OF FARM WOODLANDS

Harlow and Harrar—
TEXTBOOK OF DENDROLOGY

Kittredge—
FOREST INFLUENCES

Marquis—
ECONOMICS OF PRIVATE FORESTRY

Matthews—
COST CONTROL IN THE LOGGING INDUSTRY
MANAGEMENT OF AMERICAN FORESTS

Stoddart and Smith—
RANGE MANAGEMENT

Trippensee—
WILDLIFE MANAGEMENT

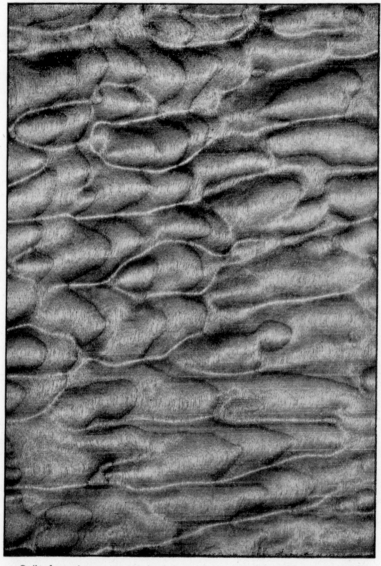

Quilted maple veneer obtained from selected stock of *Acer macrophyllum* Pursh. Material supplied by P. J. Landry, Kelso Veneer Company, Kelso, Wash. (Four-fifths natural size.)

TEXTBOOK OF WOOD TECHNOLOGY

Volume I

Structure, Identification, Defects, and Uses of the
Commercial Woods of the United States

Formerly published under the title
COMMERCIAL TIMBERS OF THE UNITED STATES

by H. P. BROWN, PH.D.
PROFESSOR OF WOOD TECHNOLOGY, THE NEW YORK STATE COLLEGE OF FORESTRY

A. J. PANSHIN, PH.D.
PROFESSOR OF FORESTRY, MICHIGAN STATE COLLEGE

and C. C. FORSAITH, PH.D.
PROFESSOR OF WOOD TECHNOLOGY, THE NEW YORK STATE COLLEGE OF FORESTRY

FIRST EDITION

McGRAW-HILL BOOK COMPANY, INC.
NEW YORK   TORONTO   LONDON
1949

TEXTBOOK OF WOOD TECHNOLOGY, VOLUME I

THE MAPLE PRESS COMPANY, YORK, PA.

THE AMERICAN FORESTRY SERIES

The American Forestry Series is intended for the college student, the practicing forester, and men in the forest industries. It is designed to provide text and reference books under a unified or coordinated plan. There will be many authors; each volume will be complete in itself, standing or falling on its own merits; but the subject matter of the series as a whole will be carefully planned so that wherever possible one volume will carry forward at the point where another has stopped, enabling the student or reader to develop his knowledge in logical sequence. There must be some overlapping, but every effort will be made to minimize unnecessary duplication. This policy will not be allowed to interfere with the inclusion in the Series of more than one book covering the same subject whenever circumstances arise making it desirable to add the new volumes. The plan is to build through many years a series which it is hoped will ultimately cover the entire field of forestry as completely as is feasible. In a sense, the Series should gradually become a manual of forestry. This should remain true even when the Series ultimately offers the choice of alternative volumes in each of several fields.

It may not be inappropriate to state in detail the viewpoint which has determined the plans and policies for the Series:

Forestry is a profession. It involves the application of biological science, engineering or physical science, and economics. It involves further the wise use of the experience of decades or centuries gained by the foresters of many lands. It involves to an unusual degree sound judgment and plain common sense. Judgment and common sense are indispensable because conditions in the forest are complex and extremely variable; because economic handicaps are of fundamental importance; and because the maturing of the forest crop is so long a process that mistakes and virtues in forest-management decisions may be decades in disclosing themselves.

Forestry is not an exact profession. A forest is the most complex biological society, in both plant and animal life, with which man works in any phase of his land-utilization enterprises. The forest yields to man a wider range of services than is provided by any other form of land utilization. The growing crop is exposed to many vicissitudes—enemies and profound economic changes—for perhaps eighty or a hundred years between seed time and harvest. Forestry applies many factors to the many-sided affairs of the forest and its products. The profession is therefore based on the ability to perceive, analyze, and wisely balance many seriously conflicting elements. These factors arise in each of several widely separated fields of human knowledge. A plan of handling a given forest may be sound from the standpoint of biology and in the light of known experience from other regions, yet most unwise because of the economic conditions in the locality concerned. Economics may indicate a certain forest policy as being the most advantageous, yet this policy may be impracticable because of handicaps in tree species, tree competitors, soil, or climate.

Forestry is not a science. In America, forestry has not yet attained even a strong foundation of underlying science on which to build. In his profession, the engineer can base most of his important planning on precise data and on known laws of physics and mathematics. The American forester must work without the precise data, and without much knowledge of the complex reactions of forest soil, climate, animal, tree, and competing plant. Forestry should be scientific at every point at which a scientific basis is available. The scientific basis should be strengthened through research as rapidly as possible. But it will be long before American forestry can become truly scientific; and even then it will probably be, like agriculture, a meeting ground of sciences rather than a science in itself.

True forestry is statesmanship of the finest type. With the forester lies the responsibility for directing land-use policies with wisdom as to the century-long future. The area over which he has the stewardship is almost or quite as great as that devoted to cultivated farm crops.

In Europe, progress in forestry consists of further refinements in an already going system. In all the Americas, forestry is a project in pioneering. In Canada and the United States, our foresters have entered the second era in their progress. Pioneering effort to establish public appreciations begins to make way for pioneer work in the woods. From Mexico on through the central and southern Americas, the first effort has started. In these nations of Central and South America, with their vast forests, there will come to pass in due time one of the world's great forestry developments.

The American Forestry Series is to be professional in character, with as much sound science as it is possible to include. Books as well as men must be pioneers. It is the hope of the publishers, the editor, and the authors that the Series may do its part in helping a pioneering profession on two continents gradually to become more exact, more scientific, and wiser in judgment. In some of the volumes, the aim will be to present the best exact factual data available at the time. In other fields, the method will be to recount the results of experience, to give such scientific facts as are at hand, and to suggest viewpoints and methods which may help the practicing forester to evaluate the conditions under which he is working. In the volumes of the latter class, the student need not expect to find precise formulas that will do his thinking for him, automatically solving his problems without mental effort on his own part. Rather, the aim will be to provide essential backgrounds for the development of individual professional judgment.

What is the field of forestry? For the purposes of this Series, we are assuming that the field open to us includes true forest, brush, and range lands—all lands of the open country that are potential producers of useful non-cultivated plant crops. We are concerned with the management of these lands and with their products and services to man. It may well be that not all of this is forestry. But certain it is that in due time someone is to manage for man's use the various classes of productive untilled lands in the open country. Who better than the forester and his close allies, skilled in the ways of the outdoors? Our interest centers, not primarily in the definition or exact scope of forestry, but in the work to be done for man's welfare.

June, 1934

The above statement of the aims and policies of the American Forestry Series appeared in 1934 in the first volume of the Series, "Identification of the Commercial Timbers of the United States," by H. P. Brown and A. J. Panshin. In 1940, it was reprinted in the successor to that text, "Commercial Timbers of the United States," by the same authors.

FOURTEEN YEARS LATER

On September 22, 1898, at Cornell University, the first classes in technical forestry in America began, with Dr. B. E. Fernow lecturing to about half a dozen students, of whom the writer had the rare good fortune to be one.

A busy half-century! In American forestry education, as in the profession itself, it has been the pioneer half-century. Now things are changing. There is not the slightest doubt that forestry in America is rapidly emerging as a true profession. It will grow through the years: in extent, in soundness, in the stature of its service. We are entering the first professional half-century. From pioneer to professional is a profound change. The American Forestry Series, in company with other groups of technical forestry books, should contribute its share to the developments of the coming decades.

Walter Mulford
Consulting Editor

Berkeley, Calif.
December, 1948

PREFACE

The text "Commercial Timbers of the United States" appeared as a one-volume work in 1940 and dealt with structure, identification, properties, and uses. It has now been in use in many forest schools for nearly a a decade and is well known to some generations of students. This Volume I of a "Textbook of Wood Technology" is a revision of the earlier text, with such changes, additions, and deletions as seem to be in order.

The justification of a new book is twofold. During the Second World War, wood technology received a tremendous impetus because of the imperative need for further and more accurate information on the properties of wood to permit its efficient use in tremendous quantities in national defense. How well wood technologists throughout the country rose to this responsibility is now a matter of record; this is evidenced by a backlog of factual data hitherto unavailable. The text, "Commercial Timbers of the United States," required revision for this, if for no other reason. But there was a second and fully as cogent a reason for the revision. It has become increasingly evident to the authors through the years that the book as originally written was not sufficiently comprehensive in subject matter to place it in the category of a textbook of wood technology. The need for such a text requires no defense; in it, the whole field of wood technology should be covered; within its covers, the gamut of information on wood should be so set down in logical sequence that a student is not forced to acquire factual information piecemeal but rather finds it all within one text.

Once the authors were committed to the plan of preparing a book dealing with the entire field of wood technology, it became evident that the inclusion in one volume of the information required for such a text would make it unwieldly for student use. Two volumes were necessary, and this plan has been followed in the present edition. Volume I deals with the structure, identification, defects, and uses of wood; Volume II is concerned with physical properties, mechanical properties, and the chemistry of wood in so far as its chemistry should be known to forestry students and to wood utilists other than chemists.

Fortunately the original text, as written, permitted the incorporation of its subject matter into the larger work without great change. By certain minor additions and deletions, it has been possible to bring this into line with Vol. II, the scope of which has already been stated.   How well the authors have succeeded in their endeavor to prepare a well-rounded text covering the entire field of wood technology, only time can tell.   At least a start will have been made toward bringing together all the available, worth-while information on the commercial woods of the United States.   Such a text should be invaluable to students specializing in wood technology and to wood utilists engaged in the fabrification of wood as a livelihood.

Volume II will contain a brief preface setting forth the objectives sought in the second part of the new text.   The general preface to the two-volume work presented here terminates with citation of the changes made in converting the original book into Vol. I within this cover.   This is desirable because the sequence of subject matter covered in the original text is so well known, especially to teachers.

Perhaps the most striking change is in nomenclature.   The American Code in the first book is replaced by the International Code.   This change was necessary because the U.S. Forest Service recently adopted the International Code, and the authors were pleased to accede to this change in the interests of uniformity.   The combining of binomial common names such as osage-orange, tulip-poplar, and honey-locust, into one word has not, as yet at least, proved acceptable to the authors.   If followed without variance and particularly where the common name is trinomial, it leads to an unfamiliar jumble of letters, which is liable to prove confusing.   In such instances in the text, if the common name is a binomial, resort has been made to the hyphen (as above), which procedure may be considered conservative.

The sequence of the presentation of subject matter has been altered in several places to ensure greater clarity of understanding.   For example, some of the subject matter in Chap. X, Miscellaneous Information on Wood, in the first edition, has been brought further toward the front of the text.   And, as stated subsequently, the remainder of what was originally Chap. X has been changed materially.

Chapter IV, Sec. IV, The Nature of the Wall of a Mature Xylary Cell has been rewritten.   This was necessary to bring it into line with advances in knowledge in this field since the publication of the first book. Acknowledgment is made at this time for the assistance rendered by Messrs. W. M. Harlow and V. A. Holmberg of The New York State College of Forestry in checking the subject matter now appearing in this section.

Chapter X, Miscellaneous Information On Wood, of the earlier text is replaced by five chapters: X, Variable Quality of Wood within a Tree-species; XI, Figure In Wood; XII to XIV, Defects in Wood; XV, Natural Durability of Wood.

Citation of references has been checked throughout. Many new references have been added and old references brought up to date where bulletins, etc., originally listed have been superseded by newer editions under the same or a new title.

The number of text figures has been increased by twelve; Text Fig. 3 is replaced by a new one. Three new tables have been added and one new plate. This last was necessary because of the inclusion of Jack Pine (*Pinus banksiana* Lamb.), which was omitted in the first text.

The two master keys toward the back of the book have been completely checked and a third key to the identification of coniferous woods, based on gross and minute features, has been added. This should prove especially helpful to students since it will enable them to employ both gross and minute features at the same time, the last obtained by the preparation of temporary, unstained mounts.

Finally, the Glossary at the back of the book has been considerably enlarged. Many technical terms used in the original text and omitted through oversight are now included, and new terms employed in the additions in the revision have been added.

The authors are greatly indebted for the constructive criticisms advanced for the revision by college teachers and others who have used the original text. Among these Prof. Emanuel Fritz of the University of California deserves special mention. In most instances, these suggestions were very timely, and many changes have been made in the manuscript as a result. L. E. Partelow, who was mentioned in the acknowledgments in the original edition, has prepared a number of new text figures and is accorded thanks for the excellence of his work.

THE AUTHORS

SYRACUSE, N. Y.
EAST LANSING, MICH.
December, 1948

PREFACE TO "COMMERCIAL TIMBERS OF THE UNITED STATES"

This is the first edition of a new book intended to replace the "Identification of the Commercial Timbers of the United States" by the same authors, which is now out of print. The title "Commercial Timbers of the United States, Their Structure, Identification, Properties, and Uses" is indicative of the greatly enlarged scope of the present text. In addition to the information in the original publication, which was pertinent only to the identification of domestic timbers, the new book incorporates within its covers an exhaustive treatment of the structure, properties, and uses of these woods, information that should be included according to the general consensus of teachers who used the former text. The result is a well-rounded textbook, complete as to subject matter and entirely suitable for use by forestry students and majors in plant anatomy, and also by engineers, architects, and others who wish to become thoroughly conversant with wood.

The fore part of the text consists of ten chapters; seventy-five new text figures have been inserted in this section. In the first nine chapters of the book the aim has been twofold: first, to tell the "story of wood" in narrative form, which implies the citation of related facts in the proper sequence; secondly, to make this story dynamic rather than static and thus retain the interest of the reader. A suggested procedure for compiling anatomical information on woods is included. The tenth chapter is devoted to miscellaneous information on wood, under a number of topics; this information is not a part of the narrative of wood but serves to round out the text, including as it does much pertinent subject matter that might otherwise have been omitted.

The two Keys for the identification of woods that appeared in the original book have been retained in the present publication. One of these is based on features visible with the naked eye and hand lens (10×) and is illustrated with photographs across the grain at low magnification; the other is concerned with minute features, that is, with features that require a compound microscope for their determination. An innovation that ensures greater accuracy in wood identification has been introduced into this second Key; photomicrographs depicting the ray crossings of conifers and the nature of the intervessel pitting in hardwoods have been inserted at the proper places. Both Keys have been thoroughly revised, and in several instances, additional information that is more specific in nature and, hence, of greater value diagnostically has been included. Provision has also been made for the identification of a number of woods which were not included in the original Keys.

The descriptions of woods by species, a feature of the original publication, has been retained, but with three very important additions. The more important uses of each wood are recorded at length, and wherever possible these have been linked to the structure and properties of the wood; this serves to indicate why a given wood is peculiarly fitted to the specific uses to which it is put. Selected references on the uses of the respective woods, listed at the end of each description, should prove invaluable to the reader seeking to become conversant with the more recent literature dealing with the utilization of domestic timbers. A number of new species have been added.

The book terminates with a Glossary and an Index. The Glossary is much more comprehensive in scope than that in the first text.

Throughout the book, the technical anatomical terms adopted by the International Association of Wood Anatomists have been used in describing the structures of wood, with certain exceptions that seemed warranted to the authors. This procedure should serve to bring the new text into line with books of similar nature in other countries and at the same time, through standardization, assist in reducing the confusion that exists in the literature in the use of technical terms employed in descriptive wood anatomy. Under the two captions, "General Characteristics and Properties" and "Uses," respectively, information is included relative to the properties of domestic woods and the bearing of these upon the use of these timbers. Numbered among such properties are strength in bending, stiffness, ability to withstand endwise compression, shock resistance, tendency to split, working and gluing qualities, nail-, screw-, and paint-holding ability, seasoning qualities, extent of shrinkage, tendency to stay in place with use, and durability. The standard terms for describing the properties of wood recommended by L. J. Markwardt and G. E. Heck (see under "Hardness," page 56) have been followed in these sections of the text, another timely step toward standardization. Data on the major uses of the various woods are based upon the United States Department of Agriculture publication entitled *Lumber Used in Manufacture;* although this was published in 1933, it is the last compilation of this nature that has appeared to date.

Due acknowledgment should be made at this time of the sources of information and materials used in the preparation of the text. Publications of the United States Department of Agriculture, the United States Department of Commerce, the United States Forest Products Laboratory at Madison, the Canadian Forest Service, as well as those of various trade associations, were freely consulted.   The series from the United States Forest Service entitled *American Woods* (now under the authorship of H. S. Betts) proved especially serviceable for information on the uses of wood.   Many citations are made, especially in the ten chapters in the fore part of the text, to articles appearing in various technical periodicals and trade journals.   Special mention should be made here of papers by I. W. Bailey, Thomas Kerr, D. B. Anderson, G. J. Ritter, and J. H. Priestley (England).

Most of the photomicrographs in the text were made by the authors. Photographs depicting figure in wood were supplied by the Veneer Association, the American Walnut Manufacturers' Association, Mersman Bros. Corporation of Celin, Ohio, the Mahogany Association, and by P. J. Landry of the Kelso Veneer Company of Kelso, Wash.   Text Fig. 6 portraying the ontogeny of a young tree stem was taken, by permission, from Eames and MacDaniels's "Introduction to Plant Anatomy." Thanks are likewise due to the United States Forest Products Laboratory and to the Canadian Forest Service for the use of certain photographs; also, among others, to W. M. Harlow, A. H. MacAndrews, and H. L. Henderson of the New York State College of Forestry, to E. Fritz of the University of California, to Bror L. Grondal of the University of Washington, and to Henry Hopp of the Soil Conservation Service.   Acknowledgment is made in the legends accompanying the text figures of the source of all photographs from outside sources.

Finally, the authors are indebted to D. S. Drnochod of the Veneer Association for editing certain parts of the manuscript devoted to figure in wood; to W. J. Baker of Michigan State College; and to C. C. Forsaith, W. M. Harlow, E. C. Jahn, L. E. Wise, and R. R. Hirt of the New York State College of Forestry for constructive suggestions as the compilation of subject matter for the text progressed.   Thanks are also due to Carl de Zeeuw and L. E. Partelow for preparing the drawings used as illustrations in the text.

H. P. Brown
A. J. Panshin

Syracuse, N. Y.
East Lansing, Mich.
November, 1940

CONTENTS

CHAPTER I

THE PLANT ORIGIN OF WOOD

CHAPTER II

THE TREE

CHAPTER III

THE GROSS FEATURES OF WOOD OF VALUE IN IDENTIFICATION

CHAPTER IV

THE WOODY PLANT CELL

CHAPTER V

THE CAMBIA OF TREES

CHAPTER VI

THE MINUTE STRUCTURE OF CONIFEROUS WOODS

CHAPTER VII

THE MINUTE STRUCTURE OF CONIFEROUS WOODS (*Continued*)

CHAPTER VIII

THE MINUTE STRUCTURE OF POROUS WOODS

CHAPTER IX

THE MINUTE STRUCTURE OF POROUS WOODS (*Continued*)

CHAPTER X

VARIABLE QUALITY OF WOOD WITHIN A TREE-SPECIES

CHAPTER XI

FIGURE IN WOOD

CHAPTER XII

DEFECTS IN WOOD

CHAPTER XV

NATURAL DURABILITY OF WOOD

Keys for Identification

Descriptions of Woods by Species

CHAPTER I

THE PLANT ORIGIN OF WOOD

I. TYPES OF PLANTS PRODUCING WOOD

Wood comes from trees; therefore, wood is of plant origin. But not all plants are productive of timber; hence, to trace wood to its source botanically, one must have a clear conception of the characteristics of woody plants and of plant classification.

A. CHARACTERISTICS OF WOODY PLANTS

Plants may be woody or nonwoody. The following criteria will serve to distinguish woody plants.

1. They must be **vascular plants,** *i.e.*, must possess specialized conducting tissues consisting of xylem and phloem.[1] The xylem is lignified (for explanation, see page 82) and is the wood of the mature plant. Plants devoid of vascular tissue cannot produce wood.

2. They must be **perennial plants,** *i.e.*, must live for a number of years. Annuals complete their life cycle within a season and are tided over the winter by their seed. Biennials live for 2 years; they usually grow vegetatively the first year and store reserve food for the production of flowers and fruits the second, but the 2-year life span precludes their inclusion among typical woody plants.

3. They must possess a **stem** that persists from year to year. In the case of the tree, this is also called the "bole" or "trunk." Many perennials fail to be classed as woody plants because they die back to the ground each autumn, the roots persisting through the winter and producing a new stem the following spring. Other plants possess persistent creeping stems and hence fall into the category of woody plants, even though they appear to be herbaceous.

4. In addition to the above, typical woody plants exhibit **secondary thickening;** *i.e.*, they have a means of thickening their stems by subsequent growth in diameter which is not traceable to terminal growing points. This is achieved through the activities of a growing layer, or cambium, which is situated just outside the last-formed layer of wood and beneath the inner bark (phloem); this produces new wood and new phloem yearly, which are inserted between the older wood and bark. In

[1] The veins of leaves are composed of this kind of tissue.

1

this manner, in the case of trees, the trunk eventually attains a diameter sufficient to make it profitable to convert it into lumber.

B. Kinds of Woody Plants

Woody plants are of three types, **trees, shrubs,** and woody **lianas,** between which no hard and fast lines can be drawn. For example, a plant may be shrubby near the limits of its range and arborescent elsewhere. Certain species of *Ficus* (figs) begin life as woody lianas but eventually become arborescent. Many woody plants that are reduced to dwarfed, scraggly shrubs in the boreal zones or at high elevations attain to the dignity of large shrubs or even trees to the southward or at lower altitudes where they are not forced to contend with such a hostile environment. In general, the kinds of woody plants may be defined as follows:

1. A **tree** is a woody plant that attains a height of at least 20 feet in a given locality and usually (not always) has but a single self-supporting stem or trunk.

2. A **shrub** is a woody plant that seldom exceeds 20 feet in height in a given locality and usually (not always) has a number of stems. Many shrubs have prostrate primary stems embedded in the soil or leaf mold; these send up persisting secondary branches at intervals (Ex., *Gaultheria procumbens* L.—aromatic wintergreen), which appear as separate individuals.

3. A woody **liana** is a climbing woody vine. Woody lianas climb by twining, clambering, aerial roots, tendrils, etc., and are characteristic features of tropical rain forests in many parts of the world (Ex., *Calamus spp.*—rattans).

II. PLANT CLASSIFICATION

In classification, plants are first divided into large divisions which have certain gross features in common, then successively into smaller divisions. The characters enumerated under the successive divisions are increasingly specific and of narrower latitude.

There are four main divisions in the Vegetable Kingdom (each divided further into classes, orders, families, genera, and species, as necessity demands), *viz.,*

Thallophytes................ Algae, fungi, bacteria, etc.
Bryophytes.................. Liverworts and mosses
Pteridophytes............... Ferns, scouring rushes, horsetails, club mosses, and quillworts
Spermatophytes............. All seed plants including coniferous and broad-leaved trees

Thallophytes constitute the lowest division of the Vegetable Kingdom and include the simplest forms of plants. The plant body, or thallus, exhibits little variation or specialization in structure (though often a wide range of form) and usually carries on its life activities either in water or on a moist substratum. Included in this group are the algae (pond scums, seaweeds, etc.), and the fungi (mushrooms, bracket fungi, etc.), both of which exhibit a remarkable variation in form and size of the thallus, but extreme simplicity in its structure. Many of the simplest Thallophytes are unicellular, and some are free-swimming and resemble minute animals. Sexuality has become well developed in many forms, whereas in others it is totally lacking, possibly through degeneration occasioned by a parasitic or saprophytic habit.

Bryophytes are best represented by the mosses, although a second group, the liverworts, is also included. The Bryophytes show a distinct advance in specialization over the Thallophytes. This is evinced through the definite establishment of a sexual stage in which the sexes may be distinguished, and an "alteration of generations," whereby a sexual stage or generation is followed by a semidependent, asexual stage, which in turn again gives rise to sexual forms. Though more specialized than Thallophytes, Bryophytes are, relatively speaking, simple plants. The plant body is an elementary structure, which possesses chlorophyll and is in some cases thalloid, whereas in others it develops a primitive stem and leaves. True vascular tissue (vascular bundles) is entirely lacking.

Vascular plants made their appearance for the first time in the **Pteridophytes**, a group that includes the true ferns and the forms that are recognized as fern allies, the horsetails, scouring rushes, club mosses, and quillworts. True roots, stems, and leaves equipped with special conducting or vascular tissue, composed of xylem (wood) and phloem, have become established as definite structures and function as in the seed plants. As in the Bryophytes, there is a sexual stage in which the sexes may be distinguished, but the sexual organs have become increasingly specialized. A fertilized egg develops without pause into an asexual stage in which sexless individuals, through spore formation, again give rise to sexual forms. In the higher Pteridophytes, it is the asexual or sporophytic stage that has become dominant, and the sexual generation has been relegated to an obscure, independent existence or has become actually dependent on the asexual generation. Pteridophytes were formerly represented by a vast assemblage of plants, many of which were aborescent and flourished during the Carboniferous period, contributing largely to the formation of our coal deposits of today. Owing to an altered environment and the development of seed plants, which are better adjusted to withstand present-day conditions, the group is now on the wane and is represented by only some 4000 species.

The dominant plants of today are the **Spermatophytes,** or seed plants.

They are vascular plants, which represent the highest type of specialization to date, though not necessarily the final type. As in the Pteridophytes, the asexual, or sporophytic, stage bears true roots, stems, and leaves and is independent; the sexual, or gametophytic, stage has undergone further reduction and is wholly dependent on this. The most striking difference between Spermatophytes and Pteridophytes lies in the formation of seeds in the first-mentioned group; these are dormant structures entailing a pause in the development of the young sporophyte that has developed from a fertilized egg nucleus. Seeds permit of the wider and more rapid dissemination of the plants possessing them and tide the plants over unfavorable periods. Sexuality is a necessary part of the life cycle of Spermatophytes and is brought about through the transfer of male nuclei to the proximity of the female nuclei by means of pollen grains. Following the fusion of the sex nuclei, made possible by the formation of a pollen tube serving as a siphon, a young sporophyte (embryo) is formed within the ovule (developing seed), which, as the latter matures, passes into a dormant condition. Upon subsequent germination of the seed, the young sporophyte again assumes an active existence.

The Spermatophytes in turn are divided into two subdivisions: the **Gymnosperms** and the **Angiosperms,** distinguished by the manner in which the seeds are borne. The word "gymnosperm" is derived from the Greek γυμνός, meaning naked, and σπέρμα, seed, and includes those Spermatophytes in which the seeds are not enclosed in an ovary but are borne naked, subtended by scales or fleshy structures. "Angiosperm" comes from the Greek ἀγγεῖον, meaning vessel, and σπέρμα, seed, and embraces those forms in which the seeds are enclosed in an ovary, which may or may not dehisce at maturity. The boundary between the two groups is sufficiently clear to serve the purposes of classification, although it in no way indicates the disparity in numbers and size.

Gymnosperms are very ancient and, in terms of numbers, form but a small part of the present seed-plant vegetation. Some 650 living forms exist today, grouped in four orders, which are to be regarded as the surviving remnant of a vast phylum that had its genesis in the Carboniferous and flourished during the Triassic. Angiosperms were evolved comparatively recently (lower Cretaceous) in a geological sense and now are represented by a vast assemblage of at least 150,000 species, which comprise the bulk of the seed-plant vegetation of the present day.[1] The most obvious characters that set off this group from the Gymno-

---

[1] One school of thought holds that the Angiosperms have been able to attain and hold the ascendancy over other groups because of adaptive features which they have developed to meet the environmental conditions in force at the present time.

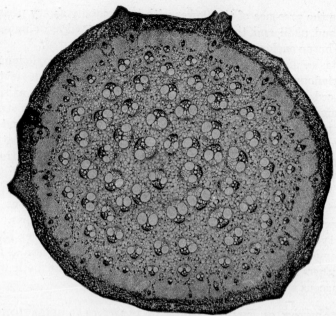

Text Fig. 1.—Transverse section of a monocotyledenous stem, *Smilax hispida* Muhlb., showing scattered vascular bundles (15 ×).

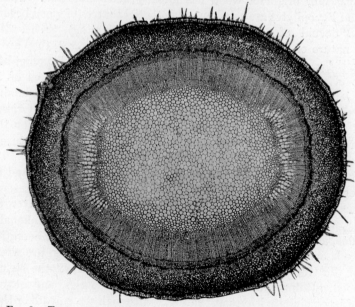

Text Fig. 2.—Transverse section of a 1-year dicotyledonous stem, *Fraxinus pennsylvanica* Marsh., showing a vascular cylinder (wood and phloem) surrounding the pith. The cylinder is bounded to the outside by cortex, periderm, and epidermis, in the sequence stated (25 ×).

sperms are the presence of the flower with its generally showy perianth, stamens, and pistil and the manner in which the ovules, or immature seeds, are borne enclosed in an ovary.

Two classes of Angiosperms are recognized, the **Monocotyledons** and the **Dicotyledons.** As the terms imply, the Monocotyledons are featured by one seed leaf (cotyledon), which is terminal on the axis, the Dicotyledons by two seed leaves, which are lateral. Another striking difference between these plants, and an important one in plant anatomy, rests in the fact that the vascular bundles of Monocotyledons are scattered in the stem (Text Fig. 1), whereas those of the Dicotyledons are arranged in a ring, or the stem contains a vascular cylinder enclosing a pith (Text Fig. 2). Monocotyledons are now held to be the more modern group that arose originally from the Dicotyledons. They include at least 30,000 species and are arranged in 7 orders embracing 48 families. The larger division, the Dicotyledons, embraces 30 orders, and over 120,000 species; some of these orders are represented wholly by herbaceous forms whereas others consist wholly of woody plants or contain both woody and herbaceous species.

III. POSITION OF TIMBER TREES IN PLANT CLASSIFICATION

The vascular origin of wood has already been indicated. Thallophytes and Bryophytes are ruled out as potential sources of wood because they are devoid of vascular (specialized conducting) tissue. The vascular nature of Pteridophytes was pointed out on page 3; they are all woody in the sense of possessing persistent stems, but they have not been a source of wood commercially in modern times. The stems of the great majority are too small and short-lived for conversion into lumber; further, the structure of the stem (arrangement of the vascular tissue) is not of the type that characterizes the higher plants, a situation that holds for the arborescent ferns even though they attain the stature of trees.

Lumber-producing trees are restricted to the Gymnosperms and the Angiosperms of the Spermatophytes; but, here again, certain reservations must be made. The Gymnosperms, like the Pteridophytes, are all woody, and four living orders are recognized: **Cycadales, Ginkgoales, Coniferales,** and **Gnetales,** listed in the probable order of their evolution. The Cycads consist of nine genera and about 80 species and are woody plants of the tropics that resemble tree ferns and palms;[1] the stem is unbranched, attains a height of 60 feet in some species, and bears a cluster of large pinnate leaves at the top. Although the stature of these

---

[1] They are most closely related to the ferns.

trees is such as to permit of their conversion into lumber, the structure of the stem is not of the normal type, precluding this possibility.

The next order, the Ginkgoales, is restricted to a single species, *Ginkgo biloba* L., of China and Japan.[1] This is a deciduous tree with the habit of a conifer and fan-shaped leaves like the pinnae of the maidenhair fern; hence the name "maidenhair tree." The growth is of the normal type, and the wood is quite suitable for commercial use; but the tree is sacred and is too limited in its range to make it a factor in the production of wood.

Nor are the Gnetales, probably the most recent order of Gymnosperms in a phylogenetic sense, a source of wood: some sixty odd species are recognized, grouped in three genera. One, *Welwitschia mirabilis* Hook. f., is a monotype, found in the deserts of western South Africa, with the habit of a large turnip from the top of which two broad, flat, strap-shaped leaves are borne; the others (species of *Ephedra* and *Gnetum*) are vines, shrubs, or small trees.

The Coniferales (Coniferae) alone among Gymnosperms are productive of timber on a commercial scale; the various members of this group are known as conifers, evergreens, or softwoods and are the source of the softwood lumber of the trade. Forty-six genera[2] and about five hundred species are recognized, many of which are important timber trees; in fact, the chief economic product of this order is wood, and it occupies a unique position in this respect which is out of all proportion to its size botanically. This situation holds for the following reasons:

1. Coniferous trees are frequently gregarious and often cover wide tracts with almost pure stands, or stands consisting of relatively few species. The economies involved in the logging of such stands are less complex than of stands composed of a greater number of species.

2. Coniferous forests attain their maximum development and area in the temperate zones where, to date, industry, with its many demands for wood, has attained its greatest impetus.

3. Coniferous trees exhibit excurrent (monopodial) growth, *i.e.*, possess stems that continue through the crown and end in a terminal leader, frequently with little taper below; such stems convert well into lumber, with the minimum amount of wastage.

4. Coniferous woods are of a type entirely different from those pro-

---

[1] Widely grown as an ornamental tree in the United States.

[2] Forty-seven genera if the new monotypic genus *Sequoiadendron* proposed by Bucholz is accepted. For further information, see J. T. Bucholz. The Generic Segregation of the Sequoias. *Amer. Jour. Bot.*, Vol. 26, No. 7, pp. 535–538. 1939. Recently, still another monotypic genus, *Metasequoia*, has been described from China, increasing the total to forty-eight genera.

duced by broad-leaved trees; they lend themselves to many uses for which the woods of broad-leaved trees are unsuited.

As has been previously pointed out, the Angiosperms, in comparison with the Gymnosperms, comprise a very large and dominant group of at least 150,000 herbaceous and woody plants, which in turn are divided into Monocotyledons and Dicotyledons. Many Monocotyledons are arborescent (palms, yuccas), and some attain to the dignity of large trees. Their trunks are not infrequently used "in the round" for house posts, posts, etc., but cannot be sawn into lumber of the normal type because the vascular bundles retain their individuality as such and are scattered in the stem.

Dicotyledons are the source of the hardwood lumber of the trade. This heterogeneous group includes herbaceous and woody plants, the latter consisting of shrubs, trees, and lianas. As stated on page 6, 30 orders and many families are recognized, some of which are represented only by herbaceous forms whereas others consist wholly of woody plants or of both woody and herbaceous species. Hardwoods, as such, are readily distinguished from softwoods by certain easily recognized characters, to be explained subsequently. Since the botanical group producing hardwoods is much larger than the group to which softwoods are traceable, greater diversification in structure may be anticipated in the former, a situation that holds. This explains why the identification of hardwood timbers is less difficult than that of softwoods.

By way of summation, it is well to make note again of the fact that two types of wood are recognized: softwood and hardwood. Softwood is produced by various genera and species, mostly evergreen, belonging to the Order Coniferales of the Gymnosperms; hardwood trees are Angiosperms of the subgroup known as Dicotyledons and are distributed in many orders and families. These terms are sufficiently convenient to meet the needs of the trade, indicating as they do the general relationship that holds between these two classes of wood. But they are not specific to species; hard pine is a "softwood" in this sense, and basswood is a "hardwood"; yet the former is much harder than the latter.

IV. PLANT FAMILIES CONTAINING TREES IN THE UNITED STATES

Experience has taught that it is convenient to think of woods in terms of plant families; following this procedure, the families and genera containing trees in the United States are listed in botanical sequence in Table I; those in boldface type are the sources of the commercially important woods of the United States.

TABLE I

PLANT FAMILIES CONTAINING TREES IN THE UNITED STATES

Gymnosperms

Pinaceae

Taxodiaceae

Cupressaceae

Taxaceae

Angiosperms

Palmaceae

Liliaceae

Casuarinaceae

Juglandaceae

Myricaceae

Leitneriaceae

Salicaceae

Betulaceae

Fagaceae

Ulmaceae

Moraceae

Proteaceae

Olacaceae

Polygonaceae

Nyctaginaceae

Magnoliaceae

Anonaceae

Lauraceae

Capparidaceae

Moringaceae

Hamamelidaceae

Platanaceae

Rosaceae

Leguminosae

Zygophyllaceae

Malpighiaceae

Rutaceae

Simaroubaceae

Surianaceae

Burseraceae

Meliaceae

Euphorbiaceae

Anacardiaceae

Cyrillaceae

Aquifoliaceae

Celastraceae

Staphyleaceae

Aceraceae

Hippocastanaceae

Sapindaceae

Rhamnaceae

Tiliaceae

Malvaceae

Sterculiaceae

Theaceae

Canellaceae

Tamaricaceae

Koeberlinaceae

Caricaceae

Cactaceae

Punicaceae

Lythraceae

Rhizophoraceae

Myrtaceae

Melastomaceae

Combretaceae

Araliaceae

Nyssaceae

Cornaceae

Ericaceae

Myrisinaceae

Theophrastaceae

Sapotaceae

Ebenaceae

Symplocaceae

Styraceae

Oleaceae

Apocynaceae

Boraginaceae

Verbenaceae

Solanaceae

Scrophulariaceae

Bignoniaceae

Rubiaceae

Caprifoliaceae

Compositae

V. FACTORS CONTROLLING THE SELECTION OF A COMMERCIAL WOOD

Chapter I may well be concluded with a discussion of the factors that control the designation of a wood as commercial. Most certainly it is more than the one fact that the arborescent plant producing it attains sufficient stature for the production of logs.

In different parts of the world, the richness of the arborescent flora fluctuates between wide extremes and is probably at a peak in the watershed of the Amazon River and in the Malay Peninsula. A conservative estimate places the number of tree species in the first-mentioned area as at least 5000, and fully 2500 trees are known from the Peninsula. Nearer home, 973 tree species, 226 varieties, and a large number of horticultural varieties and forms were recorded in Sudworth's Check List of 1927. The revised interim Check List of 1944, which was prepared under the direction of Dr. E. L. Little of the U.S. Forest Service and is now in force, lists 1015 species and 167 varieties, *i.e.*, nearly 1200 kinds of trees as occurring in the United States. But there is no such number of commercial timber species in this country. This leads to the observation that, for one reason or another, the number of timber species in a given area is never so large as the number of tree species; in fact, the ratio is about 1 to 6.

The paucity of timber species per area in comparison with the total number of species is explainable when a number of facts are comprehended. Many arborescent species never attain a size that would make them of merchantable value in terms of saw logs; for this reason, the total number available is greatly reduced. Second, the quality of the wood is of prime importance; trees that may have the necessary stature are often ruled out, *i.e.*, are still "weed trees" because the wood is of little value.

The question of accessibility also comes to the fore although this is of less significance in the United States than elsewhere because of the development of the country. We have extensive stands of Englemann spruce in the West, for example, that have scarcely been touched, largely because this is a montane species that cannot be logged readily. There are many valuable timbers in the tropics, the exploitation of which has been retarded for lack of navigable rivers and harbor facilities. African mahogany is frequently rafted well offshore, but this practice is too expensive to be followed with utilitarian woods of lesser value.

Closely coupled to accessibility is the matter of quantity obtainable. Supplies must be available, at a price that will not be prohibitive to the consumer. Our recognized domestic timbers are so firmly established that scant thought is given to this question. But such a factor becomes momentous when a wood unknown to the American public, for example, an ornamental wood, is introduced to the trade. It would prove futile indeed to expend many thousands of dollars in advertising and in working up a market, only to learn that a constant supply was unobtainable owing either to a scarcity of the tree within its range or for other reasons.

The quota of commercial timbers in a country or area is also never so large as the number of tree species because woods frequently cannot be separated with certainty "to species." The commercial timbers of the United States run to about 90, but many more than 90 tree species contribute to the production of these. Six oaks, for example, produce the bulk of the white oak lumber of the trade, and the same holds for red oak; white ash in the East may be almost any ash but brown ash (*Fraxinus nigra* Marsh.).

It must not be inferred from the preceding paragraphs that the number of commercially important timbers produced by a country or a section thereof is fixed for all time. Far to the contrary; the quota of usable woods depends on various conditions in force such as local scarcity of better woods in the area in question, improvements in manufacture, particularly in seasoning, and a better knowledge of the technical properties of wood. In the United States some species that were considered "weed trees" 50 or even 25 years ago are important today. Red-gum (*Liquidambar styraciflua* L.) and western hemlock [*Tsuga heterophylla* (Raf.) Sarg.] may be cited as cases in point. The former quickly attained commercial significance when methods were devised to kiln-dry it properly. The intrinsic worth of western hemlock was not fully recognized at first because it inherited the unsavory name and reputation of its eastern counterpart.

From the above and for other reasons, it is patent that commercial woods become such by rigorous selection, selection as regards the size of the tree species producing them, the quality of the wood formed, and the accessibility and volume of the stands of a given kind of timber; the number is still further reduced because frequently several timber species contribute but one kind of wood, in terms of trade standards.

CHAPTER II

THE TREE

I. PARTS OF THE TREE AND TREE SEEDLING DEFINED

A tree has been defined as a perennial, vascular, woody plant which attains a height at least of 20 feet and usually (not always) has but a single, self-supporting stem. Although trees, like other vascular plants, exhibit a surprising range of variation in size, form, and structure and are, in reality, complex organisms, they are constructed according to a simple, uniform plan. The plant body consists of a continuous cylindrical axis which bears lateral appendages.

The main portion of the axis above ground is the **stem, trunk,** or **bole;** this divides successively into **limbs, branches,** and **branchlets,** often in a manner characteristic for the tree species. The remainder of the axis is embedded in the earth; like the portion above ground, it divides again and again and forms the **root system.** The stem provides mechanical support for the crown, serves as an avenue for conduction between the crown and the roots, and, on occasion, may store appreciable amounts of reserve food. **Roots,** in contrast, are organs of anchorage and support which in addition perform the functions of absorption by means of root hairs or mycorhiza, of conduction, and of storage. Both roots and stems exhibit radial symmetry when cut transversely; *i.e.,* the various parts are arranged around a common center. Trees are different from the higher animals in which bilateral (right and left) symmetry is the rule.

The appendages of the cylindrical axis, aside from the root hairs, are restricted to the stem portion and are of three ranks: (1) those which contain vascular tissue (**leaves, thorns**), (2) those devoid of vascular tissue into which the outermost portions of the stem, *i.e.,* epidermis and cortex enter (**emergences—prickles** of the **rose**), (3) those which arise as extensions from the epidermis or exodermis only (**hairs, root hairs**). Since wood commercially is never obtained from appendages, further discussion of these structures is irrelevant in a text of this nature.

Nor is it necessary to digress here to describe the other organs of a tree, *viz.,* **flowers, fruit,** and **seed,** except to explain their relationship to the cylindrical axis and its appendages. Flowers are essential parts of a tree but not fundamental parts; the sporophylls (cone scales) of Gymnosperms and the sepals, petals, stamens, and carpels (one or more compos-

12

ing the pistil) of Angiosperms are appendages (modified leaves) which are attached to the stem portion of the cylindrical axis. The significance of pollination, fertilization, and seed formation in Spermatophytes has been described on page 4; the formation of fruits is but incidental. The significant thing to note is that the **seed embryo,** like the parent plant from which it springs, begins life with a cylindrical axis with a growing point at or near (cotyledon terminal in monocotyledons) either end; further, that the **cotyledons** (seed leaves) are the first appendages of the stem. With the reawakening of growth (**germination**), the growing point at the lower end of the axis (**radicle**) starts to elongate and gives rise to the root system of the developing seedling. A bit later, the **plumule** (growing point at or near the opposite end of the axis) becomes active; the stem system of the plant is composed of the tissues arising from this, and from the portion of the primary stem (**hypocotyl**) below the cotyledon(s).

II. HOW A TREE GROWS

Wood on a commercial scale is obtained only from trees of some maturity. Since the processes of growth in length and in thickness in trees are identical with those that take place in the production of seedlings from seeds, and trees from seedlings, a discussion of the manner in which growth proceeds in the mature tree will serve the purpose of this text.

A tree, as previously noted, consists of a branched cylindrical axis to which appendages of various sorts are attached. The trunk and much-branched crown compose the portions of this above the ground; below the surface of the ground, the axis divides more or less abruptly into a wide-spreading root system which in size and bulk compares favorably with the crown. Until the tree attains maturity, enlargement of the crown and root system proceeds at a fairly rapid pace, in later years undoubtedly more sluggishly. But elongation, at least in some parts of the crown and root system, never stops during successive growing seasons, *i.e.*, as long as the tree lives.

Elongation of the branched cylindrical axis is traceable to **apical growing points,** and to these alone. Through growth proceeding in these, the axis increases in length, branches according to the plan characteristic of the species, and adds new appendages acropetally (toward the apices), meanwhile (and sometimes in season—leaves) casting its older appendages. The length growth in the main stem and the branches thereof controls the form assumed by the mature plant, except that certain of the secondary axes may be shed (Ex., twigs through cladoptosis) or destroyed. The growth that is traceable to apical growing points and is responsible for the elongation of the main and secondary axes, both in stems and roots, is called **primary growth.**   Tissues arising from such apical growing points are termed **primary tissues.**

But little thickening would occur in the branched cylindrical axis of the tree were it dependent upon primary growth alone.   Obviously, the growing points, as they forge ahead, leave tissues to the rear which alter to varying degree as they mature.   However, the number of cells that can arise in an apical growing point is limited, which means in turn that the volume of tissue derived from it must of necessity be restricted, in fact, too restricted to ensure the necessary strength to support the crown of the tree.   In trees, growth in thickness is traceable to a **cambium** (growing layer) between the bark and the wood throughout the tree; the cambium continues to live for a good many years and annually produces new wood and bark between the old bark and wood.[1] Growth of this sort from a lateral cambium is responsible for most of the thickening of the stem; it is designated as **secondary growth** or **secondary thickening,** to distinguish it from growth in length traceable to apical growing points.   Tissues originating laterally through secondary thickening are known as **secondary tissues.**   Such tissues add to the bulk of the plant body, especially of the vascular (conducting) tissue, and strengthen the stem; they do not, however, fundamentally alter its structure, nor are new types of cells usually formed.

III. ORIENTATION OF THE TISSUES IN A YOUNG TREE STEM (TWIG)

The massive trunk of a tree is but a main stem in which primary growth (growth in length) has ensued each year at the apex and in which secondary growth (growth in thickness) has proceeded throughout its length.   Once secondary growth is initiated, it continues periodically as long as the tree lives.   Hence, a proper understanding of the manner in which a tree bole is built up, year by year, entails a knowledge of the tissues present in a young stem and their orientation as regards one another, this prior to and after secondary thickening is under way.

Text Fig. 3 illustrates diagrammatically the tissues present in four segments of a 1-year twig, "as is" at different heights; the tissues are depicted in longitudinal sectional view.   Segment *A* is obviously through the twig-tip; toward the apex, there is a region of persisting initiating cells, the **promeristem,** in which cell division proceeds rapidly.   The cells cut off to the rear continue to divide, but the tissue composed of them

---

[1] Much has been written about seasonal growth in thickness in trees; it does not begin at the same time at different heights in the tree.   According to Priestley, each spring, when length growth is resumed as the buds open, growth in thickness commences in the new leaf primordia at the shoot apex and from thence spreads down the tree.   PRIESTLEY, J. H., The Growing Tree, Abs. from the Presidential Address to Section K and Department K, British Association, York, England, 1932.

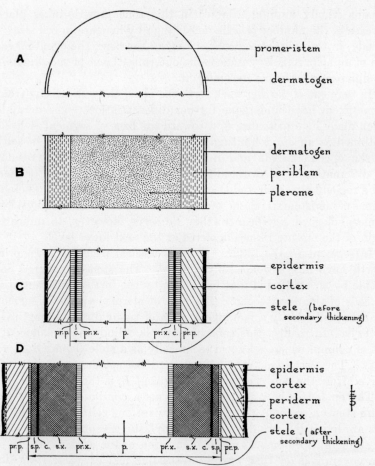

A — promeristem
— dermatogen

B — dermatogen
— periblem
— plerome

C — epidermis
— cortex
— stele (before secondary thickening)

pr.p. | c. | pr.x. | p. | pr.x. | c. | pr.p.

D — epidermis
— cortex
— periderm
— cortex
— stele (after secondary thickening)

pr.p. | s.p. c. s.x. | pr.x. | p. | pr.x. | s.x. c. s.p. | pr.p.

TEXT FIG. 3.—Schematic drawings illustrating the tissues present in four segments of a 1-year twig, taken at different heights; the tissues are depicted in longitudinal sectional view. Segment *A*. Twig-tip showing region of persisting initiating cells (promeristem) and the initial development of the dermatogen. Segment *B*. Somewhat farther back from the tip. The dermatogen is still in evidence; the promeristem has differentiated further into a core of plerome surrounded by a layer of periblem. Segment *C*. Still farther back in the twig. The primary tissues are now completely differentiated and consist of an epidermis derived from the dermatogen, a cortex formed from the periblem, and a stele that has arisen from the plerome; the stele consists of pith and primary vascular tissue composed of primary xylem and primary phloem, separated by a cambium. Segment *D*. Basal segment in which secondary thickening has ensued. The pith and primary xylem occupy the same positions and space as in segment *C*; the cambium has moved outward, leaving a layer of secondary xylem to the rear, outside the primary xylem; the cambium is bounded on the outside by secondary phloem, under the primary phloem that has been pushed farther to the outside; the cortex is still in evidence but the casting of the epidermis is presaged by the appearance of the first periderm immediately under it. Once secondary thickening has become established, as in segment *D*, it proceeds year on year in a tree member as long as it remains alive.

remains wholly undifferentiated; in this zone growth takes place by increase in the number of cells rather than by increase in cell size. But already, in the sides of segment *A* toward the base, the eventual formation of an epidermis is presaged; the outermost layer of the promeristem has differentiated into a **dermatogen.**

In segment *B*, farther back from the apex, the cells arising from the promeristem have undergone further differentiation. The dermatogen which made its appearance first toward the base of segment *A* has been continued as an outer limiting layer. Meanwhile, changes in cell size, cell shape, cell contents, and in the arrangement of cells have resulted in the differentiation of two additional regions, a central core or **plerome** and a region between it and the dermatogen, the **periblem.** These three regions of meristematic tissue shown in segment *B* have little physiological or morphological significance; they do serve, however, to indicate the origin of the mature tissues depicted at the next lower level.

In segment *C*, the tissues (primary tissues) resulting from primary growth have now become fully mature. The stem is covered on the outside by an **epidermis** that has arisen by the further differentiation of the cells of the dermatogen. The core of plerome visible in segment *B* has been replaced by a rectangular area of tissue directed lengthwise of the twig. In reality, this zone of tissue is cylindrical in shape; it is a sort of column which is known technically as a **stele** (from Greek στήλη, post). The tissue between the stele and the epidermis, *i.e.*, the tissue derived from the periblem shown in segment *B*, is the **cortex.**[1]

The epidermis of a young stem forms a continuous layer over the entire stem in segment *C*. It is rarely over one cell in thickness. The cells are living but are devoid of chloroplasts, except the guard cells at the stomatal openings. The chief function of the epidermis is to serve as a covering layer that prevents excessive loss of water from deeper lying tissues. In most instances it is the better equipped to perform this because the outer surfaces of the cells are usually waterproofed with a layer of waxy material (cutin), which acts as a varnish.

The stele in evidence in segment *C* consists of a central pith that appears unusually large at this stage. It is bounded on the flanks by a narrow zone of primary vascular tissue. The pith, like the entire stele, is actually cylindrical and is completely sheathed by vascular tissue.

The cylinder of vascular tissue in the stele depicted is composed of **primary xylem** (primary wood) and **primary phloem.** The primary xylem forms a continuous layer around the pith. The primary phloem

---

[1] Roots also possess a stele which is sheathed by cortical tissue.

is situated outside the primary xylem and, like it, is arranged in a continuous layer.[1]

The chief functions of vascular tissue, both of primary vascular tissue and of secondary vascular tissue, are conduction and support, although, on occasion, it may assume a third function, that of storage. Xylem conducts water and substances in solution absorbed from the soil upward; the tissue is rendered woody, and for this reason, most of the stiffness of the stem is traceable to it. The phloem carries food previously elaborated in the leaves downward.[2]

The pith inside the xylem is composed of tissue that is usually soft and quite different in nature from the vascular tissue; in twigs, the pith may store appreciable amounts of food, but in the mature tree-trunk, its cells are dead and no longer participate in the vital processes of the tree.

The cortex between the stele and the epidermis varies from a few to many layers of cells in thickness and is essentially parenchymatous although the cells composing it vary greatly in nature. Frequently they are thickened at the corners (collenchymatous) and serve to some extent as mechanical tissue. Fibers, grit (stone) cells, and oil or storage cells are often present. In many twigs, the cortical cells immediately under the epidermis are strongly lignified (sclerenchymatous) and occur in sheets or strands. In such cases, they supplement the epidermis as an additional protective layer and form a **hypodermis;** they also provide the necessary strength in the twig prior to the time when sufficient wood has accumulated through secondary thickening to meet this need.[3]

---

[1] In some stems the primary tissue is not continuous around the pith but is arranged in fascicles (strands) which appear as patches (vascular bundles) in transverse sections. In such instances the primary xylem and primary phloem have the same relative positions with respect to one another and are separated by a fascicular cambium. Subsequently interfascicular cambium forms between the strands and unites the fascicular cambia. Thereafter, secondary thickening proceeds in the usual manner in the meristematic layer thus formed.

[2] See footnote 3, p. 40.

[3] At this time, it is advisable to describe two other layers of tissue that are mentioned in the literature devoted to the anatomy of stems and roots, *viz.*, the **endodermis** and the **pericycle.** These structures are not illustrated in Text Fig. 3 since they are generally not distinguishable as definite layers in woody stems; their position is indicated, however, in the explanation of diagrammatic Text Fig. 5. The explanation of these terms is timely in the text at this point, since they are best understood in connection with the information that has been imparted in the preceding paragraphs.

The pericycle is, in reality, the outermost layer of the stele and is composed of one to several rows of cells. When it is only one or two rows of cells in thickness, it consists normally of parenchyma; but where it is thicker, the cells are often lignified

It remains to indicate how secondary growth proceeds in a twig following the maturation of the primary tissues depicted in segment *C*. This situation is portrayed in segment *D*. The diameter of the stem has now increased appreciably owing to the formation of **secondary xylem** and **secondary phloem** between the primary xylem and the primary phloem. These secondary tissues trace their origin to the activities of the cambium. The cylinder of pith and the zone of primary xylem continue to occupy the same positions and the same space as previously. The cambium meanwhile has moved outward, and a wide band of secondary xylem surrounds the primary xylem, bounded on the outside by the cambium. The cambium is likewise responsible for a zone of secondary phloem underlying the primary phloem, and this last-mentioned tissue has meanwhile been pushed farther to the outside. The cortex is still intact, which means that it has been enabled to adjust itself to the expanding girth of the stele. Not so the epidermis. This has been ruptured since there was no provision for its areal expansion; it has been replaced by a protective layer of periderm, the origin and functions of which are subsequently described on pages 27–31.

IV. THE ONTOGENY OF THE YOUNG TREE STEM (TWIG)

This title requires explanation since its relationship to the subject matter included under Sec. III (page 14) might otherwise be obscure. By the ontogeny of a young tree stem is understood the history of its development, step by step. Thus far in the text the nature of the tissue at the apical growing point and the tissues, both primary and secondary, that are present in different segments to the rear of it have been described briefly, resorting to diagrammatic figures. Sequence of tissue development has been indicated. It now remains to answer the question whether

and may even be fibrous (pericyclic fibers in stems). The pericycle is bounded internally by the primary phloem and externally by the innermost layer of the cortex. From it, underground lateral roots develop; likewise the first cork cells (periderm) in roots.

In roots the endodermis is distinguishable immediately to the outside of the pericycle and is in reality the innermost layer of the cortex, which has been modified and set off from the remainder of the cortex to meet certain needs of the plant. It is a cylindrical sheet of cells, one layer thick, without intercellular spaces and with structural features quite different from neighboring cells (cell walls suberized or cutinized, at least in part). It seems to be a sort of watertight layer between the cortical tissue and the stele, comparable to a dam, separating regions of different osmotic pressure and acting as a diffusion layer, preventing loss of mineral nutrients and food from the vascular tissues. An endodermal layer features the roots of nearly all plants; since it is usually absent from the stems of Gymnosperms and from angiospermous stems generally, no further mention will be made of it in tracing the development of the woody stem.

or not the primary xylem comes into being before, simultaneously with, or after the primary phloem; also whether or not each of these and other tissues, as seen in serial transverse sections of a twig, is suddenly formed completely at a given level or develops from a focal point of origin, whence all differentiation spreads laterally as the tissue ages. Since the various tissues of an axis are continually formed as long as the growing point is forging ahead, a panorama of tissue development is presented when transverse sections, cut in sequence over a distance of 1 to 2 inches below the growing point, are examined.[1] All stages in the development of a mature tissue in terms of time (days or even hours) are here portrayed spatially. This condition holds, of course, so long as growth is proceeding during a given growing season.[2]

In the higher plants with specialized tissues, as has been previously stated, the formation of new cells and growth (enlargement of cells) is restricted to certain definite regions—in a tree, to the tips of the twigs and roots, and to the growing layer (cambium) under the bark. The tissues in these regions are composed of thin-walled cells, which are undifferentiated and capable of repeated division. Such a tissue is said to be a **meristematic tissue** (generative tissue), to distinguish it from a tissue in which the cells have become fully differentiated and generally incapable of cell division, *i.e.*, a **permanent tissue.** The meristematic tissues at the apices of the tree are called **apical meristems;** the growing layer, or cambium, under the bark is a **lateral meristem.** Since growth in length (primary growth) of necessity predates secondary growth (growth in thickness), a description of the tree stem (ontogeny of the stem) should begin with the apical growing point.

Text Fig. 4 is a longitudinal section of such an apical growing point of white pine (*Pinus strobus* L.), subtended by bud scales in various stages of development. It is at once patent that the apical growing points of the stems of this tree are multicellular, and the same holds for the roots. In general, apical meristems are of two sorts, those consisting of a single cell and those composed of two to many cells. Single-celled growing points characterize the majority of the ferns, the Equisetums, and some other Pteridophytes. The Monocotyledons and some of the Dicotyledons have 2- or 3-celled growing points. On the other hand,

[1] Growth in length is restricted to this region.

[2] Growth in length usually ceases by midsummer, and, in many trees (Exs., elm, basswood, etc.) the growing point dies by midsummer and is cast off; in such instances, the uppermost axillary bud functions as a terminal bud the following spring. Growth in thickness continues for a time; it is completed first at the base of the growth of the season, last toward the apex. It follows that during the resting period (winter) the panorama of tissue development would be too foreshortened to yield satisfactory results when sections are prepared.

the timber trees of the United States without exception possess multicellular growing points of the type portrayed in the figure.

The promeristem of the growing point in this instance is in the tri-
angle, the corners of which are designated *a-a-a*; as stated previously,
this is a region of persisting initiating cells. Behind this is the pith
(*b-b*) which seems unusually large at this stage in the development of the
twig. The initial stages in the development of the primary vascular

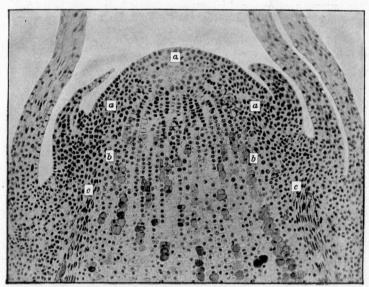

Text Fig. 4.—Photomicrograph depicting the dormant, multicellular growing point
at the tip of a white pine shoot, lateral sectional view. Promeristem, *a-a-a*; pith, *b-b*;
procambium, *c-c*. (50 ×). (*Photograph by W. M. Harlow.*)

system can be seen farther back in the growing point (*c-c*); this zone of
tissue is the **procambium.**[1] The cells of the procambium have already
begun to elongate vertically and eventually, as they mature, form a
cylinder of primary vascular tissue surrounding the pith.

Text Fig. 5 will serve to indicate the sequence of the development of
the tissues behind an apical growing point in a 1-year stem. The promeristem mentioned in the explanation of Text Fig. 3 is at the apex (*a-a*).
As the cells of the promeristem become older (are left farther behind),
they undergo changes in size, shape, wall thickness, etc., which are indicative of the cell types into which they are destined to develop.[2] But

[1] The procambium may be a continuous layer (which is seen in longitudinal sectional view in Text Fig. 4) or may consist of longitudinal strands.

[2] When length growth is progressing vigorously, these changes take place very
rapidly (in days or hours).

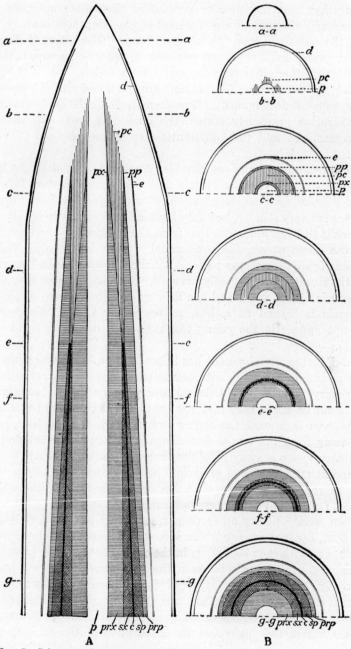

TEXT FIG. 5—Schematic drawings portraying the ontogeny of a young tree stem (twig). The explanation is given in the text.   (*After Eames and MacDaniels.*)

the transition from meristem to permanent tissue does not take place simultaneously throughout a given level in the axis; there is an overlapping of the meristem upon the mature tissues. The series of diagrammatic transverse sections present evidence to this effect, since one mature tissue after another appears in the successive sections.

At *b-b*, the dermatogen (*d*), procambium (*pc*), and pith (*p*) are shown in early stages of development. The dermatogen is the outermost layer, from which, as previously stated, the epidermis eventually develops. The procambium and pith differentiate from the plerome (see Text Fig. 3).

The appearance of the procambium marks the initial stages in the development of the vascular system and usually at the start takes the form of definite, isolated, longitudinal strands, arranged in a ring. At first these are very slender, but they increase rapidly in size by the addition of cells through differentiation from the adjacent promeristem.

In the plane at *c-c*, the procambial strands have united through extensions from their flanks to form a hollow cylinder. In tree stems, this is the situation that usually prevails. The first phloem tissue (**protophloem**) is visible at *pp* and the first xylem (**protoxylem**) at *px*. An endodermis is figured at *e*, but, as previously noted, this probably would not appear in the young tree stem as a definite structure (see page 17).

At *d-d*, further development has taken place in the procambium, and this tissue is reduced in amount because more of it has been transformed into primary phloem (**metaphloem**) and primary xylem (**metaxylem**). Note should be made here that the continued development of the primary phloem is toward the center (centripetal), that of the primary xylem away from the center (centrifugal). When the development of the primary xylem is away from the center, as in this instance, it is said to be **endarch;** this order of procedure holds for the stems of our timber trees. In roots, on the contrary, the development is in the opposite direction, *i.e.*, toward the center, and is described as **exarch.**[1] The stems of certain woody plants other than trees also possess exarch primary xylem (Ex., *Lycopodium spp.*). In some of the ferns, the arrangement is **mesarch,** *i.e.*, with the protoxylem in the center, encircled by metaxylem.

Somewhere in the axis between the transverse planes *d-d* and *e-e*, respectively, the remaining layer of the procambium was completely transformed into primary xylem and primary phloem, except for a thin layer between these tissues which then became the cambium. The establishment of this layer and the maturation of the primary xylem

---

[1] The strands of primary phloem and primary xylem alternate in roots; *i.e.*, they are on different radii of the cross section.

and primary phloem mark the completion of primary growth so far as the vascular tissues are concerned.

At the *e-e* level, not only is the cambium in evidence but it has started to produce secondary vascular tissue which is inserted between the primary phloem (*prp*) and the primary xylem (*prx*). The secondary xylem (*sx*) assumes the form of a ring which, in the transverse section, lies immediately outside of the ring of primary xylem. The cambium meanwhile has moved out and now bounds the secondary xylem upon the outside. Secondary phloem (*sp*), likewise formed by cell division in the cambium as it moved outward from the center, has accumulated on the outer face of this layer and now underlies the primary phloem (*prp*). Upon indicating the cambium as *c* and using the letters cited to indicate primary and secondary vascular tissues, the sequence of letters before and after secondary thickening would be: (before) *prx, c, prp*; (after) *prx, sx, c, sp, prp*.

At *f-f* the secondary tissues have increased in amount. The cambium has continued to move farther to the outside, forming more secondary xylem and secondary phloem. The band of primary phloem (*prp*) has become narrower owing to the compression of this tissue.

A more advanced stage of the condition illustrated in *f-f* is shown in *g-g*; further secondary growth has occurred, resulting in wider rings of secondary xylem and secondary phloem. The primary xylem occupies the same space as in *f-f* and *e-e*, respectively; but the ring of primary phloem has been further narrowed.

The conditions portrayed in *g-g* may be cited as indicating the fact that the *status quo* in the manner of growth that will prevail in the tree from this point onward has become established. Primary tissues were first formed through growth resulting from an apical promeristem, not contemporaneously but in orderly sequence, and secondary growth, traceable to a lateral cambium, has become established. Except for dormant periods, the lateral cambium will continue to function, year on year, forming new zones (increments) of secondary xylem and secondary phloem which will be interpolated between like tissues formed the preceding year.

V. EXTENT OF SECONDARY THICKENING IN A TREE STEM DURING THE FIRST YEAR

Text Fig. 6, *A*, is a schematic drawing of a transverse section of a white pine twig about 1 inch back from the growing point; the primary tissues are mature and are portrayed as to position. Secondary thickening has not begun. The figure illustrates the situation that prevailed in segment *C* of Text Fig. 3. The legend accompanying the figure provides sufficient explanation so that further description is unnecessary.

Text Fig. 6, *A*, however, is not indicative of the situation that prevails throughout the twig at the end of the growing season, *i.e.*, at the time when the twig becomes dormant; this is shown in Text Fig. 6, B (which should be compared to segment *D* of Text Fig. 3).   Thickening, traceable to a lateral cambium, has taken place meanwhile.   The segments of

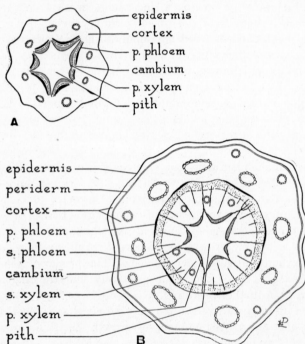

Text Fig. 6.—Schematic drawings of transverse sections of a young pine twig (*Pinus strobus* L.), showing the arrangement of the tissues prior to and after secondary thickening. *A*. About 1 inch from the apical growing point; the primary tissues are complete, but secondary thickening has not begun.   *B*. At the end of the growing season; secondary thickening is well advanced.

cambium visible in *A* have united through lateral extension.   Cell division started in the cambium.   This, as it moved outward, formed a ring of secondary xylem, at the same time producing a corresponding ring of secondary phloem to the outside in advance of itself.   One other structure in Text Fig. 6, *B*, requires brief mention.   A periderm has formed in the cortex, under the epidermis.   The significance of this layer is subsequently explained in Sec. VII of the present chapter.

Several deductions are obvious from the comparison of *A* and *B* of Text Fig. 6.   Secondary thickening in a stem[1] begins the first year. Most of the first annual ring is composed of secondary wood.   The

[1] Also in roots.

primary xylem continues to occupy the same position and volume (area in the transverse section) around the pith as it did following its formation through apical growth. The primary phloem is pushed farther to the outside, is crushed, and becomes a vestigial tissue which is eventually cast from the tree. The first periderm, at least in some twigs, forms the first year.

VI. DEVELOPMENT OF THE TREE-TRUNK FROM THE YOUNG TREE STEM

The preceding pages should suffice to show the manner in which secondary thickening becomes established in a twig during its first year. It now remains to describe the procedure whereby a twig develops into a tree trunk.

Two types of branching are recognized in trees. Those possessing a terminal leader such as pine and spruce are said to have "excurrent" (monopodial) growth; in such trees, barring accident, the main stem outstrips all the others in vigor and height growth and, as it thickens, becomes the trunk of the tree. Such stems characterize coniferous trees.

In the majority of hardwood trees, the steps in the development of the trunk are not quite so evident. The branching of the mature tree is usually "deliquescent"; *i.e.*, the crown is composed of a number of ascending or wide-spreading limbs. The question then arises as to how the tree manages to develop a single trunk; the inference would be that, since the young tree must have been considerably branched, the mature tree would possess several trunks instead of one, arising at or near the ground. Two reasons may be set forth to explain the actual condition that prevails. In a tree with deliquescent branching, the branches seldom possess equal vigor; those at the top or near the center of the crown are favored because of better light and possibly because they are in direct line with vertical sap flow. Lower branches and branches near the margin of the crown, as the tree increases rapidly in height during youth, are shaded out of existence or become dwarfed. Trees also possess a second method of controlling crown shape and density of crown. The majority of the branchlets are shed before they attain much size, the process (cladoptosis) being comparable to leaf fall and quite as natural. When the tree is young, only the most favored stems develop beyond a certain stage; one of these eventually becomes the trunk.

Text Fig. 7 depicts diagrammatically the manner in which the main stem (trunk) of an excurrent tree increases in circumference over a period of years through secondary thickening. For reasons that will be explained subsequently, the growth layers (increments of wood) may be seen; they are shown in longitudinal and transverse section. As has been stated previously, tree stems exhibit radial symmetry; *i.e.*, the parts are arranged around a center (pith). The growth increments appear as concentric rings when cut transversely (as seen on the end of a log) and as superposed, cone-shaped, or parabolic zones of tissue when viewed in longitudinal section. They approach in shape a hollow

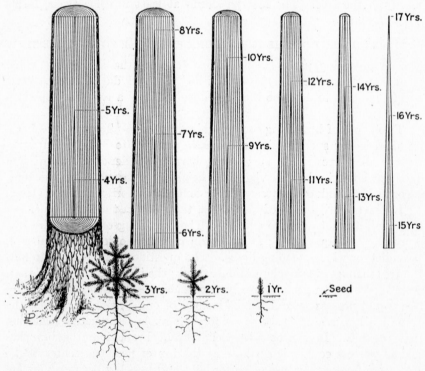

Text Fig. 7.—Schematic drawing of a 17-year-old coniferous tree showing the manner in which the trunk increases in thickness through the addition of annual increments.

cone or a hollow paraboloid, and the successive increments are telescoped, the last one ending at the top of the terminal leader of the year, the preceding one where the tip of the terminal leader was the preceding season, etc. The tree in question was seventeen years old. Fourteen annual rings show on the stump, not 17; it took the tree 4 years to attain stump height, and an annual ring would not show at this height until the terminal leader had grown past this plane.[1]

[1] An example of the type stated below will serve to focus the attention of a student upon the manner in which trees grow:

Given a tree in the winter condition 52 feet 9 inches in height and 62 years of age which grew in height as follows:

17 inches in height at the end of 3 years
9 inches in height per year for the next 9 years

VII. THE MATURE TREE-TRUNK

Even the layman is conversant with the fact that the trunk of a mature tree is composed of a core of wood covered by a layer of **bark** on the outside. The manner in which wood accumulates in the bole through periodic growth of a lateral meristem (cambium) has already been explained. The significance of bark formation in trees now deserves attention.

For a short time, the young stem (twig) is protected from desiccation, and to some extent from mechanical injury, by the epidermis. The outer surface of this is more or less cutinized to prevent undue loss of moisture, and it is generally pierced by stomatal openings which ensure the proper aeration of deeper lying tissues. But in the great majority of woody plants no provision is made for the areal increase of the epidermis as the twig enlarges in girth through secondary thickening. It soon ruptures (usually during the first year) and is sloughed off promptly in most cases. Were the twig left without an insulating layer on the outside, it would soon dry out and die, but this contingency does not occur. Before the epidermis is ruptured, a new protective layer, the **first periderm,** is formed under it. This serves to protect the stem from desiccation after the epidermis is ruptured (Text Fig. 8). It is provided with lenticels (breathing pores) in lieu of stomates.

Structurally, a periderm consists of three layers: (1) the **phellogen** (cork cambium), (2) the **phellem** (to the outside) which is composed of layers of cork cells, and (3) the **phelloderm** (to the inside) composed of one or more layers of thin-walled, nonsuberized cells. The phellogen occupies the medial position, and the other two layers originate from it through cell division. In stems, as a rule, it arises from mature, living parenchymatous cells underlying the epidermis that have remained thin-walled and begin dividing, cutting off cells parallel to the outer surface of the twig. The insulating qualities of the periderm are traceable to the phellem layer which is heavily suberized to prevent or at least inhibit the passage of moisture and gases.

---

1 foot 4 inches in height per year for the next 12 years
15 inches in height per year for the next 5 years
11 inches in height per year for the next 7 years
7 inches in height per year for the next 17 years

and at a uniform rate in height per year for the remaining time.

1. How many annual rings would appear on a transverse surface one-half the distance from the apex to the base (fractional answers not permissible)? *Ans.* 37.

2. How many annual rings would appear on a transverse surface one-third the distance down from the apex? *Ans.* 28.

The first periderm in twigs (see Text Fig. 2) is more or less cylindrical and in transverse sections is usually annular, underlying the surface. It may arise (1) in the epidermal layer (Ex., *Acer pennsylvanicum* L.), (2) in the primary cortex, which is the usual condition (Exs., *Tilia spp.*, *Juglans spp.*, *Plantanus spp.*), or in the pericycle (Exs., *Thuja spp.*,

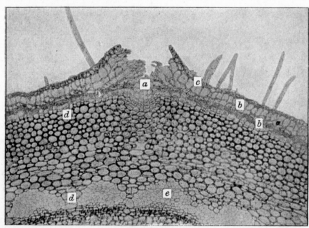

Text Fig. 8.—Outer portion of a red ash twig (*Fraxinus pennsylvanica* Marsh.), in transverse section, showing a lenticel (*a*), the first periderm (*b-b*), the epidermis with epidermal hairs (*c*), the collenchymatous cortex (*d-d*), and masses of pericyclic fibers (*e*) (100 ×). (*Photograph by C. de Zeeuw.*)

Juniperus spp.).   The evidence available points to the fact that, in the first two instances, it is initiated under or near the stomates, the segments thus formed spreading laterally and coalescing to form a layer that is uninterrupted except for the lenticels.

Once established in the tree, the phellogen producing the first periderm may continue to function for many years; *i.e.*, it is perennial like the true cambium, becoming active in the growing months and remaining dormant during the winter.[1]   Most of the cell divisions are in the periclinal plane (parallel to the outer surface of the twig), but occasionally anticlinal divisions take place which permit the phellogen to increase in

---

[1] In trees like beech (*Fagus grandifolia* Ehrh.), cell division in the phellogen proceeds slowly; a few phellem cells are cut off each year from the cork cambium, this to compensate for those shed as small particles from the outer surface of the periderm. There is no evidence of layering (zones of growth) in the phellem, and the outer bark remains smooth, the tree seemingly not shedding its bark.   In white birch (*Betula papyrifera* Marsh.), in contrast, distinct periodic (possibly annual) zonation is present in the phellem in the form of successive layers of thin-walled and thick-walled cells. Peeling of the bark is made possible since it splits readily along the zones of thin-walled cork.   The erroneous impression prevails in many quarters that white birch may be peeled because of the presence of successive concentric periderms, the break occurring in the phelloderm layers.

girth (as seen in transverse sections) and provide for its retention without rupturing near the outer surface of the twig. The tissue (epidermis, cortical cells) to the outside is cut off from the physiological activities of the tree, dies, and eventually sloughs off. Thereafter, the stem is encased by the primary periderm for some years and remains comparatively smooth. Roughening of the bark indicates the inception of deep cork formation, a feature that will be discussed subsequently.

During this period while the primary periderm is functioning, secondary thickening proceeds from the true cambium in the normal manner; each year, layers of new xylem and of new phloem are inserted between older layers of the same sort, and the stem increases in girth. In this way, the volume of vascular tissue (xylem and phloem) steadily mounts, but it still remains enclosed within the first periderm. The layers of xylem are lignified (woody) and accumulate in the tree, forming a permanent part of the bole. Not so the phloem which is formed year by year outside the cambium; this tissue is pushed farther and farther to the outside, as new phloem forms under it, and eventually is cast off as bark.

The bark on a mature tree is never so thick as the wood, for three reasons, *viz.:*

1. The layer of xylem formed a given year is usually six to eight times as thick as the corresponding layer of phloem; for this reason, wood in a tree stem does not accumulate in direct proportion to the phloem but much faster.

2. Phloem always contains sieve tubes, accompanied by one or more of the following longitudinal elements: companion cells, phloem parenchyma, bast fibers. Bast fibers possess lignified walls and hence do not crush easily; phloem parenchyma may become lignified on occasion. But the walls of sieve tubes and companion cells are never woody and, in trees, generally function for 1 year only. During this period while the sieve tubes are fluxed with protoplasmic contents, they retain their shape, but, when bast fibers are not present, they usually collapse the second year, owing to bark pressure. In such instances the older phloem tissue is compressed radially and no longer occupies as much space as formerly. Evidence of such compression is visible in transverse sections of the inner bark, cambium, and last-formed wood of *Pinus strobus* L. (Text Fig. 23, *A*), in which the phloem rays pursue a serpentine course after passing through the zone of functioning sieve tubes next to the cambium.[1]

[1] It follows that the older phloem tissue under the periderm is stretched tangentially as it is pushed farther to the outside. In many tree species, tension in the tangential direction is relieved by ray flares (Text Fig. 10, *B*). The cells in the phloem portion of certain rays divide by anticlinal walls; this permits the ray to open out fanwise as it progresses toward the outside and prevents actual rupture of the tissue.

3. Finally, old phloem tissues, where these have accumulated to such an extent as to be an impediment to further growth, are shed. This

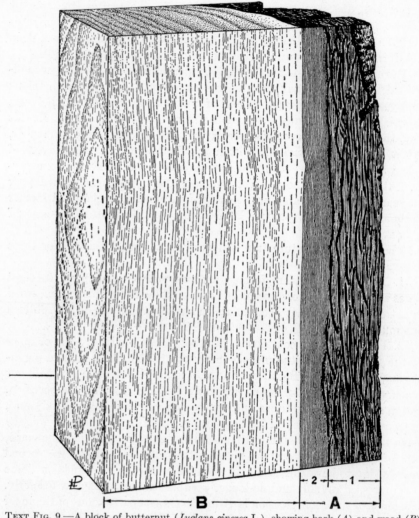

TEXT FIG. 9.—A block of butternut (*Juglans cinerea* L.), showing bark (*A*) and wood (*B*)· The outer dead brown bark (1) can be distinguished from the inner living bark (2); the former consists of islands of dead phloem tissue bonded by darker zones of periderm (six-tenths natural size).

process consists in the formation of **secondary periderms** which, in transverse and radial sections, take the form of short arcs or lunes, that branch off (*a*) first from the inside of the primary periderm and (*b*) subsequently from the last-formed secondary periderms, cutting off patches of tissue. If the primary periderm is situated in the outer part of the cortex, which is the usual situation in the stems of timber trees, the remainder of the cortex is the first tissue to turn brown, as

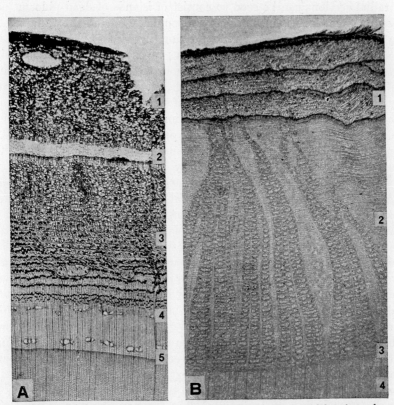

TEXT FIG. 10.—Bark and periderm formation in trees. *A*. Bark and last-formed wood of *Picea rubens* Sarg., showing the outer dead brown bark (1), the last periderm (2), the inner living bark (secondary phloem) (3), location of the cambium (4), and the wood (5) (12 ×). *B*. Bark and portion of the last annual ring of *Tilia americana* L., showing the outer dead brown bark composed of four successive periderms alternating with bands of dead phloem tissue (1), a wide band of inner living bark (secondary phloem) in which some of the rays have flared (2), position of the cambium (3), and portion of the last annual ring (4) (12 ×).

it is cut off from participation in the vital processes of the tree. New lunes of secondary periderm continue to form ever deeper in the tissues, and sooner or later the older (outer) portions of the phloem are invaded. In the phloem, the new phellogens arise from living phloem parenchyma which, unlike the sieve tubes, has continued to function. The invasion of the phloem by lunes of periderm marks the beginning of deep cork formation in trees; it is at this time that the outer surface of the bark becomes rough.[1]

At this stage, and this holds for mature trees, the bark (Text Fig. 9, *A*) consists of two parts: an **outer, dead** (dark) **bark** which in transverse or radial sections can be seen to consist of islands of dead phloem (and possibly of cortical tissue on the extreme outside) bounded by anastomosing lunes of periderm (1); an **inner, living** (light-colored) **bark** composed of accumulated phloem in which the sieve tubes are no longer functioning except in the layer immediately contiguous to the cambium but in which the phloem parenchyma is still living (2). The width of these two layers varies greatly in different kinds of trees, in individuals of the same species growing under different conditions, and at different heights in the same tree. For example, in *Picea spp.*, the layer of brown bark is comparatively thin, because it weathers off fairly rapidly; as a result, the outer surface of the tree-trunk is scaly but relatively smooth. In big trees [*Sequoia gigantea* (Lindl.) Decne.] and Douglas fir [*Pseudotsuga taxifolia* (Poir.) Britt.], on the other hand, brown bark 1 to 2 feet in thickness is occasionally encountered. This may be the accumulation of several hundred or a thousand years of more of old phloems which the tree has been tardy in casting, once they were cut off by lunes of secondary periderm. The surface of the bark of such trees is often deeply fissured.

The number of successive periderms persisting outside the living bark and hence visible in transverse sections, is variable and is not necessarily indicative of the thickness of the dead bark. In Text Fig. 10, *A*, which is a photomicrograph of red spruce, only two such layers are in evidence. The outer of these marked the position of the surface of the tree trunk; the inner delimited the boundary between the dead and the living bark. Four periderms can be counted in Text Fig. 10, B, over a shorter distance. In both *A* and *B*, the strips of bark depicted in the photomicrographs are too narrow to indicate that the periderms anastomosed to the right and left.

---

[1] The classification of trees as ring-barked and shell-barked is no longer valid in the sense that ring-barked trees possess a series of concentric periderms. The first, or primary, periderm is perennial and often continues to function for many years. Sooner or later, though it may be greatly delayed, deep cork formation is initiated in all domestic timber trees.

CHAPTER III

THE GROSS FEATURES OF WOOD OF VALUE IN IDENTIFICATION

I. THE NATURE OF GROSS FEATURES

This text is concerned with the principles involved in teaching wood identification. In approaching this subject, the logical procedure is from the gross to the minute, especially for the neophyte in this field: features visible or evident at little or no magnification thus receive attention first; those evident only at high magnifications and hence largely unknown at the start are reserved until the last. This plan has been pursued in the pages that follow.

The gross features of wood are, in general, of two kinds: those traceable to its structure, its **gross structural features,** and those which fall in the category of **physical properties** as, for example, color, odor, taste, weight, etc. Certain features of the first type, such as the fact that the grain always runs lengthwise of the log, hold for commercial timbers in general; others are specific for certain woods and hence are of diagnostic importance as offering a basis for separation in Keys. Whether general or specific, gross structural features are discussed here because the hand-lens identification of woods requires an all-round knowledge of their gross anatomy.

The physical properties of wood are, in general, less reliable in distinguishing species than its structural features because they exhibit greater fluctuation. However, accurate identification should seldom be made dependent upon one feature alone but on a number of characters considered in unison. Here, certain of the nonmechanical physical properties are frequently of value, which renders necessary their inclusion in this portion of the text.

II. GROSS STRUCTURAL FEATURES

A. The Planes in Which the Structural Features of Wood Are Studied

Before proceeding to the study of the gross and eventually to the minute features of wood, the student must orient himself as to the planes in which wood is customarily examined. This can be done best by

33

reference to Text Fig. 11 which portrays a wedge-shaped block, taken from the trunk of a mature tree.

A and *B* designate the bark; the significance of outer dead bark (*A*) and inner living bark (*B*) was explained in the preceding chapter. The sapwood is at *C*, the heartwood at *D*. *E* indicates the position of the pith. The wood is depicted in three planes of section.

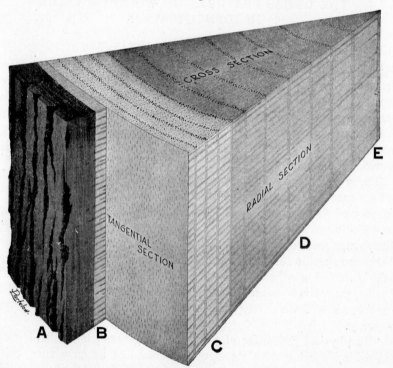

TEXT FIG. 11.—A wedge-shaped block from the mature trunk of a hardwood tree. *A*. Fissured outer, dead brown bark. *B*. Inner living, light-colored bark. *C*. Sapwood composed of four growth increments. *D*. Heartwood composed of seven growth increments. *E*. Pith.

The face that is exposed when wood is cut or sawed at right angles to the grain is the transverse surface (cross section). The end grain is visible in this plane; it is the surface that is presented on the end of a log.

The radial and tangential surfaces (sections) of the wood are at right angles to the transverse surface; *i.e.*, they extend along the grain. The first is so made that the cut follows a radius of a cross section of the log. Such a surface, if it was truly accurate as to direction and was continued, would pass from the bark through the pith of the tree. The tangential face of wood is exposed when the bark is peeled from a tree. This surface, of course, is curved. In practice, when wood is cut or sawed tangentially, the surface exposed is flat and is then a chord of the curved surface under the bark, so aligned that it is approximately at right angles to the wood rays.

B. GROWTH INCREMENTS

Growth increments are generally prominent features of woods grown in temperate regions and are usually visible, at least in thin sections, in timbers from the tropics. As stated previously, in trees with excurrent growth such as pine, they approach the form of hollow cones or hollow paraboloids in the main stem, one inserted above another and inseparably joined throughout to the preceding and succeeding structures of like nature. In broad-leaved trees with deliquescent branching, the shape is far less regular.

1. Annual Rings of Normal Type.—The appearance of normal growth increments, as seen in wood, depends on the plane in which they are viewed (Text Fig. 11). On the end of a log, they show as a succession of growth rings around the pith. When but one such layer is produced a year, it is called an **annual ring.** Ring counts on the stump hence may indicate the approximate age of a tree but not its actual age since the seedling stages are not recorded at this height (Text Fig. 7). In longleaf pine (*Pinus palustris* Mill.), error would result not only because of this but for another reason; during the "grass stage" of this species, which may last from 4 to 12 years or more, no distinct annual rings are produced in the stem and root.[1] False rings and discontinuous rings (see page 37) also lead to errors in ring counts. Dendrochronology, the correlation of annual rings with periods of time, has been a very effective tool, particularly in the arid Southwest, in determining the age of prehistoric ruins and in tracing climatic cycles.[2]

On the faces of boards, the figures resulting from growth increments vary according to the plane of the wood that is exposed. In edge-grained (quartersawn) stock, the increments assume the form of parallel striae (Text Fig. 11). Concentric and nested U and V patterns are the rule in flat-sawn stock.

Growth increments stand out in wood to varying degrees, because the growth intensity and consequently the density of the wood produced are not uniform throughout the growing period.[3] Usually, increase in

[1] PESSIN, L. J. Annual Ring Formation in Pinus palustris Seedlings. *Amer. Jour. Bot.*, Vol. 21, pp. 599–603. 1934.

[2] STALLINGS, W. S. Dating Prehistoric Ruins by Tree-rings. Laboratory of Anthropology, Sante Fe, N. M. 1927.

[3] In trees in temperate regions, the growth increments are usually annual, *i.e.*, one is formed each season and appears as an annual ring when cut transversely. In

thickness is rapid during the flush of growth at the beginning of the season but the **growth rate** slows down very appreciably as the season advances. The portion of the growth ring formed in the spring when growth is resumed abounds in conductive cells and is often quite porous and hence frequently low in density; this tissue is commonly designated as **early-** or **springwood.** Wood produced later in the season is called **late-** or **summerwood;** it is usually denser and hence darker, as viewed with the naked eye or at low magnifications. It is best adapted to ensure strength to the stem and probably does not participate in sap conduction to the same extent as earlywood. The discrepancy in color between the denser and darker latewood of a given increment and the more open, lighter colored earlywood of the succeeding zone is responsible for the delineation of growth zones.

As is to be expected, growth increments differ greatly in width and density in different tree species, in individual trees of the same species, and at different heights in a given tree. Certain trees, for example, poplars (*Populus spp.*) and the catalpas (*Catalpa spp.*), are naturally fast growing and under normal conditions develop wide rings; in the pineries of the South, slash pine (*Pinus caribaea* Morolet) is a more vigorous tree and almost invariably has wider rings than longleaf pine (*P. palustris* Mill.), growing on the same or on slightly better drained sites. On the other hand, 30 to 40 or more rings per inch are not at all unusual, especially in broad-leaved trees and also in the trees of such coniferous genera as *Taxus*, *Thuja*, and *Juniperus*.

Site likewise has a direct bearing on ring width. Some species do not thrive well when overtopped by others, and under these conditions the rings frequently are narrower than usual. On the same site and at the same age, individuals of a given species may exhibit appreciable differences in ring width depending on the crown class, *i.e.*, according to their competitive position. A moisture-loving species on a dry site may manage to survive under the conditions imposed, but its struggle for existence is then reflected in the stem by growth zones much reduced in width. Eastern arbor-vitae (*Thuja occidentalis* L.) may also be cited as a tree in which site conditions have a direct bearing on rate of growth. In the Northeast, this species occurs on two very distinct sites, in deep swamps[1] where the water gives an acid reaction, and on comparatively

---

tropical woods, on the other hand, the annual origin of the growth increments is very questionable, for not infrequently two or more seasonal rings may be formed in a given year. In describing such woods, it is best to avoid the terms "annual increments" and "annual rings," for they are likely to prove misleading.

[1] Associated with balsam fir [*Abies balsamea* (L.) Mill.], red maple (*Acer rubrum* L.), and other moisture-loving species.

dry limestone outcrops. By preference, arbor-vitae seems to be a calcicole, for it has wider rings and seeds more prolifically when growing on limestone soils.

Finally, in a given tree the ring width must of necessity vary at different heights, for only in this way can the tree retain its shape. Lengthwise in the merchantable stem[1] of such a tree, grown under optimum conditions, a given increment is widest toward the top and narrowest toward the base. The same departures would also be found in transverse sections of the bole of such a hypothetical tree; the widest rings would occur nearest the pith, the narrowest at the periphery of the wood. But trees seldom if ever grow under optimum conditions; consequently, ring width, as viewed in wood samples, fluctuates widely.

As a rule, the rings of shade-enduring trees vary more in width than those of light-demanding trees that do not readily recover from suppression. Alternating zones of narrow and broad increments are frequently visible in comparatively small samples of hemlock (*Tsuga spp.*); the growth increments of firs (*Abies spp.*), on the other hand, are usually fairly wide and quite uniform in thickness, indicating the lesser tolerance of these trees at maturity. Butt swell at the base of the bole and where large limbs join the trunk, uneven distribution of the weight of the crown in the stem, fluting of the trunks of certain species (Ex., *Carpinus caroliniana* Walt.) for no apparent reason, etc., likewise result in many idiosyncrasies in the thickness of growth increments along the stem.[2]

2. Annual Rings of Abnormal Type.—Rings of abnormal type, when present, course around the pith like normal rings. Owing to the idiosyncrasies of tree growth, however, and for other reasons subsequently explained, they exhibit features different from those presented under normal conditions. The discussion that follows is devoted to the various types of these abnormalities.

Not infrequently, particularly in very old trees with one-sided crowns or in trees in which growth is proceeding very sluggishly, some of the rings are interrupted, *i.e.*, they are **discontinuous rings** (Text Figs. 12 and 13, *B*).[3] This results from the fact that the cambium on the outer surface of the previously formed wood remained dormant at one or more places throughout its contour during a current growing season, meanwhile functioning as usual elsewhere. The new ring thus produced must, of necessity, be interrupted at the point or points where cell division

---

[1] The portion of the trunk above the butt swell.

[2] Growth increments are also visible in roots, but they are usually not so clearly delineated as in stems.

[3] Fritz, E., and J. L. Averell. Discontinuous Growth Rings in California Redwood. *Jour. Forestry*, Vol. 22, No. 6, pp. 31–38. 1924.

did not ensue. This results in a situation in which the new growth layer appears to run into the preceding ring at the place or places in question.

At this time, the fact should be stressed that there is no break in the continuity of the tissue when discontinuous rings are produced, for the cambial cells do not die but remain dormant for one or more growing seasons.[1] The temporary dormancy of the cambial cells at one or more

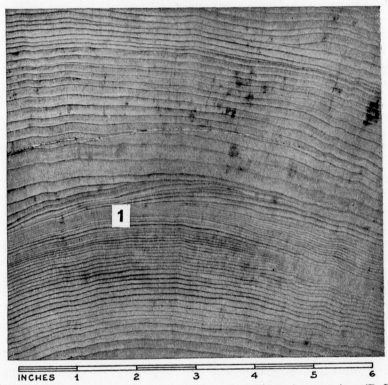

INCHES   1   2   3   4   5   6

TEXT FIG. 12.—Discontinuous rings (above 1) in redwood [*Sequoia sempervirens* (D. Don) Endl.] (*Photograph by E. Fritz.*)

places in the cambial ring may possibly be due to impoverishment through failure to receive sufficient nourishment, occasioned in turn by a one-sided tree crown. A situation of this sort can be readily envisioned in very old trees; or possibly other factors are responsible.

The conditions resulting in the formation of discontinuous rings may hold for only one season; in such cases but one ring is interrupted at a given point, the additional layers of wood to the outside being normal in

[1] Had these initials died, scar tissue would have formed, an eventuality that does not arise.

every way. Or the same conditions may hold in a given vicinity for two or more seasons; in such instances, a like number of rings are discontinuous. Since, as was previously stated, there is no interruption in the continuity of the tissue, the quality of the wood is little, if at all, impaired.

Discontinuous rings are not infrequent in wood taken from large, overmature trees. For example, they are often visible in redwood and bald cypress. They also occur occasionally in stock obtained from

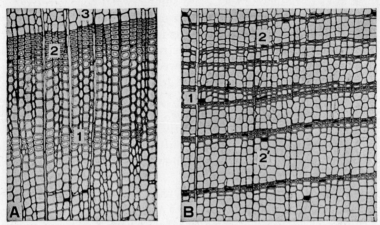

TEXT FIG. 13.—Discontinuous and false rings.

A. False rings in bald cypress [*Taxodium distichum* (L.) Rich.].   1. Flattened, thicker-walled tracheids denoting outer boundary of a false ring; the cells grade into wider-lumened tracheids above and below (55×).   2. Dense summerwood marking the true boundary of the ring.   3. Springwood of the succeeding ring.

B. Discontinuous rings in redwood [*Sequoia sempervirens* (D. Don) Endl.]   (70×). 1. A discontinuous ring.   2, 2¹. Normal rings above and below.

younger trees, especially of species that normally have narrow rings. Hop-hornbeam may be cited as illustrative of the second situation. Many rutaceous woods exhibit rings of this type.

False rings (Text Fig. 13, *A*) are usually of more frequent occurrence in wood than discontinuous rings and often lead to erroneous estimates of tree age. False rings are wholly included within the boundaries of true rings. A band of what appears to be summerwood is formed which simulates normal summerwood in appearance and density; this is followed exteriorly by tissue resembling springwood, after which true summerwood is produced.

False rings can be distinguished from true rings in that the cells composing the false summerwood grade gradually, not only to the inside but also to the outside, into more porous tissue in the regions mentioned. In other words, springwood appears to grade into summerwood both within and without. This, of course, is contrary to the situation that holds for normal rings in which the springwood grades into the summer-wood exteriorly but in which there is an abrupt transition in cell size and density of the wood between the summerwood of a given ring and the springwood of the succeeding ring.

If but one false ring is included in the true ring, the latter is designated as a **double ring;** if several such false rings occur within the boundaries of the true ring, the latter is said to be a **multiple ring.**[1] The term "false ring" is used to designate each false summerwood zone, irrespective of whether the true ring contains but one or more than one of these layers.

Annual rings of abnormal type arise for various reasons. Late frosts resulting in temporary defoliation, destruction of foliage through insect infestation, periods of drought followed by heavy precipitation and temperatures suitable for growth, and resumption of growth in the late summer or early autumn occasioned by unseasonably warm weather may be cited as contributory causes. In early life, multinodal pines such as *Pinus echinata* Mill. frequently exhibit false rings in the first growth increment.[2] These are apparently occasioned by a slowing down or a pause in secondary thickening following the formation of each false whorl of lateral branches.

3. Annual Rings in Relation to Quality of Wood.—The quality of wood is affected by ring width in most and probably in all tree-species. This subject is discussed at some length in Chap. X. Rings of unusual width frequently mean lumber of inferior quality; in the past, serious errors undoubtedly were made in the choice of tree-species for reforestation through overemphasis on fast growth as a criterion. Quality as well as quantity in the production of the future timber crop should be kept ever to the fore. Even when chemical conversion of the wood is contemplated, quality is an important consideration.

C. SAPWOOD AND HEARTWOOD

For a time while a tree is young, the period varying greatly in different kinds of trees and in the same species under different site conditions, the wood that has accumulated year by year in the core continues to perform the functions of sap conduction (up the trunk),[3] of ensuring the necessary

---

[1] ANON. Multiple Growth Layers in the Annual Increments of Certain Trees at Lubbock, Texas. *Tex. Sci.*, Vol. 91, pp. 98–99. 1940.

[2] MATTON, W. R. Life History of Shortleaf Pine. *U.S. Dept. Agr., Bul.* 244, p. 19. 1915.

[3] The general consensus is that food substances elaborated in the leaves move down the tree in the inner bark (sieve tubes of the phloem) and that mineral salts in very dilute solution and reserve food that has again been rendered soluble after the winter resting period travel up the stem in the sapwood. Girdling experiments, the apparent inability of the sieve tubes to transport food in sufficient quantity, etc., have

strength to the stem, and of providing, to some extent at least, for the storage of reserve food. The wood performing these functions is termed **sapwood.** It is still a physiological part of the tree by which it is to be understood that a portion of the tissue (3 to 40 plus per cent) remains alive and is in communication with living tissues in the bark, meanwhile participating in the vital activities of the organism.[1] Later, however, as the trunk increases in girth, for reasons as yet not satisfactorily explained, all the living cells in some of the wood to the inside (next to the pith) die. This core of dead tissue in the stem is called **heartwood** (Text Fig. 11, *D*); its main function is mechanical support, and it no longer participates in the vital activities of the tree.[2] Once heartwood formation is initiated in a tree at a given level, its formation is progressive toward the outside; but meanwhile the tree maintains a layer of sapwood under the bark sufficient to provide for the necessary sap conduction.

The formation of heartwood (duramen) is usually evinced through an appreciable darkening of the tissue,[3] causing it to contrast more or less strongly with the sapwood (alburnum) which is generally whitish. The zone of demarcation may be abrupt or gradual. Various organic compounds are produced that possibly are by-products occasioned by the death of the parenchyma as it is included in the core of dead tissue in the tree. In any case, substances of this nature are infiltrated into the cell walls and, if copious in amount, may even accumulate in cell cavities, generally in the form of amorphous deposits.[4] The net result

raised some question as to the accuracy of this assumption; but until further proof is brought forward to the contrary, the original conception is accepted as valid in this text.

[1] There is some evidence to the effect that sapwood is not equally efficient in conduction throughout. If dyes in solution are injected into a tree when the sap flow is at a near peak, certain parts of the sapwood color more deeply than others.

[2] Statements to this effect are frequent in the literature on this subject. However, MacDougal and Smith (*Science*, Vol. 66, No. 1715, pp. 456–57. 1927) have shown that in redwood [*Sequoia sempervirens* (D. Don) Endl.] some of the ray cells remain alive for at least a century, even when they are 70 annual layers deep in the heartwood. Further investigations should be made.

[3] Species of *Picea*, *Abies*, *Tsuga*, *Populus*, etc., are devoid of heartwood in terms of color and are frequently spoken of as *sapwood trees;* it is quite probable, however, that heartwood is present in a physiological sense, *i.e.*, that the central portion of the stem consists entirely of dead tissue. In other species such as common hackberry (*Celtis occidentalis* L.) and persimmon (*Diospyros virginiana* L.), the production of heartwood is greatly delayed, and the zone of dark tissue about the pith, even in mature trees, is very narrow.

[4] The number of these compounds is legion, comprising tannins, dyestuffs of various sorts, gums, resins, the salts of organic acids, etc. Valuable extractives are obtained from the heartwood of some trees. On the other hand, the presence of infiltration compounds may act as a deterrent to the use of the heartwood for certain purposes.

of this change is a heartwood usually appreciably darker than the sapwood, the color in our domestic woods ranging for the most part through
shades of yellow, orange, red, and brown.

Heartwood differs from sapwood[1] not only in color and infiltration
content but usually in weight and sometimes in the correlated property of
strength; also in its relative durability and permeability. At the same
moisture content, it is generally somewhat heavier because of its greater
infiltration content, but exceptions occur, particularly in the conifers;
the sapwood of these, as it comes from the tree, is usually much wetter
than the heartwood (often up to 200 per cent of the dry weight) and not
infrequently is heavier. In most cases, there is no marked difference in
strength between heartwood and sapwood at the same moisture content
provided they are otherwise comparable; this is traceable to the fact that
the hardening (lignification) of the tissue takes place quickly behind the
cambium, not when the tissue passes over into heartwood. But again,
exceptions occur; for example, the heartwoods of certain trees such as
redwood [*Sequoia sempervierns* (D. Don) Endl.], western red cedar
(*Thuja plicata* D. Don), and black locust (*Robinia pseudoacacia* L.) have
been found to be considerably stronger in certain kinds of tests than the
sapwood; if, on the other hand, the extractable materials are removed,
there is no appreciable difference in the strength of the heart- and sapwood
of these species.

The greater durability and lesser permeability of heartwood are likewise explained, in part at least, by its higher infiltration content; some of
the products deposited in heartwood are often more or less toxic to fungi
and obnoxious to insects, rendering it more or less immune to attack. In
general, the deeper the color of the heartwood, the greater its durability.
This does not always hold, however; the heartwood of some of the light-
colored cedars, such as northern white cedar (*Thuja occidentalis* L.) and
Atlantic white cedar [*Chamaecyparis thyoides* (L.) B.S.P.] is not highly
pigmented owing to the presence of more or less colorless infiltration but
has unusual lasting qualities. The movement of moisture and air in the
heartwood of certain hardwood trees is also greatly inhibited by the
development of tyloses,[2] which occlude vessels. As a result, fungal
growth is discouraged. Both tyloses and infiltration products, especially
if the latter are copious in amount, undoubtedly are responsible for the
lessened permeability of heartwood. This varies, of course, in different

---

Butter, for example, is very subject to taint; for this reason, relatively few woods are
suitable for food containers.

[1] ANON. Differences between Heartwood and Sapwood. *Forest Prod. Lab., Tech.
Note* 189. Undated.

[2] Tyloses are described subsequently in the text (see p. 207).

trees; where the heartwood is quite impenetrable, it serves well for tight cooperage, tanks, etc. Sapwood is usually much easier to season and takes preservatives more readily.

Once heartwood is initiated at a given level in a tree, it continues to increase in diameter throughout the life of the tree. The sapwood, on the other hand, may be widest in youth and narrow materially as the tree ages, its area remaining approximately the same or increasing proportionally with the increase in the size of the crown; this is possible because the circumference of the band increases as the trunk becomes larger.[1]

Within a species, crown class appears to be the controlling factor governing the width of sapwood. Vigorous trees with large crowns frequently possess a sapwood fully as wide at a given level as other individuals of a different crown class many years younger.

Accurate data are not available as to whether heartwood formation is a gradual process over a period of years, or cyclic, *i.e.*, progressing for a time, this period followed by a pause in development extending over one or more seasons. In the majority of trees, the heartwood is quite uniform in color, lending weight to the first assumption; but lighter and darker zones of deposition are occasionally visible in some tree species (Ex., *Betula lutea* Michx. f.). There is also a void in the literature relative to the time during the year when new heartwood is formed. Premature heartwood formation, expecially along certain radii of the log, may be induced by wounding.

Periodic growth in trees, as expressed in terms of growth increments, bears no direct relation to heartwood formation. A given increment may be in the sapwood at one place along its contour and in the heartwood elsewhere; in other words, growth increments do not pass over as entities into heartwood.

The width of the sapwood in linear measurement and also in terms of the number of rings comprising it varies in individuals of the same species and at different heights in the same individual. Dominant specimens tend to postpone heartwood formation longer and hence to possess wider sapwood than suppressed individuals. Within a given tree, the sapwood is wider in the upper (younger) portions of the trunk than toward the base. Wide variations in width may also be noted in different species. For example, longleaf pine (*Pinus palustris* Mill.) has a very narrow sapwood, whereas in slash pine (*P. caribaea* Morolet) and loblolly pine (*P. taeda* L.) it is very wide, in the latter species often composing half of the trunk. This feature plays an important role in the utilization of southern yellow pine, especially for pulp for which sapwood is preferred.

[1] For the reason stated, the volume of sapwood in a segment of the stem may remain fairly constant or even increase as a tree ages.

It is not unusual to find 150 to 200 rings comprising the sapwood of ponderosa pine (*P. ponderosa* Laws.).[1] Fully as much variation occurs in the ring counts of the sapwood of hardwood trees, as is indicated in Table II.

TABLE II
NUMBER OF RINGS COMPRISING THE SAPWOOD OF HARDWOOD TREES*

Scientific Name of Tree	Number of Rings in the Sapwood
Catalpa speciosa Ward	1–2
Robinia pseudoacacia L	2–3
Castanea dentata (Marsh.) Borkh	3–4
Prunus serotina Ehrh	10–12
Gleditsia triacanthos L	10–12
Juglans nigra L	10–20
Fagus grandifolia Ehrh	20–30
Magnolia acuminata L	25–30
Acer saccharum Marsh	30–40
Cornus florida L	30–40
Cornus nuttalli Audub	30–40
Acer saccharinum L	40–50
Betula lenta L	60–80
Magnolia grandiflora L	60–80
Nyssa sylvatica Marsh	80–100
Nyssa aquatica L	100

* This information was taken from C. S. Sargent. Manual of the Trees of North America. Houghton Mifflin Company, Boston, 1926.

Sometimes, as a result of pathological disturbances, the parenchymatous cells in the sapwood are killed which under normal conditions remain alive; this frequently happens in the vicinity of wounds. The tissue containing such dead cells darkens prematurely and simulates normal heartwood. It is designated as **wound heartwood.**

Pathological heartwood not infrequently forms in species that do not possess normal heartwood on the basis of color. Such tissue is termed **false heartwood.** Its presence in nonheartwood trees is denoted by a grayish-green, brown, or reddish-brown core of wood which, because of its position in the trunk, resembles true heartwood. False heartwood has been thoroughly investigated in European beech (*Fagus sylvatica* L.f.); it also occurs in American beech, birch, maple, poplar, pine, and other species.

False heartwood in nonheartwood species is believed to result from fungal infection. The mycelium of certain fungi that grow in the dead branches and branch stubs of the tree spreads into the central portion (core) of the trunk, killing the living parenchyma. Physicochemical

[1] This species exhibits great variation in the width of the sapwood.

changes are induced which cause browning of cell contents and stimulate the formation of tyloses. Depending largely upon the amount of available air, either the infection progresses beyond the incipient stage, producing typical decay, or quite frequently it is arrested. In the latter instance, the only apparent effect on the wood is the change in color; its strength and other physical properties, likewise its durability, are little affected.

Occasionally, streaks of light-colored wood that have the appearance and properties of normal sapwood are found embedded in heartwood; such tissue is described as **included sapwood.** There is no exact information relative to the causes leading up to the inclusion of such light-colored tracts of tissue in heartwood. Included sapwood may occur in any tree species; it is especially common and evident in western red cedar.

Lighter zones or streaks are often present in heartwood and simulate included sapwood. They form as a result of incipient decay. In such instances, portions of the darker heartwood are bleached as a result of fungous action.

D. Wood Rays

Everyone is familiar with the fact that wood splits more or less readily along the grain and that it can be broken but does not split across the grain. The explanation of this phenomenon rests upon its cellular structure. It is a cell aggregate consisting of untold millions of tiny units known as cells, each with a wall enclosing a cell cavity. The cells of wood are usually much elongated in a given direction; in fact, in most timbers some of them are one hundred or more times as long as they are wide. The majority of these elongated cells have their long axes aligned vertically or nearly vertically in the standing tree, *i.e.*, along the grain. This explains why wood usually splits readily lengthwise of the log but refuses to split across the grain.

But here and there in the wood are cell aggregates extending horizontally and radially in the standing tree in which part or all the cells also have their long axes arranged radially.[1] These aggregates are known as wood rays or xylary rays. Wood may be likened in structure to a textile in which the threads run at right angles. In this analogy the rays would represent the cross threads (woof), and the remaining tissues of the wood, consisting of cells elongated along the grain, the long threads (warp).

Wood rays are in reality sheets or plates of horizontal tissue which appear to arise on the outer surface of the wood (next to the bark)[2] and

[1] These cells, though elongated, are much shorter than the fibers running lengthwise of the tree.

[2] Only the xylary portion of the ray is included in the wood. In reality, the ray

extend for varying distances into the trunk toward the pith, so oriented that the face of the plate appears in surface view as a fleck when the wood is split along the grain in the radial direction (Text Fig. 11, radial section). On the ends of logs (across the grain), they take the form of lines of varying width and proximity, usually running at right angles across the growth increments. In flat-sawn lumber, they assume still another form. Where a portion of the face of the board is truly tangent to the growth rings, the plates are cut transversely, *i.e.*, the ends are exposed (Text Fig. 11, tangential section). Rays are least conspicuous in this plane and may or may not show as a gross feature. When visible, they usually appear as short, more or less crowded lines which are usually staggered. Several domestic woods and many tropical timbers are peculiar in possessing storied rays; in such instances, the ray ends are arranged in tiers like windows in a building, causing transverse ripple marks on the tangential surface of the wood at low magnifications.

Rays in the secondary vascular tissues of trees serve as transverse avenues of conduction. Carbohydrate food is elaborated in the leaves through photosynthesis. Most or all of this in its original or in a changed form moves out of the leaves through the vascular tissues (veins), continues through the leaf traces leading into the trunk, and is transported down the tree in the inner living bark (phloem). Here it comes in contact with the phloem portions of the rays and is moved inward to the cambial region. If growth is progressing vigorously, probably little food gets past the cambium; in periods of slow growth, however, especially toward the close of the growing season, some food in soluble form may be moved through the cambium and stored in the xylary portions of the rays and even in the longitudinal parenchyma.

Commercial woods without exception possess wood rays. They exhibit wide variations in size and grouping, facts that are duly recorded in the Keys as a means of separation.

E. Wood Parenchyma

The trifold primary functions that wood performs in the life economy of the tree have already been enumerated. It serves as a channel for the movement of sap upward to the crown; only sapwood participates in this way. It supplies sufficient strength to the stem to enable it to support the crown; both sap- and heartwood are concerned in this function. Finally the sapwood, or, better, that portion of it which consists of living cells, performs the storage function. In all trees, but especially in young, vigorous individuals, appreciable amounts of food materials accumulate

---

extends through the cambium into the secondary phloem; in this tissue this portion is designated as a phloem ray.

toward autumn. This reserve food is utilized for seed production (which may occur only at intervals of several years) and for growth in length and thickness the following spring. Length growth, and not infrequently growth in thickness, start before the new leaves have attained a size sufficient to permit them to be effective in the manufacture of new food. Storage takes place in the cortex (in parts of the tree where it is still present), in the inner bark (older portions of the stem), and in the living parenchymatous cells in the sapwood of the stem(s) and roots.

The cells which serve for storage and are therefore living[1] while they are in the sapwood, collectively, form a parenchymatous system in the wood. Since they are probably not concerned to any great extent in conduction, they are comparatively short. Such cells are enabled to remain alive not only because they are in touch with other units of like nature but because they are in communication through the cambium with living cells in the inner bark of the tree which form a comparable system. By far the majority of the cells that are left behind by the cambium as it moves outward during a given year soon lose their contents[2] and thereafter perform only the functions of providing sufficient strength to the stem, and of conduction.[3] Collectively, they are known as prosenchyma.

The parenchyma of wood consists of **ray parenchyma** and **longitudinal parenchyma,** and of **epithelial parenchyma** if resin passages are present. The rays are composed largely or entirely of the first; hence the name. The longitudinal parenchyma, as the term implies, extends along the grain as strands of cells which may or may not be grouped further into larger, cablelike masses of tissue.

Ray parenchyma offers little of diagnostic value in the identification of wood at low magnifications except as its volume has a bearing on ray size. The same holds for epithelial parenchyma if this is present; the cells composing it are too small to permit their nature to be determined under the conditions stated. Longitudinal parenchyma, on the other hand, may or may not be visible as a gross feature. Individual strands sometimes show along the grain with a hand lens as beadlike structures

---

[1] It is an axiom of plant physiology that cells must be living in order to act as food reservoirs; a living protoplast is essential not only to permit the cell to store food within its boundaries but also to move this food in a soluble form out of the cell when there is a demand for it elsewhere in the plant. The corollary follows that dead cells, although unable to perform this function, may add strength to the stem, especially if their walls have been rendered woody; they also function in the conduction of sap. This latter phenomenon is, therefore, not vitalistic in the sense that it is confined to living cells; in fact, most if not all of the sap flow up a tree takes place in dead tissue.

[2] This takes place the season of their formation.

[3] They are usually greatly elongated in a given direction.

because of the dark contents of the cells [Ex., bald cypress (*Taxodium distichum* (L.) Rich.]; in transverse sections, such filaments appear as separate cells which are usually too small to show clearly, even if the contents are dark-colored. When massed in bands or encircling the pores, however, longitudinal parenchyma is often visible at low magnifications, in fact, may be quite conspicuous. Frequently, under such conditions, it is arranged in a more or less regular and constant manner and provides a diagnostic feature of no mean value. Specific terms, defined subsequently in the text and in the Glossary, are employed to designate the different types of arrangement and are used in many places in the Keys.

The longitudinal parenchyma of wood is discussed at further length in those portions of the text devoted to minute features.

F. Softwoods and Hardwoods

The features that have been described in the preceding pages are common to all commercial woods. The subdivisions into which woods naturally fall may now be considered to advantage.

Commercial woods are divisible into two general classes, popularly known as **softwoods** and **hardwoods;** these terms are frequently somewhat confusing, for some softwoods, such as hard pine (*Pinus palustris* Mill., etc.), are much harder than some of the hardwoods, such as basswood (*Tilia spp.*), and vice versa. They are therefore to be considered as used in a general sense, to indicate a type of wood rather than the physical characteristics of a given wood.

The softwoods, otherwise known as coniferous woods, are produced by coniferous and usually evergreen trees such as the pines, spruces, and hemlocks. The leaves are needlelike, linear, awl-shaped, or scalelike, and the seeds are borne either in cones in the axil of a scale, or naked. Since the majority of these trees bear cones, they are placed by botanists in the Coniferales, or Coniferae, which means literally "cone bearers." The hardwoods, on the other hand, are obtained from broad-leaved trees such as elm, ash, oak, and poplar, scattered through various plant orders and families. The leaves are broad except in rare instances and are usually deciduous in the temperate zones. The seeds are enclosed in a fruit (ripened ovary), which is either fleshy or dry at maturity.

Softwoods are sometimes designated as **nonporous woods** and hardwoods as **porous woods.** The basis of this classification lies in the fact that porous woods possess vessels or ducts extending along the grain which appear as pores and are often visible with the naked eye on the transverse surface. The vessels are in reality tubes which are jointed at frequent intervals because they arise through the fusion of cells in a longitudinal row, the joints indicating where two members of the row are in contact.

In some hardwoods, the vessels in the springwood are much larger than those farther out in the ring, and the transition from one type to the other is more or less abrupt. Such timbers are designated as **ring porous** as, for example, oak (*Quercus spp.*). In **diffuse porous** woods, such as maple (*Acer spp.*) and birch (*Betula spp.*), on the other hand, the vessels do not vary appreciably in size throughout the ring.

Vessels do not occur in coniferous woods; hence the designation, nonporous, which is sometimes used for the timbers of this group. When the transverse surface of a coniferous wood is viewed under a lens (Plates XXIII–L), it appears to consist of uninterrupted radial rows of cells (tracheids) of approximate size, inserted between very narrow wood rays. If the summerwood is pronounced, this condition is occasioned by the fact that the tracheids toward the outer margin of the ring are flattened and thicker walled and hence appear darker *en masse*.[1]

In summation, it is well to bear in mind that all woods are porous in the broad sense of possessing air space; a given wood is said to be porous or nonporous in the restricted sense of possessing or not possessing vessels or ducts that appear as pores on the transverse surface.

That porous wood differs in general appearance from coniferous wood soon becomes patent to the student, even to the novice just beginning the study of wood who quickly learns to separate the one from the other. The gross visual differences that serve to distinguish softwoods and hardwoods defy description, but they are nonetheless present. In essence, by a fleeting glance one acquires an impression that in reality is an intuitive summation of a set of anatomical and physical characteristics sufficiently different from a second complementary and comparable set to permit recognition of the one or the other kind of wood. In other words, the eye receives a different impression when a piece of coniferous wood is viewed from that which it receives when viewing a porous wood.

G. RESIN CANALS

Another gross anatomical feature of coniferous woods, the presence of resin canals in certain species, requires description here, the more since these structures are sometimes confused with vessels (pores) which

---

[1] Most porous woods also differ from coniferous woods in the prominence of the wood rays. In conifers, these structures are generally uniseriate except where they contain resin canals; consequently, they are relatively inconspicuous on the transverse surface and form a poorly defined fleck on the radial surface of the wood. In contrast, the rays of porous wood are several to many seriate in most instances; hence, they are relatively prominent on transverse surfaces and often produce a conspicuous ray fleck on the radial surface.

characterize hardwoods. Resin canals are in reality tubular intercellular spaces sheathed by secreting cells, *i.e.*, places where the cells have separated. The definition includes not only the cavity but the cells surrounding it. Resin canals differ from vessels in that the latter arise through the fusion of cells in a longitudinal row.

Resin canals are a normal feature of the woods of pine, spruce, larch or tamarack, and Douglas fir; such canals are known as **normal resin canals.** They serve to distinguish these timbers from those of other domestic conifers. **Traumatic canals**, so called, occur in certain coniferous genera, purportedly as a result of injury, in woods which are normally devoid of canals [Exs., hemlock (*Tsuga spp.*); fir (*Abies spp.*); redwood (*Sequoia sempervirens* (D. Don) Endl.].[1]

Normal resin canals extend both longitudinally (along the grain) and transversely (across the grain). The former are the larger and are restricted for the most part to the central and outer portions of the growth increments. Traumatic canals in our domestic woods are confined for the most part to those of the longitudinal type. They sometimes simulate normal longitudinal canals but differ in that they usually occur in a row near the inner boundary of the ring, the row often extending 1 inch or more in the tangential direction.

Normal resin canals vary greatly in size. They are most conspicuous in pine where, in sugar pine (*Pinus lambertiana* Dougl.), the openings are frequently visible with the naked eye on the transverse surface and the canals form prominent dark streaks on the faces of boards and planks[2]. In the other genera mentioned, on the other hand, they usually appear as scattered white or dark flecks toward the outer portion of the ring which are either visible with the naked eye or require a hand lens (10×) for their detection. In Douglas fir [*Pseudotsuga taxifolia* (Poir.) Britt.], more or less of a tendency is expressed toward the grouping of normal canals in short tangential lines of 2 to 30 plus; in such instances, they can be readily distinguished from traumatic canals of like nature by their position and by the fact that the tangential lines are much shorter.

Resin canals provide an important diagnostic feature for the identification of coniferous woods. Their presence as normal structures indicates that the wood in question must belong to one of four genera.

---

[1] Traumatic canals are also occasionally present in the wood of red-gum (*Liquidambar styraciflua* L.).

[2] Ponderosa pine (*Pinus ponderosa* Laws.) also generally has unusually large canals; the other extreme in the genus is represented by such species as lodgepole pine (*P. contorta* var. *latifolia* S. Wats.) and red pine (*P. resinosa* Ait.) in which they are small and approach those of eastern spruce (*Picea spp.*) and tamarack [*Larix laricina* (Du Roi) K. Koch.] in size.

H. Texture and Grain

Texture is concerned with the size and quality of wood elements.[1] To have specific meaning, the term must be preceded by a qualifying adjective. Such expressions as "fine-" and "coarse-textured," "even-" and "uneven-textured," "harsh-" and "smooth-textured" are frequently encountered in descriptions of wood.

In conifers, the best measure of fineness of texture is the tangential diameters of the tracheids (the cells that appear in radial rows in transverse section); the openings of such cells in many woods are visible at low magnifications, and their relative size, even as viewed with a hand lens, is of diagnostic importance. Proof of this assertion is readily forthcoming when a coarse-textured timber such as bald cypress [*Taxodium distichum* (L.) Rich.] is compared with a fine-textured wood such as eastern red cedar (*Juniperus virginiana* L.). The photomicrographs of coniferous woods across the grain (Plates XXIII to L) portray accurately the texture gradient of the coniferous woods of the United States. It is at once evident that such species as sugar pine, Idaho white pine, bald cypress, and redwood are usually coarse-textured, whereas the other extreme is represented by the cedars and by Pacific yew. Within a genus, this character is also important; for example, western larch is almost invariably coarser textured than its eastern counterpart tamarack.

In hardwoods, the tangential diameter of the vessels and the size of the wood rays, and the number of these per unit of volume, serve best as measures of texture. Chestnut [*Castanea dentata* (Marsh.) Borkh.], for example, is coarse-textured because the earlywood pores are unusually large; in comparison, the fine, lacelike appearance of basswood (*Tilia spp.*) in transverse section bespeaks the finer texture of this timber, which is sometimes called "fine-grained" (erroneous usage of term from the standpoint of the definition of "grain" as stated subsequently.) Oak (*Quercus spp.*) is coarse-textured, not only because of its large earlywood pores, but also because it possesses large rays as well. Woods such as oak, ash, chestnut, and walnut, with large earlywood pores, are termed "open-grained" by painters because they require a filler before the paint is applied.

Terms such as "harsh-textured" and "smooth-textured" are expressive of the quality of wood elements—how the wood works and finishes under tools. For example, eastern red cedar (*Juniperus virginiana* L.) is

---

[1] Texture varies within a species but not to the extent one might imagine. The cambial initials (cells) in a tree from which xylem and phloem elements are derived gradually enlarge during the first 20 to 40 years; thereafter, they remain fairly constant in size.

the premier pencil wood of the world for a number of reasons, among others because of its fineness and evenness of texture, and because of its compactness (body), which is traceable to the quality of its cells (thick-walled tracheids).

Grain, as used for wood, has to do with the alignment and sorting of wood elements; the latter is tied up with the width of annual increments because the sorting is frequently different in wide and in narrow rings. Like "texture," the term "grain" must be preceded by an adjective modifier to connote special meaning.

A straight-grained wood is one in which the elements are aligned parallel to the long axis of the log or timber. Spiral grain results from spiral alignment of the fibers. When such spirals reverse at intervals, interlocking grain results. Undulations in the fiber alignment are responsible for wavy and curly grain.

In woods such as maple and birch the transition between springwood and summerwood, and hence between the growth rings, is often scarcely evident; such woods are even-grained. If, on the other hand, the nature of the earlywood is quite different from that of the latewood, as in normal-run southern yellow pine, the wood is said to be "uneven-grained." It follows that unusually wide-ringed stock from the vicinity of the pith or from trees which, for some reason, grew faster than the average (Ex., coppice-grown stock) would, in general, be more uneven-grained than normal stock; this is because the range of variation in the nature of the tissue in all likelihood would be greater under these conditions. Such wood is often termed "coarse-grained" when, as a matter of fact, it is actually "uneven-grained"; lumbermen call it "second-growth" stock, which may be a misnomer since not infrequently the tissue in question resulted from growth 200 to 1000 or more years previously, at a time when the tree was young. It follows that, in the future, the lumber of many tree-species will be more uneven-grained than that on the market at the present time; it will have resulted from the growth of trees in man-managed forests under a shorter rotation than that required for climax forest, in some instances through "coppicing." In fact, this situation already exists; for example, it is becoming increasingly difficult to obtain the mellow stock of yellow-poplar that recommends this wood for many purposes.

For further discussion of grain and of figure in wood, see pages 267 to 281.

III. THE PHYSICAL PROPERTIES OF WOOD OF VALUE IN IDENTIFICATION

The physical properties of wood may be divided into the mechanical and the nonmechanical. Mechanical properties require stress for their determination; the wood is put under stress, and strain, proportionate up to a certain point, results. The nonmechanical physical properties of wood do not require stress for their determination, and some of these are of value in wood identification and hence deserve brief treatment here.

A. Color

The aesthetic value of wood as a medium of construction is traceable to two sources, its color and its figure. Both are variable, not only in different kinds of wood but within that of a given species. It is this characteristic which makes possible the achievement of unique effects when things are made of wood; each piece of furniture has its own individuality, a fact that is of the greatest value as a selling point. Color in wood, where striking and unusual, is also sometimes important in wood identification, in spite of its variability. For this reason, it is desirable to devote some attention to it in this portion of the text.

Sapwood may be white, or nearly so, or tinted with yellow, pink, red, etc. Where some coloration is present, it is usually not deep enough to render it of diagnostic value.

The significance and manner of heartwood formation in trees have already been explained. The hues produced through the deposition of infiltration products cover a wide range and are traceable to the four spectral colors, red, orange, yellow, and violet, and to various blendings of these. Of the intermediate colors, brown is most frequent. Jet black (in terms of physics) is not represented among our domestic woods but is a feature of genuine ebony (*Diospyros ebenum* Koenig), native to southern India and Ceylon. The narrow heartwood of persimmon (*D. virginiana* L.) ranges from dark brown to nearly black.

The color of heartwood may or may not be distinctive. The rich chocolate or purplish heart of black walnut (*Juglans nigra* L.) may be cited as an example of the first possibility since this is undoubtedly the most reliable and most readily recognized feature in the identification of this wood. The same holds for the characteristic purplish or rose-red heartwood of eastern red cedar (*Juniperus virginiana* L.) which ages to a dull red or reddish brown. In many other trees, however, the color of the heartwood varies too much to serve as a means of identification. Frequently, moreover, the same or nearly the same color will characterize a number of related or unrelated species, making its use impossible diagnostically.

The heartwood of some trees darkens appreciably upon exposure, that of others tends to bleach. Shades of dark red usually age to reddish brown. The heart of red mulberry (*Morus rubra* L.) is orange-yellow to golden brown when first exposed but soon turns russet in the light. The rich wine-red of mahogany is also of photogenic origin; in fact, the ability of this wood to darken upon exposure to light, creating an impression of substantiality and age, is one of the factors that recommends it so highly. Light-yellow woods such as those belonging to the Orange Family (Rutaceae) not infrequently fade.

In trade practice, the color of heartwood is sometimes an asset, at other times a liability. For example, in selecting stock of ponderosa pine (*Pinus ponderosa* Laws.) for interior finish or hard maple (*Acer saccharum* Marsh.) for flooring, heartwood is avoided wherever possible because of its darker color. The colors of sap- and heartwood are often altered through manipulation. The sapwood of black walnut is some- times steamed with shavings or sawdust of the heartwood, to darken it, or stained outright with a dye. Ammonia fumes are frequently used to obtain shades of gray. Harewood in the trade is the product of *Acer pseudoplatanus* L. of western Europe; greywood is made by treating harewood with a solution of iron salts which supposedly combine with tannic substances present in the wood, darkening it appreciably. Holly wood (*Ilex opaca* Ait.), dyed black, is used as a substitute for ebony. Unusual effects have also been obtained by injecting dyes into the sap- wood of certain trees, notably white birch (*Betula papyrifera* Marsh.), at the proper time of the year so that they are carried upward by the sap stream; the trees are subsequently felled and converted into lumber, but wood, colored in this way, has never met with favor in the United States.

Fungi (and probably bacteria) are frequently causal agencies in the discoloration of wood. For further information upon this subject, see under Defects Caused by Wood-staining Fungi, page 331. At other times, the stain in sapwood is of oxidative origin, as in *Alnus* and *Aesculus spp.;* discoloration in such instances may result within a few minutes and is traceable to chemical changes which take place in substances in the sapwood.

Previous to the advent of aniline dyes, the heartwoods of various trees, particularly of those belonging to the Leguminosae and Moraceae, were a source of coloring material. In some instances, the coloring principle is ready formed in which case it is free or chemically combined; in other cases it occurs as a chromogen which requires further treatment, such as fermentation, to produce the final color. Some heartwood pig- ments are freely soluble in water [Ex., Osage-orange (*Maclura pomifera* Raf.) Schneid.]; others require alcohol, alkalies, or other solvents before they will dissolve, or are insoluble. The aqueous or alcoholic solutions not infrequently exhibit fluorescent qualities.[1]

[1] Fluorescence is defined in optics as that physical property which some media

It is clear from the preceding paragraphs that in the identification of wood, the use of color, particularly the color of the heartwood, is fraught with difficulty. This is due not only to the variations in this feature that occur naturally or are traceable to causal agents of one sort or another but also to the fact that the average student is unfamiliar with the terms describing such fluctuations, particularly terms referring to shades of color. It is best to use this character with caution, tempered by experience, and to avoid the use of too many descriptive terms. "Color" has been used in the Keys only when a sharp contrast is registered and then particularly where other criteria might fail or need additional substantiation.

B. LUSTER

Luster is the property of wood that enables it to reflect light,[1] in other words, the property of exhibiting sheen; woods are lustrous or dull in proportion as they possess or do not possess this characteristic. Luster is distinct from color and also from the ability of the wood to take a good polish. This last feature is of first importance in the selection of ornamental woods, but many of these are comparatively lusterless in the unfinished state. One of the first evidences of incipient decay in wood frequently is loss of luster. Lumbermen call such wood "dead."

The luster of wood varies undoubtedly according to its anatomical structure and the infiltration products contained in it, and likewise according to the plane of section in which it is viewed and the angle at which light strikes it (and hence is reflected). The effect of wood structure on sheen is difficult to explain, but it does have a direct bearing. Oily or waxy substances detract from luster; the corollary follows that woods with comparatively little infiltration are often quite lustrous. For the same reason, sapwood may possess greater sheen than heartwood, but the reverse may hold true; *i.e.*, extractable material in the heartwood may

---

have of emitting light when exposed to the action of certain rays of the spectrum. Such light is distinct from that reflected at the surface (which is responsible for surface color) and from that transmitted by the medium.

The fluorescence of wood may be tested by placing a few grains of sawdust or some shavings in a test tube with water or ethyl alcohol and permitting them to stand for a few days. During this time, some of the substances infiltrated into the wood leach into the liquid. The solution is then filtered and the filtrate is viewed in strong sunlight or in a beam of artificial light; the angle of observation should be approximately at 90 degrees to the beam of light. An effect comparable to that of changeable silk or that observed in solutions of eosin, denotes fluorescence. This feature is of diagnostic value in identifying certain tropical woods, for example, species of *Pterocarpus* and *Eysenhardtia*.

[1] ANON. Light Reflecting Properties of Woods. Electrical Handbook, pp. 64–65. J. Crabtree & Co., London. 1941.

be the direct cause of sheen. Quartersawn lumber generally reflects light more strongly than flat-sawn stock, largely because of the presence of numerous ray flecks which reflect the light strongly. The effect of the angle of incidence of light is also very apparent in certain kinds of figure; for example, when the pattern is of the ribbon or roe type (see Glossary for definition of these terms), the alternating light and dark zones shift according to the directions of the light rays.

Luster or lack of luster is sometimes of value in wood identification. Eastern spruce (*Picea spp.*) is not infrequently confused with northern white pine (*Pinus strobus* L.) by the neophyte in wood identification but is readily distinguished by its greater luster.[1] Lack of sheen is an earmark of such woods as bald cypress [*Taxodium distichum* (L.) Rich.] and eastern red cedar (*Juniperus virginiana* L.).[2] Among porous timbers, the lustrous wood of catalpa (*Catalpa speciosa* Ward.) cannot easily be confused with sassafras [*Sassafras albidum* (Nutt.) Nees], which is dull. The same discrepancy exists between white ash (*Fraxinus spp.*) and brown ash (*F. nigra* Marsh.), and other cases could be cited. The great majority of domestic woods are intermediate in luster; in such instances, sheen or a lack of sheen is of secondary importance, or of no value whatsoever, in their identification.

C. Odor and Taste

To have odor, a substance must possess the property of emitting free molecules into the air. The ability of substances to register this phenomenon in turn is dependent upon their vapor pressure; those in which this is high will lose more molecules than those in which it is low. But not all substances reacting in this way possess scent; the presence of such free molecules may or may not be registered by the olfactory nerves. The various animals including man differ greatly in their ability to record and to interpret odors. Furthermore, odors that are attractive to some animals (carrion beetles) are very obnoxious to others (man).

At ordinary temperatures, wood substance itself[3] has no scent; *i.e.*, it does not emit free molecules into the air. When an odor is present, it is due to substances deposited in the wood (infiltration products) or formed through the action of fungi or microorganisms. Compounds of the second type may result from the activities of wood-destroying fungi which penetrate and may eventually destroy cell walls; through their action, by-products of various sorts are deposited in the tissue that

---

[1] In the literature, this has been described as "pearly" (nacreous).

[2] When unpolished.

[3] The material of which cell walls are composed.

remains, and these frequently give off strong scents.[1] Or the odor, at least in the sapwood, may be due to the decomposition of reserve food products present in the parenchyma.   These are of three general sorts: carbohydrates, proteins, and fats and oils.   Proteins, particularly, give off very disagreeable odors when undergoing decay.   This explains why the sapwood of trees felled during warm weather is frequently strongly and disagreeably scented.

The odor of sound wood, in the majority of instances, is either too faint to be registered by man or insufficiently distinctive to be of value. Such woods are generally considered to be unscented, and no further attention is given to this feature.   Some timbers, however, particularly those belonging to certain plant families such as the Cupressaceae, Lauraceae, Santalaceae, and Myristicaceae, have characteristic odors of varying degree of persistence which serve as earmarks in their identification.   To this class, among our domestic woods, belong sassafras [*Sassafras albidum* (Nutt.) Nees] and California laurel [*Umbellularia californica* (Hook. & Arn.) Nutt.], and also the various cedars; the scents of these woods are pleasant to most people and distinctive but, like all odors, must be learned from known material, to be of value diagnostically. Malodors are not unusual.   Dark samples of bald cypress [*Taxodium distichum* (L.) Rich.] with a high infiltration content often smell rancid; catalpa (*Catalpa speciosa* Ward.) frequently has an odor reminiscent of kerosene.   The fetid odor of nannyberry wood (*Viburnum lentago* L.)[2] is very penetrating and lasting and is especially obnoxious to human beings.   Many tropical timbers such as sandalwood, genuine rosewood, stinkwood, and camphorwood possess strong characteristic scents.

Odor in wood, when traceable to infiltration products, is more pronounced in green wood than in seasoned wood, is usually more evident in heartwood than in sapwood, and is generally stronger on surfaces that have been freshly exposed.   Prolonged exposure to air or water, and kiln drying, tend to dull this feature and to mullify its value in wood identification.

The scent of wood may be an asset or a liability in its utilization for a given purpose.   For example, the odor of red cedar is said to be obnoxious to insects, recommending this species for chests in which woolens and furs are to be stored; in the Orient, strongly scented camphorwood (*Cinnamomum camphora* Nees & Eberm.) is used for the same purpose. Cigars are packed in boxes of Spanish cedar,[3] toon and calantas (*Cedrela*

---

[1] Bacteria, slime molds, and possibly wild yeasts play a role in the final stages of wood decay.   Odors are undoubtedly due in some cases to these organisms.

[2] Not included in the Keys since it is not a commercial wood.

[3] Sometimes also wrapped individually in veneer stock.

spp.) in the belief that the scent of the wood enhances the aroma of the tobacco. From time immemorial, powdered sandalwood has been burned on altars in the Orient because it gives off a strong, pleasant scent. On the other hand, certain comestible products, such as butter and beer, are especially subject to taint. Fir (*Abies spp.*),[1] spruce (*Picea spp.*), and ash (*Fraxinus spp.*), woods with little infiltration content and hence largely devoid of scent when dry, are preferred for butter tubs. The interior of wooden tanks in breweries is coated (kotited) to prevent the beer from coming in actual contact with the wood and thus acquiring taint.

It will be evident from the preceding paragraphs that odor in wood as a means of identification must be used with caution. It cannot be defined except by comparison with some previously known scent, and people vary greatly in the interpretation of odors and in the keenness of their olfactory sense. Moreover, odor in wood is traceable to different sources; only when it originates from infiltration products that are sufficiently constant and copious in the wood in question and of a specific nature does it become characteristic and hence of value diagnostically.

The senses of odor and taste are akin; many woods have taste, but this is seldom distinctive. Among domestic woods, in the one instance in which this feature is distinctive [incense cedar (*Libocedrus decurrens* Torr.)], directions are given in the Key for making this test.

D. Weight

The weight of wood is sometimes of value in wood identification; this holds particularly when the discrepancy between species under comparison is unusually great. For this reason and because weight data are included subsequently in the text under Descriptions of Woods by Species, this subject is accorded treatment here.

The **weight of wood** should not be confused with the **density of wood.** The weight varies (*a*) according to the amount of wood substance (cell-wall substance) present per unit of volume, (*b*) according to the amount of infiltration in the wood, and (*c*) according to its moisture content. Strictly speaking, the **actual density of wood** is concerned only with *a*, *i.e.*, with the amount of cell-wall substance per unit of volume. In practice, however, only **the relative density of wood** is computed since it is impractical to attempt to separate the infiltration products from the wood substance proper. Figures of relative density, therefore, include both *a* and *b*.

Throughout woody plants, cell-wall substance is remarkably uniform in its physical and chemical composition.[2] Its density has been com-

---

[1] The ill scent of fir wood generally disappears as the wood dries.

[2] This does not hold for the various layers in cell walls but in cells as a whole.

puted in various ways, and different values have been obtained to indicate its specific gravity.[1] The general consensus is to the effect that the correct figure is in the neighborhood of 1.53.[2] Since 1 cubic foot of distilled water at its greatest density (4°C.) weighs 62.4 pounds, 1 cubic foot of solid wood substance, if it were possible to obtain this, would therefore weigh 95.47 pounds. Expressing this in a different way, any wood, were it not for the air space in it, would sink immediately. Driftwood becomes waterlogged and eventually sinks because some or all of the air in the cavities of the cells composing the wood is replaced by water; since the cell-wall substance is over half again as heavy as water and buoyance was lost through loss of the entrapped air, the wood sinks.

The amount of cell-wall substance per unit of volume (actual density of the wood) varies according to (*a*) the size of the cells and (*b*) the thickness of the cell walls, and, of course, (*c*) the number of cells of various kinds in terms of *a* and *b* that are present. Fibers, particularly, since they have small transverse dimensions (which permit of the massing of great numbers in a relatively small volume), have a decided bearing on weight; if thin-walled or wide-lumened, or both, the wood will be light; if the reverse, heavy. Note should be made at this time of the fact that unusually light woods do not necessarily have a high pore count (vessel volume); in fact, the reverse is usually the case.

The **infiltration in wood** is of two sorts, inorganic or "mineral" infiltration, as it is called, and organic infiltration. The **inorganic infiltration in wood** seldom comprises more than 1 per cent of the dry weight of the wood and is left behind in the ash when the wood is burned. According to Hawley and Wise,[3] the principal metallic components in wood ashes are calcium, potassium, and magnesium. The common acid radicals are—CO_3,—PO_4, and—SiO_4. Besides these, small amounts of sodium, manganese, aluminum, iron, sulphates, and chlorides are almost invariably present. Crystals of calcium oxalate are not infrequent and are usually set aside in special parenchymatous cells or in locules resulting from the division of such cells. Wood ashes were the source from which our forefathers obtained lye (potash) for soapmaking.

The **organic infiltration in wood** may be scanty or copious. It is most abundant in heartwood where, as has already been pointed out, it impregnates cell walls and, if unusually abundant, may collect in cell cavities as well, particularly in parenchyma and in the pores (vessels).

[1] The ratio, expressed fractionally or decimally, between its weight and the weight of an equal volume of water.

[2] STAMM, A. J. Calculations of the Void Volume of Wood. *Indus. and Engin. Chem.*, Vol. 30, p. 1280. 1938.

[3] HAWLEY, L. F., and L. E. WISE. The Chemistry of Wood, p. 119. Reinhold Publishing Corporation, New York. 1926.

Woods with little organic infiltration are usually not highly colored and, in many cases, are not durable; the reverse generally holds for dark-colored woods. The relative density of the wood may be influenced in no small measure by the organic infiltration in it; its strength may or may not be. As stated previously, the compounds composing the organic infiltration of wood cover a wide range and are extremely complex chemically. Gums, resins, dyes, tannins, etc., are very frequent, and many of these are of decided economic importance.

The **moisture content of wood**[1] has a direct bearing on its weight, and moisture contents in excess of 100 per cent are not at all unusual. The sapwood of conifers is usually much wetter than the heartwood (the moisture content may be as high as 200 per cent);[2] in hardwoods, the water may be fairly evenly distributed throughout the tree or higher in certain parts of the trunk than in others. In some species, the heartwood toward the base is wetter than that higher up; a butt log may have a moisture content considerably in excess of 100 per cent; when the weight of such a log exceeds 62.4 pounds per cubic foot, it will not float. In this case it is called a "sinker." In a given cross section, certain layers may be much drier than other; furthermore, the sequence of wet and dry layers may change from month to month. The total water content of the wood of a tree does not appear to fluctuate widely at different times during the year; trees bleed more readily in the spring than later in the season, a situation explained by the fact that the sap is under greater pressure in the wood at that time.

Different kinds of trees also vary greatly in the wetness of the wood as it comes from the trunk. Under these conditions, the wood of balsam

[1] It is customary to express the moisture content of wood as a percentage of the ovendry weight. Thus, a sample with 200 per cent moisture would lose two-thirds of its weight in passing to the ovendry condition and half of its weight if it contained 100 per cent moisture. Expressing this in a different way, in this instance, the oven-dry weight of the wood may be considered as $100x$; the weight of the moisture in the wood would then be $200x$, the total weight of the block before it was ovendried, $300x$. The following formula may also be used to determine moisture content:

Percentage of moisture =

$$\left(\frac{\text{wt. of the wood before oven-drying—wt. of the ovendry wood}}{\text{wt. of ovendry wood}}\right) \times 100$$

This equation can also be expressed in this form:

$$\text{Percentage of moisture} = \left(\frac{\text{wt. of the wood before oven-drying}}{\text{wt. of the ovendry wood}} - 1\right) \times 100$$

[2] According to Newlin and Wilson (Mechanical Properties of Woods Grown in the United States. *U.S. Dept. Agr., Bul.* 556. 1917), tamarack [*Larix laricina* (Du Roi) K. Koch] and bald cypress [*Taxodium distichum* (L.) Rich.] are exceptions to this rule in that the moisture content is fairly uniform throughout the tree.

The wall of the plant cell is formed by the protoplast and is more or less rigid. As will be pointed out subsequently, it consists of one or more layers. The cell wall provides the room in which the protoplast is housed.

III. ONTOGENY OF THE WOODY PLANT CELL

The cells composing wood are mature in the sense that they have passed through certain phases in arriving at this state. The changes through which a woody cell has passed constitute its life history, or ontogeny. It is of decided advantage at this point in the text to discuss the ontogeny of the woody cell.

A. PHASE OF ORIGIN

Woody cells, in fact, cells of any sort whatsoever, never arise *de novo* but always through division or fusion of preexisting cells. All the working (somatic) tissues of plants[1] including wood are traceable to the first source. They are composed of cells that have arisen as a result of cell division. The formation of new individuals through fusion occurs only where sexuality is involved. In such a union, each nucleus possesses inherent transmittable characters of coordinate rank that can be conveyed to the next generation. The dominant characters prevail in the fusion nucleus, and some are drawn from each parent cell. The sex impetus derived from such a fusion may continue for generations of vegetative cells. For example, in trees produced from seed, the developing ovule in the pistil of the flower contains a female nucleus which is fertilized by a male nucleus brought to it through the agency of a pollen grain and tube. Following fusion, vast numbers of vegetative cells are produced which in the aggregate compose the mature tree. Wood arises directly through cell division but indirectly through cell fusion since trees as organisms would not long survive were the stimulus of fertilization to be withdrawn prior to seed formation.

Cell division may be direct or indirect.[2] **Direct division** (amitotic division) occurs in the lowest primitive plants or sometimes in senile vegetative cells that have nearly ceased to function. The nucleus

---

[1] The same holds for animals.

[2] In cell division, the nucleus is the most important organ because it is the "bearer of heredity." It follows that a study of cell division is largely a study in nuclear dynamics; the cytoplasm and plastids, when present, are passive agents in the process and continue to live as well with the one as with the other daughter nucleus, though provision is made that ensures the presence of these organs in each of the new cells. Details of nuclear structure and division can be deciphered only in cells that have been properly killed and stained, and it is customary to resort to chemical treatment to bring this about. The technique is involved but affords satisfactory results if the material is properly selected.

becomes dumbbell shaped and divides through simple fission. An annular thickening meanwhile is formed on the interior of the old cell wall, and through the extension of this centripetally a new cell wall is formed between the daughter nuclei. In by far the majority of cases, however, **indirect division** (mitotic division) takes place which ensures the halving of nuclear material between the daughter nuclei. This consists in the formation of a number of nuclear figures which follow one another in regular sequence. The nuclear membrane delineating the nucleus from the cytoplasm disappears, and the nuclear reticulum of the resting nucleus is replaced by a **nuclear spindle. Chromosomes** are formed from chromatin material, and these congregate at the equator of the spindle. In **indirect vegetative division,** these split lengthwise, the half-chromosomes thus resulting going to opposite poles. The number of chromosomes congregating at the respective poles is therefore the same as in the original mother cell. **Indirect reduction division** which results in the formation of sex cells differs from the above in that the chromosomes line up in pairs at the equator and whole chromosomes proceed to one or to the other of the respective poles. Sex cells therefore possess the half (haploid) number of chromosomes, the full (diploid) number being restored when such cells unite. Following the division or separation of the chromosomes through nuclear division, the daughter nuclei assume the characteristics of a normal, plant-cell nucleus, and a cell wall forms between them. For a time at least, this is penetrated by a large number of extremely fine strands of protoplasm, called **plasmodesma,** whose function is to ensure direct communication between the protoplasts of adjacent cells. As the contiguous daughter cells develop further, the number of plasmodesma is greatly reduced since many of them are ruptured.[1]

B. Phase of Enlargement

The second phase in the life history of a woody cell, in fact, of any cell, is that of enlargement, and considerable variation is manifested in this respect. At this stage, the protoplast is encased by a **primary wall.**[2] In some cases, little change takes place in the cell either in shape or in size following its origin through cell division. The wall may remain thin or may thicken in the manner described in the next section, and the cell

[1] The distribution of plasmodesma in a cell wall is not uniform. For the most part they are in groups the distribution of which is determined by the shape of the cell and its points of contact with neighboring cells. The larger groups occur in small areas which, as wall thickening proceeds, remain thin. Each such area becomes a pit, a structure which is subsequently described in this chapter.

[2] As was previously stated, the primary walls of contiguous cells are held together by intercellular substance.

becomes a corporeal part of a mature tissue. As a rule, however, there is an increase in the dimensions of the cell, and enlargement from a few to several hundred times takes place. Under such circumstances, the primary wall and the layer of intercellular substance between cells tend to become thinner and considerably modified in form. Were the cell able to enlarge in all directions without restraint, growth could proceed equally over the whole surface of the wall, and the mature cell would be a replica of the original except in size. In tissues such as wood, however, enlarging cells no longer act as units; they exert considerable pressure upon one another. Tissue tensions[1] result, and mutual adjustments must be made. In such instances, areal growth may be confined to certain portions of the wall, and the adult cell may assume quite a different shape or size from that of the juvenile cell which gave it birth. For example, cells through which food or "sap" is conducted in a given direction, as radially in a tree or up the stem, usually elongate farther in the direction of flow. Examples of this sort are found in wood rays where the cells are lengthened horizontally and radially in the standing tree, and also in the longitudinal elements which course vertically between the rays and through which, while they are a part of the sapwood, "sap" is conducted up the tree; such cells are often very long vertically and may on occasion (fibers) become one hundred or more times as long as they are wide.

Water plays a very important role in cell enlargement, and tissues that are increasing rapidly in volume are always fluxed with it. This is due in part to the fact that the protoplasts of the cells composing these consist largely of water, in part because plant cells, as they enlarge, develop vacuoles which act as reservoirs for cell sap.[2] The cell is no longer completely filled with protoplasm as it was in the embryonic condition, for the protoplast fails to keep up with the increase in the volume of the cell cavity.[3] As the enlarging plant cell approaches its final size, the vacuoles frequently become larger and often coalesce. Under such conditions, the protoplasm may be restricted to a parietal layer lining the wall in which

---

[1] Such stresses reach a peak in certain dicotyledonous woods, particularly in those in which some of the cells (Ex., vessel segments) increase many times in volume. The cementing substance between cells then sometimes splits lengthwise under the stresses thus set up. As a result, the cells no longer remain in contact throughout but pull apart here and there, meanwhile providing for continued intercommunication by narrow tubular processes (separated by intercellular spaces) extending between them. Cells of this sort are said to be "disjunctive."

[2] The term "cell sap" is used in the absence of a more precise expression.

[3] This constitutes one of the chief differences between plant and animal cells; in the latter, the protoplast usually continues to fill the entire cell cavity.

the nucleus is embedded, or the latter may retain its median position in the cell and be attached by strands to the parietal layer of protoplasm.

Growth and the origin of vacuoles in a cell are traceable to **osmotic pressure.**   The protoplast develops a membrane of **ectoplasm** on its outer surface which separates it from the cell wall, and this membrane possesses osmotic properties.   In addition, each vacuole is bounded by a layer of **endoplasm** with like properties.   Within the cell sap are various organic acids and their salts in dilute solution, and these, with certain crystalloid substances, are responsible for osmotic pressure.   The cell is enabled to absorb water from without its walls and to store it in vacuoles.   The latter enlarge further, the peripheral portion of the protoplast is pressed firmly against the cell wall, and turgor results.   As a consequence, stress is brought to bear on the thin wall (primary wall) of the cell which increases in surface area either through stretching or through further growth, perhaps in both ways.   In this way the cell accommodates itself to the pressure from within; in other words, it grows.

It follows that cell size is restricted within certain limits, for a number of reasons.   As the vacuoles increase in volume, the cell sap is diluted, and its osmotic pressure is correspondingly reduced.   Furthermore, some of the substances responsible for osmotic pressure are undoubtedly removed from the protoplast during the process of wall building.   In cells in which there is little or no areal growth of the primary wall, the tension in this, since it is an elastic membrane, increases as the cell enlarges.   This force impedes the further enlargement of the cell, as does also the pressure exerted by neighboring cells in contact with the unit in question.   Final cell size, obviously, is contingent upon the balance of these opposing forces.   The large cells that are a feature of certain plants may be due either to further growth of the protoplast and hence to sustained or even enhanced osmotic pressure or to initial embryonic cells of large size.

The manner in which the increase in the surface area of the primary cell wall proceeds can only be conjectured.   It is conceivable that the primary wall consists of innumerable ultramicroscopic particles[1] which are mutually attracted to one another but are separated by films of water. When turgor develops, *i.e.*, when there is pressure from within and the primary wall is stretched, the particles become more widely separated and the films of water increase in width.   Eventually, new particles are inserted between the old by the protoplast, and the surface area is thus increased.   Although the **intussusception theory** is based wholly upon supposition, it does offer a means of explaining areal growth in primary walls.

[1] Called "micelles" in the earlier literature.

C. Phase of Cell-wall Thickening

1. Manner in Which Thickening Proceeds.—During the period of enlargement, the protoplast is encased by a primary wall and by this wall only.[1]   At the time when a xylary cell attains its ultimate size or soon after, the cell wall thickens.   This is brought about by the deposition on the primary wall of a **secondary wall,** this new layer resulting from the further activity of the protoplast working within the cell lumen.   A necessary corollary to this statement follows, *viz.*, that wall thickening proceeds only in living cells; cells in which the protoplasts have disappeared cannot continue to thicken their walls.   The formation of the secondary wall marks an irreversible change in the cell; further enlargement of the cell is precluded, although not necessarily further division, provided that the daughter cells thus resulting occupy the same volume as the original cell.   A further observation should be recorded at this time.   Certain postcambial changes that take place in the secondary phloem of trees as it is pushed farther to the outside through periodic secondary thickening have already been noted (page 29).   Among these are the development of ray flares in many twigs, to provide for the increasing girth of the inner living bark; likewise the formation of cork cambia (phellogens).   According to Kerr and Bailey,[1] cell division in such instances proceeds only in those cells in the phloem (parenchyma) in which no true secondary walls have formed during tissue differentiation.   The primary walls that were present in such cells immediately following their origin in the cambium modify but slightly in form and thickness, and, as a consequence, the cells retain their capacity for further growth and enlargement.

There are two theories that seem to explain the thickening of cell walls: the **apposition theory** and the **superposition theory.**   According to the first, ultramicroscopic particles are considered to be deposited separately and individually upon the preexisting wall surface (at the start, on the primary wall), and secondary layers are gradually built up through deposition.   According to the second conception, whole layers of ultramicroscopic particles in the form of lamellae are deposited at a given time by the protoplast.   This theory of superposition gains weight from the fact that in favorable material which has been properly stained it is possible to distinguish stratification in cell walls.   Bast fibers and wood fibers not infrequently exhibit such layers, especially when cut transversely.   Possibly thickening by apposition and by super-

[1] Kerr, T., and I. W. Bailey.   The Cambium and Its Derivative Tissues.   X. Structure, Optical Properties, and Chemical Composition of the So-called Middle Lamella.   *Jour. Arnold Arboretum*, Vol. 15, p. 333.   1934.

position both take place in the wall under varying conditions depending upon the nutritive material available to the protoplast at different periods, the type of cell, inheritance, etc.; under these conditions, wall thickening would result through a combination of these processes.

The thickness of the secondary wall varies greatly in different cells; at times, it is so thin as to be easily overlooked. Cells whose functions are mainly conductive and mechanical (prosenchyma) have thicker secondary walls as a rule than those designed primarily for storage. The

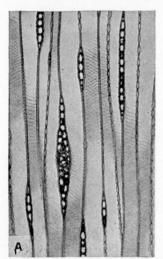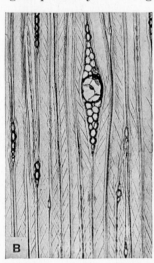

TEXT FIG. 14.—*A*. Spiral thickening in the longitudinal tracheids of Douglas fir [*Pseudotsuga taxifolia* (Poir.) Britt.] (185 ×). *B*. Spiral checking in the longitudinal tracheids of longleaf pine (*Pinus palustris* Mill.) (85 ×).

elements of oak wood may be cited as a case in point. In this timber, the strands of longitudinal parenchyma are composed of relatively thin-walled cells whose chief function appears to be that of storage; the fibers in the outer portion of the ring, in contrast, are thick-walled, in dense-wooded species often to such a degree that the cell cavity (lumen) is reduced to a mere slit.

2. Spiral Thickening.—Certain woods also possess cells in which the secondary wall not only is appreciably thickened but is equipped with spiral thickening on the inner surface next to the lumen (Text Fig. 14, *A*). Spiral bands of this sort have been described as tertiary in the literature, but they are actually a part of the secondary wall. Several such spirals extend along the inner surface of the wall at the same time, ascending usually in a counterclockwise direction. In longitudinal sections of wood where adjacent walls in surface view of two cells happen to be included, spiral thickening often produces a reticulate pattern (visible in the figure). This is due to the fact that the hatchings on the side of the wall toward the observer usually mount from right to left, those on the side of the wall away from the observer in the opposite direction. Since the wall was rendered translucent in preparing the section and the lenses of a microscope possess depth of focus, the sets of lines going in different directions are both visible at the same time, producing the effect stated.

Spiral thickening, when present, is restricted to prosenchyma where it is found in different types of elements (cells), not only in those in which the long axis is vertical in the standing tree but also on occasion in ray cells as well. Usually, the helixes extend the full length of the cell, but not always. For example, in the vessel segments of red-gum (*Liquidambar styraciflua* L.), the thickening of this sort is confined to the ligulate tips (Text Fig. 37, *B*, *f*); spirals in the fibrous cells of coniferous woods tend to run out toward the ends. The angle assumed by the helixes within a species also varies considerably, so much so, in fact, that it is only of relative diagnostic significance. In general, the thicker the cell wall and hence the narrower the lumen, the steeper the spiral. From this reasoning, it is evident that helixes in cells near the outer boundary of a growth increment would be steeper than those in cells further back in the season's growth, because they have a thicker wall and a narrower lumen. The spacing of the coils of the spirals, on the other hand, is more or less constant within certain limits in a given wood; this feature can therefore be used in the separation of species.[1]

3. Pits (Text Fig. 15).—Gaps or recesses are left as the secondary wall is laid down by the protoplast, to facilitate the interchange of materials between cells. A gap of this sort is known as a pit. A pit consists of the recess produced in this way and the membrane spanning the pit at its outer end.

Pits formed as above characterize individual cells, but they rarely occur solitarily. As a rule, a complementary pit is formed directly opposite on the other side of the middle lamella in the contiguous cell, and a pit pair is the result.[2] In this way, communication between the

---

[1] Spiral thickening should not be confused with microscopic spiral checks which sometimes form, especially in compression wood prior to or as a result of seasoning, in the thick-walled fibrous cells of conifers (Text Fig. 14, *B*). Two criteria may be used in distinguishing these. When spiral thickening is present, the angle of the spiral is usually less than 45 degrees from the horizontal; that of spiral checking is steeper. In the former, the lines are raised on the inner wall, a feature that can be determined by careful focusing of the microscope; checks are, of course, cracks in the secondary wall extending down toward or to the compound middle lamella.

[2] Pit pairs are described in detail on p. 78. A pit pair was formerly known as a pit.

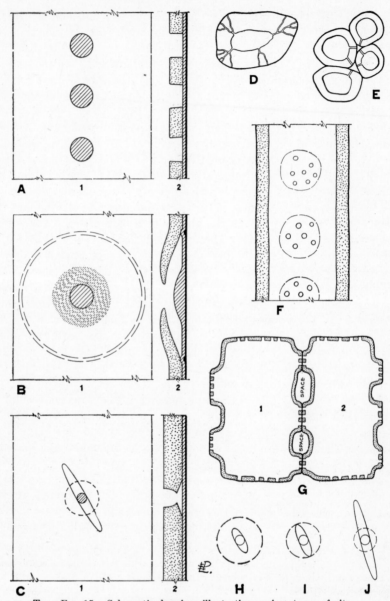

TEXT FIG. 15.—Schematic drawings illustrating various types of pits.

A. Simple pits in frontal (1) and in sectional (2) views; the recess in the secondary wall (A2) is the pit cavity; the pit membrane consists of intercellular substance (solid black) and primary walls (crosshatched), and closes the pit at the outer end; the opening of the pit (to the left) is the pit aperture. Simple pits in frontal view (A1) appear as dots or small openings in the wall.

B. A bordered pit of a coniferous wood, in frontal (1) and in sectional (2) views. The

cells while they are still participating in the vital processes of the plant is greatly facilitated. **Blind pits** leading to intercellular cavities are occasionally found in parenchymatous tissue (Text Fig. 15, *E*); it follows that in such cases the pit has no complement.

a. Parts of a Pit.—The recess in the secondary wall is the **pit cavity** (Text Fig. 15, *A*2); the membrane closing the pit at the outer end is the **pit membrane.** The first term is used to designate the space in the pit between the pit membrane and the cavity (lumen) of the cell. The pit membrane is composed (1) of the intercellular substance holding the two cells together at this particular point (indicated in solid black) and (2) the primary wall lying along its flank belonging to the cell in which the pit is located (indicated by crosshatching).

The depth of the pit cavity (length in sectional view) varies according to the thickness of the secondary wall. Thick-walled cells have longer (deeper) pit cavities than those in which the walls have remained comparatively thin (which may not show pits). In the first instance, the pit cavity may be so narrow as to appear in sectional view as a canal. The opening of a pit into a cell lumen is called the **pit aperture.**

b. Kinds of Pits.—Pits fall into two general categories according to the shape of the pit cavity, the simple and the bordered. In a **simple pit,** the pit cavity, as it progresses from the pit membrane to the cell lumen, remains nearly constant in width (as seen in sectional view), becomes slightly wider toward the cell cavity, or narrows very gradually in this direction (Text Fig. 15, *A*2). In surface view, the aperture of such a pit appears as a dot or small opening, set in the wall and without further embellishment (Text Fig. 15, *A*1). Not infrequently, simple **ramiform**

---

pit (2) consists of a dome-shaped pit chamber whose base rests on a pit membrane consisting of intercellular substance (solid black) and primary wall (crosshatched); the pit aperture is to the left and leads directly into the cell lumen; the position of the pit annulus is indicated by a thickening in the middle lamella above and below the pit chamber; the pit membrane is thickened at the center and forms the torus. In frontal view, a bordered pit in coniferous wood (*B*1) frequently appears to consist of three concentric circles; the outer is the pit annulus (indicated in the drawing by a double broken line); the inner is the pit aperture; the middle circle with an irregular contour is the torus.

    C. A bordered pit in a hardwood, in frontal (1) and in sectional (2) views. The pit (2) possesses a pit chamber and a pit canal with inner and outer apertures. The outer aperture leads to the pit chamber; the inner aperture opens (to the left) into the lumen of the cell. In frontal view, such a pit presents the appearance depicted in (1); the outer aperture is rounded; the inner aperture is flattened and is canted from the longitudinal axis of the cell.

    D. Simple ramiform pits in a thick-walled cell.

    E. Simple pits in ray cells, leading to intercellular spaces at the corners.

    F. Simple pits grouped in depressions in the secondary wall.

    G. Sieve pitting (simple pits) in the ends of the processes of two disjunctive cells (1 and 2, respectively).

    H. Pit of the type figured in *C*, with included inner aperture.

    I. Pit of the type figured in *C*, in which the inner aperture extends to the pit annulus.

    J. Pit of the type figured in *C*, with extended inner aperture.

pits (Text Fig. 15, *D*) form in stone and grit cells and in sclerosed tyloses (Chap. IX, page 208); in such instances, the narrow canals from two or more pits coalesce as they approach the lumen of the cell, or, tracing the development in the other direction, a canal leading into the secondary wall from the cell lumen branches and the ultimate divisions lead to separate pit membranes.

Simple pits characterize parenchyma (see page 46) and exhibit considerable variation in their distribution, and some variation in shape and size. Frequently, marked departures occur in their arrangement and size in the same cell, depending upon the kinds of wood elements that are in contact with it. As a rule, they are largest where they lead from the cell in question to prosenchyma. Simple pits may be quite evenly distributed over the whole cell wall or confined to certain limited areas that mark the points of contact with the facets of other cells. At other times, they are restricted to relatively small patches where they are frequently grouped in depressions caused by the failure of the secondary wall to attain normal thickness at these points, for no obvious reason (Text Fig. 15, *F*). Clustered pits also often occur in the ends of the tubular processes of disjunctive cells (see footnote 1, page 67); cribriform grouping of this type is called **sieve pitting** (Text Fig. 15, *G*).

Bordered pits, in contrast to those of the simple type, possess pit cavities that narrow more or less abruptly as the wall thickens (Text Fig. 15, *B*2 and *C*2). The result is a dome-shaped **pit chamber** whose base rests on the compound middle lamella, capped by an aperture leading directly into the cell lumen (coniferous woods) (*B*2) or into a narrowed portion of the pit cavity, the **pit canal** (*C*2). As seen in surface view, both of the above-mentioned types of pit possess a border owing to the overarching of the secondary wall over the pit chamber. Bordered pits having not only a dome-shaped pit chamber but a narrow pit canal leading from it have two apertures (*C*2). The opening of the canal into the lumen of the cell is called the **inner aperture,** that into the chamber of the pit the **outer aperture.** Canals of this sort may be of the same size and shape throughout their length, but frequently they become wider toward the cell lumen as the wall thickens; in such instances, they often assume the form of a flattened funnel, the small end of which leads into the pit chamber (*C*1).

In bordered pits, the compound middle lamella that extends across the pit gap in the secondary wall is often thicker than in places where the secondary wall is continuous. Frequently, the thickening is localized and is restricted to the margin of the pit membrane or to this and to its central portion. The narrowed thickened rim on the margin of the pit membrane is the **pit annulus** (Text Fig. 15, *B*1 and *B*2); it is, in reality, a thickening in the compound middle lamella and serves perhaps to strengthen the wall of a cell at points that would otherwise be weakened by the interruptions (pits) in the secondary wall.

If the central portion of the pit membrane is thickened, the pit is said to have a **torus** (Text Fig. 15, *B2*); the unthickened portion of the pit membrane around the torus is called the **closing membrane.** In reality, a torus is disk-shaped in surface view, with a somewhat ragged margin, and planoconvex as seen in section. Viewed in frontal aspect, the surface appears smooth but, in the case of Douglas fir wood at least, Stone[1] has shown by photomicrographs at high magnification that it actually is very irregular. The closing membrane is thin; it serves as the attachment between the torus and the pit annulus and probably provides, as is explained later, for the passage of liquids between tracheids. At moderate magnification, the closing membrane appears smooth in surface aspect. Barlike thickenings, radiating out from the torus, have been noted in woods of *Abies*, *Picea*, and *Tsuga*.[2]

When a torus is present, the large bordered pits of coniferous woods that have been properly stained frequently appear to consist of three concentric circles, as seen in surface view (Text Fig. 15, *B1*; the pit annulus is illustrated by a double broken line). The outer circle is the pit annulus, the inner circle the pit aperture leading out of the pit chamber, and the middle circle, which is less even in contour than the others, the margin of the torus.

In surface view, bordered pits vary in shape, ranging from circular to oval or polygonal, elliptical, lenticular, and linear with rounded ends. Polygonal pits result from crowding and are often six-sided, because hexagons will fit together to form a plane surface. The pit aperture may lead directly into the cell lumen when the orifice assumes, in general although not always, the same shape as the outline of the pit. When a pit canal is present, it follows that the inner aperture, if it is flattened, is quite different in shape from the pit chamber, seen in the same view (Text Fig. 15, *H*, *I*, and *J*).

The alignment of an elongated pit aperture may be transverse, longitudinal, or oblique. In pits of the last type, the angle is steepest in cells that are narrow lumened. When the orifice (inner aperture) of a pit crosses the pit annulus, as seen in surface view, it is said to be **extended**

[1] STONE, C. D. A Study of the Bordered Pits of Douglas Fir with Reference to the Permeability of the Wood to Liquids. Doctor's thesis (unpublished), University of Washington, 1939.

[2] WEST, W. I. Structural Variations in the Closing Membranes of Pit-pairs in Several Coniferous Woods. *Univ. Wash. Forest Club Quart.*, Vol. XV, No. 1, pp. 16–20. 1941–1942.

(Text Fig. 15, *J*); at other times, it may just reach the annulus (*I*), or it may not extend to the annulus, when it is designated as **included** (*H*).   In thick-walled cells (Ex., vessel members of *Gleditsia triacanthos* L. and *Diospyros virginiana* L.), flattened extended inner apertures frequently coalesce, end to end, forming grooves or depressions on the inner surface of the cell wall (Plate XX, Fig. 110).   In such instances, the slits do not extend to the primary wall, *i.e.*, to the compound middle lamella,[1] unless the cell wall has checked along the same lines as it dried.

Bordered pits of a peculiar type occur in certain dicotyledonous woods and provide a feature of some diagnostic importance.   In such instances, the pit membrane, as seen in surface view, presents a punctate or dotted appearance (Text Fig. 16, *E*) as though it was perforated with minute openings, an assumption that was held until comparatively recently. Pits of this sort in the secondary wall are called **vestured pits.**   According to I. W. Bailey,[2] the phenomenon is traceable to extremely minute and strongly refractive processes which arise as outgrowths from the free surfaces of the secondary wall (Text Fig. 16, *A, B, C,* and *D*).   They take the form of papillary projections from the margins of the inner and outer pit apertures, of corallike outgrowths from the dome-shaped walls of pit chambers, or of numberous branched or interlocking threads which fill the pit chamber.

The evidence to date is to the effect that vestured pits are very consistent in their distribution, and for this reason their presence or absence appears to be of decided diagnostic importance, particularly in the identification of tropical woods.   They may characterize the wood of one species of a genus and be lacking in the others, or they may be features of all the woods of a genus or of a subfamily or even of a family.   They are, of course, restricted to prosenchyma; here, again, variation occurs in that they may be present in all the prosenchymatous cells throughout the wood or restricted to those of certain types.

In the United States, only those commercial timbers belonging to the Legume Family possess vestured pits; hence this character can be used in their segregation "to family" but not "to genus."   However, this character is difficult to interpret, particularly by the neophyte in wood identification, requiring, as it does, thin sections that must be carefully stained and examined at high magnification.   Its value is lessened still further since artifacts frequently occur in the bordered pits of certain

---

[1] The slit is scalloped at the bottom, the depressions leading through the outer apertures of pits into pit chambers deeper in the cell wall.

[2] BAILEY, I. W.   The Cambium and Its Derivative Tissues.   VIII. Structure, Distribution, and Diagnostic Significance of Vestured Pits in Dicotyledons.   *Jour. Arnold Arboretum*, Vol. 14, pp. 259–273.   1933.

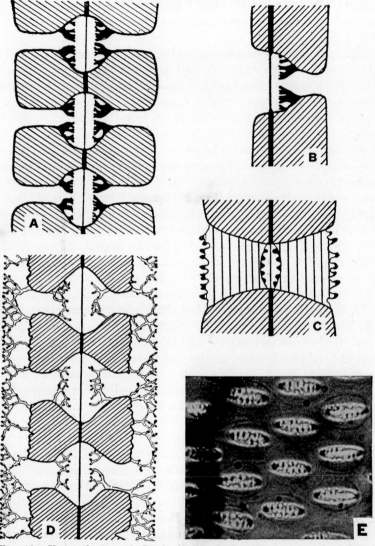

TEXT FIG. 16.—Vestured pits. *A.* Bordered pits (pit pairs) in the walls of adjacent vessels, showing coralloid outgrowths from the overarching walls of the pit chambers. *B.* Sectional view of a half-bordered pit pair in the adjacent walls of a vessel (right) and a parenchymatous element (left) (the bordered pit is vestured, the simple pit is not). *C.* Sectional view of bordered pits (of a pit pair) in the walls of adjacent fiber tracheids, showing papillary projections from the margins of both the inner and outer apertures. *D.* Sectional view of bordered pits (pit pairs) in the walls of adjacent vessels, showing branched and anastomosing projections from the overarching walls of the pit chambers and from the inner surfaces of the vessels. *E.* Vestured pits, surface view, in a vessel segment of black locust (*Robinia pseudoacacia* L.) (1360 ×). (*A, B, C,* and *D* after *I. W. Bailey.*)

timbers. [Ex., *Carya ovata* (Mill.) K. Koch. Plate XX, Fig. 111. Such pits then resemble vestured pits very closely when viewed in frontal aspect.]

Bordered pits are sometimes quite widely separated on cell walls when viewed at high magnification, so much so as to appear solitary. As a rule, however, they are arranged in longitudinal, transverse, or oblique series. The first type of arrangement is common in cells that are greatly elongated in a given direction, as vertical in the standing tree, or where the pits are linear and transversely oriented, in which instance the pitting is scalariform. The second and third types of arrangement are more frequent in cells of greater width, such as the members composing the vessels of porous woods. Here the pits may be in transverse rows extending across the cell wall [**opposite pitting**; Exs., *Liriodendron tulipifera* L. (Plate XXII, Fig. 128); *Nyssa sylvatica* Marsh. (Plate XXII, Fig. 127)] or in oblique rows [**alternate pitting**; Exs., *Populus deltoides* Bartr. (Plate XXI, Fig. 123); *Acer saccharinum* L. (Plate XXI, Fig. 121)]. Opposite pits may retain their rounded contours but frequently become squarish or rectangular. Alternate pits are frequently so crowded that they become polygonal. In some instances, as in certain coniferous woods, bordered pits are grouped in clusters in a characteristic manner.

4. Pit Pairs.—Pits rarely occur solitarily but are generally accompanied by a complementary pit directly opposite on the other side of the compound middle lamella in the contiguous cell, and reversed as to direction (Text Fig. 17). Two such complementary pits form a pit pair. The bordered pit pairs of conifers are provided with a compound torus; a torus is lacking in those of hardwoods. The pit membranes of half-bordered and simple pit pairs are unthickened. Pit pairs are of three sorts (Text Fig. 17): **simple** (*A*), **bordered** (*B*), and **half-bordered** (*C*).

Simple pit pairs connect parenchymatous cells. In wood, the cells of this type are concerned primarily with the storage of reserve food material, although they may also function in the translocation of foodstuffs, as, for example, the cells of ray parenchyma which are elongated horizontally and radially in the standing tree. Bordered, half-bordered, and simple pit pairs serve as avenues of communication between prosenchymatous cells, *i.e.*, between cells designated in the main for conduction and strength.[1] The same holds in hardwoods where parenchyma and prosenchyma are in contact.[2]

---

[1] Note should be made at this time of the fact that such cells may serve in conduction, even though they are dead, *i.e.*, have lost their protoplasts.

[2] FROST, F. H. Histology of the Wood of Angiosperms. I. The Nature of the Primary Pitting between Tracheary and Parenchymatous Elements. *Bul. Torrey Bot. Club*, Vol. 56, pp. 259–264. 1929.

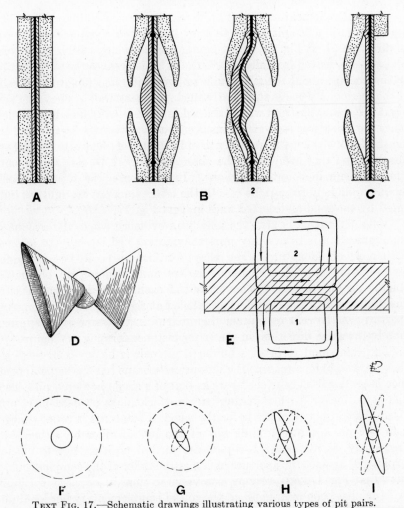

TEXT FIG. 17.—Schematic drawings illustrating various types of pit pairs.

A. Simple pit pair in sectional view (the intercellular substance is indicated by solid black, the primary wall by crosshatching).

B. Bordered pit pairs in sectional views; in 1 the compound torus occupies the medial position; in 2, it has been aspirated to the left, effectively closing the pit pair.

C. Half-bordered pit pair in sectional view; there is no evidence of a compound torus.

D. Bordered pit pair, oblique lateral view; the complementary pits have pit canals, and flattened inner apertures; the latter are reversed as to direction.

E. Schematic sketch showing the compound wall between two cells (1 and 2); the wall has been included in a section of the wood (indicated by crosshatching); in cell 1, the inner aperture is canted from right to left (note direction of the arrows); in cell 2, the reverse holds.

F, G, H, I. Diagrams of various types of bordered pit pairs in frontal view, showing changes in form accompanying reduction in size and function, and occurrence in walls of increasing thickness. As the pit chamber decreases in size, the inner aperture becomes flattened and is usually canted from the vertical. The broken lines indicate portions of the pit pair embedded in the wall or on the side of the compound wall away from the observer.

If the complementary pits of bordered pit pairs have elongated oblique apertures and hence pit canals that are like flattened funnels reversed as to direction (Text Fig. 17, *D*), X figures are frequently visible when such pit pairs are viewed frontally (*G, H, I*). This is because the pit apertures are inclined at about the same angle in two contiguous longitudinal cells. If the section of wood is sufficiently thick, the back wall of one cell (Text Fig. 17, *E*1) and the front wall of the cell to the rear (*E*2) may be included. Since the tissue was rendered translucent in preparing the section and the lenses of a microscope possess depth of focus, the pit aperture toward the observer and that away from the observer can both be seen at the same time and run in counterdirections. In such case, the former usually mounts obliquely from right to left, the latter from left to right, as indicated by the solid and dotted lines in Text Fig. 17, *G, H, I*.

V-figured pit pairs are occasionally in evidence where the avenue of communication is from a ray prosenchymatous cell laterally to a longitudinal cell of like nature. The reason for this can readily be ascertained by preparing two short paper cylinders and outlining an elongated, oblique pit aperture on the inner wall of each, properly oriented as to direction. When the cylinders are placed at right angles, the elongated apertures in the cells of contact then extend in the same or in approximately the same direction, in the latter instance forming a V figure.

The compound torus of a bordered pit pair is biconvex in sectional view for an obvious reason; the closing membrane has the same appearance in sectional and surface views as that of a single-bordered pit except that it is thicker, with radiating barlike thickenings on each face, provided these are characteristic for the wood. The torus is usually larger than the pit aperture leading out of the pit chamber on either side. Frequently, it no longer occupies the medial position but is pushed (aspirated) against the aperture of one or the other of the complementary pits (Text Fig. 17, *B*2), serving as a valve to close it.

Much has been written about the role of complementary bordered pits in the passage from cell to cell of sap and preservatives, especially in coniferous wood. The importance of such research requires no defense, particularly as regards the impregnation of wood with preservatives. Complementary bordered pits have been examined at high magnifications in an attempt, on the one hand, to find how a liquid passes through a closing membrane, on the other, to determine the extent of aspiration of tori in relation to impregnation. It is now known that aspiration to varying degrees takes place in different portions of wood and under conditions that can be controlled (seasoning, application of air and steam pressure, etc.). Brief mention of several papers in this field is now in order; space does not permit of the review of all the literature, which is voluminous and contradictory.

Bailey published an article in 1916[1] in which he reported the presence as normal structures of actual slits radiating out from the tori in the closing membranes of larch and redwood and asserted that these explained the passage of small particles of carbon in suspension (India ink) through cell walls. That such slits exist under certain conditions, of a width to permit the passage of a preservative, is irrefutable. That they occur as normal structures is questionable as they have every appearance of being microscopic seasoning checks, checks that would naturally form along lines of weakness between the barlike structures reported by West.[2] Stamm,[3] using electroendosmotic flow, hydrostatic flow, permeability to colloidal solution, and methods of overcoming surface tension in capillary structure, concluded that, if openings occur in cell walls other than those possibly present in pit membranes, they are not of a size to provide passage for the penetration of liquids. His results seem to indicate that it is through complementary pit pairs and through these alone that liquids must pass.

The approach of Miss G. J. Griffin of the Forest Products Laboratory was somewhat different in that she studied the extent of aspiration of tori in Douglas fir wood, both of the Lowland and Rocky Mountain grades, on the penetration of the wood with preservatives.[4] The objectives of her study were to determine, if possible, why Douglas fir sapwood treats much easier than the heartwood; why the summerwood both of sapwood and heartwood is more readily treated than the springwood; and finally, why Rocky Mountain Douglas fir is more resistant to a preservative than Lowland Douglas fir. Miss Griffin found departures in the ease of treatment of the two grades of fir mentioned, apparently traceable to the extent of aspiration of the tori. She also reported that air drying increased the number of aspirated pits in Mountain Douglas fir but not in the lowland form; that oven drying caused aspiration to equal degree in both; and further, that the position of the tori can be changed in both forms by air pressure and steam pressure. The results obtained by Miss Griffin led her to the conclusion that a definite correlation exists

[1] BAILEY, I. W. The Structure of the Bordered Pits of Conifers and Its Bearing upon the Tension Hypothesis of the Ascent of Sap in Plants. *Bot. Gaz.*, Vol. 62, pp. 133–142. 1916.

[2] *Op. cit.*

[3] STAMM, A. J. The Capillary Structure of Softwoods. *Jour. Agr. Res.*, Vol. 38, pp. 23–67. 1929. *Idem.* An Electrical Conductivity Method for Determining the Effective Capillary Dimensions of Wood. *Jour. Phys. Chem.*, Vol. 36, pp. 312–325. 1932.

[4] GRIFFIN, G. J. On Bordered Pits in Douglas Fir: A Study of the Position of the Torus in Mountain and Lowland Specimens in Relation to Cresote Penetration. *Jour. Forestry*, Vol. 17, pp. 813–822. 1919; *Idem.* Further Notes on the Position of the Tori in Bordered Pits in Relation to Penetration of Preservatives. *Jour. Forestry*, Vol. 22, pp. 82–83. 1924.

between the position of the tori and the permeability of wood to liquids. Subsequently, Stone[1] duplicated Miss Griffin's studies on Lowland Douglas fir and arrived at a different conclusion; according to his findings, the position of the tori has a negligible effect on the penetration of preservatives in the lowland form.

D. Phase of Lignification

The final phase in the ontogeny of a woody cell is that of **lignification.** This term is used by botanists to indicate the process whereby cell walls are rendered harder and possibly more durable, presumably by the infiltration of certain substances (known under the general term of "lignin") into them.

Prior to lignification, mature cell walls consist largely of **cellulose,** the chemical formula of which is $(C_6H_{10}O_5)_n$. Lignin is formed in the cell wall, not through the chemical alteration of the cellulose already present but as a new product that is deposited between the particles of cellulose.

Like cellulose, **lignin** at one time was considered to be a definite chemical compound; in fact, a chemical formula was assigned to it. Modern science has abandoned this idea; it is possibly a mixture of chemically related compounds in intimate association. The chemistry of lignin is not completely understood at the present time although some progress has been made in this direction. The process of lignification is known to occur in the Spermatophytes and Pteridophytes,[2] and certain constituents appear to be universally present in the lignin mixture wherever it occurs in the Plant Kingdom. Such departures as distinguish the lignin of one group of plants from that of another, for example, the lignin of Gymnosperms from Angiosperms (Maüle reaction[3]) are due to substances, probably in relatively small amounts, that respond to certain reagents.

Attention can now be focused to advantage upon the difference in the conception of the term "lignification," as held by botanists, and "lignin," as understood by chemists. As previously stated, botanists consider that lignification is a hardening and conditioning process in the physiological sense; although they concede that chemical alteration underlies this change, detectable by microchemical stains, the greater emphasis is

[1] Stone, C. D. Penetration of Preservatives in Douglas Fir as Affected by the Position of the Tori in the Pit-pairs. University of Washington, College of Forestry. Unpublished thesis, p. 20. 1936.

[2] It possibly may also take place in Bryophytes and even in Thallophytes.

[3] The Maüle test is made by treating the wood successively with neutral potassium permanganate ($KMnO_4$), aqueous hydrochloric acid (HCl), and ammonium hydroxide (NH_4OH). Angiospermous woods turn a distinct red; those of Gymnosperms an indefinite yellow or pale brown.

placed on the physical alterations that take place in the cell wall as it becomes lignified.

The approach of the chemists to the study of lignin, on the other hand, has been through the analysis of the mature tissue wood. They have proceeded in a methodical way, by relatively precise methods, to define what they consider to be lignin by the analysis of wood after it has been taken from the tree.

In the procedure of the chemists, in general, the **extractable material** is first removed by the use of water or other solvents. The residue is then ordinarily a mixture of **holocellulose,**[1] **lignin,** and a small amount of **mineral matter.** The holocellulose which consists of **alpha cellulose** and **hemicelluloses**[2] is then taken out of the mixture by treatment with cold concentrated acids under standard conditions; the lignin remains behind as a residue that can be weighed.[3] Note should be made that, by this procedure, it is also possible by appropriate methods to determine or to remove the hemicelluloses occurring in the holocellulose mixture taken out by the acid treatment. This, in turn, permits of the calculation of the approximate percentage of cellulose.

The above process may also be reversed. The lignin may be taken out of the wood by a number of different procedures, one of which is the so-called **holocellulose method** of the Forest Products Laboratory.[4] As a result of such a treatment, the cellulose matrix, in which a part of the lignin was infiltrated, is left behind in the cell wall together with the hemicelluloses.

On the whole, the chemical definition of lignin rather than the botanical conception of lignification seems to be the more workable and hence serviceable, for lignin is determined by relatively precise methods that can readily be repeated. However, it is quite probable that the oven-dry

---

[1] G. J. Ritter has defined "holocellulose" as the lignin-free carbohydrate fraction of wood freed of its extraneous materials. See RITTER G. J., and R. MITCHELL. Crystal Arrangement and Swelling Properties of Fibers and Ray Cells in Basswood, *Paper Trade Jour.*, Vol. 107, No. 6. 1939.

[2] E. Schultze first used the term "hemicellulose" in 1892. Chemists are not in agreement at present in their understanding of these substances. According to A. G. Norman, hemicelluloses are cell-wall polysaccharides, which may be extracted from plant tissues by treatment with dilute alkalies, either hot or cold, but not with water, and which may be hydrolyzed to constituent sugar and sugar acid units by boiling with hot dilute mineral acids. See NORMAN, A. G. The Chemistry of Cellulose, the Polyuronides, Lignin, etc. Oxford University Press, New York. 1937.

[3] In all probability, the lignin obtained in this way is not identical with that present in the cell wall originally; gravimetrically, at least, it approximates the amount originally present.

[4] This consists in very cautious alternate chlorinations and treatment with alcoholic ethanolamine.

samples used by chemists for analysis are not chemically identical with the wood in the growing tree.   The detection of lignification, based on the interpretation of microchemical stains, especially aniline dyes, is questionable at best.   Some workers are attempting to bridge this gap by treating thin sections of woody tissue with the reagents commonly used by chemists, meanwhile watching the reaction under a microscope. The latter do not take into consideration that wood is a heterogeneous mixture of different kinds of cell types and that even the cell wall itself, as is pointed out subsequently, consists of various layers differing from one another chemically.   Whether or not lignin, as understood by the chemist, is responsible for the process of lignification as interpreted by the botanist is a moot question.

According to data compiled by chemists, the cell walls of woody plants are composed of about 50 per cent of cellulose, approximately 25 per cent of lignin, and generally less than 1 per cent of mineral matter, the remaining 24 per cent consisting of hemicelluloses and extractable materials of various sorts.[1]   Angiosperms contain slightly less lignin than Gymnosperms (approximately 24 per cent as compared to 27 per cent); the reverse holds for hemicelluloses (approximately 26 per cent as compared to 23 per cent).

Until comparatively recently, the secondary wall was considered to be heavily lignified.   Ritter, Bailey, and other workers have now shown that the true middle lamella (intercellular substance) contains the most lignin, the primary walls lying along its flanks almost as much (the compound middle lamella is hence heavily lignified in the sense of the chemists), and the secondary walls the least of all.

In terminating this discussion, certain phenomena should be mentioned that are correlated in one way or another with lignification as understood by botanists, for otherwise they might escape attention. Lignification, like cell enlargement, can take place only while the protoplast is living; cells do not die and then lignify their walls.   The process may have been completed in the compound middle lamella and still be in progress in the secondary wall, even though this last-named layer itself is still increasing in thickness.   In other words, this change in the cell wall proceeds centripetally.   In trees, lignification is usually completed very quickly behind the cambium, usually almost as soon as the new cells have attained their ultimate size and the secondary walls have reached their final thickness (Text Fig. 24).   This explains why sapwood is as strong or nearly as strong as heartwood, at the same moisture content.   Examples of delayed lignification in cell walls are not wanting,

---

[1] The chemistry of wood is discussed at length in Vol. II, Sec. III, of this text (in preparation).

however; for example, in many trees the cells of phloem parenchyma that are devoid of secondary walls (see page 69) and are unlignified continue to live and to function for a number of years after the crushing of the sieve tubes with which they are associated. Eventually, some of these enlarge. Following this, secondary walls are formed which lignify along with the compound middle lamella. It follows that new or unusual conditions may cause the lignification of cell walls which previously have remained unlignified, provided the cells have remained living.

IV. THE NATURE OF THE WALL OF A MATURE XYLARY CELL

This section is added to the text at this point in part by way of summation, in part to clarify the conception of the reader as to the ultramicroscopic physical structure of the wall of a mature woody cell.

To repeat, each cell in a tissue is provided with a thin primary wall. Each cell is separated from the one next to it by a thin layer of intercellular substance.[1] In woody cells, the primary wall is always accompanied by a secondary wall.

The layer of intercellular substance between cells is called the **middle lamella** (see footnote, page 69); it appears to consist chiefly of lignin. It differs from the primary and secondary walls along its flanks in being isotropic, *i.e.*, its physical structure is such that it exhibits the same properties in all directions.

The primary and secondary walls of the individual cells, in contrast, are anisotropic. Although they consist basically of cellulose, they are also lignified. The primary wall is so heavily lignified that, in its reactions, it behaves much like the middle lamella (layer of intercellular substance), so much so in fact that in sections of wood stained with Haidenhain's haematoxylin or ruthenium red, it is almost indistinguishable from it. The complete wall between the cavities of contiguous cells therefore appears to consist of three layers, a dark zone bordered by lighter zones on either side. In such instances, the dark middle layer is, in reality, a **compound middle lamella** consisting of intercellular substance (the middle lamella) and primary walls along its flanks; the lighter layers are the secondary walls of the respective cells that happen to border on one another at this particular point.

The secondary wall is, of course, the last layer formed by the protoplast. Pits are gaps in this layer which are spanned at the outer end by a pit membrane. As previously stated, the secondary wall varies greatly in thickness according to the nature of the cell, and its inner surface not

[1] This layer between cells arises during cell division. The cross wall which forms between the daughter nuclei is composed of (1) intercellular substance and (2) the primary walls of the cells lying to either side of it.

infrequently is sculptured in various ways or seems to be different chemically. Some workers then recognize a tertiary wall, a practice that is to be discouraged.

Information on the nature of the primary wall other than that already recorded is meager; this is explained by the fact that it is exceedingly thin and is flanked on the one side by the middle lamella, on the other by the secondary wall. The primary wall appears to be much more retentive of its lignin than the middle lamella when treated with lignin solvents. Evidence is also accumulating to the effect that it is much more important in the chemical reduction of wood than heretofore supposed; for example, the phenomenon known as ballooning[1] may be traceable to this layer. The assumption is entirely tenable that the cellulose of this layer is comparable in every way to that of the secondary wall which is now described.

The secondary wall consists largely of cellulose although some lignin is present. It is convenient to think of the cellulose and lignin in this layer as forming two interpenetrating systems, respectively, either of which may be removed, leaving the other; further, that the cellulose is in the form of a lattice, the interstices of which are filled with lignin, hemicelluloses, and extraneous materials (see page 83). Although the highest power of the microscope reveals only a spongelike structure of the lignin, or of the cellulose, when the lignin has been removed chemically, the cellulose lattice can be broken down by proper mechanical or chemical treatment into fine threadlike structures known as fibrils (Text Fig. 18). Whether such fibrils actually exist in the untreated wall or whether they are formed upon treatment because of lines of weakness in the submicroscopic structure is a moot question. The authors lean to the second view after reviewing the literature in this field, which is highly controversial. Be this as it may, there can be no question that lines of weakness at least exist which are definitely oriented; further, that the fibrils follow the same orientation.

The composition of fibrils, either existent originally in the cellulose lattice or, as the authors believe, formed as the result of chemical treatment of the secondary wall prior to its examination, now requires attention. Note should be made of the fact that fibrils can be seen with a compound microscope or can be made large enough by swelling in alkali to be so seen; they grade down in diameter from about one micron to the

---

[1] Ballooning is not a normal phenomenon in wood but develops in fibers when wood is subjected to mechanical or chemical reduction. Segments of a fiber swell, *i.e.*, balloon; these enlargements (balloons) are separated by constrictions in which little or no swelling ensues. The discussion of fiber ballooning does not fall within the province of this text. For further information, see W. M. Harlow. The Microchemistry of Pulp Fibers. 1. The Significance of Fiber Ballooning in the Pulping Process. *Paper Trade Jour.*, Vol. 117, No. 2, pp. 27–29. 1943.

limit of visibility and probably far beyond.[1] The structures entering into the composition of these fibrils that are now discussed, however, are

TEXT FIG. 18.—Tangential wall of a delignified longitudinal tracheid of western hemlock [*Tsuga heterophylla* (Raf.) Sarg.], showing fibrils. Photographed with ultraviolet light (3500 ×). (*Courtesy of Bror L. Grondal.*)

beyond the range of visibility of the human eye, even with the most powerful lenses. Here, scientists have had to resort to such tools as X rays[2] by which the spacings of atoms and groups of atoms can be deter-

[1] The fibrillar nature of cellulose is still evident in photomicrographs obtained with an electron microscope at a magnification of 66,000 ×. See *Hercules Chem.*, No. 16, p. 21. 1946. Hercules Powder Co., Wilmington, Del.

[2] X rays are similar to light rays in all respects except that the wave length is several thousand times smaller.

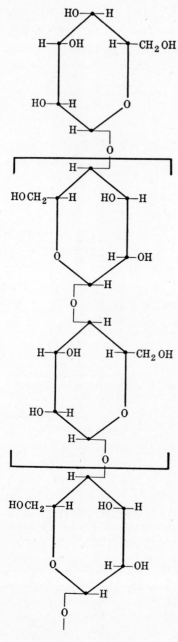

mined with great precision through diffraction interference patterns, and to cathode rays employed in the electron microscope in obtaining photomicrographic images of objects twenty or more times smaller than can be seen with an optical microscope. The literature is voluminous relative to the ultramicroscopic structure of the plant cell wall, and various theories have been evolved in an attempt to explain this.[1] Of these the Fringe Micellar Theory, or the Micellar Network Theory as it also has been called, has gained the greatest support. Reference to this will be made subsequently after certain fundamental concepts of the structure of cell-wall cellulose are discussed.

It is now generally conceded that the cellulose in plant cell walls is composed of chain molecules of the sort illustrated in Text Fig. 19. These chain molecules are made up of structural units (units of glucose anhydride) that are held together lengthwise by primary valences. It should be noted further that the even-numbered units in each chain, *i.e.*, the second, fourth, etc., are oriented at a 180-degree angle to the odd-numbered units, *i.e.*, the first, third, etc. The length of one pair of these units, *i.e.*, of a pair

[1] OTT, E. Cellulose and Cellulose Derivitives, pp. 215–222. Interscience Publishers, Inc., New York. 1943.

TEXT FIG. 19.—Portion of one end of a long-chain molecule of cellulose of the type that occurs in the cell walls of the higher plants. The black dots at five of the corners of each hexagon indicate atoms of carbon (*C*). The even-numbered units of the chain are oriented at a 180-degree angle to the odd-numbered units. The length of a pair of units (indicated by brackets) is 10.3 Å; the length of the chain depends on the number of pairs entering into its composition. The chain is 3-dimensional; the atoms to the left of the vertical in each hexagon of the diagram are in a plane above and oblique to the plane of the paper; the reverse holds for the atoms to the right of the vertical.

consisting of an even-numbered unit and an odd-numbered unit, is 10.3 Å.[1] The length of the entire chain is not known to a certainty; it has been estimated from X-ray photographs at from 4000 to 12,000 Å. Nor can a figure be set for the number of these long-chain molecules entering into the structure of a fibril; it is logical to assume that it is high, perhaps 100 or more.

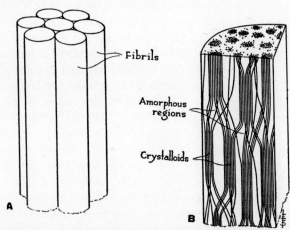

TEXT FIG. 20.—Alignment and composition of fibrils of alpha cellulose from plant cell walls. *A.* Faggotlike bundle consisting of segments of seven parallel fibrils, inclined at a slight angle from the vertical. *B.* One fibril in lateral sectional view showing zones in which portions of the long-chain molecules of cellulose have the parallel arrangement (crystallites), separated by regions in which the chain molecules are but partially parallel and disorganized (amorphous regions); there is no sharp boundary line between the crystallites and the amorphous regions.

Were the long-chain molecules of cellulose arranged in parallel throughout a fibril, cellulose would yield a continuous crystalline pattern; actually, however, the pattern of the cellulose occurring in plant cell walls is discontinuous. This is the basis of the Fringe Micellar Theory, which postulates that the long-chain molecules are parallel to each other lengthwise only at intervals (Text Fig. 20); further, that between these zones of parallelism they are but partly parallel and disorganized, resulting in so-called "amorphous" regions. There is no sharp deliniation lengthwise between the zones of parallelism and the amorphous regions, hence the employment of the word "fringe" in coining the name for this theory. The chain molecules pass successively through the regions of parallelism and the amorphous regions but usually terminate in the former. The zones of parallelism are now known as crystallites, a much more fortunate term than "micelles," which was formerly applied to the regions of

[1] The symbol Å indicates the angstrom unit, which is a hundred millionth of a centimeter, *i.e.*, 10^{-8} cm.

parallelism. The significance of this statement is explained at the end of this chapter.

The parallel portions of chain molecules composing the crystallites are believed to be held together crosswise of the fibril by fairly strong hydrogen bonds or somewhat weaker van der Waals forces.[1] The linkage in these segments of the fibril is therefore 3-dimensional. In the amorphous zones, in contrast, there is less or little linkage between the chain molecules crosswise of the fibril because of their nonparallel arrangement, but strong primary valences bind the cellulose-anhydride units together here, the valences that are in force throughout the length of the chain molecule.

Information is available relative to the size of the crystallites and their spacing laterally. The length is in the range of 400 to 600 Å, the width approximately 50 Å. The width of the spaces between the crystallites laterally varies from 10 to 100 Å.

Students who pursue this subject further in the voluminous literature may be at a loss to understand the difference between the term "crystallite" as used in modern terminology and the term "micelle" as originally coined in 1858 by Nägeli.[2] Unfortunately, as the conception of the ultramicroscopic structure of the cell wall has changed as new tools, notably X rays, became available to scientists, the term "micelle" was retained, while the understanding of it as such has altered. Nägeli, on theory alone, conceived the cell wall as consisting of discrete particles, micelles as he called them, held together by mutual attraction and interspersed in an amorphous medium, in general, lignin; water could penetrate between micelles but never into them. He had no conception of the crystalline nature of cellulose and thought of micelles much like bricks in a wall, held together by mortar. The modern concept of cell-wall structure and of the cellulose therein has already been described at some length. The discontinuous crystalline pattern of cellulose traceable to crystallites alternating with amorphous zones is an established fact. It therefore seems best in future to speak of crystallites in discussing the ultramicroscopic structure of cell walls and to discard the term, "micelles," as not synonymous.

The alignment of fibrils, as seen in a chemically treated secondary wall, is not uniform. Bailey and Kerr[3] have demonstrated the presence of three layers in normal wood tracheids, fiber tracheids, and libriform

---

[1] van der Waals forces are the forces of attraction between molecules, tending to hold them together.

[2] NÄGELI, C. Die Stärkekörner, F. Schulthub, Zurich. 1858.

[3] BAILEY, I. W., and T. KERR. The Visible Structure of the Secondary Wall and its Significance in Physical and Chemical Investigations of Tracheary Cells and Fibers. *Jour. Arnold Arboretum*, Vol. 16, pp. 273–300. 1935.

fibers.[1]   In terms of varying fibril orientation (Text Fig. 21), these are a thin outer layer next to the primary wall, a central zone that varies greatly in width depending on the thickness of the secondary wall, and a narrow inner tenuous layer bounding the cell lumen.   In the outer and inner layers, the fibrils are directed at right angles to the long axis of the

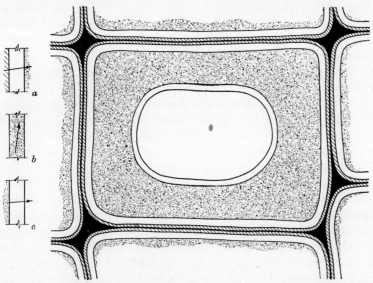

Text Fig. 21.—Diagrammatic drawing showing the layers in the wall of a fibrous xylary cell.   The solid black zone is the true middle lamella composed of intercellular substance; the crosshatched portions on either side indicate the position of the primary walls; these three layers compose the compound middle lamella and are heavily lignified.   *a, b,* and *c,* respectively, are the layers of the secondary wall; the arrows at the side indicate the orientation of the fibrils.   (*After Kerr and Bailey.*)

cell or form ascending counterclockwise helixes of very low slope.   In contrast, the fibrils in the middle layers are aligned parallel to the longitudinal axis of the cell or in counterclockwise helixes of steep slope. Bailey and Kerr noted further that deviations from the typical three-layered type of secondary wall are not infrequent; many tracheids have no clearly defined inner layer whereas others have more than three layers of varying fibrillar orientation.

Further information on fibril orientation in the secondary wall was presented in a subsequent paper by Bailey and Vestal.[2]   Thin sections of wood were given a preliminary chemical treatment and then stained with a 2 to 4 per cent iodine–potassium iodide solution.   Dark-brown crystals

[1] These xylary elements are described subsequently in the text.

[2] BAILEY, I. W., and MARY R. VESTAL.   The Orientation of Cellulose in the Secondary Wall of Tracheary Cells.   *Jour. Arnold Arboretum,* Vol. 18, pp. 185–208. 1937.

of iodine formed within the outer and middle layers of the secondary wall,[1] in the interstices between the fibrils, as a result of this treatment. These were clearly visible under a microscope and served to indicate fibrillar orientation.

The results of Bailey and Vestal substantiated those presented in the earlier paper by Bailey and Kerr relative to fibril orientation in the outer and middle layers of the secondary wall. This second paper, however, introduced a new idea: deviation of fibrils from the norm in the secondary wall occasioned by the presence of the large bordered pits that feature coniferous woods. Reference is now made to Text Fig. 22, in explaining this situation.

Text Fig. 22 is a diagrammatic representation of a segment of a coniferous tracheid, viewed in oblique radial perspective. The secondary wall only is depicted since the discussion that follows pertains to this wall alone. Beginning at the bottom of the figure, the three layers of the secondary wall appear as a series of three complete telescoping sleeves directed upward to the line x-y. Above this line, the front wall of the tracheid has been cut away to show three U-shaped half sleeves (each a wall layer), in inverse order to the sequence illustrated below the line x-y, for an obvious reason. It is patent that the wall layers (3) are illustrated successively in outer surface aspect at A, B, and C as they would appear in the front radial wall of the tracheid; in inner surface aspect at D, E, and F, as they would show in the back radial wall of the tracheid. Alignment of fibrils is indicated by dash lines; bordered pits in surface view are shown in A, B, C, and F.

In the outer layer of the secondary wall at A, the fibrils are aligned in a very low, ascending, counterclockwise spiral except within the boundary of the bordered pit where they have a concentric arrangement around the aperture. According to Bailey and Vestal, this is the situation as regards fibril arrangement in this layer except that the fibril alignment varies from helixes of low angle, as depicted, to horizontal. It is worthy of note at this point that the flattened pit aperture of the bordered pit at A does not conform in alignment to the spiraling in the wall outside the boundary of the pit but is at a steeper angle. More about this later.

Turning now to B where the middle layer of the secondary wall is shown in surface aspect, the difference in fibril alignment in this and in the outer wall layer (A) is at once apparent. The fibrils still run in ascending counterclockwise spirals, but the helixes are very steep (well above 45 degrees from the horizontal). Also, the long axis of the flattened pit aperture is parallel to the alignment of the helixes and, within the

---

[1] At the time of the publication of their paper, Bailey and Vestal had not succeeded in obtaining iodine crystals in the thin tenuous inner layer of the secondary wall.

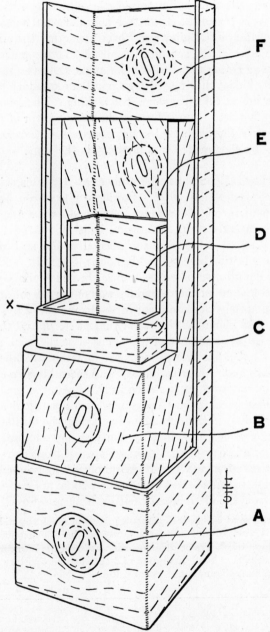

TEXT FIG. 22.—Orientation of fibrils (indicated by broken lines) in ascending counter-clockwise helixes in the layers of the secondary wall of a coniferous tracheid. The three layers of the secondary wall are shown as a series of telescoping sleeves that are cut away

boundary of the pit that is illustrated, the fibrils are not in concentric arrangement as in the pit at A, but are only deflected somewhat as they progress across the pit.   Bailey and Vestal state that the fibril alignment in the middle layer of the secondary wall may be steep as depicted, the helixes ascending counterclockwise at an angle well over 45 degrees from the horizontal, or that they may extend parallel to the long axis of the cell in which case helicoidal arrangement is lacking.   Their results indicate that it is the alignment of the fibrils in the middle layer of the secondary wall that controls the alignment of pit apertures of bordered pits when the apertures are flattened; the alignment is the same or well-nigh the same.[1]

At C, the fibril alignment is the same as at A.   This is in accordance with the findings of Bailey, *et al.*   Bordered pits of the secondary wall, of course, extend through this layer, but since Bailey and Vestal[2] were unable to demonstrate fibril orientation in it by the I-KI method, the possible deviation of fibrils from the normal within and in the vicinity of bordered pits in this layer can only be conjectured.

Attention should now be focused on D, E, and F above the cross line x-y.   The three layers of the secondary wall of the cell are again shown in surface aspect as they would appear in the back wall of the tracheid, the sequence of layers being the reverse of that at A, B, and C.

At D, the spiral alignment of the fibrils is at the same angle as at C but is reversed.   This is indicative of the fact that the low fibril helixes in this thin inner layer of the secondary wall ascend in a counterclockwise direction.   No bordered pit is shown in this layer, for the reason stated in the preceding paragraph.   The same conditions hold as between E and B, and F and A; in these homologous layers, the fibril alignment and the deviation of this occasioned by the presence of bordered pits are entirely comparable except that they are reversed but at the same angle from the vertical at E and F.   Note should again be made of the fact that it is the alignment of the fibrils in the middle layer of the secondary wall that controls the alignment of flattened pit apertures.

[1] This last statement is necessary because, in cells in which the middle layer of the secondary wall is unusually thick, it is quite possible that the alignment of the fibrils in successive concentric layers of this may vary somewhat.   It is conceivable under these conditions that the final orientation of a flattened pit aperture may be a compromise of steep fibril alignments of varying degrees.

[2] *Op. cit.*

above the level x-y.   At A and B the fibril helixes in the outer and middle layers ascend from left to right, but at different angles; they have the concentric arrangement in the bordered pit at A, but are only deflected in the pit at B; fibril helixes are not illustrated in the inner layer of the wall at C because they have not as yet been demonstrated in this layer with certainty.   Above the level x-y, the same conditions hold at D, E, and F, in inverse order, except that the fibril helixes are reversed as to direction.

Especial emphasis is placed on Text Fig. 22 because considerable confusion exists as to the alignment of fibrils in the middle layer of the walls of xylary cells; in fact, some of the illustrations depicting this situation have been erroneous in portraying spiral reversal from the vertical in successive concentric zones of this layer; in other words, in such figures, some of the helixes are shown ascending in a counterclockwise direction, others in the reverse direction. A statement of Bailey and Vestal[1] is very significant in this connection: "Regularly recurring changes from right-handed to left-handed helixes or *vice versa*, such as are hypothesized by various investigators, are rarely, if ever, encountered in the central layer of coniferous tracheids." This statement is conservative in that it pertains only to coniferous tracheids, but the assumption can at least be entertained that it holds for all longitudinal xylary cells.[2]

The contention of Bailey and Vestal relative to the directional uniformity of spiraling to one side of the vertical in the middle layer of the secondary wall of coniferous tracheids is borne out by other evidence. The orientation of flattened pit apertures, where they occur, conforms in alignment to the ascending counterclockwise fibril spirals, as has been previously pointed out; flattened pit apertures directed longitudinally in the cell denote the absence of fibril helixes; *i.e.*, that the fibrils extend lengthwise in the secondary wall of the cell. Microscopic checks of the type encountered in thick-walled coniferous tracheids in the summerwood, like flattened pit apertures, parallel the fibrils. The lack of conformance in alignment of spiral checking and of spiral thickening noted on page 71 is explainable on the basis that spiral thickening occurs on the inner layer of the secondary wall, a wall layer in which fibril alignment approaches the horizontal or is horizontal.

[1] *Op. cit.*

[2] The same statement apparently does not apply in all cases to the ray cells of wood whose long axes are directed horizontally and radially in the standing tree. In the case of basswood, Ritter and Mitchell have shown that the crystal arrangement and therefore the alignment of fibrils are crosswise of the cell, *i.e.*, in the same direction as in the longitudinal fibrous elements; the ray cells therefore shrink most longitudinally, contrary to the usual idea, and the degree of longitudinal shrinkage falls in the range of crosswise shrinkage of the longitudinal elements of the wood. For further information, see G. Ritter and R. L. Mitchell. Crystal Arrangement and Swelling Properties of Fibers and Ray Cells in Basswood Holocellulose. *Paper Trade Jour.*, Vol. 108, No. 6, pp. 33–37. 1939.

CHAPTER V

THE CAMBIA OF TREES

The origin of the cambium in trees has already been explained. It is the growing layer that underlies the phloem and covers the outer surface of the wood throughout the branched cylindrical axis. In trees in the temperate zones, the cambium passes through active and dormant periods annually; all the secondary tissues are traceable to it, and through its activities the tree continues to increase in thickness year by year.

I. CAMBIAL ZONE AND CAMBIUM

Reference should now be made to Text Fig. 23 which depicts the dormant **cambial zone** of a coniferous and of a hardwood tree, respectively, as seen in transverse and longitudinal tangential sections. In transverse view, the inner living bark (1), the cambial zone (2), and the last-formed wood (3) are portrayed. The inner bark (phloem) of the hardwood tree illustrated differs from that of the conifer in being stratified; bands of **soft bast** (b) consisting of relatively thin-walled sieve tubes, companion cells, and phloem parenchyma alternate with those of **hard bast** (a) composed of dead fibers, several such double layers being formed each year. The phloem of the conifer, in contrast, not only is unstratified but is much more simple in structure; sieve tubes (a, a′) and phloem parenchyma (cells with dark contents) (b) are present, but there is no evidence of the companion cells and bast fibers that are features of the hardwood tree.

Throughout vascular plants, sieve tubes are a constant feature of the phloem; in conifers, these are always accompanied by phloem parenchyma and sometimes in addition by bast fibers, but companion cells are universally lacking.[1] Angiospermous trees differ from softwood species in possessing companion cells which are lateral and contiguous to the sieve tubes; both phloem parenchyma and fibers may also be present (Exs., *Liriodendron tulipifera* L.; *Tilia spp.*) or the latter may be wanting (Ex., *Platanus occidentalis* L.). The inference should not be drawn from the photomicrographs that the phloem of hardwood trees is invariably stratified and that the reverse holds for softwoods. Stratification is frequent but not universal throughout the former group; it also occurs in

---

[1] ABBIE, L. B., and A. S. CRAFTS. Phloems of White Pine and Other Coniferous Species. *Bot. Gaz.*, Vol. 100, pp. 695–722. 1938.

conifers, particularly in those (Taxodiaceae, Cupressaceae) in which bast fibers are present (these are responsible for the stringy bark in trees belonging to these families).

Distinction should be made between the **cambial zone** and the **cambium.** In transverse sections of the type shown (*A, C*), prepared from material collected during the resting season, the former (2) consists of six to eight rows of tabular cells which grade toward the outside into sieve tubes in various stages of formation. In trees, these last-named structures function for 1 year only; those whose further development is arrested by the approach of the winter season and have yet to participate in the vital processes of the tree become active the following spring. For this reason, the transition in passing from the cambial zone to the phloem, on the one hand, is more or less gradual, and from this zone to the last-formed wood, on the other, abrupt.

In reality, the cambium is composed of one layer of cells; this is one of the rows of tabular cells visible in transverse sections of the resting cambial zone. However, the cells composing this layer are so similar to the others in this region that the initial layer, or true cambium, cannot be distinguished as such. The cells composing the cambium differ from others in the cambial zone in possessing the power of repeated division when growing conditions are favorable.

During the dormant season, the tissue of the cambial zone is relatively firm. At the start of this period, the walls of the cells composing it thicken appreciably, and the protoplasts pass into what Priestley has termed the **gel state,**[1] meanwhile parting with a certain amount of water. The **osmotic pressure** of the cells is heightened, and the resistance of the cambium to frost is materially increased.

The student should not infer that the cambial zone of a tree at the height of the growing season presents the same appearance as those depicted in Text Fig. 23, *A* and *C*. With the reawakening of growth in the spring, the tissues in this region swell materially and become succulent. The nature of the cells meanwhile changes. Where before their protoplasmic contents were gelled, they now are semifluid (in the **sol state**). Concomitantly, changes take place in the cell walls; they become thinner and more plastic. This is the stage when the bark will slip easily on the wood.

Shortly after the establishment of the condition described in the preceding paragraph, repeated division begins in the uninucleate cells of the true cambium; in other words, the cambium becomes active (Text

[1] PRIESTLEY, J. H. Studies in the Physiology of Cambial Activity. III. The Seasonal Activity of the Cambium. *New Phytol.*, Vol. 29, No. 5, p. 322. 1930.

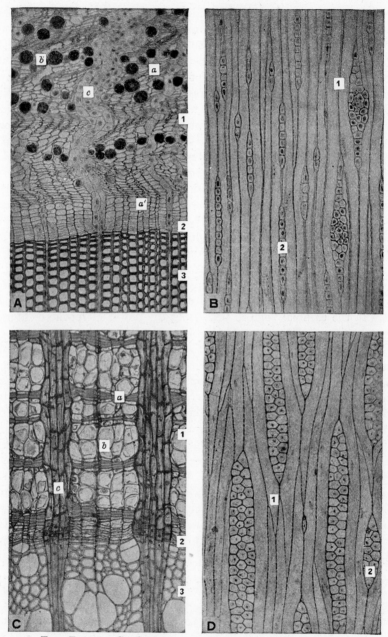

Text Fig. 23.—Cambia of trees in the dormant (winter) condition.
A. Inner bark (1), dormant cambial region (2), and portion of the last annual ring (3) of northern white pine (*Pinus strobus* L.). The sieve tubes function only for one year; they have collapsed in the older living bark (*a*) but have yet to function in the vicinity

Fig. 24; compare with Text Fig. 23, *A* and *C*). The division is of the type known as indirect (mitotic) vegetative division (see page 66). Nuclear figures are produced in regular sequence,[1] and a new wall forms between the daughter nuclei. The new walls are largely in the tangential plane. By such divisions, each cambial cell gives rise to two daughter cells. One of these continues to function as a cambial mother cell. The other, if cut off to the outside, becomes a part of the phloem; if to the inside, a part of the xylem.[2] Directly or after further division, this, then, differentiates relatively quickly into one or more elements belonging to the one or to the other of these tissues, respectively.

It follows that longitudinal xylary cells arising in this way from the repeated division of a mother cell in the lateral cambium are aligned in radial rows; further, that those of a given row, irrespective of whether they are phloem or xylary cells, are all descendants of the same mother cell in the cambium. The radial arrangement of the elements thus arising is largely retained in coniferous woods, for reasons that will be

---

[1] BAILEY, I. W. The Formation of the Cell Plate in the Cambium of the Higher Plants. *Proc. Natl. Acad. Sci.*, Vol. 6, pp. 197–200. 1920.

BAILEY, I. W. The Cambium and Its Derivative Tissues. III. A Reconnaissance of Cytological Phenomena in the Cambium. *Amer. Jour. Bot.*, Vol. 7, pp. 417–434. 1920.

[2] There are about six to eight as many divisions on the xylem side of the cambium as on the phloem side. This explains why secondary xylem in a tree accumulates much faster than secondary phloem.

---

of the cambium (*a'*); the enlarged cells with dark contents (*b*) compose the phloem parenchyma; the phloem portion of a ray is visible (*c*); the cambial region (2) consists of 6–10 rows of tabular cells (in this view), one row of which, though indistinguishable, is the true cambium. The transition from the thin-walled cells of the cambial region (2) to the mature tracheids of the wood (3) is very abrupt. (100 ×.)

B. Cambium of northern white pine (*Pinus strobus* L.) in tangential view. The cambium is composed of very long (several millimeters) longitudinal mother cells (1) with tapering ends, and short ray mother cells (2), grouped in cambial rays. Some of the longitudinal cells extend completely across the photograph, lengthwise; the tapering ends only of others are visible. Uniseriate and multiseriate fusiform cambial rays can be distinguished; the transverse resin canals which are a feature of the fusiform xylary and phloem rays of this species do not show since these structures are of post-cambial origin. (100 ×.)

C. Inner bark (1), dormant cambial region (2), and portion of the last annual ring (3) of yellow-poplar (*Liriodendron tulipifera* L.). The phloem is stratified in this species and consists of alternating layers of bast fibers (*a*) and soft bast (*b*) between the rays (*c*); the soft bast is composed of sieve tubes (large quadrangular cells), companion cells, and phloem parenchyma. The cambial region (2) consists of about six rows of tabular cells (in this view), one row of which, though indistinguishable, is the true cambium. The transition from thin-walled cambial cells (2) to the mature elements of the wood (3) is abrupt; vessels, fiber tracheids and the xylary portions of rays are evident in the latter. (100 ×.)

D. Cambium of yellow-poplar (*Liriodendron tulipifera* L.) in tangential view. The cambium is composed of long longitudinal mother cells (1) with tapering ends, and short ray mother cells (2), grouped in cambial rays. The longitudinal cells are not sufficiently long to extend completely across the photograph lengthwise, a situation which held for the comparable units in white pine. The cambial rays are 2–3-seriate except for one lone ray which consists of a single cell. (100 ×.)

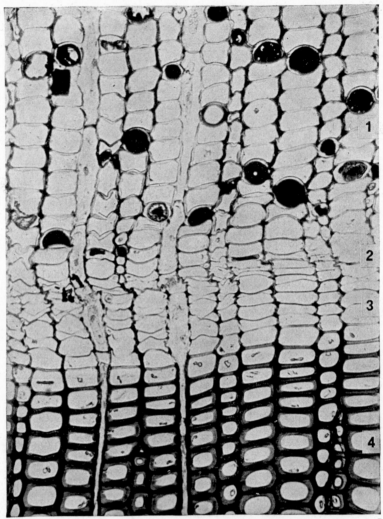

TEXT FIG. 24.—Active cambium of pine (*Pinus* sp.), in transverse section. 1. Inner living bark consisting of sieve tubes, phloem parenchyma (cells with dark contents), and phloem rays. 2. Cambium. 3. Immature longitudinal tracheids with thin walls. 4. Mature longitudinal tracheids with thick walls. (*Courtesy of the Forest Research Institute, Dehra Dun, India.*)

Note the apparent rapidity with which the xylary cells mature behind the cambium.

explained later; porous woods, on the contrary, show less evidence of it because of the postcambial enlargement of certain cells of the wood, particularly of vessel members (see page 168) which results in distortion of the tissue.

II. KINDS AND ARRANGEMENT OF CAMBIAL INITIALS (MOTHER CELLS) IN THE CAMBIUM

Inspection of photomicrographs *B* and *D* of Text Fig. 23, which depict cambia in longitudinal tangential view, will serve to show that there are two kinds of mother cell, and *two kinds only*, in the cambium. Those which have their long axes upright in the standing tree have tapering ends; these are the so-called **fusiform initials** or **fusiform cambial cells** to which all the longitudinal elements of wood are traceable.[1] The smaller cells, grouped in the form of wood rays that have been cut transversely, are **ray initials** or **ray mother cells.** Through divisions in the plane of the paper, they are responsible on the one hand for the continuation of a phloem ray to the outside, on the other, for the further building of the complementary xylary ray within the wood, these two structures together forming the complete ray that passes through the cambium at this point.

In the great majority of trees, the fusiform initials and the clusters of ray mother cells that comprise the cambial portions of the rays are staggered, as viewed in tangential sections. Not only do the former usually overlap vertically in the standing tree, *i.e.*, those which are contiguous laterally end at different heights, but the same holds for the cambial-ray areas. This situation results in an **unstoried cambium.** Emphasis is placed on this fact at the present time because a different situation holds in the cambia of certain hardwoods, in which the cambial-ray areas are storied (arranged in tiers, like windows in a building); under these conditions, the fusiform initials may also be storied, resulting in a **storied cambium,** or they may retain the staggered arrangement that is a feature of most cambia. **Ripple marks** in wood (see page 46) are traceable to storied cambial initials.

III. SHAPE AND SIZE OF CAMBIAL INITIALS IN HARDWOODS AND SOFTWOODS

Text Fig. 25 illustrates the shape, in three planes of section, of the initials in the storied cambium of a hardwood tree and likewise those of the young xylary cells arising from them. The longitudinal cells are much the larger.

The fusiform cambial initial depicted (*a*) has the shape of a thin

[1] Those which have their long axes directed along the grain.

picket which has been sharpened at each end. Such a unit has eight facets (faces), *i.e.*, it is an elongated octahedron. When seen in tangential view, a cell of this sort appears fusiform, hence the term "fusiform initial"; as viewed radially, narrowly rectangular since the sloping ends would not be evident in this plane with a microscope; when cut trans-

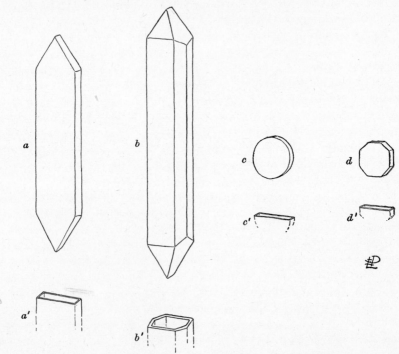

Text Fig. 25.—Initials from the storied cambium of a hardwood tree, and an immature longitudinal xylary cell. *a*. 8-sided fusiform mother cell. *a'*. A transverse section of the same. *b*. Immature, 14-sided (tetrakaidecahedral) xylary cell arising from *a* through division. *b'*. Hexagonal transverse section of the same. *c*. Coin-shaped ray mother cell in tangential aspect. *c'*. Transverse section of the same. *d*. Short prismatic ray mother cell in tangential aspect. *d'*. Transverse section of the same.

versely, tabloid (*a'*). Special note should be made of the fact that, although the sloping facets on the ends of the octahedron approach the rectangular, they are more or less rounded at the corners.

It is only in storied cambia that the fusiform initials approach the conventionalized form depicted in Text Fig. 25. Elsewhere in hardwood trees and in all coniferous trees, they are far less regular in shape, in fact, so irregular that they are scarcely to be thought of in terms of geometric figures with plane faces. This condition is explained in part by their much greater length in the trees in question.

The dimensions of the fusiform cambial initials of hardwoods vary markedly according to species and also, within narrower limits in a given species, according to age and conditions of growth. The transverse diameter in the tangential plane is in the neighborhood of 10 to 15 microns.[1] In length, they range from about ten to over sixty times these figures. The length is much more variable than the transverse dimensions, as Bailey[2] has brought out in some of his studies of the cambium. In 54 arborescent species (inclusive of tropical species) examined by him, the longest fusiform initials occurred in *Myristica philippensis* Lam. (mean, 1.31 mm.) and in *Glochidon littorale* Bl. (mean, 1.04 mm.) of the Philippine Islands, the shortest in *Robinia pseudoacacia* L. (mean, 0.17 mm.) of eastern United States. The average length for the 16 domestic species included in the larger list was 0.532 millimeter. Of these, *Betula populifolia* Marsh. had the longest initials (mean, 0.94 mm.), followed by *Nyssa sylvatica* Marsh. (mean, 0.83 mm.) and *Liquidambar styraciflua* L. (mean, 0.70 mm.). The mean lengths in the same 16 species fell between 0.30 and 0.80 millimeter, respectively, in more than 80 per cent of the cases.

In contrast to the longitudinal initials, the ray mother cells of hardwoods (Text Fig. 25, *c* and *d*), when viewed tangentially, are relatively small and are generally narrower than the fusiform cells that accompany them; they may be rounded (*c*), when intercellular spaces are usually present between them, or polygonal (*d*) and more closely fitted in the ray areas. Both of the above types, like the longitudinal initials, possess little thickness. Those of rounded contour may be described as roughly coin-shaped, with the face of the coin toward the observer in the plane in question; the angular types, in contrast, have the form of very short prisms with lateral faces which are usually unequal in length, the prisms so orientated that one base shows in the tangential plane.

The cambial initials of conifers are comparable in shape with those of hardwood trees with unstoried cambia. Particularly is the accuracy of this statement evident in the case of the ray initials which not only in form, but in dimensions as well, overlap those of hardwoods.[3] The longitudinal cambial initials of softwoods, on the other hand, are much

---

[1] A micron is $\frac{1}{1000}$ millimeter.

[2] BAILEY, I. W. The Cambium and Its Derivative Tissues. II. Size Variation of Cambial Initials in Gymnosperms and Angiosperms. *Amer. Jour. Bot.*, Vol. 7, pp. 355–367. 1920.

[3] At first thought, this situation seems illogical, for the rays of conifers are prevailingly narrow whereas those of hardwoods range from narrow to broad. The truth of the statement rests in the fact that large ray areas, as noted in cambia viewed in tangential section, do not result from large units, smaller ray areas from smaller units, etc. The size of the ray initials remains fairly constant, within rough limits; the number of cells is therefore the controlling factor in determining ray size.

longer (100 to 200 times as long as wide).   They generally measure 1 to 2 millimeters or more along the grain and 30 or more microns in width tangentially.[1]

IV. ENLARGEMENT OF YOUNG XYLARY CELLS FOLLOWING THEIR FORMATION IN THE CAMBIUM

The young xylary cells arising through cell division in the cambium remain thin-walled for a time and undergo a varying amount of enlargement.[2]   The extent of this depends upon the type of element they are destined to become, on the kind of wood of which they are to be a corporeal part, and on their position in the tree and in an annual increment.   It is convenient in discussing this phenomenon to deal with the longitudinal and transverse elements of wood separately.

A. Enlargement of Longitudinal Xylary Cells

The longitudinal cells of wood, as they mature, increase appreciably in radial diameter, to some or to considerable extent in tangential diameter, and, with the exception of the vessel segments, usually considerably in length along the grain.   A moderate increase in the radial diameter is readily understandable, for the cambium moves outward with further growth, and spatial adjustment in this direction is ensured for the enlarging cells.   Enlargement in the tangential plane, unless it is considerable as in the formation of vessel segments, apparently results from the response of the cells to the tissue tensions that prevail at this time. They become polygonal and often hexagonal in cross section (Text Fig. 25, *b'*).   In trees with a storied cambium, the longitudinal cells are actually 14-sided (tetrakaidecahedral) at this stage (Text Fig. 25, *b*); but in less specialized dicotyledons and in coniferous trees the shape is far less regular, for many more than 14 facets (points of contact with other cells) develop.   As the cells become polygonal in cross section, those in contiguous rows shift laterally with respect to one another, *i.e.*, they become staggered, but there is no change (break) in the layer of intercellular substance; this then permits of an increase in the tangential diameter (Text Fig. 26).

The unusual enlargement of the vessel members in radial and tangential diameter, on the other hand, is brought about in a different manner. The newly formed cells, which on maturity are to become vessel members, first enlarge tangentially, rapidly reaching their maximum diameter in that direction.   This is followed by extension in the radial direction

---

[1] For this reason, it was inadvisable to illustrate cells of this sort in Text Fig. 25.

[2] The same holds true of the cells in the phloem which is situated outside of the cambium.

There is considerable evidence to indicate that while this radial expansion takes place the division of the fusiform cambial initials lying opposite to an enlarging vessel is slowed down; the neighboring cambial initials meanwhile continue to divide unimpeded.[1] Increase in the cross-sectional area of a vessel member also produces considerable distortion in the neighboring cells which are pushed outward in all directions in the trans-

A   **B**

Text Fig. 26.—Schematic section of a portion of the cambial zone of a tree, depicting cells which have arisen through the tangential division of longitudinal cambial initials. *A.* Before the cells in contiguous rows have shifted laterally. *B.* After such a shift has resulted, owing to tissue tension; the tangential diameters of the cells have increased, without sliding growth. (*After Beijer, J. J. Die Vermehrung der radialen Reihen im Cambium. Rec. de trav. bot. Néerl., Vol. 24, pp. 631–786. 1927.*)

verse plane. As a result of this enlargement, the mature vessels eventually may come to have many more cells in contact with them than was originally the case. This can result only if the layer of cementing substance between contiguous cells is ruptured or is altered in such a manner that the cells can slide upon one another; this is called **sliding growth** or **gliding growth.** The student should bear in mind that the cells at this stage are devoid of secondary walls and hence pits but that at the start they did possess plasmodesma (strands of protoplasm connecting the protoplasts of neighboring cells, grouped in pit fields) which must have been ruptured.

Turning now to changes in length that ensue along the grain, the longitudinal cells destined to become vessel segments exhibit but little

[1] This phenomenon can be demonstrated most readily in ring-porous woods by counting the number of cells radially, *i.e.*, from the boundary of one ring to that of the next, selecting first a place where a springwood vessel is flanked on each side by a ray and then a place between the two rays where no large springwood vessels have been formed. Invariably, it will be found that fewer cells have been formed throughout the growing season by the cambial initials in the former than in the latter instance, thus indicating that the initials divided fewer times opposite the vessel.

or no elongation in this direction;[1] most of the enlargement in these units is in the transverse plane. The other longitudinal elements in the immediate vicinity of the vessels and elsewhere in the wood increase in length to varying degrees as they mature. The greatest elongation takes place in the developing fibers of hardwoods which frequently become four to five times as long as the fusiform initials in the cambium that gave rise to them. Coniferous tracheids, in contrast, are seldom more than 25 to 30 per cent longer than the longitudinal mother cells. However, the latter have a much greater length than those of hardwoods, as has been recorded previously.

The manner in which elongation proceeds in the longitudinal elements of coniferous and dicotyledonous trees, both in the xylem and in the phloem, is still a matter of debate. According to such investigators as Bailey, Thimann, and Kerr, the young fusiform xylary cells elongate at their ends, and the elongating ends push between and separate the cells in the tiers above and below. This is the concept of sliding growth but of sliding growth restricted to the ends of the cells involved. If this conception is correct, cleavage must result between the tips of the cells in the tiers above and below, the rupture coming in the layers of intercellular substance which originally cemented the tips together. As growth in length ensues, the complementary pit fields (places where pits would have formed subsequently when the secondary wall was laid down) shift so that they no longer match on the opposite flanks of the layer of intercellular substance. The plasmodesmic strands connecting contiguous cells must also be ruptured. With the completion of growth in length, protoplasmic contacts between contiguous cells are again established. The deposition of a secondary wall, of course, does not begin until the enlargement of the cell is practically complete.

In contrast to the above, Priestley[2] has evolved an ingenious theory to explain the elongation of the longitudinal xylary cells. He proposes the term **symplastic growth** for the process, as he visualizes it. Priestley is of the opinion that "mutual adjustment of cell position takes place between semifluid protoplasts, separated from one another by plastic walls which move as a common framework under tension, and without any slip between the wall surfaces of neighboring cells."

Further discussion of gliding growth as described by Bailey and others,

[1] A vessel segment may even be shorter than the cambial initial to which it is traceable; this is due to the fact that the top and bottom of the expanding cell are drawn together a little as the cell expands in girth. PRIESTLEY, J. H. Studies in the Physiology of Cambial Activity. I. Contrasted Types of Cambial Activity, *New Phytol.*, Vol. 29, No. 1, p. 68. 1930.

[2] PRIESTLEY, J. H. Studies in the Physiology of Cambial Activity. II. The Concept of Sliding Growth. *New Phytol.*, Vol. 29, No. 2, pp. 96–140. 1930.

ot symplastic growth as understood by Priestley, and of other theories that seek to explain the enlargement and changes in the juxtaposition of longitudinal xylary cells following their origin in the cambium does not fall within the sphere of this text. Considerable research yet remains to be done before these phenomena can be thoroughly understood.

B. Enlargement of the Transverse Xylary Cells Composing the Wood Rays

Most of the enlargement that takes place in xylary-ray cells following their origin in the cambium is in the radial direction. Evidence to this effect is forthcoming when serial tangential sections are cut through the cambial zone and last-formed wood of a tree. The cluster of cells composing a given ray, as cut transversely (*t*), are of practically the same size and of the same number, irrespective of whether the ray in question is viewed when it passes through the cambium or as it appears in the near-by wood.[1]

The young xylary-ray cells are enabled to elongate in the radial direction because sufficient spatial adjustment is assured in the xylary portion of the ray as the cambium moves outward. Sliding growth is not a necessary concomitant although the possibility of this is not precluded. The extent of the elongation is controlled apparently by the rate at which cell division proceeds in the ray initials; if division is rapid in the ray mother cells, the mature xylary-ray cells are shorter in the radial direction than if the reverse holds. The initials in a given ray area (*t*) do not divide simultaneously but at different intervals; furthermore, some divide much more rapidly than others as, for example, those engaged in the production of "upright cells"[2] as compared with those responsible for "procumbent cells." Growth in thickness lags toward the end of the growing season. Slackening of growth is recorded in the forming xylary ray in that the ray cells, as viewed in transverse and radial sections, are shorter in the late summerwood than in the springwood.

V. INCREASE IN GIRTH OF THE CAMBIUM

Another point requires clarification at this time which until comparatively recently was one of the conundrums of plant anatomy. This is the manner in which the cambium increases in circumference to permit

---

[1] Once brought into being, a ray, barring injury to the cambium, is continued as long as the tree lives. It may increase in size—in fact, it usually does—but any change of this sort is initiated in the cambium. Hence, the statement still holds that in size and in cell numbers the cambial and near-by xylary portions of a ray are practically identical.

[2] For description of upright and procumbent cells, see Chap. VIII, page 185.

the inclusion of successive increments of secondary wood in the trunk of the tree, always, of course, to the inside of the cambium.

Bailey[1] has written a classical paper upon this subject. At the start he postulates that the increase in girth of the lateral meristem may be due to one or more of the following factors:

1. An increase in the tangential diameter of the fusiform initials.
2. An increase in the length of these cells.
3. An increase in the number of these cells.
4. An increase in the tangential diameter of the ray initials.
5. An increase in the number of these cells.

That the statements listed under 1, 2, 4, and 5 hold true for many vascular plants had already been demonstrated by the same investigator prior to 1923; except in those highly specialized dicotyledons with a stratified cambium, the cambial initials of both types undergo gradual enlargement for some years (20 to 60) after which but minor fluctuations in size occur, in no way correlated with increasing age. Comparing a 1-year-old stem of white pine (*Pinus strobus* L.) with a 60-year-old stem of the same species, Bailey proceeded by computations to show that neither the increase in the tangential diameter of the fusiform initials nor the increase in the length of these cells, whereby they grow past each other vertically in the tangential plane and hence reach higher and lower horizontal levels in the stem, could fully account for the increase in the girth of the cambium. At the same time, he recognizes the fact that some of the ray initials increase in tangential diameter; but even the cumulative effect of this, added to that resulting from the enlargement of the fusiform initials, could in no wise explain the ever-widening circle of cambium.[2] The deduction follows that the cambium must increase in girth largely through the addition of new initials.

The manner in which the number of fusiform initials in the cambium of a tree is increased is illustrated in Text Fig. 27. This proceeds in one of two ways.

In the Gymnosperms and less specialized Dicotyledons, the fusiform initials, as viewed in tangential aspect, are not arranged in tiers (stories); consequently, no two end at the same or at approximate height. Most of the divisions in these initials are periclinal (in the tangential plane); but pseudo-transverse division occurs now and then, resulting in the

---

[1] BAILEY, I. W. The Cambium and Its Derivative Tissues. IV. The Increase in Girth of the Cambium, *Amer. Jour. Bot.*, Vol. 10, pp. 499–508. 1923.

[2] This is obvious since, in many cases, the circumference of the cambium when a stem is one year old, is seldom over 1 inch; at the same level when the tree is mature, the same layer may have a circumference in excess of 10 feet, an increase in this dimension of over 12,000 per cent.

formation of an oblique wall between the two new cells thus arising (*A*). The sloping ends of these cells then grow past each other, the two new cells coming to be parallel and in contact with one another in the tangential plane although they are not necessarily of the same length.

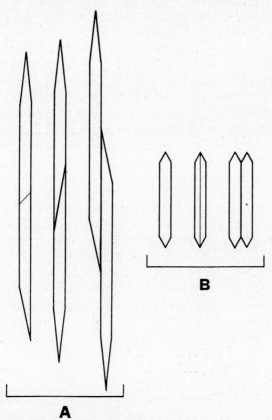

TEXT FIG. 27.—Diagrams illustrating the manner in which the increase in the girth of the cambium proceeds in nonstratified and in stratified cambia.
A. Fusiform initial from a nonstratified cambium, dividing pseudo-transversely; the daughter cells resulting from this division elongate and slide by one another in the tangential plane. B. Fusiform initial from a stratified cambium; the daughter cells resulting from the radiolongitudinal division expand laterally but do not elongate. (*After I. W. Bailey.*)

Stratified meristems are features of some of the higher dicotyledons which may (*Diospyros virginiana* L.) or may not (*Robinia pseudoacacia* L.) exhibit ripple marks on the tangential surface of the wood as a result. In such instances, the fusiform initials, as viewed in tangential aspect, are grouped in transverse tiers and end at the same or at proximate heights (*B*). When these cells divide, the division is radiolongitudinal.

The new wall runs lengthwise of the cell and is at right angles to the original tangential walls; *i.e.*, it is in the longitudinal radial plane.   As a result, the two new cells arising from the division lie parallel in the tangential plane and end at the same height.   The girth of the cambium is thus increased, in spite of the fact that the two new fusiform initials do not undergo elongation following their formation through cell division.

According to Bailey,[1] "in the dicotyledons there is a progressive reduction in the length of the fusiform initials and of their derivatives, which closely parallels stages in the differentiation of highly specialized types of vascular tissues."   Aberrant vessel-less dicotyledons such as *Drimys, Tetracentron,* and *Trochodendron* possess secondary xylem which closely resembles that of the Gymnosperms; the fusiform initials in these trees are fully as large as those in Gymnosperms.   In Dicotyledons with vessels, in contrast, these meristematic cells have shortened progressively as the tracheary elements became more specialized.   Unusually short fusiform initials characterize stratified meristems of the sort occurring in black locust and persimmon.   Coupled with these changes is the orientation of the anticlinal partition which is formed when a fusiform initial divides. In the nonstratified meristems studied by Bailey, this partition fluctuated from nearly horizontal to varying degrees of obliquity.   As the initials became shorter, the alignment became more nearly radiolongitudinal, arriving at or approximately at this orientation in stratified cambia.

In conclusion, Bailey raises the question of how much significance can be attached to the close parallelism in the sequence of changes in cell size in the cambium and in the vascular tissue arising from it.   Did the first give rise to the last, or vice versa?   Or did both these sequences arise as the result of a third set of factors?   At present, these questions must remain in the realm of speculation.

[1] See footnote 1, p. 108.

CHAPTER VI

THE MINUTE STRUCTURE OF CONIFEROUS WOODS
PART I. THE WOOD ANATOMY OF NORTHERN WHITE PINE

(Pinus strobus L.)

The main and secondary titles heading this chapter require explanation, to render understandable the sequence in which the information in
this portion of the text (Chaps. VI and VII, respectively) is presented.
The order is from the specific to the general; pedagogically, in the opinion
of the authors, it is best first to describe the minute features of a well-
known coniferous wood, then to point out the anatomical departures that
occur in coniferous woods as a group. The subtitle, as given above, is
indicative of this method of approach; it is coordinate with that in the
next chapter, Comparative Anatomy of the Coniferous Woods of the
United States.

I. DESCRIPTION OF A BLOCK OF WHITE PINE WOOD

Text Fig. 28 is a schematic drawing of a small block of white pine
(*Pinus strobus* L.) at high magnification (400×), showing the wood in
three planes of section (*A*, *B*, and *C*). Not only do the faces meet at
right angles, but the block is so cut that the two longitudinal faces (*B* and
C) are truly radial and tangential, respectively.

Experience has taught that the sense of proportion is frequently lost
in the study of wood in shifting from a hand lens to a compound microscope. For this reason, it is desirable that the student acquire at the
very start some conception of the size of the block portrayed. The area
of the faces of the cube (which are not completely shown) is in the neighborhood of $9/100$ square millimeter, or roughly, about $1/7000$ square inch;
the volume would therefore be approximately $27/1000$ cubic millimeter,
i.e., less than 1/600,000 cubic inch.

The cellular nature of wood is at once apparent from the figure;
xylary tissue consists of cells held together by intercellular substance[1]
but, what is more important, of several different kinds of cells. Cells of
similar shape and functions, collectively, comprise a type of wood element.
Those elements which have their long axes directed vertically in the

---

[1] As has been pointed out previously, the dark medial layer visible in cell walls in
the transverse section is the compound middle lamella (see p. 85).

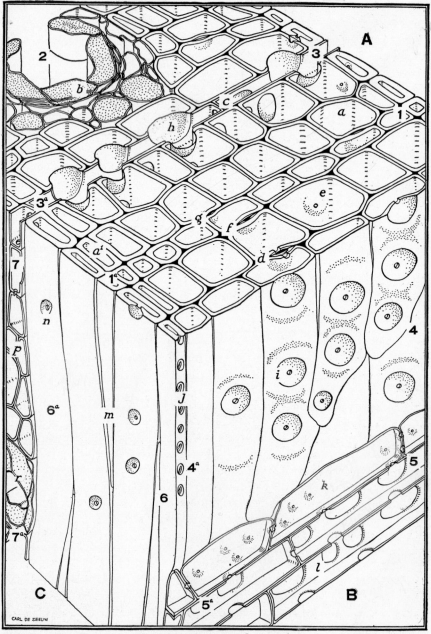

TEXT FIG. 28.—Schematic three-plane drawing of the wood of northern white pine (*Pinus strobus* L.). (400 ×.)

Surface *A*. 1-1^a, portion of an annual ring; 2, resin canal; 3-3^a, wood ray; *a-a'*, longitu-

standing tree (also vertically on the paper) are called **longitudinal elements;** as has been stated previously, they are all traceable to fusiform initials of one type in the cambium. **Transverse elements,** in contrast, are elongated transversely and radially in the tree. Collectively, they comprise the rays and result from the division of ray mother cells.[1]

The longitudinal and transverse elements of white pine wood are listed in Table III. The reader should realize that each of these is three-dimensional, *i.e.*, has length, breadth, and thickness, and further, as will be stressed later, that a given kind of element may be many times longer than another. Note should also be made of the fact that all the kinds of elements need not necessarily show in a given section of a wood. Their

TABLE III
ELEMENTS OF WHITE PINE WOOD

I. Longitudinal
    A. Prosenchymatous
        a. Tracheids
    B. Parenchymatous
        a. Epithelial cells:*
            excreting cells of
            longitudinal resin
            canals

II. Transverse
    A. Prosenchymatous
        a. Ray tracheids } Narrow rays ⎫
    B. Parenchymatous   ⎬ Narrow rays ⎫
        a. Cells of ray } Narrow rays ⎭   ⎬ Fusiform rays
            parenchyma   ⎭
        b. Epithelial cells:*
            excreting cells of
            transverse resin canals

    * Longitudinal and transverse resin canals are not listed, since they are intercellular spaces encircled by excreting cells (epithelium) and are hence not true elements. Longitudinal parenchyma is not present in white pine wood.

    [1] One point requires clarification and emphasis at this point. It follows that the longitudinal cells of white pine, as shown in Text Fig. 28, in fact, of any wood, are cut transversely (the short way) when sections are prepared across the grain and the transverse cells (ray cells) longitudinally (the long way). In sections along the grain, the longitudinal elements, of course, appear in lateral view irrespective of whether the section is radial (*B*) or tangential (*C*); the transverse elements (ray cells), on the other hand, are cut longitudinally in the radial section (*B*) and transversely in the tangential section (*C*).

---

dinal tracheids; *b*, epithelial cells; *c*, ray cells; *d*, pit pair in median sectional view; *e*, bordered pits in the back walls of longitudinal tracheids, in surface view; *f*, pit pair in sectional view, showing the margin of the torus but so cut that the pit apertures are not included in the plane of section; *g*, pit pair in which neither the pit aperture nor the torus shows; *h*, window-like pit pairs between longitudinal tracheids and ray parenchyma.

    Surface *B*. 4-4ᵃ, portions of longitudinal tracheids in radial aspect (the ends are blunt); 5-5ᵃ, upper part of a uniseriate ray; *i*, bordered pits on the radial walls of longitudinal, springwood tracheids (the base of the pit is toward the observer); *j*, small bordered pits on the radial walls of longitudinal summer-wood tracheids, in the same view in as *i*; *k*, ray tracheids; *l*, cells of ray parenchyma.

    Surface *C*. 6-6ᵃ, portions of longitudinal tracheids in tangential aspect; 7-7ᵃ, portion of a xylary ray; *m*, tapering ends of longitudinal tracheids; *n*, a small bordered pit on the tangential wall of a longitudinal summerwood tracheid; *p*, cells of ray parenchyma, *r*, transverse resin canal.

presence or absence hinges entirely on whether cells of the type in question happened to project into the plane under examination.[1]

The wood elements listed in Table III should now be considered in conjunction with Text Fig. 28. Special effort should be made at this time to obtain a clear conception of the positions that representatives of each type of cell have in the wood and of the comparative volume of the wood occupied by cells of the type in question.

In developing a logical description of the minute features of white pine wood, it is obvious that several means of approach are possible which are undoubtedly logical. In the present instance, it has seemed best to describe all the structures visible on a given surface, then to proceed to the next surface, etc. This treatment of the subject seems especially justifiable since a student never sees wood in three dimensions under the microscope at the magnification shown in the figure, but rather in one plane at a time, by means of sections.

A. Description of Surface *A* (Transverse Surface)

On surface *A*, a segment of an annual ring (1-1^a) is shown in which growth proceeded from right to left when this layer was formed. Two types of longitudinal elements, *viz.*, **longitudinal tracheids** (*a*, *a'*) and **epithelial cells** (*b*) belonging to a longitudinal **resin canal** (2), and one type of transverse element [**ray cells** (*c*) forming part of a **wood ray** (3-3^a)] are shown. The longitudinal tracheids constitute a large proportion of the volume of the wood. They are arranged in radial rows, those in the springwood (1) being thinner walled and tending toward the hexagonal in comparison with the thick-walled, rectangular (tabular) tracheids of the outer summerwood (1^a). The orderly arrangement of the cells of this type is traceable to the fact that those of a given row are all descendants of the same fusiform mother cell in the cambium; as this divides again and again, walls are formed in the tangential plane, the daughter cells thus produced to the inside of the cambium maturing into longitudinal tracheids.

Bordered pits are visible both on the radial walls and on the tangential walls of the tracheids. If surface *A* could be viewed frontally (as a section of wood is seen under the microscope) instead of obliquely, as in the drawing, only pit pairs in sectional view would be visible (*d*, *f*, *g*); as it is, some bordered pits show on back walls in oblique view, appearing as bosses perforated at the center (*e*). The pits on the radial walls, except in the extreme outer portion of the summerwood, are much larger than

---

[1] It follows that all the cell types present in a wood would appear sooner or later in serial sections, cut in any plane.

those on the tangential walls (see n of surface C). Those of the latter type are restricted to the last-formed summerwood tracheids.

The varying appearance of a coniferous pit pair as seen in sectional view now requires description. If the section is median, the two pit apertures are visible (d); if to one side of the apertures, neither of the latter shows. In the latter instance, the pit chamber appears as a biconvex cavity, inserted in the cell wall and without visible means of communication with the cell lumina lying to either side of the wall, spanned by a pit membrane. The last may be slightly thickened or unthickened depending on whether the plane of section happened or did not happen to include the edge of the torus (compare d, f, and g).

The parenchymatous uniseriate portion of a wood ray (3-3^a) crosses surface A diagonally beyond the fifth row of tracheids. Since the ray cells are seen in longitudinal sectional view in the plane in question, they are longer than the longitudinal tracheids along the flanks of the ray (which are cut transversely). Pit pairs of a peculiar type (h) are present in the walls between the parenchymatous cells of the ray and the tracheids. The pit on the tracheid side has a very wide aperture and a very narrow border; the complementary pit in the contiguous ray cell is simple. The result is a semibordered pit pair with very wide pit apertures, spanned by an unthickened compound pit membrane which often arches outward into the lumen of a longitudinal tracheid. Pit pairs of this sort are frequently described in the literature as windowlike.

The final feature of surface A requiring description is the longitudinal resin canal (2) which appears in oblique surface view on the upper left-hand portion of the figure. It is evident that this consists of a tubular cavity extending along the grain, sheathed by thin-walled excreting cells (b) (epithelium). In a transverse section, viewed frontally as in a microscope, the lateral walls of some of the epithelial cells would not show as they do in the figure; in such instances, only the rounded orifice of the canal would be visible, surrounded by epithelial cells in one plane, the cells flattened and seemingly stretched in the peripheral direction.[1]

The cavity of a canal of the type depicted on surface A is, in reality, an intercellular space, *i.e.*, a place where immature longitudinal xylary cells pulled apart, leaving a tubular cavity. The cells surrounding this meanwhile remained thin-walled and assumed the function of resin excretion. As long as the canals are a part of the sapwood, resin collects in the cavity and exudes as pitch if it is ruptured, as when logs are sawn into lumber. In heartwood, resin canals are usually plugged with tylosoids

---

[1] In lateral view, the epithelial cells are rectangular; if the epithelium is more than one layer of cells in thickness, the shortest rectangles are situated next to the cavity of the canal, the longest farthest away.

(see Text Fig. 35, *H*) and thereafter may be considered as vestigial structures.

From the above description, it is evident that a resin canal, consisting as it does of a tubular intercellular space and surrounding epithelium, as such, is not a wood element (see Table III). The epithelial cells surrounding it fall into this category, however; they are traceable to daughter cells arising from fusiform initials in the cambium which, as they mature, divide by transverse walls into a number of smaller units aligned in a longitudinal row.

It is well to note here that longitudinal resin canals, as found in the wood of white pine and other conifers, are of postcambial origin; the continuity of the cambium is not interrupted prior to their formation, nor is there any evident change in the nature of the cambial cells. As seen in transverse sections, longitudinal daughter cells, in clusters here and there behind the cambium, fail to mature into longitudinal tracheids in the normal manner but remain thin-walled and rich in protoplasm. The true middle lamella between cells near the center of the cluster splits, and an intercellular cavity is formed; resin accumulates in this, widening it further, and a canal is the result. In white pine wood, the epithelium is usually several layers of cells in thickness. The cells immediately surrounding the canal cavity remain active and do not crush; one or more layers behind these generally collapse (Text Fig. 35, *A*), permitting the cells in the first layer to enlarge further peripherally, thus increasing the size of the tubular intercellular space.

B. Description of Surface *B* (Radial Surface)

Portions of longitudinal tracheids (4-4^a) and the upper part of a uniseriate wood ray (5-5^a) are shown in lateral aspect on surface *B*. The former are rendered conspicuous by the presence of large bordered pits (*i*) which appear in surface view; the ray stands out against the background of tracheids because it extends transversely.

Three blunt tracheid ends are visible on the surface under consideration. When this is compared with surface *A*, it is evident that the longitudinal tracheids which trace their parentage to the same fusiform mother cell in the cambium, and hence are aligned in radial rows on the transverse surface, end approximately at the same height in the wood. The question now arises: Why do not all the tracheids in such a tier terminate exactly at the same height since they are daughter cells from the same mother cell? The answer to this question rests in the fact that gliding growth takes place not to an exact but to an approximate degree in these cells as they mature behind the cambium; as a consequence, the mature tracheids are only approximately equal in length. In the figure, the ends of the last three extend downward farther than the others and are covered up by the ray.

Also, were it not for gliding growth, the ends of the tracheids in the tier coming up from the bottom of the drawing would just meet those of the tier above; not only would they just meet these, but they would show on surface *B*. No tracheid ends of this tier can be seen, however, even though the presence of such a tier is indicated in that portion of the drawing immediately above the right-hand end of the ray. This means that, as the ends of the tracheids of superposed tiers in a radial plane grow past each other, they are thrust laterally out of the plane, so much so that only one series is visible at a time in radial surface aspect.

Turning again to the bordered pits (*i*) visible on surface *B*, note should be made at once of the fact that pit membranes are not shown. This is to be explained by the fact that the surface exposed is not a true plane obtained by sectioning the wood; it is rather a schematic conception of a surface obtained by splitting the wood radially in such a manner that the compound middle lamella adhered to the contact face of the other block.

In the view of the pits presented, the bases of the dome-shaped pit cavities are toward the observer; hence, the pits do not appear as bosses on the wall but as bowl-shaped recesses in the wall. According to this analogy, the pit aperture appears as a hole in the bottom of the bowl which leads, of course, to the lumen of the tracheid in back. Crassulae, of the type described on page 137, are not in evidence in the drawing although their position is indicated by stippling. As previously explained, they are in reality thickenings in the intercellular substance (the middle lamella), overlaid by primary and secondary walls. Since the compound middle lamella with its medial layer of intercellular substance was removed from surface *B*, the position of crassulae is indicated by dumbbell-shaped or lunate depressions in the secondary wall.

The bordered pits on the radial walls of the longitudinal tracheids of white pine are usually in one row, although paired pits occur occasionally, particularly when the wood is coarser textured than normally. They are largest and most conspicuous in the earlywood portion of an annual increment (*i*) and become successively smaller as its outer margin is approached (*j*). Meanwhile, the shape of the aperture changes as the pits are reduced in size; this becomes flattened and is set at an angle to the vertical, although it seldom extends beyond the annulus of the pit. As will be mentioned again elsewhere, radial pits are most numerous toward the ends of the tracheids.

Considering next the portion of a uniseriate ray showing on surface *B*, it is evident that it consists of two kinds of elements, ray tracheids (*k*) and cells of ray parenchyma (*l*), respectively. One row of the first-named cells is present on the upper margin; this is underlaid by two rows of ray parenchyma.

The ray tracheids are comparatively short cells which, since they are prosenchymatous in nature, are provided with bordered pits. Like the longitudinal tracheids, they lose their protoplasts quickly after they mature behind the cambium and thereafter apparently function only in radial conduction inward from the cambium and, of course, mechanically, never as storage cells. They are seldom more than 0.1 to 0.2 millimeter in length; the longitudinal tracheids, in comparison, are usually thirty or more times as long, *i.e.*, 3 millimeters or more in length along the grain.

Bordered pit pairs lead through the radial walls of the ray tracheids to the longitudinal tracheids in contact with the rays on the flanks. The pits on the ray-tracheid side are shown in surface view in the figure. The same type of pitting is found in the ends of the ray tracheids in the same horizontal row, the pit pairs in this instance appearing in sectional view. Half-bordered pit pairs connect ray tracheids with the cells of ray parenchyma. Here the pit is bordered in the ray tracheid; the simple complementary pit is in the parenchymatous cell.

In white pine, the ray tracheids (*k*) may be restricted to one row on the upper and lower margins of the ray, or several rows may be present on one or both margins. In such cases, the cells of the superposed rows are connected by bordered pit pairs comparable with those shown in the end walls of ray tracheids in the figure. Not infrequently, one or more rows of ray tracheids are also inserted in the body of the ray.

The cells of ray parenchyma (*l*) are comparable in their dimensions with the ray tracheids except that they are usually somewhat longer. Since, as indicated on surface *B*, they possess simple pits, it follows that the pit pairs connecting one cell of this sort with another are unbordered. The simple pit pairs in the end and horizontal walls are relatively large but nowise so large as the windowlike pits in the side walls that lead to longitudinal tracheids. As previously pointed out, these are simple on the ray-cell side (the side showing on surface *B*); since the complementary pit on the other side of the wall is narrowly bordered, the pit pair is half-bordered. As is evident on surface *A*, the membranes of these pits frequently arch into the lumina of the longitudinal tracheids.

C. Description of Surface *C* (Tangential Surface)

Surface *C* is the third and final face of the white pine block requiring description. Before proceeding to a discussion of its several features, one or two general statements are in order.

On a tangential surface of the type of C, it is evident from the manner in which xylary cells are formed from initials in the cambium that every unit shown is derived from a different mother cell. This is not the case on surface B where five cambial initials and five only[1] produced the cells there depicted. This is another way of saying that the longitudinal elements of a wood are more or less stratified in the radial plane because tiers of cells are present, those of a given tier being of common parentage (traceable to the same mother cell in the cambium) and inserted at approximately the same height.[2] Consequently, if the surface exposed is truly radial, it may be relatively wide and consist of many cells, yet these owe their origin to relatively few cambial initials.

Further examination of surface C also brings out the fact that the longitudinal elements are not tiered in this plane; *i.e.*, they do not end at the same height. This also holds for the rays, although this is not too evident in the figure since only two of them are shown. This lack of stratification of the cells of white pine in the tangential plane in turn can be traced to the cambium. As stated previously on page 101, the fusiform initials and the groups of ray mother cells (in the form of rays) may or may not be tiered[3] in a cambium; it follows that, in the latter instance, the cells (xylary cells behind the cambium) derived from them, respectively, are not tiered.

Finally, note should be made of the fact that the nature of the tissue exposed on surface C would, of necessity, vary somewhat, depending on the place where the cut or split was made in the annual increment. In the present instance the tangential aspect of the summerwood is presented; had the plane been in the springwood, certain differences would be noted, among others the absence of pits (n) on the tangential walls of the longitudinal tracheids.

Two types of structures are visible on surface C, *viz.*, overlapping longitudinal tracheids ($6\text{-}6^a$) and wood rays ($7\text{-}7^a$; portion of a ray in the lower right-hand corner). Together, these compose the structure of white pine wood, as viewed in this plane, unless a longitudinal resin canal (of the type depicted on surface A, 2) happens to be included.

The longitudinal tracheids differ in appearance from like structures on surface B not only in not being tiered, for reasons already explained, but in the nature of the ends; these taper to a point (m) quite in contrast with their blunt rounded contours in the radial plane. Several small bordered

---

[1] Parts of tracheids from two longitudinal tiers account for two of them; since there are three transverse rows of ray cells showing, the quota of five is completed by the three ray mother cells producing these.

[2] The regularity of this arrangement is upset to a varying degree, of course, by the amount of sliding growth.

[3] If one or both are tiered, ripple marks are formed on the face of the wood.

pits (*n*) in oblique surface view can be seen on the tangential walls; the pit membranes are not shown in these, for the same reason that they were not illustrated on surface *B*. The pits of this sort are comparable in every way with the larger pits on the radial walls except in respect to size. One such pit is figured in sectional view at the upper edge of the plane. Tangential pitting is a constant feature in white pine, but it is confined to the last few layers of summerwood tracheids.

The two rays extending into surface *C* are obviously of different structure. The one in the lower right-hand corner has already been described in considerable detail as it appears in lateral view in the radial plane; it is a **uniseriate ray**, *i.e.*, it is a ribbon-shaped tier of tissue one cell in thickness extending at right angles to the grain in the radial direction, composed of horizontal rows of ray tracheids and ray parenchyma.

When a uniseriate ray of the above-mentioned type is viewed in a tangential plane, it is, of course, cut transversely. Under these conditions, it appears as a uniseriate structure composed of cells aligned in a longitudinal (vertical) row along the grain. In this, the ray tracheids occupy the terminal portions (one or more cells) or these and intermediate positions as well. The last cell (ray tracheid) at each end of the row is necessarily gable-shaped, to permit the longitudinal tracheids of the wood to close in above and below the ray without leaving a large intercellular space. All or most of the body of the ray, *i.e.*, that portion between the ends, consists of ray parenchyma.

Ray tracheids can readily be distinguished in the tangential plane through the presence of small bordered pits, seen in sectional view, on their lateral walls; these form small bordered pit pairs with the complementary pit in the longitudinal tracheid in touch with the ray tracheid at this point. The walls of the ray tracheids are also somewhat thinner than those of the cells of ray parenchyma. The presence of the balloonlike pit membranes described on surface *A*, extending laterally into the lumen of the adjacent longitudinal tracheid, serves to identify ray parenchyma.

Wide variation occurs in the height of the uniseriate rays of white pine, as is to be expected. The lowest are but one cell high and may consist wholly of ray tracheids or of ray parenchyma. Ray heights of a dozen or more cells are indicative of the other extreme. The explanation of this fluctuation in ray height rests in part on the origin of new rays in coniferous wood, in part on a reduction in ray height that sometimes ensues.[1] These topics are discussed in some detail on pages 146 to 148.

In any tree, the rays diverge as they extend outward into the bark. Additional rays are formed, on occasion, between existing rays since, in

[1] Barghorn, E. S. Origin and Development of the Uniseriate Ray in Coniferae. *Bul. Torrey Bot. Club*, Vol. 67, pp. 303–328. 1940.

a given wood, the spacing of these structures on the transverse surface remains approximately constant. The new rays originate from new ray initials in the cambium (separated from ray initials already present by longitudinal mother cells), usually from one such cell which is formed as the result of the further division of a fusiform initial.[1] Once in existence such rays undoubtedly increase in size over a period of months or years; the original ray mother cell in the growing layer is meanwhile replaced by a number of ray mother cells, clustered in the form of a transverse section of a ray. Following their formation and with further addition of cells, the new ray increases in size toward the maximum for the wood in question. Were it possible, therefore, to dissect a ray out of wood, it should taper to a point toward the pith, the end indicating the place where the cambium initiated its formation.

The second type of ray characterizing white pine wood is described as a **fusiform ray.** A portion of such a ray (7-7[a]) is shown to the extreme left on surface *C*. Structurally, it consists of the same elements as the uniseriate rays, *i.e.*, of ray tracheids[2] and ray parenchyma (*p*) which occupy the same relative positions, plus the addition of epithelial cells. The latter are a part of a resin canal (*r*) which is located in the central portion of the ray. This, as a result, has become several-seriate at this point but above and below tapers to uniseriate margins similar in every way to the upper or lower parts of a uniseriate ray. When such a structure is cut transversely, as in the tangential plane of the wood, it is spindle-shaped; hence the name "fusiform ray."

The transverse canals in the fusiform rays of white pine are comparable with those of the longitudinal type except in alignment and size. Like the latter, they arise through the splitting of cell walls and are tubular intercellular cavities sheathed by thin-walled epithelial cells. These, at least above and below the canal aperture, give way abruptly to cells of ray parenchyma (*p*). The transverse canals of white pine never attain the size of those of the longitudinal type, although both are normal structures.

Here and there in white pine wood, the transverse resin passages communicate directly with the longitudinal canals, forming a canal system, so to speak. The question now arises whether or not communication also exists between the resiniferous system of the wood and that of the bark, the more since the horizontal canals extend across the grain. Such is not the case, as is indicated in Text Fig. 23, *B*; in the cambium, there is no break in the continuity of the ray mother cells that through division

---

[1] *Ibid.*

[2] Ray tracheids do not show in ray 7-7[a] since the upper and lower margins of the ray are not included in the drawing.

are concerned with the formation of a fusiform ray. This means that the canal cavity in this instance, as held in the formation of the longitudinal resin passages, is of postcambial origin.

Another point should receive attention at this time, *viz.*, the relative abundance of fusiform rays in the wood. Discussion of this topic is especially desirable because these structures, being larger and higher than most of the uniseriate rays, are more conspicuous, and therefore casual observation might lead to an erroneous conclusion. Exact figures are not available, but probably not 1 ray in 20 contains a resin passage. The number of fusiform rays per unit of area of tangential surface can be calculated; the figure is never over 5 per square millimeter when the wood is of normal structure.

II. VOLUMETRIC DATA ON WHITE PINE WOOD

In the preceding pages, the minute anatomy of white pine wood has been discussed at length, in terms of three dimensions. The detailed description, if carefully read, supplemented as it is by a three-plane drawing, should serve to create an accurate mental picture of the structure of this timber. However, the student should realize that this is not sufficient. To attain a thorough comprehension of any wood, he must also acquire a volumetric conception of it; in other words, he should have some realization of how much of its volume is occupied by the various types of cells that are recognized as elements.

Volumetric data on white pine, in fact on any wood,[1] can be compiled by one of two methods that yield appropriate although, of course, not absolutely accurate results.[2] In both, photomicrographs are prepared at a sufficient magnification. According to the first method, the area occupied by the elements of a given kind is computed with a planimeter; the total area of the wood image is then determined. Then, in general, the following proportion holds:

$$\frac{\text{The area occupied by the element in question}}{\text{The total area}} \quad \text{as} \quad \frac{\text{The volume occupied by the same type of element}}{\text{The total volume}}$$

By the second method, the weight of the paper bearing the image of the wood is first determined. Then the images of the element in question

---

[1] HUBER, BRUNO, u. GERHARD PRÜTZ. Über den Anteil von Fasern, Gefässen, und Parenchym am Aufbau verschiedener Hölzer. *Holz als Roh- und Werkstoff* (Berlin), Band I, 377–381. 1938.

[2] This statement is made to stress again the fact that wood is an organic product resulting from vital processes in a living organism and, further, that undoubtedly no two pieces of wood, even though of the same kind, are exactly alike.

are cut out with scissors and weighed together.   Then, in general, the
following proportion holds:

$$\frac{\text{The weight of the images of the element in question}}{\text{The weight of the wood image}} \quad \text{as} \quad \frac{\text{The volume of the same kind of element in the wood}}{\text{The total volume of the wood}}$$

Experience has taught that the weighing method is more accurate, for
in the other procedure, the planimeter is liable to slip.   In the case of
white pine, the ray volume can be determined from tangential sections and
the volume occupied by the longitudinal canals from transverse sections.
Of course, this procedure is based on the supposition that the cross-sectional areas of these structures does not change at deeper levels in the
wood, which does not necessarily follow.   Compiled by this method, the
volumetric composition of white pine, in round figures, is approximately
as given in the Table IV.   It is evident that over 90 per cent of the wood
is composed of longitudinal tracheids, a situation that is seldom realized.
Although the percentages are somewhat different in other coniferous
woods, it is safe to say that their tracheid volumes would compare very
favorably with this figure.

TABLE IV

VOLUMETRIC COMPOSITION OF WHITE PINE WOOD

Longitudinal tracheids	93.00 per cent
Longitudinal resin canals	1.00 per cent
Wood rays	6.00 per cent
Total	100.00 per cent

III. DETAILED DESCRIPTION OF A LONGITUDINAL TRACHEID OF WHITE PINE WOOD

Since over 90 per cent of the volume of white pine wood consists of
one kind of element, *viz.*, the longitudinal tracheid, it is quite fitting that
this chapter should end with a discussion of this type of cell.   It has
therefore been singled out for description in terms of size, shape, and
markings.   A part of this information has already been recorded, it is
true, in explaining Text Fig. 28; its inclusion again in the text is for
purposes of summation and for greater emphasis.   A comprehensive
description of the coniferous tracheid is the more in order because the
utilization of wood for certain purposes, particularly softwoods for paper-
making, frequently hinges on their fiber content.

Text Fig. 29, *A*, depicts such a cell from white pine in radial aspect,
also a portion of this (*B*) which was in contact with a ray, in the same view
but at higher magnification.   Note should be made of the fact that the
illustrations are not drawings but photomicrographs, prepared from

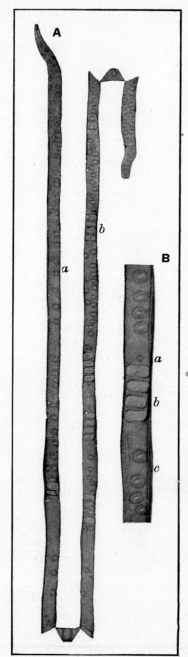

macerated material; they therefore indicate the shape of the cell and the position of its markings exactly as they were before the wood was broken down by chemical treatment into its cellular components.

A. SIZE OF THE WHITE PINE TRACHEID

The tracheid shown was so long that it was necessary to break the photograph at two points to permit of its inclusion in the figure. By actual measurement, it is over ninety times as long as it is wide.[1] The ray tracheids of the same wood, by comparison, are relatively small cells; in fact, they are not more than about one-thirtieth as long as the other type of cell. The length of the longitudinal tracheids in white pine varies in different trees, at different heights in the same tree, at the same height at different points along a radius of a transverse section, and even within an annual increment.

Average tracheid length, in fact the average dimension of any wood element in a given direction, can be obtained by recognized statistical methods; such fluctuations are governed by laws of variation that are well known. Data on average fiber length, compiled at

[1] For information on the breadth and length of white pine tracheids, see Tables VI, and VII. A micron is $\frac{1}{1000}$ millimeter.

TEXT FIG. 29.—A. A longitudinal tracheid of northern white pine (*Pinus strobus* L.) in radial surface aspect (65 ×). *a*, bordered pits leading laterally to a contiguous longitudinal tracheid; *b*, ray crossing.

B. Portion of the same, at a higher magnification, depicting a ray crossing (130 ×). *a*, a small bordered pit leading laterally to a ray tracheid; *b*, windowlike pits leading laterally to cells of ray parenchyma; *c*, bordered pits leading laterally to a contiguous longitudinal tracheid. (*Photographs by C. H. Carpenter.*)

various centers of research, are seldom in exact agreement, however, because of the varying nature of wood which requires much sampling if reliable data are to be obtained.   Paucity of material for sampling, therefore, results only in relative figures; but, even under these conditions, these should be comparable if the work is carefully done.   According to data compiled by The New York State College of Forestry, Syracuse, N.Y., the average lengths of the longitudinal tracheids of normal white pine wood, taken from the merchantable part of the tree stem and from different samples, range from 3 to 4 millimeters.

B. Shape of the White Pine Tracheid

The shape of the tracheid is shown only in one plane.   It appears as a linear cell with blunt tapering ends.   The radial diameter is, of course, the transverse diameter of the face that is exposed; reference to surface *B* of Fig. 28, in which springwood and summerwood tracheid segments are visible, will serve to indicate that the radial diameter of a white pine tracheid is not constant but is contingent on the position of the cell in the annual increment of wood.   The tracheids are widest in the radial plane at the inception of the springwood, narrowest in the last-formed summerwood.

The shape of a white pine tracheid in tangential view is comparable but not identical with that shown in the photomicrograph.   In this plane, it also appears as a long linear cell, but a cell in which the ends taper to relatively sharp points.   The shape of tracheid ends varies, therefore, according as they are seen in the radial or in the tangential plane, respectively.

The diameter of a longitudinal tracheid in the tangential plane is much less variable than in the radial plane; in fact, in coniferous woods, it is used as a measure of texture (see Table VI).   This relative constancy in width in normal wood is explained by the fact that the fusiform initials in the cambium of a coniferous tree gradually enlarge over a period of 20 to 40 years after which the size remains relatively constant.   The final length of the daughter cells (longitudinal tracheids) derived from such initials depends, therefore, on the amount of gliding growth taking place; the width of the mature daughter cells, on the contrary, is not altered appreciably by sliding growth but remains fairly constant, once the fusiform initials have attained mature size.

When cut transversely, the longitudinal tracheids of white pine are usually polygonal or rarely somewhat rounded with intercellular spaces at the corners.   In the springwood, they are frequently hexagonal, those in contiguous radial rows then alternating to form a mosaiclike surface devoid of intercellular spaces.   Summerwood tracheids, in contrast, are generally rectangular in transverse section, usually becoming more tabular and compressed in the tangential plane toward the outer margin of the ring.

Summing up the information in the last four paragraphs, it is evident that, neglecting the ends, the longitudinal tracheid of white pine is an extremely long prismatic cell, or a tubular cell if, perchance, the tracheid happens to be rounded in the transverse plane. If it is rectangular when cut transversely, it follows that it possesses four facets at right angles, two radial and two tangential faces, respectively; otherwise, the faces are set at other than right angles to each other, the tendency being toward six-sided prisms because a tetrakaidecahedral cell (see Text Fig. 25) is six-sided when cut transversely through the central portion.[1]

C. Markings of the White Pine Tracheid

Focusing attention next on the markings visible on the radial wall of the tracheid, it is evident that these are pits.[2] Text Fig. 29, *B*, is a portion of tracheid *A* at higher magnification; when this is examined, it is evident that the pits are of three sorts, *viz.*, those belonging to pit pairs that are inserted in the wall between a longitudinal tracheid and a ray tracheid (*a*), those of pit pairs that ensure communication laterally between a longitudinal tracheid and a cell of ray parenchyma (*b*), and those of pit pairs that lead from one longitudinal tracheid laterally to the next (*c*). The positions of these three kinds of pits in the wood of white pine should be traced in Text Fig. 28 in which they all appear.

Pits of types *a* and *b* occur at points where wood rays were in contact with the longitudinal tracheid; such spots are designated as "ray crossings."[3] It is interesting to note that seven such areas are visible on one radial wall of the tracheid figured. This means it was touched seven times by rays on one side; it is safe to assume that the count would be about the same on the other radial wall. This sample tracheid was therefore in contact with rays between ten and fifteen times throughout its length, on one side or the other. This statement serves to correct a misconception common among students studying transverse sections of white pine. As thus viewed, since only certain tracheids are in contact with wood rays, the assumption is that these and these only are touched

[1] For further information on the shape of the white pine tracheid, see F. T. Lewis. The Shape of the Tracheids in the Pine. *Amer. Jour. Bot.*, Vol. 22, pp. 741–776. 1935.

[2] This term is used advisedly. There are no pit pairs showing because in isolated cells of the type portrayed, obtained by macerating wood with chemicals, the intercellular substance and possibly the primary walls on either side of it are destroyed, permitting the cells to separate.

[3] They are also known as cross fields.

by rays. Above and below such a plane of section, every tracheid is touched again and again by these structures.

As has been stated previously, the pits between longitudinal tracheids (c in Text Fig. 29, B) are both uniseriate and biseriate in their arrangement. The latter condition is the more common as the ends of the tracheid are approached. On the other hand, through the central portion of the cell, extensive areas are visible on the wall that are devoid of such pits. This increase in the pit number near the ends of the tracheids should facilitate the transfer of liquids in the longitudinal direction (up the tree).

The total number of intertracheid pits on the radial walls of a longitudinal tracheid of white pine undoubtedly varies within wide limits. It probably ranges between 200 and 300 when both radial walls or the paired radial walls of springwood tracheids (when these cells are hexagonal in cross section) are taken into consideration. As will become evident later, the figure is much higher in some coniferous woods.

The presence of bordered pits on the tangential walls of longitudinal tracheids has already been mentioned. These are invariably smaller than their counterparts on the radial walls (see Text Fig. 30, A and B, for comparison as to relative size); further, they are restricted to the last few rows of tracheids in the summerwood. Pits of this sort do not show in the tracheid portrayed in Text Fig. 29 because this was taken from the springwood.

CHAPTER VII

THE MINUTE STRUCTURE OF CONIFEROUS WOODS
(Continued)

PART II. COMPARATIVE ANATOMY OF THE CONIFEROUS WOODS OF THE UNITED STATES[1]

The elements of coniferous woods are listed in Table V, which should be compared to Table III and the departures in the two tables noted. It is evident from Table V that all coniferous woods, white pine not excepted, possess few cell types and are relatively simple in structure.

TABLE V
ELEMENTS OF CONIFEROUS WOODS

I. Longitudinal

A. Prosenchymatous
  a. Tracheids
    a'. Resinous tracheids
  b. Strand tracheids

B. Parenchymatous
  a. Cells of longitudinal parenchyma
  b. Epithelial cells:* excreting cells of longitudinal resin canals

II. Transverse

A. Prosenchymatous
  a. Ray tracheids } Narrow rays

B. Parenchymatous
  a. Cells of ray parenchyma } Narrow rays
  b. Epithelial cells:* excreting cells of transverse resin canals

} Narrow rays } Fusiform rays

* Longitudinal and transverse resin canals are not listed, since they are intercellular spaces encircled by excreting cells (epithelium) and are hence not true elements.

The resinous longitudinal tracheids and the strand tracheids recorded in Table V are not present in white pine wood. The first-mentioned cell occurs in some pines and elsewhere in coniferous woods. Strand tracheids may be encountered in any coniferous wood that has resin canals or longitudinal parenchyma (subsequently described in the text, pages 142 to 146); in reality, they are transitional elements between these structures and normal longitudinal tracheids (see page 139).

Longitudinal parenchyma is likewise listed in Table V but not in Table III. Strands of such cells extending with the grain feature certain coniferous woods but are entirely lacking in others. As is pointed out

[1] For information on the comparative anatomy of the coniferous woods of the world, see E. W. J. Phillips. The Identification of Coniferous Woods by Their Microscopic Structure. *Linn. Soc. Jour., London*, Vol. 52, pp. 259–320. 1941.

subsequently, the presence or absence of longitudinal parenchyma and its position in the annual ring are of diagnostic significance.

Certain departures between the wood rays of coniferous woods in general and those of white pine should also be noted at this time. No new types of ray cells are listed in Table V which are not present in the wood of *Pinus strobus*. The differences recorded in the two tables are rather in ray composition. In white pine a ray may consist of ray tracheids or of ray parenchyma alone, or of these two kinds of elements, with or without a resin canal with its epithelial cells. In coniferous woods other than pine, the same possible combinations hold. In Alaska yellow cedar, some of the rays are wholly parenchymatous, others are composed entirely of ray tracheids; rays with both ray parenchyma and ray tracheids are extremely rare in this wood.

From what has been said concerning the elements of coniferous wood in general, in comparison to those of white pine, it is obvious that not all the cell types listed in Table V are encountered in every coniferous wood. Longitudinal tracheids are always present and constitute fully 90 per cent of the volume of the wood. Strand tracheids may occur in those coniferous woods with resin canals or longitudinal parenchyma. Strands of longitudinal parenchyma may or may not be present, as previously stated. Different ray combinations result that are traceable to varying cell composition. It is these departures in anatomical structure that make it possible to construct keys for the identification of coniferous woods "to genus" and frequently "to species."

The elements of coniferous wood are now discussed individually in the text beginning first with the cell type that is by far the most abundant, the longitudinal tracheid.

I. THE LONGITUDINAL CONIFEROUS TRACHEID

As was pointed out in the preceding chapter, in describing the structure of northern white pine, coniferous woods by volume consist largely of longitudinal tracheids. In discussing the comparative anatomy of the coniferous woods of the United States, it is therefore apropos that this type of element should be the first to receive attention.

A. THE ARRANGEMENT, SHAPE, AND SIZE OF LONGITUDINAL CONIFEROUS TRACHEIDS

In their arrangement and in shape, the tracheids of white pine may be taken as representative for coniferous woods as a group. In transverse sections, for reasons already stated, they appear as polygonal cells that are arranged in radial rows. The shape of the polygons is governed roughly by the position of the tracheid in the annual ring. In the springwood, they are rectangular or tend to be hexagonal, those in contiguous rows then being arranged in echelon; toward the outer margin of the ring, they become rectangular and even tabular.   Vertically, in the standing tree, a coniferous tracheid, irrespective of genus or species, is an extremely long, linear cell (75 to 200 times as long as wide) that tapers to a blunt end, as viewed in radial aspect, and to a relatively sharp tip in the longitudinal plane at right angles.   Neither in their grouping nor in their shape do these long cells exhibit sufficient variation to render this feature of any value diagnostically.

In contrast to the above, longitudinal tracheids manifest considerable fluctuation in size.[1]   The departures here, contrary to those occurring in arrangement and shape, are often sufficiently striking and constant in their distribution, to genus and even to species, to permit of the separation of woods on this basis that might otherwise be confused. Since characters of this kind are important in a text devoted to wood identification, they are discussed in the paragraphs that follow.

The three-dimensional nature of a longitudinal tracheid has already been explained; it possesses length, breadth, and thickness.   The long axis is, of course, directed along the grain; it is convenient to think of the transverse diameter of the cell in the radial direction as indicating the thickness of the element; the cross diameter in the tangential direction would therefore be a measure of breadth.

The radial diameter (thickness) of a tracheid varies according to its position in the annual increment; this fluctuation is not of generic or specific significance.   The tracheids of greatest radial diameter are produced when growth first starts in the spring; springwood is composed of wide-lumened tracheids which are relatively thin-walled.   As the season advances, the cells of this sort become narrower and thicker walled; the transition from one to the other type of cell may be gradual (Ex., eastern spruce) or abrupt (Ex., hard pine).   Meanwhile the nature of the tissue (summerwood) changes to a varying degree; where before its main function was apparently conduction, it now is obviously stronger mechanically and darker in color.   The narrowest (flattest) tracheids are produced on or near the outer margin of the growth increment, i.e., just before the end of the growing season.

The tangential diameter (breadth) of a longitudinal tracheid varies according to the place within its length where the measurement is made, according to the position in the tree, and, finally, according to the kind of wood.   The breadth remains about the same except at the tapering ends, where, for an obvious reason, it is less.   This explains why most of the rows of tracheids in transverse sections of coniferous wood are of

[1] The same holds for their markings.

about the same breadth, with occasional narrow rows; in the latter instance, the plane of "cut" happened to be near the ends. The relationship existing between tracheid size (including breadth) and position in the tree is discussed at length on pages 247 to 251. The variation in tracheid breadth in the coniferous woods covered by this text is indicated in Table VI.[1] *Sequoia sempervirens* and *Taxodium distichum* head the list with tracheids that attain a maximum diameter of 80 and 70 microns, respectively; the average width, of course, is much lower but is still such as to indicate the coarse texture of these woods which, incidentally, is a valuable feature in their identification. Sugar pine and western larch are almost as coarse-textured as the two above-named woods. The other extreme is represented by *Thuja occidentalis*, *Juniperus virginiana*, and *Taxus brevifolia*. The maximum breadth of tracheid in the last is 25 microns, the average being between 15 and 20 microns.

It is evident from the table that tracheid breadth in the coniferous woods listed ranges from 15 microns in *Taxus brevifolia* up to 80 microns in some samples of redwood. A definition for medium-textured coniferous wood can be set arbitrarily; it is one in which the average breadth (tangential diameter) of the tracheids is somewhere between 30 and 45 microns. Above these figures, softwoods are coarse-textured; below them, they are fine-textured.

Several other observations should be made from Table VI. It is interesting to note, for example, that the coarsest and finest textured conifers occur on the West Coast. It might be reasoned that the unusually large tracheids of redwood are due to inheritance or to the diameter that this tree attains. Most certainly they cannot be ascribed to height alone because Douglas fir is as tall but has much smaller tracheids. Further, bald cypress never approaches redwood and Douglas fir in stature yet possesses tracheids nearly as large as the first-mentioned tree. By the same reasoning, the narrow tracheids of Pacific yew may be due to inheritance.

Texture varies considerably in different species of a genus. For example, in *Chamaecyparis*, according to Table VI, *C. nootkatensis* and *C. thyoides* are identical in texture; *C. lawsoniana*, on the other hand, is a coarser wood. Not infrequently, when eastern and western conifers fall in the same genus, the western species will prove to be coarser textured than its eastern counterpart; this holds as between *Larix occidentalis* and *L. laricina*, the western firs (*Abies spp.*) compared with eastern balsam fir (*A. balsamea*), the western and eastern hemlocks (*Tsuga spp.*),[2] etc.

[1] See footnote 1, p. 404, for manner in which tracheid breadth is computed.

[2] In Table VI, western hemlock is listed as having tracheids with greater maximum diameter than eastern hemlock. The deduction should not be made, however, that

One might reason from this that regions of the United States west of the Rocky Mountains are most favorable for the growth of coniferous trees, but this line of argument is not entirely convincing.

TABLE VI

TANGENTIAL DIAMETER (BREADTH) OF LONGITUDINAL TRACHEIDS OF THE CONIFEROUS WOODS OF THE UNITED STATES
(Arranged in order of averages)

Scientific name	Diameter, microns	Scientific name	Diameter, microns
Sequoia sempervirens	80 (av. 50–65)	*Libocedrus decurrens*	50 (av. 35–40)
Taxodium distichum	70 (av. 45–60)	*Tsuga heterophylla*	50 (av. 30–40)
Pinus lambertiana	65 (av. 40–50)	*Abies balsamea*	50 (av. 30–40)
Larix occidentalis	60 (av. 38–50)	*Abies fraseri*	50 (av. 30–40)
Pinus monticola	60 (av. 35–45)	*Pinus resinosa*	45 (av. 30–40)
Pinus palustris	60 (av. 35–45)	*Thuja plicata*	45 (av. 30–40)
Pinus echinata	60 (av. 35–45)	*Tsuga canadensis*	45 (av. 28–40)
Pinus taeda	60 (av. 35–45)	*Larix laricina*	45 (av. 28–35)
Pinus caribaea	60 (av. 35–45)	*Torreya californica*	55 (av. 25–35)
Pinus ponderosa	60 (av. 35–45)	*Torreya taxifolia*	55 (av. 25–35)
Pinus jeffreyi	60 (av. 35–45)	*Pinus strobus*	45 (av. 25–35)
Abies concolor	60 (av. 35–45)	*Chamaecyparis nootkatensis*	40 (av. 25–35)
Abies grandis	60 (av. 35–45)	*Chamaecyparis thyoides*	40 (av. 25–35)
Abies magnifica	60 (av. 35–45)	*Picea glauca*	35 (av. 25–30)
Abies procera	60 (av. 35–45)	*Picea mariana*	35 (av. 25–30)
Pinus contorta var. *latifolia*	55 (av. 35–45)	*Picea rubens*	35 (av. 25–30)
Picea sitchensis	55 (av. 35–45)	*Thuja occidentalis*	35 (av. 20–30)
Pseudotsuga taxifolia	55 (av. 35–45)	*Juniperus virginiana*	35 (av. 20–30)
Chamaecyparis lawsoniana	50 (av. 35–40)	*Taxus brevifolia*	25 (av. 15–20)

The tracheid lengths[1] of the conifers included in this text are given in Table VII. The average length ranges from 1.18 millimeters in *Juniperus utahensis* to 7.39 millimeters in *Sequoia sempervirens*. It is evident that coarse-textured woods, *i.e.*, those whose tracheids are widest in the tangential plane (see Table VI), also possess the longest tracheids; conversely, those which have tracheids of narrow breadth have short tracheids. This would seem to indicate a correlation between tracheid breadth (tangential diameter) and tracheid length. Tracheids measuring 3.0 to 5.0 millimeters may be considered as average for coniferous woods. Above or below these figures, the wood in question would be considered as unusually long or short fibered, respectively.

the western species is consistently coarser textured than its eastern counterpart; as a matter of fact, the reverse holds.

[1] Computed according to recognized statistical methods.

TABLE VII

AVERAGE LENGTH OF LONGITUDINAL TRACHEIDS OF THE
CONIFEROUS WOODS OF THE UNITED STATES

(Determined from specific samples)*

Scientific name	Average length, mm.	Standard deviation	Scientific name	Average length, mm.	Standard deviation
Pinus lambertiana............	5.14	0.94	*Tsuga canadensis*............	3.37	0.57
	5.40	1.03		3.80	0.82
	5.24	0.96		4.24	0.99
Pinus monticola.............	2.83	0.59	*Tsuga heterophylla*..........	2.87	0.40
	2.97	0.58		2.91	0.58
	3.79	0.69		3.10	0.59
Pinus strobus...............	3.00	0.55	*Abies balsamea*..............	3.33	0.43
	3.70	0.66		3.37	0.50
	3.99	0.69		3.53	0.61
	4.00	0.91			
Pinus contorta var. *latifolia*....	3.19	0.44			
	3.26	0.44			
Pinus palustris.............	4.90	0.83	*Abies concolor*..............	3.79	0.63
Pinus echinata..............	4.46	0.91	*Abies grandis*...............	3.05	0.47
	4.64	0.92		3.35	0.43
	4.85	0.76		3.53	0.65
Pinus taeda.................	4.33	0.91	*Abies magnifica*.............	3.27	0.52
Pinus caribaea..............	4.58	0.87	*Abies procera*...............	3.60	0.58
Pinus rigida................	3.57	0.74	*Sequoia sempervirens*........	5.79	1.03
	3.75	0.83		7.39	1.31
Pinus rigida var. *serotina*......	2.73	0.36	*Taxodium distichum*..........	3.14	0.58
				5.23	1.42
				5.79	1.10
Pinus ponderosa.............	3.53	0.75	*Libocedrus decurrens*........	3.60	0.59
	3.71	0.86			
	4.08	0.98			
Pinus ponderosa var. *jeffreyi*...	3.20	0.61	*Thuja occidentalis*...........	2.17	0.47
				2.16	0.43
Pinus resinosa..............	2.51	0.54	*Thuja plicata*...............	3.00	0.45
	2.63	0.45		3.18	0.48
	2.67	0.27			
	2.70	0.89			
Larix laricina...............	2.86	0.39	*Chamaecyparis lawsoniana*....	3.18	0.47
	3.00	0.46			
	3.68	0.65			
Larix occidentalis...........	2.82	0.48	*Chamaecyparis nootkatensis*....	2.24	0.39
	2.97	0.55			
	4.09	0.71			
Picea glauca................	2.92	0.41	*Chamaecyparis thyoides*.......	3.20	0.45
	3.76	0.79		3.34	0.42
	3.24	0.51			
Picea mariana...............	3.25	0.40	*Juniperus virginiana*.........	2.15	0.50
	3.81	0.52			
	3.60	0.72			
Picea rubens................	3.01	0.49	*Juniperus silicicola*..........	2.38	0.62
	3.17	0.60			
	3.01	0.61			
Picea engelmanni............	2.49	0.48	*Juniperus utahensis*..........	1.18	0.29
	2.75	0.66			
	3.63	0.55			
Picea sitchensis.............	5.22	0.85	*Taxus brevifolia*..............	2.31	0.34
	5.37	1.06		2.32	0.45
	5.45	0.98			
Pseudotsuga taxifolia..........	3.00	0.31	*Torreya californica*..........	3.23	0.67
	3.32	0.39			
	3.88	1.41			
Pseudotsuga taxifolia var. *glauca*	2.85	0.45	*Torreya taxifolia*.............	2.76	0.39

* The standard deviation is a length in millimeters that, added to and subtracted from the tracheid average length, establishes limits of length within which approximately two-thirds of the tracheids will fall. Limits obtained as above by adding and subtracting three times the standard deviation will include over 99 per cent of the tracheids.

B. Markings of Longitudinal Coniferous Tracheids

Considerable variation is manifested in coniferous woods in the nature of the markings on the lateral walls of the tracheids; these are traceable in part to pits, in part to thickenings in the true middle lamella (intercellular substance) between walls and on the inner surface of the secondary wall.

The pits mentioned in the preceding paragraph are always bordered.[1] They fall into three categories depending on the coniferous wood under examination: (1) those belonging to pit pairs that lead from the longitudinal tracheids laterally into cells of like nature, (2) those of pit pairs that provide for communication between the longitudinal tracheid and ray parenchyma in contact with it, and (3) those of pit pairs that connect the longitudinal tracheid with ray tracheids provided that these last-named cells are present in the ray (see under Rays, page 149).

The pit pairs between longitudinal tracheids are generally conspicuous; the pits may or may not be provided with pit canals, depending on the thickness of the wall. Such pit pairs are invariably present in the radial walls and also occur in tangential walls under certain conditions that will be explained later. For clarity, it is convenient to discuss intertracheid pitting on radial walls and on tangential walls separately.

1. Nature of the Pits on the Radial Walls.—The pits on the radial walls of the springwood tracheids of coniferous woods are large and hence are desirable objects for study (Text Fig. 30, *A*). In surface view the pit contour is quite sharply defined by the pit annulus (see page 74). The rounded area at the center of the pit is the pit aperture. The torus behind the pit aperture is visible in the photomicrograph because the tissue was rendered translucent in making the mount and the lenses of the microscope have depth of focus; it is less even in contour and larger than the pit aperture, and the latter, for this reason, appears as a darker area near the center of the torus. In the pits portrayed, the pit apertures lead directly into the lumina of the cells on the side of the paper toward the observer; there are hence no pit canals. Each pit, in reality, is a boss on the wall the dome of which is toward the observer.

In the summerwood, radial pits undergo some modification, occasioned by the narrowing of the radial diameters of the longitudinal tracheids toward the outer margin of the growth ring. The pit annulus, as a rule, retains its rounded outline, but may be oval or even elliptical. Long before there is any evidence of this, however, the pit aperture loses its rounded contour and becomes oval, elliptical, or slitlike (Text Fig. 15, *H, I, J*). Flattened pit orifices are usually oriented obliquely to the long

---

[1] The border may be obscure.

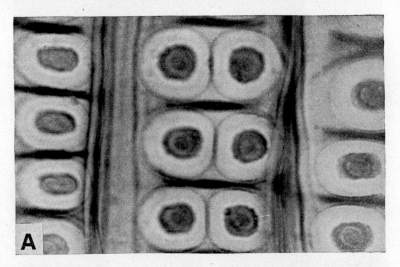

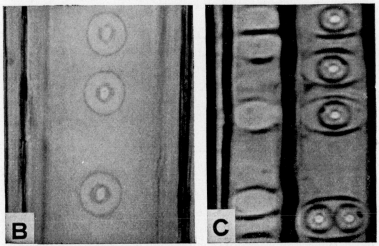

TEXT FIG. 30.—Nature of the pits on the lateral walls of coniferous tracheids.

A. Paired bordered pits on the radial walls of the longitudinal springwood tracheids of sugar pine (*Pinus lambertiana* Dougl.). The outer circle of the pit is the pit annulus; the dark irregular central area is the torus; the smaller rounded spot within the boundary of the torus is the pit aperture; the dark bars above and below the pits are crassulae (875 ×).

B. Bordered pits on the tangential wall of a summerwood tracheid of sugar pine (*Pinus lambertiana* Dougl.) taken at the same magnification as *A*; the pits are much smaller and crassulae are wanting.

C. Pit fields on the radial walls of the longitudinal tracheids of bald cypress [*Taxodium distichum* (L.) Rich.], bounded above and below by crassulae. Five of the pit fields are empty, three contain one pit each, and one has two bordered pits (230 ×). Three and four pits, aligned in a transverse row, frequently occur in a pit field in this species (see Text Fig. 33).

axis of the tracheid. Circular, oval, and elliptical pit apertures are usually "included" (*H*); slitlike orifices are generally "extended" (*J*), and
not infrequently a check develops through these as the wall dries in
lumber. A still further change may take place as the tracheids become
narrower and thicker walled. A pit canal may develop in the wall; in
such instances, the pit possesses a pit chamber, an outer aperture leading
into the pit canal, and an inner aperture opening from this into the lumen
of the tracheid (Text Figs. 15, *C*2; and 33, *C*2).

The bordered pits on the radial walls of the tracheids may be crowded
or distant; the first condition is more frequent toward the ends of the
tracheid, the second in places throughout the median portion.[1] In either
case, the pits are arranged in longitudinal series. Crosswise of the cell,
there may be but one pit in the wall at a given height, or two, three, or
four pits may be present, arranged in a transverse row.[2] This last condition is found in the springwood, but even here it does not hold throughout
the whole length of a tracheid; frequently, but one pit shows at a given
height, whereas above or below others may be paired, etc. Or the paired
arrangment will hold throughout most of the cell but will give way
through the central region to grouping in transverse rows of three or even
four. The longitudinal series of pits in tracheids in this region may therefore be uniseriate, biseriate, or even tri- or quadriseriate for short distances along the wall. The uniseriate condition prevails on the radial
walls of summerwood tracheids.

Transverse rows on the radial walls of springwood tracheids, consisting of two, three, or four pits, are indicative of coarseness of texture.
The first type of arrangment is common in western larch and sugar pine.
In *Sequoia sempervirens* and *Taxodium distichum*, rows of three to four
pits are not uncommon in the springwood (Text Fig. 33, *C*3); in the narrower tracheids of the summerwood of these same species, a lower seriation is the rule.[3]

The manner in which the bordered pit pairs of coniferous wood function in the transfer of water and solutes from one tracheid to the next was
illustrated in Text Fig. 17, *B*1 and 2. The flow is through that portion

---

[1] Figures indicating the number of bordered pits on the radial walls of white pine
tracheids were given on p. 127. The upper limit would undoubtedly be higher than
the figure stated for coniferous woods as a group.

[2] In one family of the Coniferales, the Araucariaceae, the pits are in oblique series
and, where crowded, are hexagonal. This family is largely confined to the Southern
Hemisphere.

[3] For further information on the nature of the pitting on the radial walls of longitudinal coniferous tracheids, see A. S. Pierce. Types of Pitting in Conifers. *Ill.
State Acad. Sci. Trans.*, Vol. 28, pp. 101–104. 1936.

of the pit membrane between the pit annuli and the compound torus.[1] When the latter is aspirated to the right or left, the pit pair is more or less effectively plugged by the torus.

2. Crassulae on the Radial Walls.—Several other features that are concerned with the pitting on the radial walls of tracheids require attention here. Referring again to Text Fig. 30, *A* and *C*, note should be made of the fact that the pits and pairs of pits are bounded above and below by zones or lines of darker substance. These structures are traceable to a concentration of intercellular substance at these points, possibly to strengthen the wall in the vicinity of the pits; the layer is overlaid by the primary and secondary walls of the cell on the side of the wall toward the observer but show through when the tissue is cleared with chemicals. Areas of this sort were called Bars of Sanio for a good many years, after their discoverer, but are now known as crassulae (see page 117).

Crassulae are always confined to the radial walls of tracheids. They are common throughout coniferous woods with the exception of the Araucariaceae and hence are of no diagnostic significance in wood identification.[2] They are also visible in the vessels and tracheids of certain hardwoods (see Text Fig. 42, *A*).

In most coniferous woods, the bordered pits on the radial walls of the longitudinal tracheids develop in places where the true middle lamella is thinner than elsewhere. In properly stained material, such areas stand out fairly clearly and are bounded above and below by crassulae. A thin place of this sort in the wall is called a "primary pit field" (Text Fig. 30, *C*). A primary pit field may contain one or more pits. In the second instance, the pits are arranged in a transverse row, at least in the secondary wood of tree trunks. Not infrequently, pits fail to form, resulting in an empty pit field.

3. Nature of the Pits on the Tangential Walls.—The bordered pits that are present on the tangential walls of longitudinal tracheids under certain conditions are always smaller than their counterparts on the radial walls; this fact is the more evident when *A* and *B* of Text Fig. 30 are compared, in which the magnification is the same. The three pits showing in *B* form a uniseriate vertical row, but they differ from the seried pits in radial walls in being more distant. Not infrequently, particularly in wide-lumened cells, there is no evidence of pit seriation

---

[1] As previously stated, Bailey has reported perforated pit membranes in the bordered pit pairs of *Larix* and *Sequoia*. See footnote 1 on p. 81.

[2] For further information on crassulae, see E. Gerry. The Distribution of "Bars of Sanio" in the Coniferales. *Ann. Bot.* [London], Vol. 24, pp. 119–123. 1910; I. W. Bailey. Structure, Development, and Distribution of So-called Rims or Bars of Sanio. *Bot. Gaz.*, Vol. 67, pp. 449–468. 1919.

whatsoever on the tangential walls; the pits then appear to be staggered, with wide intervals between them. The contour of such pits usually remains circular, for they are so small that they are not constricted by the close proximity of the radial walls of the tracheid; the aperture is frequently somewhat flattened and is then more or less oblique to the long axis of the cell. Crassulae never develop in tangential walls, as is evident from Text Fig. 30, *B*.

Tangential pitting occurs throughout coniferous woods with the exception of the hard pines.[1] Where present, it is confined to the last few rows of summerwood tracheids and the inner tangential wall of the first-formed springwood tracheids of the succeeding increment. Pits in this location are evidently a device to provide further for conduction in the transverse radial direction just prior to the cessation of seasonal growth in thickness. The absence of tangential pitting in the hard pines may be due to the presence of ray tracheids (see page 153) in large numbers in the rays of these woods.

The other two categories of pits occurring on the lateral walls of longitudinal tracheids, which were mentioned on page 126, are situated at points of contact of the tracheids with wood rays. These can best be described in discussing these last-named structures.

4. Spiral Thickening on the Walls of Longitudinal Tracheids.—Spiral thickening, of the type described on page 70 and illustrated in Text Fig. 14, *A*, is present in the tracheids of certain coniferous woods, not only in the longitudinal tracheids but in the ray tracheids as well. The laws governing the formation of such spirals need not be repeated again at length; certain pertinent facts stand out, however, in connection with their distribution in coniferous tracheids that make necessary the following statements:

1. Several spirals usually extend along the inner surface of the wall at the same time, in an ascending counterclockwise direction. In conifers, the number usually ranges from 1 to 4; the full number of spirals may not be present throughout the length of the tracheid.

2. The angle of the spirals is contingent on the width of the cell and the thickness of the cell wall. Cells that are narrow lumened for either of the above reasons possess steeper spirals than those with wider cell cavities. For this reason, summerwood tracheids have steeper spirals than those of the springwood. The angle of the spirals therefore possesses but relative diagnostic significance since it varies according to the position of the tracheid in the growth increment.

3. The spacing of the coils of the spirals, on the other hand, is sometimes of value in the separation of species.

[1] Red pine (*Pinus resinosa* Ait.) is an exception to this rule.

Spiral thickening is a constant feature in the longitudinal tracheids of Douglas fir,[1] Pacific yew, and the *Torreya spp.;* it is sporadic in its distribution in tamarack and loblolly pine. In Douglas fir, the spiraling is most conspicuous in the springwood tracheids, and, for the reason stated, the coils are at the lowest angle. Toward the outer margin of the growth increment, the turns of the spiral become steeper and less conspicuous; spiral thickening may disappear completely in the outermost tracheids. The tracheids of *Taxus brevifolia* and of *Torreya spp.* are spiraled throughout the annual layer of wood; Pacific yew differs from *Torreya* in possessing steeper angled and more compact spirals, features that appear to be of generic significance although they are not used in the Key based on minute features in this text. When present as a sporadic feature in tamarack and loblolly pine, spiral thickening is confined to the tracheids of the summerwood. In such cases, it is too irregular in its distribution to be of importance.

C. LONGITUDINAL RESINOUS TRACHEIDS

As longitudinal coniferous tracheids of the normal type pass from sapwood into heartwood, resinous material sometimes accumulates in these cells at or near the places where they are in contact with wood rays. Such deposits are usually reddish brown or nearly black and are amorphous in nature. In transverse sections, if the plane of the cut happens to include them, they appear to fill the cell either completely or partly. Along the grain, they assume the form of transverse plates extending across the cell and simulating cross walls, or of lumps on the wall on one or both sides of the tracheid. Tracheids with such inclusions are designated as "resinous tracheids."

Resinous tracheids are comparatively rare in coniferous woods. They are most frequent in *Agathis* and *Araucaria* of the Araucariaceae. Penhallow[2] reported them as occasional in *Abies fraseri* and *A. grandis;* they also occur sporadically in some of the soft pines and possibly elsewhere.

D. LONGITUDINAL STRAND TRACHEIDS

Strand tracheids (Text Fig. 31), like longitudinal tracheids, are prosenchymatous in nature and lose their protoplasts relatively quickly as they mature to the rear of the cambium. They differ from longitudinal tracheids in being shorter elements and, further, in possessing end walls one or both of which are at right angles to the longitudinal walls; when the second condition holds, the cells are narrowly rectangular along the

---

[1] It is also present in the ray tracheids.

[2] PENHALLOW, D. P. North American Gymnosperms, p. 58. Ginn & Company, Boston. 1907.

grain. Both the end and the radial walls are provided with bordered pits of the normal type.

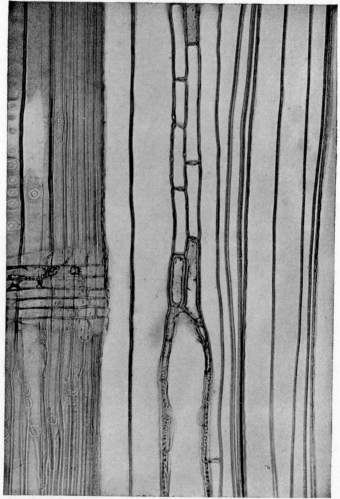

Text Fig. 31.—Strand tracheids in western larch (*Larix occidentalis* Nutt). The strands are mixed, passing over above and below into epithelial cells (120 ×).

Tracheids of this sort arise through the further division of a cell which otherwise would have developed into a longitudinal tracheid. All the segments thus produced through the formation of cross walls may become prosenchymatous; or some of them may remain parenchymatous, a "mixed strand" then resulting.

Strand tracheids may well be regarded as elements transitional between longitudinal tracheids on the one hand and epithelial or longitudinal parenchyma on the other.[1] This assumption is strengthened by the fact that they are frequently associated with cells of the one or the other of these types. If present in a wood, they are to be found in the vicinity of the longitudinal resin canals, on the outer face of the annual increment (terminally), or in or near traumatic tissues. Terminal strand tracheids are sometimes present in *Larix spp.* and in Douglas fir where they apparently replace the strands of longitudinal parenchyma that occupy the same position and are sporadic in their distribution in these genera.

E. Trabeculae in Longitudinal Coniferous Tracheids

Trabeculae are described at this point in the text because they are occasionally present in the longitudinal tracheids of coniferous woods.[2] A trabecula is a cylindrical, barlike structure extending across the lumen of a tracheid from one tangential wall to the other (Text Fig. 32). The ends are somewhat enlarged where they join the sides of the cell. In the earlywood, the rods of this kind are quite thin but become shorter and thicker in the narrow-lumened tracheids of the latewood.

The origin of a trabecula can be traced back to the cambium. For reasons as yet in question, a delicate filament of wall substance forms across a fusiform initial which, through division, is giving rise to a tier of tracheids in the radial plane. A secondary wall is then laid down about this in the same manner and at the same time that wall thickening is progressing elsewhere in the cell.[3]

Trabeculae are best seen in radial and transverse sections of wood, particularly in the former, since they appear in lateral view in these planes. They seldom occur solitarily, but as a rule one is formed at the same height in each of a number of tracheids in the same tier, *i.e.*, in tracheids that arose from the same mother cell in the cambium. A

---

[1] Cells of this last type do not occur in white pine and hence were not mentioned in Chap. VI, which was devoted to a description of this wood. They are described on p. 142 of the text.

[2] They have also been reported in certain hardwoods.

[3] T. A. McElhanney and his associates at the Forest Products Laboratories of Canada ascribe the formation of trabeculae to the hyphae of cambial fungi. They state that "the rods seem to be due to the result of the deposition of cell-wall material about a fungus filament in the cambium, with the result that the structure is perpetuated in the series of cells developed from the cambial cell." Strength is added to this contention since trabeculae are likely to be present in regions where the cambium has been exposed to fungal infection, noticeably in wood formed after wounding and in close proximity to fungous cankers. See McElhanney, T. A., *et al.* Canadian Woods, Their Properties and Uses, p. 66. *Forest Prod. Lab. Canada.* 1935.

transverse series of trabeculae at the same height in the wood is the result, extending across the grain.   Not infrequently, a number of such series are superposed in the radial plane.

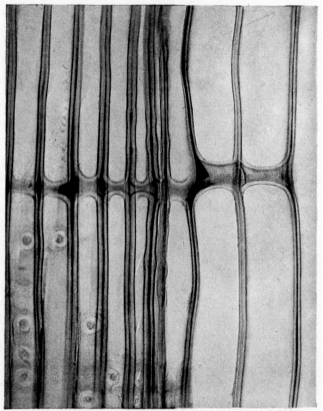

Text Fig. 32.—Trabeculae in Alaska yellow cedar [*Chamaecyparis nootkatensis* (D. Don) Spach.]   (360 ×).

Bars of the kind known as trabeculae occur sporadically throughout all gymnospermous woods and hence are of no diagnostic value.   They are also occasionally present in dicotyledons.

II. LONGITUDINAL PARENCHYMA IN CONIFEROUS WOOD[1]

The scope of the terms "parenchyma" and "prosenchyma," as applied to wood, was explained on page 46.   This information should be scanned again.   Three types of parenchyma are recognized in coniferous wood, *viz.*, "longitudinal parenchyma," "ray parenchyma," and

[1] Longitudinal parenchyma was not listed in Table III because it is not present in the wood of white pine.

"epithelial parenchyma." In discussing the parenchyma of softwoods, it is convenient to deal with ray parenchyma in conjunction with wood rays; epithelial parenchyma had best be described in conjunction with

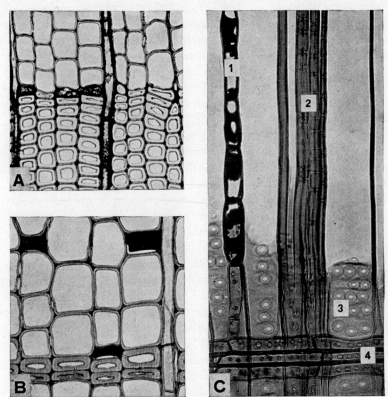

TEXT FIG. 33.—Longitudinal parenchyma in coniferous woods.

A. Terminal parenchyma in western hemlock [*Tsuga heterophylla* (Raf.) Sarg.] (three cells on the outer margin of an annual ring) (200 ×).

B. Metatracheal-diffuse parenchyma in redwood [*Sequoia sempervirens* (D. Don) Endl.] (three dark cells in the early spring wood) (200 ×).

C. Portion of a strand of longitudinal parenchyma of bald cypress [*Taxodium distichum* (L.) Rich.], radial view (165 ×). (1) strand; (2), bordered pit pairs in sectional view, the pits with pit canals; (3) bordered pits in transverse rows of three on the radial walls of spring-wood tracheids; (4) wood ray in radial aspect.

resin canals. The following paragraphs are devoted to a discussion of longitudinal parenchyma in these timbers

The longitudinal parenchyma of softwoods occurs in the form of strands extending along the grain (Text Fig. 33, *C*1). When cut transversely, such a strand appears as a cell that is usually thinner walled than the neighboring tracheids and frequently contains dark contents (Text Fig. 33, *A* and *B*). Each strand arises by the further division of a daughter cell cut off from a fusiform initial in the cambium. Complete strands are seldom if ever visible in prepared sections of coniferous wood, for two reasons. They extend for a considerable distance (several millimeters) along the grain, too far, in fact, to permit of their inclusion in the field of the microscope at the magnifications at which wood is usually studied. Second, they seldom pursue a truly straight course in the wood and possess little thickness; consequently, they quickly fade out of a thin section of any size. Strands of longitudinal parenchyma are usually widest in the tangential plane, but this does not always hold; if they happen to be in the earlywood, the radial diameter may be fully as great as the tangential.

The number of cells composing a strand is undoubtedly variable in different coniferous woods, in different samples of a given species, and even in the same sample. No definite figures can be cited because of the length of the strands which precludes accurate counts. In certain woods (*Larix spp., Pseudotsuga spp.*), the strands consist in part of prosenchymatous cells (strand tracheids) (see page 139); in such instances, there is no fixed sequence in the arrangement of such cells and of those which are parenchymatous in nature.

The units composing a strand vary in shape according to their position. Those at the ends are square or rectangular at the base and taper abruptly or gradually to a point; the remainder of the strand consists of cells that approach the rectangular as viewed in longitudinal sections, although a certain amount of distortion often results through the bulging of the lateral walls to the right and left.

Pits may be observable if the walls attain appreciable thickness; they are invariably simple. The grouping varies somewhat, of course, and is contingent upon the kinds of cells that are in contact with the parenchymatous cell in question. The arrangement of the pits is not of any significance in the separation of species. The pit pairs leading to prosenchyma (longitudinal and ray tracheids) are half-bordered; those in the walls between parenchymatous cells, simple. Pierce (see footnote 3, page 136) recognizes two sorts of pitting in the end walls separating units in the same strand.

The strands of longitudinal parenchyma may be inserted separately in coniferous wood (Text Fig. 33, *B*); or several such strands may be in contact laterally, especially in the tangential plane (*A*). If the cells (strands cut transversely) are confined to the outer margins of the growth rings, the **parenchyma** is said to be **terminal,** if to the body of the ring, **metatracheal** or **metatracheal-diffuse.** The term metatracheal signifies that the cells of this kind are relatively abundant in number and are then often loosely grouped in a belt within the ring boundaries. The expression metatracheal-diffuse is indicative of the fact that the arrangement is more open, the cells then occurring at wide intervals and hence being sparse in their distribution. These two types of arrangement intergrade.

True longitudinal parenchyma is present in some coniferous woods and wanting in others; it does not occur, for example, in *Pinus*, *Taxus*, and *Torreya*[1] among the genera represented by species in the United States. Such cells are present in the root wood of *Picea* but have disappeared from the trunk wood, *i.e.*, from the wood of the merchantable part of the tree. Elsewhere in domestic conifers, true longitudinal parenchyma is invariably present or at least occurs sporadically. Bald cypress and redwood may be cited as typifying the first condition; Douglas fir, the larches, and various *Abies* species, the second. Certain trees, such as *Thuja occidentalis* and *T. plicata*, are peculiar in that some samples contain appreciable amounts of longitudinal parenchyma whereas in others it is entirely lacking. At other times, in these same woods, a given ring may contain these cells in appreciable number, but they will be wanting in neighboring rings.[2]

Much has been written about the phylogenetic significance of the distribution of longitudinal parenchyma in coniferous woods. According to Jeffrey,[3] paleozoic gymnosperms to which modern conifers are traceable were devoid of typical annual rings, and the pitting was confined to the radial walls. During the Mesozoic, seasonal increments and tangential pitting in the terminal region thereof became established as definite features, probably as a result of the cooling of the earth and the development of seasons. Owing to the latter, trees could no longer grow continuously; this change to periodic growth was accompanied by the appearance, in the wood of some of the ancient conifers, of strands of longitudinal parenchyma. These appeared first on the outer surface of the growth increments during the Jurassic (Middle Mesozoic), arising through the segmentation of cells which up to this time had always

[1] The same holds for *Araucaria* and *Agathis* of the Southern Hemisphere.

[2] Further insight into the distribution of longitudinal parenchyma in coniferous woods can be gleaned by referring to Table I, Plant Families Containing Trees in the United States, p. 9. The coniferous woods are grouped in four families: Pinaceae, Taxodiaceae, Cupressaceae, and Taxaceae. True longitudinal parenchyma is wanting in *Taxus* and *Torreya* of the Taxaceae, as already stated. Its absence in *Pinus* and the stem wood of *Picea* has been recorded. In the other genera of the Pinaceae represented in the United States (*Larix*, *Pseudotsuga*, *Tsuga*, and *Abies*), longitudinal parenchyma is sporadic in its distribution and is either terminal or metatracheal, or both. Domestic woods belonging to the Taxodiaceae (*Sequoia* and *Taxodium*) and to the Cupressaceae (*Thuja*, *Chamaecyparis*, *Cupressus*, *Libocedrus*, and *Juniperus*), in contrast, are, as a group, featured by fairly abundant metatracheal parenchyma.

[3] JEFFREY, E. C. The Anatomy of Woody Plants, Chap. V. University of Chicago Press, Chicago. 1917.

developed into longitudinal tracheids.　The juxtaposition of such cells to the cambium rendered the food stored therein easy of access.

Once the strands of parenchyma became established in gymnosperms as a permanent feature of the wood, they increased in number as evolution proceeded.　Not only did this happen, but they were no longer confined to the margin of the ring, and the type of arrangement known as meta-tracheal developed.　Modern conifers include some forms wholly devoid of longitudinal parenchyma or in which these cells are strictly terminal; the metatracheal arrangement has become well established in the Taxo-diaceae and the Cupressaceae.

III. RAYS OF CONIFEROUS WOODS

General information relative to the shape, alignment, and function of wood rays was recorded on pages 45 to 46.　The two types of rays present in white pine wood were described in minute detail in Chap. VI, as they appear in three planes of section.　It now remains to point out the anatomical variations that are encountered in these structures when they are examined in the various domestic conifers.

A. KINDS OF RAYS IN CONIFEROUS WOODS

At the start, note should be made of the fact that a coniferous wood may contain but one type of ray or that two types may be present.　The first condition holds when transverse resin canals are not normal to the wood; in such instances, the rays are uniformly narrow and are usually uniseriate, as viewed in the tangential plane, although a tendency toward the biseriate condition is manifested in certain species.　The presence of transverse resin canals in the wood (which are invariably accompanied by longitudinal passages of like nature) results in the formation of fusi-form rays; this term is used to designate these structures because the rays containing such canals are spindle-shaped when cut transversely (Text Fig. 34, *C*, *D*, and *E*).

The narrow rays of coniferous woods vary in height as viewed in tangential sections, both in number of cells and in linear measurement. This holds not only for different woods but in the same wood and in dif-ferent samples thereof.

The minimum height of the narrow ray is one cell and in the neighbor-hood of 15 to 30 microns.　Such low rays can be found in tangential sections by careful examination and trace their origin to the manner in which new rays arise in the cambium.　In any tree, the rays diverge as they extend outward through the wood into the bark.　Additional rays are formed, on occasion, between existing rays since, in a given wood, the spacing of these structures on the transverse surface remains approxi-

mately constant. The new rays arise from the division of the fusiform
mother cells in the cambium in a manner different from that which results
in the formation of new longitudinal elements in the xylem and phloem.
Barghorn[1] has described four quite different ways in which new rays may
arise in the secondary tissues of conifers through the division of fusiform
initials, but one type is by far the most frequent. In this, division and
the formation of a cell wall near the upper or lower end of a fusiform initial
results in the production of a new cambial ray one cell in height. The
fusiform mother cell is shortened as a result of this process, provided the
entire apex of the fusiform initial is involved; if, on the other hand, the
new cell wall twice intersects the same side wall of the initial, the latter
remains the same length. As long as the cambial portion of a ray is
unicellular, it follows that the xylary portion of the ray derived from it is
but one cell in height.

Once a new cambial ray, 1 cell in height, has come into being, arising
as described above and separated from other cambial rays by fusiform
mother cells, its increase in height is effected most frequently by simple
transverse anticlinal division. In this way two ray initials replace the
lone initial originally present in the cambium and the xylary ray resulting
from the periclinal division of these cells is 2-celled in height. This
increase in ray height frequently occurs shortly after the origin of the
new ray in the cambium. The process generally continues in this way
until that portion of the ray in the cambium has attained a height of 4 or
5 cells. Thereafter, the formation of new ray initials is confined to the
margins of the cambial ray; there are neither vertical nor transverse
anticlinal divisions in the center of the ray. Increase in the height of the
cambial ray in cells and linear measurement results, of course, in higher
xylary rays.

Not infrequently, the rays of conifers decrease in height after attaining
a peak height. This is brought about by two mechanisms: (1) either
through the loss of ray initials from the body of the cambial ray or (2) by
the division of one high cambial ray into two through the intrusion of
the apex of an elongating fusiform cambial initial into the intercellular
substance between two ray initials, thus forcing them apart. It follows
that in the second instance, high cambial rays undergo separation into
two lower cambial rays more readily than do low rays.

The upper limit in the height of coniferous xylary rays varies according
to the kind of wood and the sample thereof. The highest figures are
reached in *Taxodium distichum* and *Sequoia sempervirens* in which rays
40 to 60 plus cells and 500 to 1000 plus microns in height are occasionally
found although the averages are much lower. *Juniperus virginiana* and

[1] *Op. cit.*, p. 120.

Chamaecyparis lawsoniana are illustrative of the lower figure; in these woods the tallest rays are seldom over 6 cells and never over 300 microns in height. The mean maximum height of the narrow rays of conifers, taken as a group, is somewhere in the neighborhood of 10 to 15 cells.

Low xylary rays are sometimes characteristic for a group of coniferous woods, in terms of botanical classification. For example, the rays of the Cupressaceae are lower, on an average, than those of the Pinaceae and Taxodiaceae. At other times, the height of the tallest rays may be of generic or specific significance;[1] it is used in the Key based on minute features, usually as a secondary character and only when the magnitude of the difference is such as to render this character reliable. The firs (*Abies spp.*) have taller rays than the hemlocks (*Tsuga spp.*); the same holds as between *Taxodium distichum* and *Sequoia sempervirens*. Other cases might be cited.

As stated on page 246, the narrow rays of conifers are usually uniseriate, and this frequently holds for all the rays in the wood. In certain species, however, more or less of a tendency is expressed toward the biseriate condition; in such instances, the usual condition is generally one or more pairs of cells in the body of the ray. Rays completely biseriate throughout are sometimes encountered in *Sequoia sempervirens*. When present, rays that are in part or wholly biseriate may be a concomitant of coarse texture, but *Taxus brevifolia*, the finest textured coniferous wood in the United States, not infrequently has paired cells in the rays. At other times, biseriation may be of traumatic origin, but frequently no reason can be given for this condition. Most certainly rays in part biseriate in a wood is of no diagnostic significance since, in the 15 genera of coniferous woods covered in this text, paired seriation occurs sporadically in 11.

Fusiform rays, when present in coniferous wood, are always decidedly in the minority. The numerical proportion of such rays to narrow rays cannot be definitely set, but it is in the neighborhood of 1 to 20. The number of fusiform rays per square millimeter of surface in the tangential plane is on the order of 2 per square millimeter. As a rule, but one canal is present, but rarely two canals are included in the same ray (Text Fig. 35, *D*).

In the coniferous woods included in this text, fusiform rays are invariably present in *Pinus*, *Picea*, *Larix*, and *Pseudotsuga*. They do not occur elsewhere in domestic softwoods as normal structures although enlarged rays containing resin cysts are sometimes encountered [Exs.,

---

[1] Data on the height of the average ray, computed under standard conditions, undoubtedly would prove to be more reliable, but they are not available at the present time.

Cedrus deodora Loudon; *Picea sitchensis* (Bong.) Carr.], apparently as a result of injury.

Some insight can be gained relative to the size attained by fusiform rays in the four genera enumerated in the preceding paragraph by reference to Plates XXIII to CII, under Descriptions of Woods by Species; in each instance, one photomicrograph depicts the wood in tangential aspect at 75×. Fusiform rays are of the greatest width in certain pines because the transverse canals attain their maximum diameter in these trees; those of *Picea*, *Larix*, and *Pseudotsuga* are generally narrower. The height in cells is variable and apparently is of no diagnostic significance; the upper limit may be set at about 30. The erroneous deduction is often made that fusiform rays are higher along the grain than the narrow rays because most of the latter are lower; however, a careful search will bring out the fact that there is little to choose between the height of the tallest narrow rays and that of the fusiform rays accompanying them.

B. Composition of Rays in Coniferous Woods

The rays of coniferous woods are composed of **ray parenchyma,** of **ray tracheids,** or of both of these kinds of cells. The cells of ray parenchyma are equipped with simple pits if a secondary wall is present.[1] They remain alive as long as they are a part of the sapwood. Ray tracheids, in contrast, are provided with bordered pits and, like the longitudinal tracheids in the sapwood, lose their protoplasts quickly following their origin in the cambium. Being empty, they usually stain somewhat differently from ray parenchyma in sections of sapwood.

Among domestic conifers, the walls of ray parenchyma are thin and unpitted (in the sense of not possessing a secondary wall making pits possible) in Pinus, the Taxodiaceae, the Copressaceae, and in the Taxaceae. The local nodular thickenings in the end walls of the ray cells of *Juniperies virginiana* and *Libocedrus decurrens* are not due to pitting. Truly pitted ray parenchyma is therefore confined to *Picea*, *Larix*, *Pseudotsuga*, *Tsuga*, and *Abies*.

The nature of the pitting serving for communication laterally from

[1] This stipulation is necessary because of the results reported by Bailey and Faull. These investigators state that the ray cells of the Taxodiaceae, Araucariaceae, Taxaceae, Podocarpaceae, Cupressaceae, and Cephalotaxaceae are devoid of a true secondary wall such as features the ray of the tribe Abietoideae of the Pinaceae (*Picea*, *Larix*, *Pseudotsuga*, *Tsuga*, *Abies*); such being the case, pits cannot be present since these are gaps in the secondary wall. See Bailey, I. W., and Anna F. Faull. The Cambium and Its Derivative Tissues, No. IX. Structural Variability in the Redwood, *Sequoia sempervirens*, and Its Significance in the Identification of Fossil Woods. *Jour. Arnold Arboretum*, Vol. 15, pp. 233–253. 1934.

the ray parenchyma to longitudinal xylary elements in contact with it is of diagnostic significance and hence requires description. Such pitting is encountered in what are termed ray crossings.[1] A **ray crossing** is the area bordered by the horizontal walls of the ray parenchyma cell in question and the lateral (vertical) walls of the longitudinal tracheid in back (or in front) of it. The pitting in ray crossings is composed of half-bordered pit pairs only when the cells of ray parenchyma possess secondary walls as in *Tsuga* and other genera of the Abietoideae of the Pinaceae. Elsewhere in native conifers, as has been previously pointed out, this layer is lacking; in such case the pit in a longitudinal xylary element is not accompanied by a complementary pit in the wall of the ray cell and the term, pit pair, applied under these conditions is, strictly speaking, a misnomer. Irrespective of whether a ray crossing possesses pit pairs or only pits, the appearance of a pit in it in frontal aspect is that of the pit in the longitudinal wall of the longitudinal xylary cell in contact with the ray at that point. Nothing is lost, therefore, in describing the pits in the ray crossings of conifers, viewed frontally, in lieu of pit pairs where these are present.

Phillips[2] has described five fairly well-defined types of ray-crossing pits in conifers. Radial sections are required and the crossings should be examined in the springwood. The various types are depicted in Text Fig. 34.

The pits figured in *A* are described as windowlike. The pit aperture is very broad and has an overhanging border so narrow that careful focusing is frequently required to determine its presence. In lateral view, such pits present a broad expanse of unthickened pit membrane much like a pane of glass in a window; hence the term "windowlike."

Windowlike pits feature the woods of the commercial soft pines, and of red pine, among native woods. They are also present in Scotch pine, *Pinus sylvestris* L.

Pits of a type described as pinoid are illustrated in *B* and *C*. They differ from windowlike pits in being smaller, and they are more variable in size and more numerous per ray crossing. A border may (*B*) or may not be (*C*) discernible. If one is present, it is usually wider on one side of the aperture than on the other, giving the pit a lopsided appearance.

Pinoid pitting features all native pines aside from those with windowlike pits. In the legend accompanying the chart for recording anatomical data on coniferous woods, page 165, provision is made for this type of pitting under *I, A, f*.

The type of ray-crossing pits designated as piciform is shown in *D*.

[1] They are also called "cross fields" and "ray cross fields."
[2] *Op. cit.*

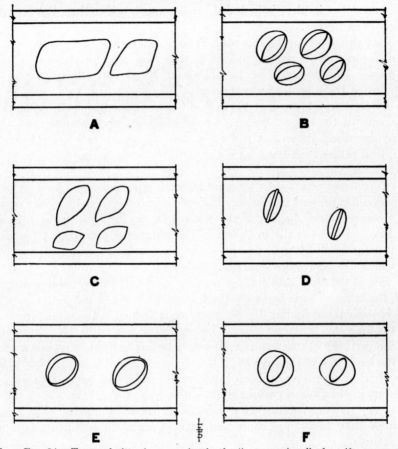

TEXT FIG. 34.—Types of pit pairs occurring in the "ray crossings" of coniferous woods. *D, E,* and *F* after E. W. V. Phillips. *Op. cit.,* p. 128.

A. Windowlike pit pairs of the type that characterize the three commercial soft pines, and red pine (*Pinus resinosa* Ait.)

B and *C.* Pinoid pit pairs of the type occurring in the hard pines other than red pine (*Pinus resinosa* Ait.) A border may (*B*) or may not (*C*) be present.

D. Piciform pit pairs of the type encountered in *Picea, Larix,* and *Pseudotsuga.*

E. Taxodioid pit pairs of the type that feature *Sequoia* and *Taxodium* of the Taxodiaceae, *Abies* of the Pinaceae, and *Thuja* of the Cupressaceae.

F. Cupressoid pit pairs of the type that occur in *Chamaecyparis, Libocedrus,* and *Juniperus* (but not in *Thuja*) of the Cupressaceae, and in *Tsuga* of the Pinaceae.

They are generally elliptical, have a narrow and often slightly extended aperture, and posses a wide border.

Picea, Larix, and *Pseudotsuga* possess pits of the piciform type. Mixed with other types they are also encountered in timber genera elsewhere (Exs., *Araucaria, Cunninghamia, Cedrus*).

E illustrates pitting of the taxodioid type. The pit aperture ranges from oval to circular, is included, and is much wider than the narrow, fairly even border.

Taxodioid pitting features the Taxodiaceae, which include *Taxodium* and *Sequoia*, although cupressoid pitting may also be present in bald cypress. It is also present in *Abies* and *Thuja* and offers a means of separating these woods from those of allied genera.

Cupressoid pits are depicted in *F* and, as the adjective modifier implies, characterize the Cupressaceae. A cupressoid pit approaches the piciform type described above but differs in that the aperture is included and elliptical rather than linear as in the piciform type; the border meanwhile remains wide.

Cupressoid pits feature all cupressaceous woods except *Thuja* and are occasionally present in *Tsuga*. Elsewhere in foreign conifers they occur in *Araucaria* and *Agathis* of the Araucariaceae, in *Podocarpus spp.*, in *Taxus*, and occasionally in *Cedrus*. The number of pits per ray crossing is usually small (1 to 4) except in the Araucariaceae and in *Taxodium*, in which the figures are somewhat higher.

Pits of the *D*, *E*, and *F* types may be nearly orbicular, oval, or elliptical, the last two sorts being the more frequent. When the contour of the pit is other than circular, the pit aperture is aligned in the same direction as the long axis of the pit; it may be vertical or canted to the right or left of the vertical. If the canting ascends from left to right, the pit is seated in the back wall of the ray cell; if the reverse holds, it is in the front wall.

Mention has already been made of the fact that ray tracheids are present in the rays of certain coniferous woods; further, that they differ from ray parenchyma in being prosenchymatous in nature. The paragraphs that follow are concerned with information pertinent to these structures.

The pits of ray tracheids are bordered because of the nature of these cells. Hence, pit pairs leading from a ray tracheid to another cell of like nature are doubly bordered, and the same holds for pit pairs serving for communication between ray tracheids laterally to longitudinal tracheids. Half-bordered pit pairs connect ray tracheids with longitudinal parenchyma and with ray parenchyma.[1]

---

[1] Mention has already been made of the significance of flattened pit apertures on the lateral walls of ray parenchyma, apertures that are canted to the right or left from the vertical. To repeat, if the canting ascends from right to left, the pit is seated in the back wall; if the situation is the reverse, it is in the front wall. The same holds for sloping pit apertures in comparable positions in ray tracheids. Stress should be placed at this time, however, on the fact that the X figures (Text Fig. 17, *G*, *H*, *I*), which characterize doubly bordered pit pairs with flattened apertures in the walls of longitudinal tracheids, are never present in ray tracheids. This is explained by the fact that the canting of the apertures of the pit pairs between ray tracheids and longi-

Ray tracheids may or may not be present in a coniferous ray, as has already been stated. When present, they are marginal and may be present in the body of the ray as well. Given a coniferous ray containing ray tracheids, viewed in lateral aspect (as seen in a radial section), the question arises as to how to distinguish ray tracheids from ray parenchyma. Search should first be made along the upper and lower margins of the ray to determine whether the cells in these positions appear to be different from those in the body of the ray. As noted previously, ray tracheids frequently stain differently from ray parenchyma and hence can be distinguished for this reason. Another usable criterion is the size of the pits on the lateral walls of the two kinds of cells in question except in the genus *Pinus*. The doubly bordered pit pairs showing where ray tracheids cross longitudinal tracheids resemble in shape and in the orientation of the aperture the half-bordered pit pairs where ray parenchyma contacts longitudinal tracheids, but they are larger (see Plate XVIII, Figs. 102 and 103). Finally, ray tracheids are indicated beyond question of doubt by the presence of doubly bordered pit pairs, seen in sectional view, on end walls. The pit pairs of ray parenchhma are simple in this position or the end walls are devoid of pitting.

Ray tracheids occur normally in the Pinaceae and are constant features of the woods of *Pinus, Picea, Larix, Pseudotsuga*, and *Tsuga;*[1] they are sporadic in certain species of *Abies* of the same group. Throughout the Taxodiaceae (*Taxodium, Sequoia*) and the Cupressaceae (*Thuja, Chamaecyparis, Libocedrus, Juniperus*), they are very erratic in their distribution.[2] In the last-named group, they are extremely rare except in one instance; cells of this sort are invariably present in the wood of Alaska yellow cedar [*Chamaecyparis nootkatensis* (Lamb.) Spach.] and serve as a ready means for the identification of this timber.

In point of numbers, ray tracheids attain their best development in the genus *Pinus*, more specifically in the hard pines. In this genus, one or more rows are present on the upper and lower margins of the ray, and not infrequently additional rows are distributed throughout its median portion as well. The low rays of hard pines frequently consist wholly of ray tracheids. In the other genera of the Pinaceae in which ray

tudinal tracheids is in the same direction. A "V" figure may result, or if the pit apertures on different sides of the compound wall coincide in direction, only one aperture will be in evidence.

[1] The four genera first enumerated possess fusiform rays; ray tracheids are present in these as well as in the narrow rays.

[2] HOLDEN, R. Ray Tracheids in the Coniferales. *Bot. Gaz.*, Vol. 55, pp. 56–65. 1913; GORDON, M. Ray Tracheids in Sequoia sempervirens. *New Phytol.*, Vol. XI, pp. 1–7. 1912.

tracheids are normal, they are present in far fewer numbers. Not only are they wanting in the body of the ray in most instances, but a strong tendency is also manifested toward the reduction of the marginal rows to one. This lone row, too, is often interrupted at different points along its course. Alaska yellow cedar is peculiar in that ray tracheids and ray parenchyma seldom occur in the same ray; *i.e.*, a ray is composed wholly of either the one or the other type of cell, both types being present in the wood. The sporadic distribution of ray tracheids elsewhere in coniferous woods has already been recorded; in such instances, they are confined to the margins of the rays.

Much has been written about the phylogenetic significance of ray tracheids. As previously stated, they are most abundant in *Pinus* which, for reasons that need not be discussed here, is considered to be the oldest living genus of conifers. Their presence as constant features in four other genera that are considered to be closely allied botanically to *Pinus*, but in decreasing numbers, is understandable. They are sporadic in *Abies* which may be considered as a transitional genus. In the Taxodi-aceae and Cupressaceae with the exception of *Chamaecyparis nootkatensis* in which, for some reason, they have been retained, they have disappeared as normal structures through evolution. According to this line of reason-ing, unusual conditions such as wounding may result in a reversion to an ancestral condition; in such instances, ray tracheids again appear, a situation that explains their sporadic distribution in certain woods.

The ray tracheids of Douglas fir possess spiral thickening comparable with that in the longitudinal tracheids of this wood. A peculiar modifi-cation of the ray tracheid has also resulted in hard pines which serves as an important diagnostic feature in the identification of these woods. The inner wall thickens in an irregular manner before the cell dies, the thicken-ings, if not too pronounced, appearing like teeth when viewed laterally (Plate XVII, Figs. 97, 98, 99). At other times, projections from the walls (not necessarily only the upper and lower walls) meet near the center of the cell lumen, much as a stalactite may unite with a stalagmite in a cave, forming a rodlike structure extending across the cell. Ray tracheids with either of the types of thickening described above are said to be "dentate" (toothed); they are confined exclusively to the hard pines and provide a ready means of identifying these woods.[1]

As previously stated, the low rays in hard pines are frequently com-posed entirely of ray tracheids. The segregation of such cells and of parenchyma into separate rays has already been recorded in Alaska

---

[1] The ray tracheids of *Picea spp.* are slightly dentate, and the same holds some-times in *Larix spp.* The dentations are too shallow, however, to be confused with those that feature the hard pines.

yellow cedar.   Elsewhere in the conifers, wherever ray tracheids occur, they are always associated with ray parenchyma.   More and more of the ray tissue is given over to cells of this type as the ray tracheids wane in number; in what are recognized as the highest conifers, the rays come finally to consist entirely of ray parenchyma except in instances where ray tracheids may be called back by reversion to an ancestral condition, as already stated.   This condition holds in *Abies*, in the Taxodiaceae, and in the Cupressaceae with the exception of Alaska yellow cedar.

C. Average Ray Volumes of the Coniferous Woods
of the United States

In their spacing, the wood rays of coniferous woods exhibit no marked departures that are of diagnostic significance.   Across the grain they usually range from 6 to 9 per millimeter.   Considerable differences in ray volume are encountered, however, as indicated in Table VIII[1] and compiled by the method described on page 123 of the text.

TABLE VIII
AVERAGE RAY VOLUMES OF THE CONIFEROUS WOODS OF THE
UNITED STATES
(Arranged in botanical sequence, by genera)

Scientific name	Average ray volume, per cent	Variation in samples examined, per cent	Scientific name	Average ray volume, per cent	Variation in samples examined, per cent
Pinus lambertiana	5.7	0.7	Picea sitchensis	7.2	3.1
Pinus monticola	6.5	2.6	Pseudotsuga taxifolia	7.3	2.1
Pinus strobus	5.3	0.4	Tsuga canadensis	5.9	0.7
Pinus contorta var. latifolia	5.7	0.9	Tsuga heterophylla	8.0	0.4
Pinus palustris	8.3	3.7	Abies balsamea	5.6	2.3
Pinus echinata	8.0	3.3	Abies concolor	9.4	1.8
Pinus taeda	7.6	1.6	Abies grandis	6.6	5.2
Pinus caribaea	11.7	1.8	Abies procera	6.5	2.1
Pinus rigida	7.2	2.7	Sequoia sempervirens	7.8	2.5
Pinus ponderosa	6.7	2.4	Taxodium distichum	6.6	2.6
Pinus jeffreyi	8.1		Libocedrus decurrens	8.9	0.9
Pinus resinosa	7.0	1.4	Thuja occidentalis	3.4	0.6
Larix laricina	11.0	4.2	Thuja plicata	6.9	1.4
Larix occidentalis	10.0	1.1	Chamaecyparis lawsoniana	5.5	1.7
Picea glauca	7.0	0.4	Chamaecyparis thyoides	5.1	2.4
Picea rubens	4.9	2.7	Juniperus virginiana	6.2	1.3
Picea engelmanni	5.9	2.5			

The average ray volume for all the coniferous woods examined is relatively low (7.08 per cent) compared to that of porous woods (see page

[1] Myer, J. E.   Ray volumes of the Commercial Woods of the United States and Their Significance.   *Jour. Forestry*, Vol. 20, pp. 337–351.   1922.

233); the lowest figure of 3.4 per cent was recorded for *Thuja occidentalis* L; the highest of 11.7 per cent for *Pinus caribaea* Morolet. Considerable variation in ray volume occurs in the pines, topped by that of slash pine (*P. caribaea*). The maximum figure for this species is possibly to be attributed to its vigor of growth manifested by a dense crown. The two larches, with ray volumes of 11.0 and 10.0 per cent, respectively, rank next; this situation might be attributed to their deciduous habit and the greater need for storage in the wood, but the same reasoning applied to *Taxodium distichum* (L.) Rich., does not hold as the average ray volume of this wood is only 6.6 per cent.

The low ray volumes of coniferous woods occasioned by narrow rays can undoubtedly be ascribed to their ancient origin and the persistence of the evergreen habit in most coniferous trees. Conifers developed and went through their greatest morphological variation far back in the Mesozoic when the climate was equitable. Consequently, there was no need in the wood for the storage of food in longitudinal and ray parenchyma to provide for accelerated growth following unfavorable periods. Such periods did not exist, and hence the rays served primarily for radial conduction and remained narrow.

During the adverse conditions of the late Cretaceous and the later cold epoch, only those species that could endure these profound changes continued to exist, with little alteration in the organization of the wood. Modern conifers have inherited their narrow rays from their Mesozoic progenitors; they have probably been enabled to retain these structures because appreciable amounts of reserve food could be stored in the persisting foliage during the cold season, food that had to be stored elsewhere in the deciduous trees of temperate and subarctic zones. Reasoning thus, the lower ray volume of bald cypress, in contrast to those of the larches, may be due to inheritance rather than to their deciduous habit, or to the influence of environment.

IV. NORMAL RESIN CANALS IN CONIFEROUS WOOD

(Text Fig. 35)

General information relative to the origin, distribution, and size of resin canals in coniferous woods is given on pages 49 to 50; this portion of the text should be reread. To reiterate, structures of this sort are of two classes, those normal to the wood and those which, supposedly at least, arise as a result of wounding. Normal canals are constant features in *Pinus*, *Picea*, *Larix*, and *Pseudotsuga* and extend both longitudinally and transversely, forming a resiniferous system in the wood. Traumatic canals, *i.e.*, canals formed supposedly as a result of injury, in contrast, are sporadic in their distribution, are not confined to the aforementioned genera, and, in domestic conifers, are usually longitudinal.

The manner of the origin of a normal longitudinal canal in white pine has already been recounted.   In coniferous woods, these tubular structures, when they are present, are postcambial in their development and arise through the separation (fission) of cells at the true middle lamella, *i.e.*, schizogenously.   The cells surrounding the tubular cavity thus formed originate from fusiform initials in the cambium, in fact, from the same initials that give rise to longitudinal tracheids; instead of maturing into tracheids, such cells remain parenchymatous, and cross walls form at intervals, at the closest intervals when the long mother cells abut directly on the resin cavity.   The units formed in this way, collectively, comprise the epithelium which sheathes the resin cavity.

The normal transverse canals of coniferous wood arise in an entirely comparable manner, *i.e.*, through cell fission followed by alteration of the cells surrounding the tubular cavity.   In this instance, there is no further division by transverse walls of very long cells into shorter units; some of the cells of the ray, instead of developing into ray parenchyma or ray tracheids, are metamorphosed directly into epithelium.

Since the origin of normal resin canals is identical throughout coniferous woods, such departures as occur in these structures are traceable to variations in the relative number and grouping, in the size, and in the nature of the epithelial cells.   Some of these are of diagnostic significance.

Normal resin canals are more abundant and more evenly distributed in *Pinus* than in the other three genera in which they occur.   In the pines, the number of such longitudinal canals per square millimeter of cross-sectional surface runs from zero to five, the average being nearer the lower limit (Text Fig. 35, *F*); the same holds as regards the normal transverse canals on the tangential surface of the wood.   It follows also that the phrase "evenly distributed" is used in a relative sense only; the count of either type might be five in a given square millimeter of surface in one portion of a plane, three in another, and zero in a third.

In *Picea*, *Larix*, and *Pseudotsuga*, fully as much variation occurs in the number of normal canals per square millimeter as in *Pinus; i.e.*, the maximal and minimal counts remain about the same.   The increased number of canals in the wood of *Pinus*, in comparison with the other three genera, is explained by the fact that fewer square millimeters of surface fall in the lower count brackets.

The distribution of normal longitudinal canals is far less regular in the spruces, larches, and Douglas fir than in pine; possibly the same holds for the normal transverse canals, although no data are available on this point. In transverse sections where portions of a number of concentric annual

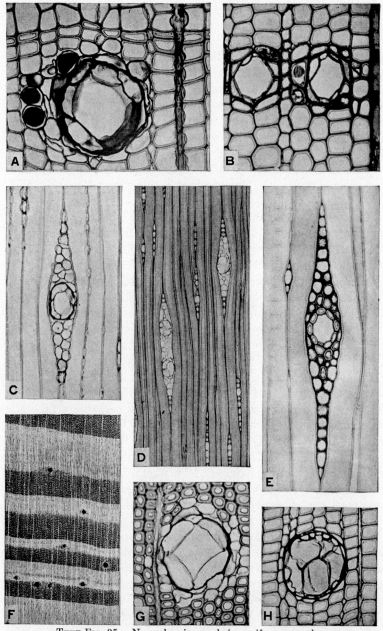

TEXT FIG. 35.—Normal resin canals in coniferous woods.
   A. Longitudinal resin canal in transverse section, with thin-walled epithelial cells.
Northern white pine (*Pinus strobus* L.) (150 ×).   (*Photograph by W. M. Harlow.*)
   B. Two longitudinal resin canals in transverse section, with thick-walled epithelial

rings are visible, the longitudinal canals may approach those of pine in number and spacing; on the other hand, they may be lacking entirely in some of the other ring segments. Douglas fir is peculiar in that the normal canals of the sort being described are solitary in some samples and fairly evenly distributed in the outer part of the ring; in others, a strong tendency is manifested toward the grouping of the canals in tangential rows of 5 to 30 or more in the rings. Some samples of spruce, especially eastern spruce, also exhibit the same tendency although the number of canals in the row is seldom so high. Where several normal longitudinal canals are proximal in a coniferous wood, two or more may be in actual contact; canals that are paired in the tangential plane are frequently separated by a wood ray that courses between them.

Normal resin canals vary in size in coniferous woods not only according to whether they are longitudinal or transverse but also according to the genus containing the wood and the species of the genus producing the wood. In a given wood, the longitudinal canals are invariably larger than those of the transverse type (in Text Fig. 35, compare A to C, B to E); this situation is also indicated in the Descriptions of Woods by Species. For example, in northern white pine, the longitudinal canals attain a maximum diameter of 200 microns and the average diameter ranges between 135 and 150 microns; in this same wood, the transverse canals are usually less than 80 microns in diameter. Reference to the descriptions in this same portion of the text of the other coniferous woods possessing normal resin canals will bring to light further examples. Some correlation also exists between the size of the longitudinal canals and the transverse canals in the same wood; if the former are unusually large or unusually small, this situation is reflected in the transverse canals by a corresponding change in size.

Normal longitudinal and transverse canals are largest in *Pinus*, the genus in which they attain their greatest abundance. Those in *Picea*,

cells. Sitka spruce [*Picea sitchensis* (Bong.) Carr.] (150 ×).

C. Transverse resin canal in a fusiform ray, cut at right angles, with thin-walled epithelial cells. Northern white pine (*Pinus strobus* L.) The magnification is the same as in *A*.

D. Transverse resin canals in fusiform rays, cut at right angles; the canals are occluded with tylosoids; rays with two canals are relatively rare. Longleaf pine (*Pinus palustris* Mill.) (75 ×).

E. Transverse resin canal in a fusiform ray, cut at right angles, with thick-walled epithelial cells. Sitka spruce [*Picea sitchensis* (Bong.) Carr.] The magnification is the same as in *C*.

F. Distribution of longitudinal resin canals in longleaf pine (*Pinus palustris* Mill.) (8 ×).

G. Longitudinal resin canal of longleaf pine (*Pinus palustris* Mill.) in transverse section; the canal is bounded on the left by a ray and elsewhere by thick-walled summer-wood tracheids (125 ×).

H. Longitudinal resin canal of red spruce, (*Picea rubens* Sarg.) in transverse section; the orifice of the canal is occluded with tylosoids (150 ×).

Larix, and *Pseudotsuga* are invariably smaller with the possible exception of Sitka spruce, the size showing no marked variation in these three genera. The greatest disparity in size is found in the pines; some species possess large canals (up to 300 microns in diameter) whereas others are characterized by much smaller passages of this type, the discrepancy being of such magnitude sometimes as to be an aid in the separation of species. Sugar pine, western white pine, and northern white pine may be cited as a case in point (see Descriptions of Woods by Species); the largest canals are found in the first, the smallest in the third, western white pine occupying the intermediate position. Ponderosa pine is also generally characterized by unusually large canals; the other extreme is found in red pine and lodgepole pine. Among *Picea* species, Sitka spruce stands out from the other species because of the greater size of its canals.

The nature of the epithelial cells and the number of these cells encircling the cavities of normal transverse canals, when these are cut transversely in a tangential section, offer a further means of separating coniferous woods. Two types of epithelium can be distinguished: the thin-walled and the thick-walled. *Pinus* is always characterized by thin-walled epithelial cells (Text Fig. 35, *A* and *C*). They are generally devoid of pits and are apparently unlignified. Some of the epithelial cells are always thick-walled in *Picea* (Text Fig. 35, *B* and *E*), *Larch* and *Pseudotsuga* while others, presumably those excreting resin, remain thin-walled. The thick-walled cells are generally provided with pits and appear to be lignified.

Tangential sections for an obvious reason are required in employing the number of cells encircling the cavity of a transverse canal as a diagnostic feature. Six cells per duct is characteristic of *Pseudotsuga; Picea* usually has 7 to 9 cells and *Larix* up to 12 or more.

Considerable space has been devoted in the literature to the process whereby pitch is excreted and accumulates in the cavity of a normal resin canal, but this phenomenon is not clearly understood at the present time. The chemical nature of the resin in the sapwood is somewhat different from that in the heartwood. There is also some evidence to the effect that the contents of the canals in the living tree are somewhat different chemically from those present after the tree is felled and converted into lumber. For example, commercial pine oil is obtainable from converted wood (lumber, old stumps, etc.), but not directly from the oleoresin flowing from a wound in a living tree.

Naval stores (turpentine, pine tar, rosin, etc.) are obtained by tapping longleaf pine and slash pine in the South and from several other pines in foreign countries. The bark[1] and the wood are scarified, resulting in the

---

[1] The bark contains resin cysts.

rupture of some of the normal canals; the oleoresin oozes out and is collected for distillation.   Repeated wounding results in the production of an abnormal number of canals in the new wood which forms in subsequent years in the vicinity of the wound; when these are broken by repeated tapping, the flow of pitch is increased.

As normal resin canals pass from sapwood into heartwood, they cease to function and are frequently occluded with **tylosoids** (Text Fig. 35, *H;* compare to *G* in which tylosoids are not present).   These result from the proliferation of unlignified epithelial cells,[1] frequently until the canal is entirely plugged throughout or at various points along its course.   Tylosoids are of no significance except that they may possibly enhance the durability of the wood.

V. TRAUMATIC RESIN CANALS IN CONIFEROUS WOOD

Traumatic resin canals in coniferous wood may be longitudinal or transverse; the two sorts seldom occur in the same sample, although deodar (*Cedrus deodora* Loudon) is an exception to this rule.   Longitudinal traumatic canals differ from longitudinal canals of the normal type in that they are generally arranged in a tangential row (Text Fig. 36, *A*), rarely in more than one row, as viewed in cross sections of wood.   Such a row may extend for an inch or more along a ring.   They differ further from normal canals in that they are usually restricted to the springwood portion of the growth increment (often at the very beginning of the increment); in contrast, normal longitudinal canals are not in long tangential rows (*x*) and are confined for the most part to the outer half of the ring.   Along the grain, the traumatic longitudinal canals of a given row anastomose in the tangential plane.

The traumatic transverse canals of coniferous wood, like normal transverse canals, are confined to wood rays.   They are much larger than the normal canals occurring in this position, however, and the wood rays are greatly enlarged as a result.   Traumatic transverse canals may accompany transverse canals of the normal type [Ex., Sitka spruce, *Picea sitchensis* (Bong.) Carr.] or may occur in a wood devoid of such canals (Ex., deodar, *Cedrus deodora* Loudon).   When present in coniferous wood, transverse traumatic canals frequently show as radial streaks extending across the grain in edge-grain stock.[2]   Their presence does not produce serious distortion of the grain and, in wooden members in which in use the stress is low, their presence is not a serious defect unless they are present in unusually large numbers.

[1] In *Picea, Larix,* and *Pseudotsuga,* some of the epithelial cells remain unlignified; tylosoids arise from these, not from lignified units of this sort.

[2] GERRY, E.   Radial Streak (red) and Giant Resin Ducts in Spruce.   *Forest Prod. Lab., Mimeo. Rpt.* 1391.   1942.

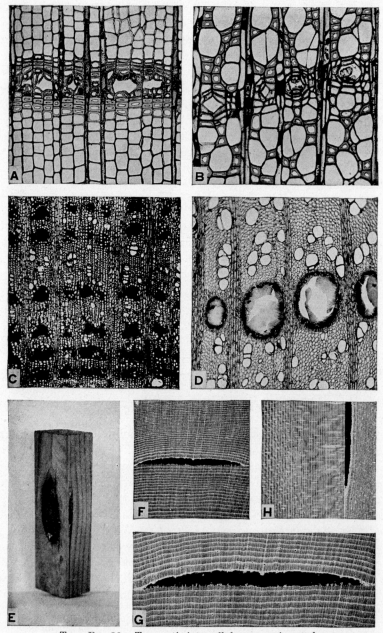

TEXT FIG. 36.—Traumatic intercellular spaces in wood.

A. Traumatic schizogenous resin canals (x) in western hemlock [*Tsuga heterophylla* (Raf.) Sarg.]; such a row may extend some little distance in the tangential direction (95 ✕).

B. Traumatic schizogenous gum canals (x) in red-gum (*Liquidambar styraciflua* L.); as in *A*, a row may extend some distance in the tangential direction (95 ✕).

The traumatic resin canals of coniferous wood, irrespective of whether they are of the longitudinal or transverse type, are of schizogenous origin; *i.e.*, they result from the cleavage or separation of cells, in a manner entirely comparable to that which ensues in the formation of normal canals. The middle lamella between cells splits or disappears, and the cells separate; those bordering the tubular cavity thus formed assume the function of excretion, *i.e.*, become epithelium. The epithelial cells are, as a rule, thickened and pitted, and show every appearance of being lignified.

VI. CRYSTALLIFEROUS ELEMENTS IN CONIFEROUS WOOD

Crystalliferous elements (cells) are rarely encountered in coniferous wood, in contrast to the situation that holds for porous wood. The crystals are exceedingly small and are hence easily overlooked. They occur in the form of cubes, octahedra, or rectangular prisms and, in certain instances at least, consist of calcium oxalate.

Crystal-bearing cells are restricted to the woods of the Pinaceae. Peirce[1] has reported hexagonal, rarely rectangular, prismatic crystals as present in the longitudinal tracheids of the monotypic genus, *Pseudolarix;* this is unusual, for one ordinarily associates crystals with parenchyma. Samples of *Picea* and *Abies,* among domestic woods, not infrequently have small crystals in the ray parenchyma; they also occur in this position in *Pseudolarix, Cedrus,* and *Keteleeria* of the Old World.

The presence of crystals in coniferous wood is of such rare occurrence and so sporadic that it is of no diagnostic significance. Crystals are usually considered as by-products of metabolism.

VII. SUGGESTED PROCEDURE FOR RECORDING ANATOMICAL DATA ON CONIFEROUS WOODS

A comprehensive understanding of the comparative anatomy of the coniferous woods of the United States cannot be acquired only by reading this chapter. Suitably stained mounts of each wood must be available

[1] PEIRCE, A. S. Anatomy of the Xylem of Pseudolarix. *Bot. Gaz.,* Vol. 95, pp. 667–677. 1934.

C. Traumatic lysigenous gum cavities (x) in the branch wood of grapefruit (*Citrus paradisi* Macf.) occluded with black gum (45 ×). (*Photograph by A. S. Rhoads.*)

D. Traumatic lysigenous gum cavities (x) in black cherry (*Prunus serotina* Ehrh.) (50 ×).

E. A pitch pocket in red spruce (*Picea rubens* Sarg.) in tangential (surface) and in radial (edge-grain) views (⅖ ×).

F. End-grain view of a pitch pocket in black spruce [*Picea mariana* (Mill.) B.S.P.] (2½ ×).

G. The same as *F.* (5 ×.)

H. Radial view of a pitch pocket in black spruce [*Picea mariana* (Mill.) B.S.P.]

STUDENT'S NAME:

CHART FOR RECORDING ANATOMICAL DATA, CONIFEROUS WOODS

No.	Scientific name	I Longitudinal tracheids A (a b c)	I B (d e f g)	I C	II Parenchyma A	II B (a b)	III Resin canals A (a b)	III B (a b)	III C	III D	IV Wood rays A (a b c)	IV B a	IV B b	IV C a	IV C b (1,2 3,4)	IV D Sketch of ray crossing	IV E Pits in ray crossing a	IV E b	IV E c	Remarks
1	*Pinus strobus*	a	d e	30μ	A	a b	a b	a	0–5	110μ	c	1–15	16–395μ	a	2 3		1–2	1	2	Two windowlike pits frequent in ray crossings
2	*Abies balsamea*	a	d g₂	33μ	A		A				a	1–34	18–740μ	a	3		2	1	3	Ray tracheids not observed

LEGEND FOR CHART ON CONIFEROUS WOODS

I. Tracheids

  A. Pits

    a. Pits on the radial walls of the first springwood tracheids in one longitudinal row or occasionally paired laterally (4 or more consecutive pairs never present)

    b. Pits on the radial walls of the first springwood tracheids in 1–2 longitudinal rows (record as *b* only when four or more consecutive pairs occur)

    c. Pits on the radial walls of the first springwood tracheids in transverse rows of 3–4 (record as *c* if any pits are arranged as above). (Text Fig. 33, *C*3)

    d. Pits present on the tangential walls of the last-formed summerwood tracheids

    e. Pits in the ray crossings of the first-formed springwood tracheids windowlike (Text Fig. 34, *A*)

    f. Pits in the ray crossings of the first-formed springwood tracheids lenticular or narrowly oval [Text Fig. 34, *B* and *C* (pinoid)]

    g. Pits in the ray crossings of the first-formed springwood tracheids appearing as normal bordered pits [Text Fig. 34, *D* (piciform), *E* (taxodioid), *F* (cupressoid)]. Record subtypes as g_1, g_2, g_3, respectively.

  B. Spiral thickening [avoid misinterpretation of spiral checking (Text Fig. 14)]

    a. Wanting

    b. Present

  C. Average tangential diameter in microns (see footnote 1, page 404)

II. Longitudinal parenchyma

  A. Wanting

  B. Present

    a. Strictly terminal (Text Fig. 33, *A*)

    b. Metatracheal or metatracheal-diffuse (Text Fig. 33, *B*)

III. Longitudinal resin canals

  A. Wanting (Plate XLV, Fig. 177)

  B. Present and normal

    a. Epithelium thin-walled (Text Fig. 35, *A*)

    b. Epithelium thick-walled (Text Fig. 35, *B*)

  C. Number per sq. mm.

  D. Maximum tangential diameter (see footnote 3, page 400)

IV. Wood rays

  A. Seriation

    a. Strictly uniseriate

    b. In part biseriate

    c. Fusiform with transverse canals

IV. Wood rays (*Continued*)

  B. Minimum and maximum height of narrow rays

    a. In cells

    b. In microns

  C. Composition

    a. Homogeneous (without ray tracheids) (Plate XIX, Fig. 105)

    b. Heterogeneous (with ray tracheids)

      1. Ray tracheids strictly marginal

      2. Ray tracheids marginal and interspersed

      3. Ray tracheids nondentate (Plate XVII, Fig. 100)

      4. Ray tracheids dentate (Plate XVII, Fig. 98)

  D. Sketch of ray crossing (springwood), to show number, shape, and arrangement of pits

  E. Pits in ray crossing (springwood)

    a. Average number

    b. Number of horizontal rows

    c. Greatest number per horizontal row

which permit of the study of the tissue in three planes of section with a microscope.   Directions for the preparation of such mounts will be sent by the authors upon request.   The procedure is laborious but is conducive to satisfactory results if followed meticulously.

As anatomical data are compiled on each wood or samples of a given wood, they should be filed in a form that permits of ready reference. This is especially important where comparative studies are to be made. Various ways of filing such information have been devised, some of which are undoubtedly meritorious.   Where the number of woods to be examined is relatively few, the chart method will prove entirely satisfactory in classes in wood anatomy.

A tentative chart and explanatory legend are presented on pages 164 and 165.   The legend should prove entirely comprehensible if the descriptive information on the comparative anatomy of the coniferous woods in the forepart of the present chapter has been thoroughly mastered. Two woods have been recorded in the chart to illustrate the system that is followed.   Mimeographed charts of the type shown, on a scale convenient for class use, can be obtained in quantity at a nominal cost from the Department of Wood Technology, The New York State College of Forestry, Syracuse, N.Y.

As data on each wood are compiled by the student and recorded in the chart, they should be checked for accuracy by the instructor.   When information has been assembled on all the woods assigned, the preparation of a key can then proceed along logical channels.   In the preparation of such a key those characters which are most constant should have first preference.   Coordinate characters should be recorded only when the degree of magnitude of their departures is such that they cannot be misinterpreted.   A dichotomous key of the type used in the text is recommended; in this, structures and features of coordinate rank are brought together at the same place, permitting of ready comparison.

CHAPTER VIII

THE MINUTE STRUCTURE OF POROUS WOODS

PART I. THE DIFFERENCE BETWEEN POROUS WOOD AND CONIFEROUS WOOD, AS VIEWED AT HIGH MAGNIFICATIONS

The anatomical departures that distinguish porous wood from coniferous wood at low magnifications, and information on the gross visual differences between these two kinds of timbers, have already been recorded. In summation, porous woods possess vessels or ducts extending along the grain that appear as pores on transverse surfaces; hence the name. Vessels are wanting in coniferous wood which is said to be nonporous in the restricted sense of not possessing such pores.   It is also quite possible in most instances to separate porous woods from coniferous woods at a glance, for they differ in gross appearance (see paragraph 4, page 49). It now remains to point out wherein these two kinds of wood are dissimilar at high magnifications.

The plates under Descriptions of Woods by Species, pages 443 to 612 will show at once the striking anatomical departures that exist between hardwoods and softwoods.   As was brought out in Chaps. VI and VII, respectively, which are devoted to the structure of coniferous wood, when transverse surfaces of these timbers are viewed at a sufficiently high magnification, the longitudinal tracheids show as polygonal or somewhat rounded cells which are regularly arranged in radially aligned rows between the wood rays.   The true radial alignment of such rows is little, if at all, distorted as they course through successive annual rings except that they fork occasionally; this is explained by the fact that most of the enlargement in the cross-sectional area of the longitudinal tracheids results through an increase in the radial diameter, the tangential diameter meanwhile being little altered.   Since the longitudinal tracheids, as viewed in transverse sections, are arranged in radial rows, it follows that the rays inserted here and there between the rows must, of necessity, pursue a well-nigh straight course except in the relatively few coniferous woods in which longitudinal resin canals are present.

In hardwoods, on the contrary, the radial alignment of the longitudinal elements on transverse surfaces is either lost entirely or is more or less obscured.   This is due in part to the presence of vessels which, in the

167

which will be subsequently described as the description of red-gum wood proceeds.

Two items of structure are worthy of note at the start in connection with the vessels. They are relatively thin-walled, especially as compared with the fibers, and they are more or less angled. The last condition evidently results from the first. As the vessels and fiber tracheids mature behind the cambium, the latter become angled and develop thick walls which undoubtedly resist the pressure exerted by the enlarging vessels. Since one or more fibers impinge upon every vessel, the vessels are forced in turn to become angular. Although this condition is repeated in other domestic woods to varying degree, angling of the vessels to the extent registered in red-gum is the exception rather than the rule. This, then, constitutes an anatomical feature of diagnostic importance in the identification of this wood.

Some of the pores (vessels in transverse section) shown on surface A are entirely surrounded by fiber tracheids (a); others are margined only in part by such units, cells of one or more other categories completing the boundary. At a^1, a^2, and a^3, respectively, two pores are in contact, one larger than the other.* The pore at a^3 not only is in contact with a smaller pore but also is touched by a cell of longitudinal parenchyma; in the other two instances mentioned, contiguous longitudinal parenchyma is not evident, but all the cells surrounding the vessel are not shown. At a^4, the vessel at one point is in contact with a procumbent ray cell, at another with a cell (c^1) of longitudinal parenchyma. Two other combinations are possible, one of which is depicted on surface A. The ring of fibers around a pore is sometimes interrupted only by longitudinal parenchyma, at other times only by ray parenchyma. The vessel at a^5 is in touch with two ray cells and hence illustrates the second situation. The possible combinations of cells bounding the pores of red-gum are, therefore, as follows:

1. Boundary of pore consisting entirely of fiber tracheids.

2. Boundary of pore consisting of fiber tracheids and one or, rarely, two contiguous pores.

3. Boundary of pore consisting of fiber tracheids, a pore, and a lone cell of longitudinal parenchyma.

4. Boundary of pore consisting of fiber tracheids and a lone cell of longitudinal parenchyma.

5. Boundary of pore consisting of fiber tracheids and one or more cells of ray parenchyma.

---

* The frequent pairing of the pores of red-gum in the tangential plane is explained subsequently.

6. Boundary of pore consisting of fiber tracheids, a cell of longitudinal parenchyma, and a cell of ray parenchyma.

The pairing of pores in red-gum was mentioned in the preceding paragraph. The question now arises whether paired pores on transverse surfaces of the wood are always indicative of parallel vessels in the wood. Referring again to surface A, special note should be made of the difference in the conditions prevailing at a^1 and a^2, respectively, and at a^3. In all three instances, two pores are in contact, and the assumption might be in order that, in each case, two vessels are parallel along the grain. This is the actual situation at a^3* where the smaller pore lies somewhat to the rear of the larger, the alignment of the two orifices with respect to one another being radial. For red-gum, the general statement can be made that, where two or more contiguous pores are aligned radially, this denotes a like number of vessels that are parallel along the grain.

The situation at a^1 and a^2, on the other hand, is quite different, even though two pores are in contact at these points. In these instances, the alignment of the pores with respect to one another is in the tangential direction in the wood. One is large whereas the other is usually smaller, by comparison. Both are transverse sections of the same vessel, a condition that scarcely appears credible at first thought.

The situation mentioned above is explained by the manner in which vessels are formed in porous woods. They consist of segments that are derived from the same longitudinal initials in the cambium as the other cells composing the longitudinal xylary tissue. Cells in a longitudinal row that are destined to become vessel segments enlarge in cross-sectional area to the rear of the cambium; the end walls that lie parallel to one another and the intercellular substance between them are then absorbed, either wholly or in part and in such a manner that the opening or openings in one segment check with those in the other. In this way, ready communication, endwise, between contiguous vessel segments is ensured.

In the vessels of hardwoods, the end walls deviate more or less strongly from the vertical and are so oriented that they slope toward the wood rays. Inclination results to such degree in the springwood vessels of oak, chestnut, ash, etc., that the end walls appear to be set almost at right angles to the longitudinal. Much less canting occurs in red-gum, and consequently the sloping ends of the segments overlap for an appreciable distance along the grain. When such overlapping ends are cut transversely at some point along their line of juncture, as happens when wood is sectioned at right angles to the grain, they appear as twin pores that are tangentially aligned with respect to one another. They may be

---

* Although it is not evident in the drawing.

nearly of the same size, or one may be considerably larger. This explains why so many of the pores of red-gum are paired in the tangential plane.

Markings show in the back walls of the vessels at several points on surface A. These are of two types: perforations of a peculiar type in the sloping end walls of vessel segments (a^1, a^2), and pits (a^3, a^4, a^5, a^6).

The vessel perforations of red-gum can best be explained by including certain information in the text at this point relative to the nature of these structures in porous wood. Their origin through the absorption of a portion of the wall where two vessel segments are in contact was indicated on page 177. Originally, one large pit pair or a series of parallel, transversely orientated pit pairs were present in this wall; these may have been bordered, half-bordered, or simple. Subsequently, the pit membrane of the pit pair, or the pit membranes if a series of pit pairs were present, were absorbed, leaving one or a series of parallel openings, respectively.

That portion of the common wall between two vessel segments that is directly involved in the formation of one or of a series of parallel, transversely oriented perforations in close proximity is known as a perforation plate. Vessel segments usually possess two such half-plates which are located at or toward the ends of the member. The term "plate" indicates a surface that is relatively flat. A perforation half-plate has a complement in the wall of the succeeding vessel segment above or below (along the grain) which is reversed in direction and, of course, matches it exactly.

In the perforation plates of red-gum that are depicted at a^1 and a^2, it is evident that these are of the type known as scalariform because of their ladderlike appearance. Within the boundary of a plate, a series of parallel, linear apertures, aligned at right angles to the long axis of the segment, is portrayed, separated by bars which in reality are the remnants of the plate between the openings. The number of bars is, of course, not evident from surface A alone, since only portions of plates appear at a^1 and a^2. However, from the situation at the lower corner of the cube where a plate is shown in its entirety (surfaces A and B), it is obvious that it possesses many thin bars; in fact, 23 show in the plate in question. In red-gum, the number is not fixed but usually falls between 20 and 25. These many-barred scalariform perforation plates serve as an important diagnostic feature in the identification of this wood.

The nature of the pits showing on the back walls of the vessels on surface A is contingent upon the type of cell that happens to be in contact with the vessel at that point. Since depth of focus is not brought out in the drawing, only the apertures or inner apertures of such pits are recorded. In this connection, it is well to bear in mind that the vessel segments of hardwoods are prosenchymatous in nature and hence are generally although not always equipped with bordered pits (they are provided with bordered pits in red-gum). The other complement of the pit pair may be simple or bordered.

Where one vessel is in contact with another that parallels it along the grain, the situation at a^3, the pit pairs are bordered and the complementary pits are similar in shape. In such instances, the apertures of the pits on the side of the wall toward the observer are linear and transversely oriented if the pits are linear (as shown); otherwise, they are narrowly elliptical. Sometimes the linear apertures are long enough to indicate that a linear pit extends the full width of the facet of the vessel in which the pit is located (the width of the facet is controlled by the size of the cell in contact with the vessel at this point); at others, two or rarely three apertures form a transverse series, indicating the presence of as many pit pairs between two vessel segments at this point.

The pit pairs between the vessels and fiber tracheids are also bordered, since the fiber tracheids are provided with bordered pits. However, in this instance, the complementary pits are quite different. In the vessel wall, the pit is dome-shaped, has a rounded aperture (a^6), and is devoid of a pit canal. The complementary member of the pit pair in the fiber tracheid, in contrast, possesses a narrow canal leading down to a pit chamber. Consequently, this pit is provided with both an inner and an outer aperture. A pit pair of the type described above is figured in sectional view at a^4 (pit pair leading to the left into a fiber tracheid).

At a^3, a vessel is in contact with a cell of longitudinal parenchyma; at a^5, with two "upright" cells (ray parenchyma). In both cases, the pit pairs are bordered, and one of the bordered members is situated in the vessel wall toward the observer. This is not equipped with a canal, and the aperture is rounded. In frontal view, such pits are very similar in shape and size to those in the vessel wall which lead to fiber tracheids.

2. Fiber Tracheids (Surface A).—Among hardwoods, the term "fiber tracheid" is applied to longitudinally directed cells that not only are fibrous in the sense of being very long cells but possess pits with a distinct border and a lenticular or slitlike aperture. The fibrous elements of red-gum fall within this definition; on surface A, as drawn, they (b, b^1, b^2, b^3, b^4) outnumber all the other elements, and it follows, of course, that an appreciable volume of the wood is occupied by cells of this type.*

More careful inspection of the top face of the cube will serve to

* Although the fibers of red-gum outnumber all the other elements, it should not be inferred that they occupy the greatest volume in the wood. Over 50 per cent of the wood, volumetrically, is composed of vessels (see Table X).

accentuate four outstanding characteristics of the fiber tracheids of red-gum: (1) they are not definitely aligned in radial rows like the longitudinal tracheids of conifers; (2) they vary in size on the transverse surface shown, a condition that holds, no matter where the plane of the cut happens to fall; (3) they are strongly angled; (4) they possess unusually thick walls. The first two features are not specific to the wood under discussion since they are repeated over and over again in other timbers. The reason underlying the failure of the longitudinal fibrous cells of hardwoods to retain the radial alignment that characterized them as they arose through the repeated division of the same cambial initial was explained on page 167; it is due to the presence of vessels that enlarge appreciably in cross-sectional area behind the cambium. Variation in the size of the fibrous elements that are visible on surface A is traceable to two causes. Like the tracheids of conifers, they are exceedingly long cells with tapering ends. Since they are not stratified tangentially in the wood, it follows that those showing in a given transverse section are cut at different heights, the size of the fiber depending on where the plane of section happened to pass through it. Discrepancy of fiber size in transverse sections is also explained by the fact that the fibers near the outer margin of a ring are somewhat flattened in the tangential plane (indicated by 1-1^a on surface A in the text figure); such cells are followed by others in the succeeding ring that are much larger in cross section, even when they have descended from the same cambial initial.

On the other hand, the strong angling of the fibers of red-gum and the unusual thickness of the fiber wall, which, in turn, results in a small lumen, may be considered as characteristic for this wood. These features, however, are not specific in the sense of permitting of the separation of this wood from all others on these bases alone. But considered in conjunction with other features, such as the many-barred perforation plates, they offer a combination of characters the interpretation of which invariably points to red-gum among domestic timbers.

The pits connecting fiber tracheids are bordered, since these cells are prosenchymatous in nature. Not only are both of the pits constituting such a pit pair bordered, but both are provided with long pit canals and hence inner and outer pit apertures (b, b^1, b^2, b^3); the pit canals have the form of flattened funnels (Text Fig. 17, D).

Surface A of Text Fig. 37 is canted somewhat toward the observer; hence, portions of the back walls of fiber tracheids show, a situation that was true, also, of the vessels. But the expanse of wall exposed in surface view, however, is much less because of the nature of the fibers as compared with that of the vessels. In spite of this, portions of the pit pairs connecting the fiber tracheids show in surface view in the back walls of these elements (b, b^1, b^2, b^3). The pit canal (only the lower half is portrayed) is slitlike and oblique to the long axis of the fiber.

The nature of the pit pairs between fiber tracheids and vessels has already been described (page 179); they are bordered, but the complementary pits are quite different in shape. Bordered pit pairs are present where fiber tracheids are in contact with parenchyma, both ray and longitudinal. Sectional views of such pits are shown at b^3 [at the right, leading to longitudinal parenchyma (c)] and at b^4 (at the right, leading to an upright cell in ray 2^b-2^c). In such instances, the pits in the walls of the fiber tracheids possess a flattened pit canal; the complementary pit in the contiguous parenchymatous cell lacks such a canal.

3. Longitudinal Parenchyma (Surface A).—As viewed across the grain, the cells of longitudinal parenchyma in red-gum have the angular shape and dimensions of fiber tracheids but are much thinner walled. Four such cells are visible on surface A (c, c^1, c^2, c^3) which were located as to position on page 175. As illustrated, these cells are destitute of contents, but they possessed protoplasts when they were in the sapwood, in contrast to the neighboring prosenchymatous cells.

Several observations relative to the distribution of longitudinal parenchyma in red-gum are now in order, from evidence presented on the transverse surface of the block. The cells of this nature are relatively sparse; only four show on surface A. Not only are the units of this kind few in number in the plane under observation, but no two are in contact; each is separated from its fellows by other kinds of cells, *i.e.*, by vessels, fiber tracheids, and ray parenchyma, in various combinations. In red-gum, the cells of longitudinal parenchyma are rarely contiguous when viewed across the grain; as will become evident when surface B is described, they form strands along the grain and hence are in contact, end to end.

The longitudinal parenchyma of red-gum is provided with bordered and simple pits. The pits are bordered, and the complementary members of the pit pairs are also bordered when the contiguous cell is a vessel segment or a fiber tracheid. In such instances, the pits are comparatively large. Structures of this sort are shown in surface and sectional views in the cell at c; in this instance, a fiber tracheid is situated in the rear of the parenchymatous cell. The pit aperture of the pit shown in surface view is rounded and of appreciable size. The complementary pit of the pit pair on the other side of the wall would conform, of course, to that typical for a fiber tracheid. It follows that the pit pairs between longitudinal parenchyma and contiguous vessels would be of the same nature and of approximately the same size.

Where longitudinal parenchyma abuts on ray parenchyma, the nature of the pitting, in contrast, is quite different (see to the right of j on surface B). Here the pit pairs are simple, but, in addition, the pit apertures are smaller, in fact, minute where the pit pairs lead to procumbent ray cells. Another departure exists in that these minute pits are grouped in a characteristic manner in pit fields, in depressed areas of the cell wall. Pitting of this sort between cells of xylary parenchyma occurs in many hardwoods and hence is of no diagnostic significance.

4. Ray Parenchyma Composed of Upright (d) **and Procumbent** (e) **Cells (Surface** A).—Attention has already been called to the fact that two rays course diagonally across surface A from left to right and, further, that these two rays, as seen in this plane, consist of different kinds of cells, respectively, on the basis of shape. These two types of cells and the nature of their pitting can best be described as viewed on surface B where they are seen in lateral aspect.

B. Description of Surface B (Radial Surface)

Portions of five of the six elements listed in Table IX as occurring in red-gum wood are visible on surface B.* Three of these are of the kind designated as longitudinal; the end of one vessel segment appears at f and the median part of another at f^1; short lengths of five fiber tracheids are included in the drawing (g, g^1); a strand of longitudinal parenchyma (h), with three cells showing, extends along the grain. The fourth (i) and fifth (j) types of cells are situated in a wood ray ($3\text{-}3^a$), the upper portion of which can be seen extending from left to right across surface B, at the base. The short, conspicuously pitted ray cells (i) are of the type known as upright; in that part of the ray showing, they are restricted to a single row on the upper margin. Two rows of "procumbent" cells (j) underlie the lone line of upright cells.

Before proceeding further with the description of surface B, it is necessary to acquire a clear conception of the manner in which the plane of section, as portrayed, passed through the tissue. The tip of the vessel segment at f and all the ray cells (i and j) are shown in lateral sectional aspect. The remainder of the tissue is depicted in surface view, *i.e.*, as though the line of cleavage sheared the compound middle lamella which, as in the case of the white pine block depicted on page 112, adhered to the contact face of the tissue that was excised. Consequently, the cells in this portion of surface B are pictured in lateral aspect but not in lateral sectional aspect. The observer views them as from the outside, with the compound middle lamella removed. This situation is responsible for the manner in which the pits are portrayed on the back walls.

---

* Epithelial cells do not appear, since the longitudinal gum canals that sometimes occur in red-gum wood are not illustrated in the drawing.

1. Vessels (Surface B**).**—The vessel segment at f projects downward and ends in a blunt tip. No idea of the length of this vessel member can be gained from the drawing, since the upper portion is cut off by surface A. That it extends for some distance along the grain is borne out by data presented in Table XI at the end of this chapter; in fact, its length is such that only a small portion of it is included in the drawing.

The scalariform perforation plate which shows on one back wall of this vessel was described on page 178; to repeat, this consists of a series of transversely aligned, linear apertures separated by thin bars. This plate has a complement, reversed as to direction and situated directly behind it, belonging to a vessel segment extending into the block from below; the tapering end of this second vessel segment shows in surface C (k^2) and overlaps that of the vessel segment f (indicated as k^1 on surface C). The end of this second vessel segment which runs up from below is excised by surface A; in that plane, it appears as a small pore contiguous to the larger pore that is a cross section of vessel segment f.

Several pit apertures show in the back wall of vessel segment f, below the scalariform perforation plate. The complementary perforation plates in red-gum do not occupy all of the area where the sloping ends of contiguous vessel segments overlap. Bordered pit pairs frequently occur above and below these structures which provide for additional communication between adjacent members of the same vessel.

One further feature that is diagnostic for red-gum is portrayed in vessel segment f: spiral thickening is present on the inner wall at the tip. Thickenings of this sort are not at all unusual in vessel walls, being present in cherry, basswood, maple, etc., where they constitute a diagnostic feature that can be used with others to identify these woods. In such cases, the spirals usually occur throughout the length of the segment, at least on the radial walls. The restriction of thickenings of this sort to the tapering tips of the vessel segments in red-gum may be considered as unusual.

The portion of a vessel segment visible at f^1 is of interest only in that it serves to confirm the nature of the pit pairs where two vessels are in contact in red-gum. In this instance, another vessel to the right (not shown in the figure) paralleled vessel f^1 along the grain. One facet of this was in contact with the vessel appearing in the drawing. The linear pits that are in evidence in the wall of vessel segment f^1 are therefore the back halves of pit pairs that originally connected these two vessels. They are bordered because the domes of the pit cavities point away from the observer. Directionally, the situation is the reverse of that which held in vessel a^3 on surface A where only the apertures of the front members of such pit pairs show on the wall.

2. Fiber Tracheids (Surface B).—The portions of five fiber tracheids (g, g^1) visible in lateral aspect on surface B appear as rectangles, the long axes of which are directed along the grain. These cells are possibly descendants of the same longitudinal cambial initial. There is no certainty of this, however. In hardwoods the radial alignment of cells from the same cambial initial is often distorted, for some of them enlarge at right angles to the grain to the rear of the cambium and become vessel segments. It chanced that none of the fibrous cells illustrated terminate on the radial face of the block. A situation of this sort is quite probable when a small block of red-gum is portrayed at high magnification; in the present instance, the fiber tracheids extended well beyond the upper and lower faces of the cube.

The pits on the lateral walls of the fiber tracheids are aligned in a uniseriate row. They are members of pit pairs of the kind depicted in Text Fig. 17, D, *i.e.*, they are bordered, and the pit canals have the shape of flattened funnels. Hence, the inner aperture of each of the complementary pits is slitlike and extended, and departs but slightly if at all from the vertical in the cell wall. But the pits showing on the lateral walls of the fiber tracheids on surface B have no such apertures. Again, this situation is traceable to the plane of cleavage which in the drawing followed the layer of intercellular substance that originally cemented the cells shown to others to the right of surface B. The pits, as depicted, are small and bordered. They are directed away from the observer and hence only the small dome of the pit is in evidence, perforated at the top (back) by a small, rounded inner aperture leading to a flattened pit canal embedded in the wall to the rear.

The nature of the pit pairs between fiber tracheids and vessels, and between these cells and the units composing the strands of longitudinal parenchyma, was discussed under Fiber Tracheids (surface A). In each instance, both pits of the pair are bordered. The pit in the vessel or parenchymatous cell has no canal and hence but one aperture; that in the fiber tracheid has a long pit canal and outer and inner apertures, the latter of which is slitlike.

3. Longitudinal Parenchyma (Surface B).—The three cells of longitudinal parenchyma at h are a part of a strand that extends for some distance along the grain. The whole strand arose from the same kind of longitudinal mother cell in the cambium that also gave rise by successive divisions to vessel segments and fibrous cells. Following its origin through cell division in the lateral meristem and usually after some elongation, a daughter cell divided further by cross walls into a series of units that remained parenchymatous in nature; these now collectively constitute the strand a portion of which is depicted. The end cells of the series are not included in the drawing; if visible, they would taper to a point, for an obvious reason.   The central portion of the strand is composed of prismatic cells which owe their shape to the pressure exerted upon them by the surrounding tissues at the time of their formation.

The length of the strands of parenchyma in red-gum and the number of units comprising them vary.   They are so long that they tend to run out of the plane of the cut when thin sections of the wood are examined; consequently, length measurements and cell counts are difficult.   The over-all length of a strand is usually greater than that of the vessel segments with which it is associated but less than that of the fiber tracheids. Seven or more cells usually enter into the composition of such a strand.

The strand parenchyma of red-gum falls into the general category of tissue designated as parenchymatous; the cells of such tissue may possess simple or bordered pits.   The pits depicted in surface view on surface *B* are of the second type; not only are they bordered but the pit chamber is relatively large.   In red-gum, bordered pits of this sort are present in the walls of the longitudinal parenchyma wherever it is in contact either with vessels or with fiber tracheids; the complementary pit of the pit pair is, of course, also bordered, the shape of this pit depending upon whether it is in a vessel wall or in that of a fiber tracheid.

Where longitudinal and ray parenchyma are contiguous, the pit pairs are simple.   In those which connect strand parenchyma with upright ray cells, the complementary pits on either side of the wall are of the shape and size depicted at the bottom of surface *B* (*i*).   These are similar in shape and size to those in other upright cells of the same row that lead to fiber tracheids and vessel segments, but they differ in being simple.   On the other hand, where longitudinal parenchyma comes in contact with procumbent ray cells, the pit pairs approach the minute and are clustered in depressions in the secondary wall, as illustrated to the right of *j* on surface *B*.   The clusters of simple pits (sieve pittings) in this instance are viewed from the ray side of the common wall, but they would have the same appearance if surveyed from the opposite direction in the strand parenchyma behind the ray.

4. Ray Parenchyma Composed of Upright and Procumbent Cells (Surface *B***).**—Mention has already been made of the heterogeneous nature of the wood rays of red-gum.   They consist of two kinds of cells: upright units (*i*) on the margins of the ray and also frequently in the body of the ray as well, and procumbent cells (*j*).   These two cell types are portrayed in the portion of the ray visible at the bottom of surface *B*. In each instance, they are aligned, end to end, in transverse rows that extend across the grain in the radial direction. Data as to the numbers of such rows present in red-gum are included subsequently in the text.

The upright cells can readily be distinguished from the procumbent because they differ in shape and pitting. The word "upright" is indicative of the fact that these cells are shorter across the grain radially and higher along the grain than those designated as procumbent. Their form, as figured on surface *B*, is comparable to that of a very steep-gabled roof, *i.e.*, they are wedge-shaped. The shape described above, of course, holds only for the cells on the upper and lower margins of the ray. Where units of this sort are included in the body of the ray, they continue to be high along the grain and short across the grain, but they are then short-prismatic in shape.

The most striking feature of the upright cells of red-gum is the nature and copiousness of the pitting on their radial walls. This shows to advantage on the back walls of the cells visible at *i* and stands out the more because the procumbent cells possess so few pits in the comparable location. This would seem to indicate a division of labor among the cells composing the ray since communication laterally with the longitudinal tissue along its flanks must be largely restricted to the upright cells.[1] The pits in the back walls of the upright cells are bordered or simple, depending on whether the cell to the rear is prosenchymatous or parenchymatous. In the first instance, they are bordered, and the complementary pit in the fiber tracheid or vessel is also bordered (this would possess a slitlike aperture when leading to a fiber tracheid and a rounded orifice when leading to a vessel). Where the pits in the back walls of the upright cells lead to strand parenchyma, they are simple, and the complementary pits of the pit pairs in the wall away from the observer are also simple.

Communication radially between upright cells in the same row, or vertically (in the direction of the grain) when there is more than one row of upright cells, is assured by simple pit pairs. The complementary pits in such instances are smaller than those in the radial walls; a number are shown in sectional view in the drawing. The same condition also holds as regards the pit pairs between upright and procumbent cells, the communication in this instance being in the vertical direction.

Turning now to a description of the procumbent cells, it is evident from surface *B* that they are longer horizontally (in the radial direction) and somewhat lower vertically than the upright cells. The length is usually several times greater than the height, although this does not necessarily follow in all cases. Procumbent cells contrast strongly with

---

[1] This situation is repeated in other woods with heterogeneous rays, notably in *Salix spp.*

the upright cells not only in shape but, as has already been stated, in the paucity of the pitting on their radial walls. Few pits lead laterally from these units to the longitudinal elements of the wood.

In the drawing, communication laterally with the fiber tracheids behind the ray is indicated here and there by bordered pits. These are much smaller than their counterparts in the back walls of the upright cells; but, like those, they are members of bordered pit pairs. A somewhat greater pit concentration is to be noted where the horizontal ray cells are in contact with strand parenchyma. The nature of this pitting has already been described on page 185. It is indicated to the right of j on surface B. Simple pits with unusually small apertures are clustered in depressions in the secondary wall (sieve pitting). These clusters are matched by similar pit aggregations on the other side of the wall, the pit pairs being simple. But here, again, the provision for communication laterally from the rays scarcely seems ample.

Numerous simple pits ensure ready communication between the procumbent cells, both along the grain and at right angles to it in the radial direction. These are shown in sectional view in the drawing as lines. Had the portion of the ray depicted on surface B been biseriate instead of uniseriate, numerous simple pits of this type would have been in evidence in the back walls of the procumbent cells, leading to like cells to the rear of them. As stated previously and as shown in the figure, the procumbent cells are also in communication with the upright cells lying above (or below) them by simple pit pairs.

C. Description of Surface C (Tangential Surface)

The wood of red-gum is shown in tangential aspect on surface C; only a part of this face of the cube is included in the drawing. A portion of a vessel (k), the overlapping ends of two vessel segments (k^1, k^2), short lengths of several fiber tracheids (l), and the lower part of a heterogeneous ray $(4\text{-}4^a)$, cut transversely, occupy this area. The longitudinal elements are depicted in lateral surface view, the ray cells in sectional view. Strand parenchyma is conspicuous by its absence; this does not mean that longitudinal parenchyma is never visible on the tangential surface of red-gum but rather, that the plane of section of surface C did not happen to traverse such a strand.

1. Vessels (Surface C).—The nature of the pitting on the vessel wall (above k) is of the type that occurs where two vessels are in contact along the grain. It is comparable in every way with that illustrated at f^1 on surface B except that in this instance the linear pits are accompanied by oval pits, arranged in two transverse rows of three each. This same grouping of the pits might well have occurred in a vessel wall on surface B.

More or less of a tendency toward this sort of pitting is manifested in some samples of red-gum although the situation illustrated on the vessel wall on surface B is by far the more common. It is evident from the information presented above that the nature of the intervessel pitting is identical in red-gum in the radial and tangential planes. Since intervessel pitting occurs more frequently, however, in tangential sections of the wood, they serve best to illustrate this feature.

The overlapping ends of the two vessel segments (k^1, k^2) which are visible on surface C require little in the way of additional description since the situation that holds there has already been explained at some length. The end of one segment projects into the cube from below, and the tip was excised by surface A. The other vessel member enters the cube from above and can be traced downward to where it terminates on surface C. It is evident from the drawing that the vessel members of red-gum overlap some little distance along the grain and, further, that the length of this juncture is duly recorded on the tangential face of the wood.

2. Fiber Tracheids (Surface C).—The portions of fiber tracheids (l) that show on surface C present no features that were not visible in the same cells on surface B. The pits on the fiber wall are aligned in a uniseriate row, are viewed at about the same angle, and have the same shape.* The fiber tracheids of red-gum are equipped with pits both on their radial and on their tangential walls; the pits are somewhat less abundant, however, on the tangential walls.

3. Longitudinal Parenchyma (Surface C).—No longitudinal parenchyma is in evidence on surface C, owing to the plane of the cut. Had a strand happened to be included, it would have the same appearance as strand h on surface B, even to the nature of the pits.

4. Ray Parenchyma Composed of Upright and Procumbent Cells (Surface C).—The final structure requiring description on surface C is the lone wood ray ($4\text{-}4^a$) which is visible in oblique sectional view. A second structure of this kind ($2^b\text{-}2^c$), composed of upright cells in the plane of the section, crossed surface A, but this was too far beyond ray $4\text{-}4^a$ showing on surface A as $2\text{-}2^a$ to be included in the portion of the tangential face of the cube depicted in the drawing.

Note should be made at once that ray $4\text{-}4^a$ is biseriate through the central portion and possesses uniseriate extensions above and below. This leads to the observation that, in red-gum, some of the rays at least are partly biseriate. Further discussion of this matter is reserved until later in the description.

Continued inspection of ray $4\text{-}4^a$ on surface C serves again to accentu-

---

* The nature of these pits and their shape, as portrayed, were explained under the description of surface B on p. 184.

ate the fact that the rays of red-gum are heterogeneous, a situation that was substantiated on surface B. Its lower end terminates in an upright cell (m) which is narrower and higher along the grain than the other cells located above it in the body of the ray. The cell in question is a member of a row of such units on the lower margin of the ray. The condition in ray 4-4^a is therefore the same as that portrayed at the base of surface B except that the marginal row of upright cells is at the bottom rather than at the top of the ray. The remainder of ray 4-4^a on surface C is composed of procumbent cells (n) of the type showing in longitudinal sectional view in ray 2-2^a, on surface A, and as j in the ray on surface B. As stated previously, they are lower along the grain and several times longer across the grain than the upright cells. This explains the disparity in the height of upright and horizontal ray cells, as viewed in tangential sections of the wood.

The nature of the pitting on the walls of the ray cells was discussed at length when surface B was described. Although such pits are not shown in ray 4-4^a because too many details would lead to confusion, many pit pairs that are bordered or simple, depending on the nature of the cell in contact with the ray at that point, lead laterally from the upright cells to longitudinal cells along the flanks of the ray, few laterally from the horizontal cells. Also, the ray cells themselves, irrespective of their kind or position in the ray with respect to one another, are joined by numerous simple pit pairs. A few of these are visible in surface and sectional views in ray 4-4^a. In two instances, blind simple pits lead through the wall of a ray cell to an intercellular space. Such blind pits, of course, have no complement. Intercellular spaces of the type portrayed in ray 4-4^a are present in many woods; *i.e.*, they are a normal feature.

The actual situation as regards the composition and seriation of the rays in red-gum is not evident on surface C, for a very small portion of the tangential face of the wood is portrayed. Reference should be now made to Plate LXXXI, Fig. 266, in which a larger area of the wood is visible at a lower magnification. Several points are at once evident from the photomicrograph. Some of the rays, the lower ones, are strictly uniseriate; three such rays can be seen, one consisting of seven cells, the other two of eight cells each. Other and much taller rays are 2–3-seriate at one or more places throughout their length but 1-seriate elsewhere. When the 2–3-seriate condition prevails at but one point in the ray, the margins terminate in uniseriate extensions above and below. If the ray possesses the increased seriation at several points, it is unusually high, then appearing to consist of two or more rays of the first type which are confluent along the grain. The rays of this kind not only terminate above and below in uniseriate extensions but the 2–3-seriate portions are linked by uniseriate segments.   Dimensional and volumetric data on the rays of red-gum are included subsequently in the text.

The uniseriate rays may be homogeneous, *i.e.*, may consist entirely of upright cells; or both types of ray cells may be present, in which case these rays are heterogeneous.   The 2–3-seriate portions of the wider rays are composed of procumbent cells and the uniseriate segments of upright cells, or of these and procumbent cells.   The same holds when two or more 2–3-seriate segments are linked by uniseriate portions.

II. VOLUMETRIC COMPOSITION AND THE SIZES OF THE CELLS OF RED-GUM WOOD

The information recorded in the preceding pages should have permitted the student to acquire an accurate knowledge of the kinds and the shapes of the cells composing red-gum wood, their arrangement with respect to one another, and the nature of the pitting whereby communication is assured between them.   But this is not enough to ensure his complete understanding of this timber.   As was the case with white pine, he must now proceed to gain a clear conception of the wood, volumetrically, using data compiled by the weighing method described on page 122; by this procedure, he will arrive at a realization of the percentage of the wood, based on volume, that is occupied by each kind of cell.   Finally, he must master dimensional data placed at his disposal which will permit him to visualize the different types of cells, in terms of size.   Then and only then can he assume that he is thoroughly conversant with the xylary anatomy of red-gum wood.   The remainder of this chapter is devoted to the fulfillment of these last two objectives.

The volumetric composition of red-gum wood, in round figures, is approximately that stated in Table X.   It must be understood, of course, that these data cannot be other than proximate; for, as is stated in a subsequent chapter, the structure of wood is materially affected by a number of factors, among others, by its position in the tree and the growth rate prevailing when it was formed.

TABLE X

VOLUMETRIC COMPOSITION OF RED-GUM WOOD*

Vessels	54.9 per cent
Fiber tracheids	26.3 per cent
Longitudinal parenchyma	00.5 per cent
Wood rays	18.3 per cent
Total	100.00 per cent

* Data taken, with one slight change, from G. E. French.   The Effect of the Internal Organization of the North American Hardwoods upon Their More Important Mechanical Properties.   Thesis submitted in partial fulfillment for the degree of Master of Forestry, The New York State College of Forestry, Syracuse, N. Y.   1923.

It is evident from the table that over 50 per cent, by volume, of red-gum wood is composed of vessels.[1] These are unusually thin-walled which possibly explains why red-gum is relatively soft and has the objectionable feature of denting easily when struck by a hard object. The fibers constitute 26.3 per cent of the wood; *i.e.*, they occupy less than half as much space as the vessels. The amount of longitudinal parenchyma, by volume, is negligible, composing less than 1 per cent of the wood. This is to be expected, for strand parenchyma is never abundant in this timber. The wood rays comprise a little less than one-fifth of the wood, volumetrically.

The average dimensions of the elements of red-gum wood, in three planes, are given in Table XI (the figures, as recorded, are based on the

TABLE XI

DIMENSIONAL AND NUMERICAL DATA ON RED-GUM WOOD*

1. Longitudinal Elements

Vessel segments: Length along the grain, 1.32 ± 0.30 mm.; diameter in the radial plane, 68 ± 15 microns; diameter in the tangential plane, 58 ± 7.7 microns; thickness of the vessel wall, ±3 microns; number of vessels (pores) per square millimeter on the transverse surface, 125–145.

Fiber tracheids: Length along the grain, 1.82 ± 0.16 mm.; diameter in the radial plane, 22 ± 5.7 microns; diameter in the tangential plane, 34 ± 6.2 microns; thickness of the wall, 7 ± 1.2 microns.

Cells of longitudinal parenchyma: Length (height) along the grain, 156 ± 38 microns; diameter in the radial plane, 22 ± 6.7 microns; diameter in the tangential plane, 26 ± 7.6 microns; thickness of the wall, ±2.5 microns.

2. Transverse Elements

Ray parenchyma

Upright cells: Length (height) along the grain, 54 ± 11 microns; diameter in the radial plane, 54 ± 9.4 microns; diameter in the tangential plane, 14 ± 2.9 microns; thickness of the wall, ±3 microns.

Procumbent cells: Length (height) along the grain, 25 ± 4.5 microns; diameter in the radial plane, 120 ± 42 microns; diameter in the tangential plane, 12 ± 3.7 microns; thickness of the wall, ±3 microns.

3. Height of Wood Rays in Cells and Microns

1-seriate rays		2–3-seriate rays	
In cells	In microns	In cells	In microns
2–19	30–585	8–49	150–1300

* For interpretation of the figures in Table XI, see footnote at bottom of Table VII.

[1] In this respect, Text Fig. 37 is misleading, for fiber tracheids occupy the greater area on surface *A*. Were the cube larger, the actual situation prevailing would be apparent.

analysis of one sample).   Perusal of these data will serve to indicate the wide discrepancies in cell size that exist in this wood.   Information is also included relative to the number of vessels (pores) per square millimeter that are visible on the transverse surface, and on the height of the rays on the tangential face of the wood in terms of number of cells and of microns.

CHAPTER IX

THE MINUTE STRUCTURE OF POROUS WOODS
(*Continued*)

PART III. THE COMPARATIVE ANATOMY OF THE COMMERCIAL POROUS WOODS OF THE UNITED STATES

The anatomical departures that serve to separate porous woods from nonporous woods were discussed at some length in Part I, Chap. VIII. Not only do porous woods possess vessels, structures that are never present in the secondary xylem of conifers, but they are much more complex in structure. Without further comment or repetition, the student can now logically proceed to an examination of the anatomical features of the commercially important porous woods of the United States.

TABLE XII
ELEMENTS OF POROUS WOOD

I. Longitudinal
  A. Prosenchymatous
    1. Vessel segments
    2. Tracheids
      a. Vasicentric tracheids
      b. Vascular tracheids
    3. Fibers
      a. Fiber tracheids
      b. Libriform fibers
  B. Parenchymatous
    1. Cells of longitudinal (strand) parenchyma
    2. Fusiform parenchyma cells
    3. Epithelial cells; excreting cells encircling the cavities of longitudinal gum canals*

II. Transverse
  A. Prosenchymatous
    1. None†
  B. Parenchymatous.
    1. Cells of ray parenchyma.
      a. Procumbent cells } Homogeneous } Heterogeneous rays
      b. Upright cells } rays }
    2. Epithelial cells; excreting cells encircling the cavities of transverse gum canals*

* Longitudinal gum canals, apparently of traumatic origin, are occasionally present in red-gum. They are not found elsewhere in the woods covered by this text. Longitudinal and transverse canals are normal features of certain tropical timbers, but the two types seldom occur in the same wood.

† None in domestic hardwoods.

I. THE ELEMENTS OF POROUS WOOD COMPARED
WITH THOSE OF NONPOROUS WOOD

Table XII lists the elements of porous wood although it must not be inferred that all the cell types enumerated are present in every hardwood. Different combinations occur which, coupled with variations in sorting, in cell size, and in the thickness of cell walls, explain the *raison d'être* of the many kinds of porous wood.

Table XII should be compared with Table V. The more complex structure of porous wood is at once apparent, for a greater number of elements are recorded. Yet another deduction may be drawn from this comparison. The wood rays of domestic porous woods are entirely parenchymatous, in spite of the fact that two kinds of ray cells can frequently be distinguished on the basis of shape and often of pitting. Ray tracheids, *i.e.*, prosenchymatous elements, are present in the rays of certain conifers.[1]

In discussing the comparative anatomy of porous woods, the elements composing them are first traced to their ultimate source in the cambium and the manner in which the various types arise through the maturation of young xylary cells, formed as a result of the division of cambial initials, is duly recorded. Then, following the plan pursued in Chap. VII which dealt with coniferous wood, each type of element is discussed in detail, reserving for attention last the cells that enter into the composition of wood rays.

II. DEVELOPMENT OF THE ELEMENTS OF POROUS WOOD
FROM CAMBIAL INITIALS

Text Fig. 38 serves to emphasize again the fact that the longitudinal elements of wood are all derived from the same type of cambial initial. A cell of this kind, of the sort that occurs in a storied cambium, is shown in the center at *A*. In a ring-porous wood, daughter cells cut off from this in the plane of the page mature, without or with little elongation, into **springwood vessel segments** of the type depicted at *B* or into **summerwood vessel segments** of the kind figured at *C* and *D*, respectively.

A **vascular tracheid** is illustrated at *G* and a **vasicentric tracheid** at *H*; these are mature imperforate cells which are described subsequently in the text. The vasicentric tracheid (*H*) is the longer of the two cell types, but both grew somewhat in length as they matured, for they are obviously longer than the undifferentiated fusiform cell (*A*).

---

[1] Note has already been made of the fact that prosenchymatous xylary cells lose their protoplasts shortly after they mature, whereas parenchymatous cells remain alive for some time, presumably as long as they are a part of the sapwood.

A **fibrous cell** is portrayed at *I*. Its exact nature cannot be determined for the type of pitting is not indicated, but this is of no concern at this time. The long fibrous elements of porous wood arise from the same type of fusiform initial that produces the vessel segments, tracheids, etc.

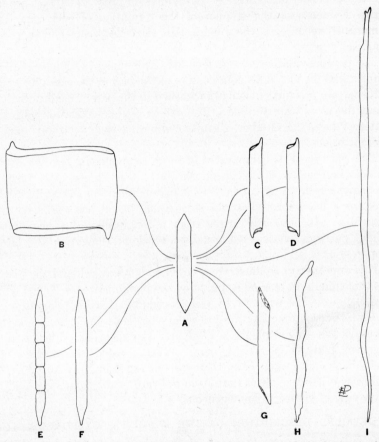

TEXT FIG. 38.—Schematic drawings indicating the manner in which the longitudinal elements of porous wood are derived from fusiform cambial initials. The cells are illustrated in lateral aspect.

A. Fusiform cambial initial. *B.* Springwood vessel segment. *C* and *D.* Summerwood vessel segments with caudate ends, on the opposite and on the same side, respectively. *E.* A strand of longitudinal parenchyma. *F.* A fusiform parenchyma cell. *G.* A vascular tracheid (in shape, it is similar to a summerwood vessel segment but is imperforate). *H.* A vasicentric tracheid. *I.* A fibrous cell.

As the fibrous cells mature, they increase in length several hundred per cent, meanwhile becoming narrower and hence more fibrous in nature.

The longitudinal elements (*B, C, D, G, H, I*) thus far described in Text Fig. 38 are all prosenchymatous; the remaining types, *E* and *F*, respectively, are parenchymatous.   The cells of type E are designated as **longitudinal parenchyma** and are grouped in strands.   Such a strand obviously results through the partition of a longitudinal fusiform cell, by the formation of cross walls.   The number of cells in a strand arising in this way depends, of course, on the number of cross walls that are laid down.   Evidence of the manner of the formation of such strands is permanently recorded in the wood in that the cells at each end taper to a point.

The parenchymatous strand depicted (E) is somewhat longer than the fusiform initial (A).   This is indicative of the fact in the case illustrated, that a certain amount of elongation ensued in the parent longitudinal cell before the cross walls formed.   The extent of this elongation and, as a matter of fact, the number of units composing such a strand, vary in different woods.[1]

The cell type F is comparatively rare in commercial hardwoods but abounds in the woods of certain shrubs.   It is known as a **fusiform parenchyma cell.**   Such an element is parenchymatous in nature in that it retains a living protoplast for some time, but it has the shape of a short fiber.   It obviously arises from a longitudinal fusiform initial, without partition of this, but usually after some elongation and lateral compression.

It is unnecessary to illustrate a young xylary-ray cell and the mature cells that differentiate from it, pursuing the plan followed in Text Fig. 38, since little would be achieved by this procedure.   Except in length in the horizontal-radial direction, mature xylary-ray cells, in shape, are largely replicas of the ray initials in the cambium which, through division in the tangential plane, give rise to them.   When a wood ray contains both procumbent and upright cells, there are corresponding ray initials in the cambium; otherwise, all of the ray initials are of the same type and the xylary ray, of course, is homogeneous.

III. DETAILED DESCRIPTION OF THE ELEMENTS OF POROUS WOOD

It will now prove advantageous to discuss the elements of porous woods in detail, meanwhile adding certain pertinent information which will serve to emphasize the fact that the timbers of this type vary widely

---

[1] *Longitudinal epithelial parenchyma* is not portrayed in Text Fig. 38, for gum canals do not occur as normal structures in any of the woods included in this text. When longitudinal canals are present, the epithelial cells encircling the cavity of a canal arise in the same manner as longitudinal parenchyma, *i.e.*, by the further division, through the formation of cross walls, of a daughter cell traceable to a fusiform cambial initial.   Longitudinal epithelial cells are usually wider than their counterparts in longitudinal strand parenchyma; as viewed transversely, they are curved, to conform to the cavity of the canal.

in their anatomical topography. These cell types are discussed in the order in which they are listed in Table XII.

A. The Longitudinal Prosenchymatous Elements of Porous Wood

The longitudinal prosenchymatous elements of porous wood, as indicated in Table XII, consist of vessel segments, various types of tracheids, and libriform fibers. Such cells are primarily concerned in performing the function of conduction, or the mechanical function, or both. For the most part, they are elongated in the direction of the grain of the wood.

Like all xylary cells, the prosenchymatous elements of porous wood mature rapidly following their formation from the cambium. They differ from the parenchymatous elements with which they are associated in that their protoplasts disappear as soon as or shortly after these cells attain full maturity. The observation is in order at this time that a wood element need not necessarily be living to serve in conduction and to ensure sufficient strength to the stem.

1. Vessel Segments.[1]—A vessel segment is a mature perforate element. As was stated in Sec. II of the present chapter, a vessel segment develops from a longitudinal cell that arises through cell division in the cambium; it is one unit of the larger structure which is known as a **vessel.** In its early stages of development, the forming vessel segment is provided with a primary wall and a protoplast, and is imperforate. At this time, it is in contact with only 6 to 8 other cells in the transverse plane. Enlargement from a few to several hundred times takes place transversely, but there is no or little elongation along the grain. The cell is enabled to increase in size because it possesses a turgid protoplast. At maturity, a large vessel segment may be bounded laterally by 30 cells or more. This situation can be brought about only if the neighboring cells shift position with respect to one another; they are enabled to do this because the layer of intercellular substance between contiguous cells is ruptured or altered chemically, permitting them to glide past each other and to adjust themselves to the tissue tensions that undoubtedly prevail at this time. After the vessel segment has attained its maximum size, a secondary wall is formed by the protoplast, working from within. Gaps (pits) are left in this, and sometimes the inner wall of the vessel becomes sculptured further by localized thickening. Openings form at or near the ends of the segment, and shortly afterward the protoplast disappears.

Vessel segments vary greatly in shape and size (Text Fig. 39), in their sculpturing, and in the nature of their inclusions. They can be studied to best advantage in macerated wood.

[1] In the literature, vessel segments are also called **vessel members** and **vessel elements.**

a. The Shape and Size[1] of Vessel Segments.—In shape, as viewed laterally, vessel segments range from drum-shaped (Text Fig. 39, *F*) and barrel-shaped to short- or long-oblong (*C, D, E, H,* etc.) and linear, with or without tapering or ligulate extensions at one or both ends. If the segment is rounded in cross section, its central portion, at least, is cylindrical; not unfrequently, as in red-gum, vessel segments are angular when seen in transverse section and hence are prismatic in lateral view, with one or more facets visible.

As a vessel segment forms from an immature fusiform cell, there is no or little elongation along the grain; the enlargement at right angles to the grain, in contrast, is appreciable, as has been previously stated. If the enlargement is restricted to the central portion of one side of the fusiform initial or to the central portion and one end, the resulting vessel segment will then possess ligulate extensions (tails) at both ends (Text Fig. 39, *G*) or at one end (*C, D,* and *E*), respectively; or the end(s) will be sloping (*H*). In the first case, when such a segment is viewed in lateral aspect, the ligulate or sloping tips may both be on the same side of the vessel segment (*G*) or arranged diagonally with respect to one another (*H*). Ligulate extensions are to be regarded as vestigial structures in the sense that they are portions of the original immature xylary cell that did not participate in the enlargement during the formation of the vessel segment. Vessel segments with sloping ends are blunt in radial aspect (*A* and *B*) and taper to a sharp point, when viewed in tangential aspect (*G, H*).

Vessel segments vary considerably in length in different woods (Table XIII), in spite of the fact that little or no elongation ensues along the grain as they enlarge in the transverse plane.[2] This is because the longitudinal cambial initials of trees are of different length (see page 101). If by chance these happen to be unusually long, then the vessel segments arising through the longitudinal division of such cells will be very long; if the reverse holds, particularly if the cambium is storied, then short vessel segments are the rule. As the secondary tissues of woods have

[1] The International Association of Wood Anatomists has adopted descriptive terms defining length of vessel segments, width of pores, etc. The listing of these is beyond the scope of this text. For information upon this subject, see the following references: ANON. Standard Terms of Length of Vessel Members and Wood Fibers. *Yale Univ., School Forestry, Trop. Woods,* No. 51, p. 21. 1937; ANON. Standard Terms of Size for Vessel Diameter and Ray Width. *Yale Univ., School Forestry, Trop. Woods,* No. 59, pp. 51–52. 1939.

[2] They may also vary in length to lesser extent in the same wood, particularly as between the springwood and summerwood portions of the ring in ring-porous trees such as oak or chestnut. This disparity in length in such instances is largely explained by the fact that the vessel segments in the springwood shorten appreciably as they increase greatly in diameter and become annular, barrel-shaped, etc., not because any of the vessel segments increase materially in length as they mature.

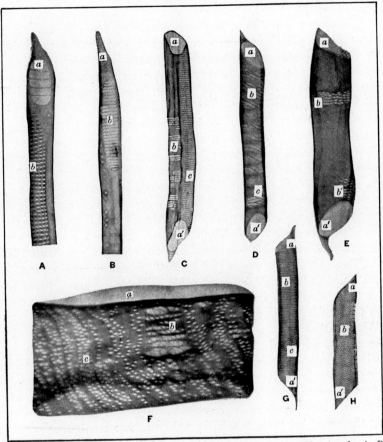

TEXT FIG. 39.—Types of vessel segments in hardwoods (115 ×). (*Photographs A, B, D, E, F, G, and H, inclusive, by C. H. Carpenter; photograph C by W. M. Harlow.*)

  A. Portion of a vessel segment of yellow-poplar (*Liriodendron tulipifera* L.) showing a scalariform perforation plate with few bars (*a*), and opposite pitting (*b*).

  B. Portion of a vessel segment of red-gum (*Liquidambar styraciflua* L.) showing spiral thickening at the tip (*a*), and a scalariform perforation plate with many bars (*b*).

  C. A vessel segment of cucumber magnolia (*Magnolia acuminata* L.) showing simple perforations at the ends (*a, a'*), several ray crossings on the radial face (*b*), and scalariform pitting composed of linear pits on the tangential wall (*c*).

  D. A vessel segment of yellow buckeye (*Aesculus octandra* Marsh.) showing simple perforations at the ends (*a, a'*), spiral thickening (*b*), and a ray crossing (*c*).

  E. A vessel segment of black willow (*Salix nigra* Marsh.) showing simple perforations at the ends (*a-a'*), and two ray crossings (*b-b'*).

  F. Annular (ring-shaped) vessel segment from the springwood of chestnut [*Castanea dentata* (Marsh.) Borkh.] showing simple perforations at the upper end (*a*), a ray crossing (*b*), and strips of pits leading to vasicentric tracheids (*c*).

  G. A vessel segment of silver maple (*Acer saccharinum* L.) showing caudate ends (*a-a'*) on the same side, spiral thickening (*b*), and pits leading to longitudinal parenchyma (*c*).

  H. A vessel segment of butternut (*Juglans cinerea* L.) showing caudate ends (*a-a'*) on opposite sides, and intervessel pitting on the tangential wall (*b*).

become more specialized, there has been a progressive shortening of the cambial initials which in turn has resulted in shorter vessel segments, these changes accompanied meanwhile by others that will be described shortly.

A vessel segment is presented in transverse aspect when it is cut at right angles to the grain. It then appears as a **pore**. The term pore embraces not only the actual orifice but the encircling wall as well.[1] Pores may be solitary or grouped in various ways. A **solitary pore** is generally rounded;[2] the oval shape predominates with the long axis directed radially. When two or more pores are in contact or the fibrous elements of the wood are unusually thick-walled and the vessel segments thin-walled, the configuration of the pore is more or less altered; in such cases, it has one or more flat sides or becomes angled throughout. Not infrequently, several pores are contiguous, one with another, in a radial row. As a rule, in such cases, they are flattened, and the walls are thicker at the points of contact. Such a pore cluster appears as one pore consisting of several divisions; it is known as a **pore multiple. Pore chains,** *i.e.,* radial lines of pores in contact or in close proximity, characterize holly (Plate LXXXVIII, Fig. 279) and other timbers. Nested summerwood pores (**pore clusters**) are an important diagnostic feature of coffeetree wood (Plate LXXXIV, Fig. 271).

When two or more pores are in contact, this condition may indicate a like number of vessels that are parallel and contiguous along the grain. This is not necessarily so, however, for the course of vessels is sometimes so irregular, especially in the tangential plane, that several segments of the same vessel may show as contiguous pores in the same plane. If the ends of the segments of the same vessel overlap for an appreciable distance along the grain, as, for example, in red-gum, two contiguous pores may show on the transverse surface of the wood; these, of course, lead into different segments of the same vessel.

The pores of wood vary greatly in size. The tangential diameter is the more conservative and hence is the dimension that is usually measured. The smallest pores have a tangential diameter in the neighborhood of 20 microns; the other extreme is found in the oaks, chestnut, etc., where pores at the beginning of a ring are frequently 300 plus microns in width. Lianas such as the grape and woodbine have even larger pores.

As noted in the section of the text devoted to the gross features of wood, hardwoods can be divided into two groups on the basis of pore size. If the pores formed in the spring are much larger than those formed later

---

[1] The same expression is used to indicate the cross section of a vascular tracheid (Text Fig. 38, *G*).

[2] In a wood like red-gum (*Liquidambar styraciflua* L.), the pores are angular; this is because the fibers are thick-walled and the vessels thin-walled.

in the season, the wood is **ring porous** (Exs., chestnut, oak, elm, black locust, ash); on the other hand, if the pores are fairly uniform and quite evenly distributed throughout the ring, the wood is said to be **diffuse porous.** Certain woods, such as the *Juglans spp.* and persimmon, are intermediate in this respect; they are classed as **semi-ring porous** or **semi-diffuse porous.** (These two terms may be regarded as synonyms.)

The nature of the porousness of hardwoods in terms of ontogeny and phylogeny has been a subject of discussion. The evidence is to the effect that the diffuse porous condition is a more primitive characteristic than ring porousness. It has been shown, for example, that the hypocotyls of seedlings of ring-porous trees possess diffuse porous wood; further, that the same condition holds likewise for the cotyledonary node and, in most of the species examined, carries over into the wood of the first-year seedling stem.[1] These plant parts are recognized as conservative regions, *i.e.*, regions in which a primitive condition persists.

Turning now to phylogeny, Jeffrey[2] has shown that the beginning of annual ring formation dates back to the late Carboniferous, with the geographical origin in what are now the boreal regions. The earliest known fossil woods of a definite angiosperm nature exhibit no sign of ring porousness, even though well-developed vessels are present. The evidence is to the effect that ring porousness represents an evolutionary advance from the diffuse porous condition. This was possibly first brought about by increasing aridity, and later by the physiological aridity of winter months, followed by a wet vernal season and summer drought that had, as a necessary concomitant, marked seasonal inequalities in the available moisture supply. The factor of moisture supply was probably in force during the Miocene and the Pliocene. Persisting diffuse porousness in the woods of genera of plant families that are considered well advanced in terms of specialization is explained on the basis that trees have undergone other adaptations which have enabled them to retain diffuse porous wood, in spite of the general urge toward the ring-porous condition. Be this as it may, it is conceded that ring porousness was accompanied by the appearance of structural features of an advanced nature in terms of increasing specialization. Numbered among these features, subsequently described in the text, are simple perforations in the end walls of vessel segments, the paratracheal distribution of longitudinal parenchyma, and the presence of only simple pits in the walls of wood fibers.

[1] GILBERT, S. C. Evolutionary Significance of Ring Porosity in Woody Angiosperms. *Bot. Gaz.*, Vol. 102, pp. 105–119. 1940–1941.

[2] JEFFREY, E. C. Anatomy of Woody Plants. University of Chicago Press, Chicago. 1917.

The nature of the porousness of present-day hardwoods can be summed up as follows: Truly ring-porous woods are restricted to the North Temperate Zone; there are no listed indigenous ring-porous trees in the South Temperate Zone. Woods of the same genus, and even supposedly of the same species, may be ring porous in one region of the North Temperate Zone but exclusively diffuse porous farther south. The first few rings of ring-porous trees retain a certain degree of diffuse porousness because the springwood pores do not attain maximum size in successive rings for a number of years.

The spacing and number of pores per square millimeter of surface are also very variable. In some woods, tracts of tissue of this size can be found that are entirely devoid of pores whereas in neighboring tracts of the same area a dozen or more pores can be counted. In boxwood (*Buxus sempervirens* L.), the pores average about 180 per square millimeter and for a few other woods there are even higher figures. Pore counts between 6 and 20 per square millimeter may be considered as average.[1]

b. The Sculpturing of Vessel Segments.—The sculpturing of vessel segments is occasioned in part by the nature of the openings that form at or near their ends, in part by the nature of their pitting and by localized thickening, provided that this is present, on the inner surface of the secondary wall.

(1) NATURE OF THE OPENINGS BETWEEN VESSEL SEGMENTS (Text Fig. 40).—Ready communication, lengthwise, between each two segments of a vessel is ensured through the formation of an aperture or a series of parallel, transversely oriented apertures through the common wall between them. The portion of the wall involved in this process is known as a **perforation plate.** As the term implies, a perforation plate is flat; it may occupy nearly all the wall at the juncture of two vessel segments or only a portion of it.

Perforation plates vary in shape, according to how they are inclined. When two large springwood vessel segments abut squarely on one another (Text Fig. 39, *F*) and the plate is nearly horizontal, it is circular to oval or nearly so in contour. If the vessel segments taper to oblique or ligulate ends, the plate is canted farther from the horizontal (Text Fig. 39, *A, B, C,* etc.); in such cases it may be elliptical, oval, or oblong with rounded ends.

A perforation plate really consists of two **half plates** that are reversed as to direction and belong to different vessel segments meeting at that point. Ordinarily, a given vessel segment possesses two half perforation plates, one at or near each end; but occasionally more than two are

---

[1] The vessel volume of a wood can be computed by the method explained on p. 122. In domestic timbers, it ranges from about 6 to over 50 per cent.

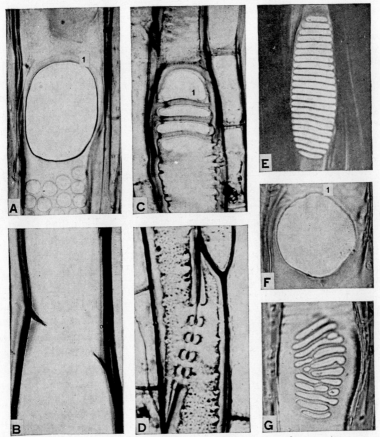

TEXT FIG. 40.—Types of perforations between vessel segments.

A. Simple perforation in cottonwood (*Populus deltoides* Bartr.) in oblique surface (radial) view; the perforation rim (1) is visible on the upper margin of the orifice (550 ×).

B. A similar perforation in sectional (tangential) view, at the same magnification as *A*.

C. Scalariform perforation plate with three thick bars (1) in a summerwood vessel in sassafras [*Sassafras albidum* (Nutt.) Nees] in oblique surface (radial) view (550 ×).

D. A similar plate in sectional (tangential) view, at the same magnification as *C*.

E. Scalariform perforation plate with many thin bars, in red-gum (*Liquidambar styraciflua* L.) in oblique surface (radial) view (170 ×).

F. Simple perforation plate in farkleberry (*Vaccinium arboreum* Marsh.) in oblique surface (radial) view; the perforation rim (1) is visible at the upper margin of the orifice (1240 ×).

G. Foraminate perforation plate in farkleberry (*Vaccinium arboreum* Marsh.) in oblique surface (radial) view (1240 ×). Both simple (see *F*) and foraminate perforations occur in this wood.

present, indicating that the vessel segment in question opened into as many other segments.

The process whereby a perforation or a series of parallel, transversely oriented perforations (a **multiple perforation**) is formed in a perforation plate was described on page 178. To repeat, such a plate originally possessed one large, bordered, half-bordered, or simple pit pair or a number of parallel, transversely oriented pit pairs of like nature. One or more openings developed in the perforation plate when the membrane of each pit pair was absorbed.

When a number of parallel, transversely oriented apertures are present in a perforation plate, it is called a **scalariform perforation plate** (Text Fig. 40, *C, E*); if but one aperture is in evidence, the perforation is a **simple perforation** (*A, F*). In either case, that portion of the margin of the plate remaining after perforation is accomplished is called a **perforation rim** (*A*,1). In the formation of scalariform plates, remnants of the plate are also left between the perforations which, since they are rod-shaped, are called **bars** (*C*, 1). The number, thickness, and spacing of such bars vary in different hardwoods and hence are of diagnostic significance. For example, in red-gum (Text Fig. 40, *E*), the plate usually possesses 20 to 25 thin bars in close proximity; in contrast, in the vessel segments in the summerwood of sassafras (*C*), the bars are few in number, not so closely spaced, and unusually thick. Various modifications of scalariform perforation plates occur. In some woods, the bars exhibit a tendency to branch, whereas in others a reticulate pattern is produced (*G*) when the plate is said to be foraminate.[1]

In a given wood, the perforations may be wholly simple or wholly multiple (scalariform or foraminate), or both types may be present (Text Fig. 40, *F* and *G*). Birch (*Betula spp.*) has vessels with latticed perforations, but those of maple (*Acer spp.*) are invariably simple. Since these two woods are frequently confused, the nature of the perforations alone will serve to distinguish them. Frequently, perforations of a given type may characterize all the species of a genus or an entire family. They are always simple, for example, in the poplars and aspens (*Populus spp.*), in the willows (*Salix spp.*), and in ash (*Fraxinus spp.*); red-gum, in comparison, invariably possesses the latticed type. Both simple and multiple perforations occur in beech, chestnut, sycamore, sassafras, *Vaccinium arboreum* Marsh. (Text Fig. 40, *F* and *G*), although the simple type

---

[1] Such plates occur in *Vaccinium arboreum* Marsh., also in *Ephedra* and *Gnetum* of the Gnetales. In the two last-mentioned genera, a number of openings are grouped in a rounded cluster in the plate, and each is about the size of the membrane of a large bordered pit.

usually predominates.   In ring-porous woods containing the two types, such as chestnut and sassafras, the large springwood vessel segments, which abut more or less squarely on one another, are usually equipped with simple perforations; the segments of the smaller vessels in the summerwood, with oblique end walls, then possess multiple latticed perforations with a few stout bars, or both types may occur in these elements. In cucumber magnolia (*Magnolia acuminata* L.), multiple latticed perforations are present in the first annual increment, in the vicinity of the primary wood; elsewhere in the wood, they are simple.   In the related evergreen magnolia (*M. grandiflora* L.), simple and multiple perforations are usually present throughout the secondary wood.

Perforation plates show to best advantage in longitudinal sections of wood that are fairly thick (25 microns or more).   If a plate is horizontal or nearly so, a situation that frequently occurs in the large springwood vessels of ring-porous woods, it varies little in appearance irrespective of whether or not it is viewed in the radial or in the tangential aspect.   This is because the plate not only is rounded in contour but also is little or not at all canted from the transverse plane.   The same condition does not hold, however, if a plate is oblique, for, in such case, it slopes toward rays. Consequently, it is presented in oblique surface aspect in a radial section (Text Fig. 40, *A*, *C*, *E*, *F*, and *G*) and in oblique sectional view (*B* and *D*) when the section is tangential.[1]

Evidence that has been accumulated during the past 35 years is to the effect that scalariform perforation plates are indicative of a continuing primitive condition in the dicotyledons.   They occur in their most highly developed form in vessel segments with steep end walls, in those whose length is usually above the average.   With increasing specialization, the members of vessels, as has already been stated, became shorter and the end walls more nearly transverse.   Meanwhile, latticed perforations gave place to those of the simple type.

(2) NATURE AND EXTENT OF THE PITTING ON THE WALLS OF VESSEL SEGMENTS.—The nature and the extent of the pitting on the wall of a vessel segment vary greatly and are contingent upon the kinds of cells that happen to be in contact with the segment at the places in question. Pit pairs between a vessel segment and another prosenchymatous cell are usually bordered.   Where they lead to parenchymatous elements, they may be bordered, half-bordered, or simple.   In such instances, the type

[1] In Text Fig. 40, a simple perforation of poplar is depicted as it appears in a radial (*A*) and in a tangential (*B*) section, respectively.   The plate was canted at an angle of about 30 degrees from the horizontal.   *C* and *D* present the same views of a steeply aligned scalariform perforation plate of sassafras.

of pitting in the parenchymatous cell is controlled largely by the degree of specialization of the wood.[1]

Points of contacts of vessel segments and rays usually stand out, not only because of the characteristic clustering of the pits in areas where ray cells were attached to the vessel, but also because the pits are frequently different in size and in nature (Text Fig. 39, *C, D, E,* and *F*) from those leading to longitudinal elements. Long vessel segments may be touched by rays a number of times on the same side. Large springwood vessel segments such as occur in chestnut and oak, often show ray contacts on both flanks, in spite of the fact that such contacts are always confined to the one or the other side of the longitudinal initials in the cambium. This is to be explained by the readjustments, entailing sliding growth, that take place between the cells in the immediate neighborhood of the vessel segment as it enlarges greatly in the transverse plane.

Intervessel pitting appears to best advantage on the tangential faces of a vessel segment, *i.e.,* on the one or the other face presented in a tangential section. It is frequently of diagnostic significance. The pits are usually in close proximity and vary in arrangement and in size in different hardwoods. As was stated on page 78, various types of grouping are recognized: **alternate pitting** (Plate XX, Fig. 116; Plate XXI, Fig. 121), **opposite pitting** (Plate XXII, Figs. 127 and 128), and **scalariform pitting** (Plate XXI, Fig. 120). The pits in the first type range from circular to oval if they are uncrowded; if crowded, they are polygonal and frequently hexagonal. Where the opposite arrangement prevails, they are often rectangular. The pits in the arrangement known as scalariform are linear with the long axis directed across the vessel. Scalariform pitting, like scalariform perforation plates, is indicative of a persisting primitive condition in wood.

Inspection of Plates XX, XXI, and XXII serves to show the variation that may be anticipated in the size of intervessel pits. Persimmon (Plate XX, Fig. 110) has unusually small pits (these are of the type illustrated in Text Fig. 17) and the flattened inner apertures of several pits are frequently confluent across the vessel. The pits of birch (Plate XXII, Fig. 126) are also unusually small; the maples (Plate XXI, Fig. 121), in contrast, have much larger intervessel pits, so much larger that this feature can be used in the separation of these woods which are frequently confused by students.

Where vessel segments are in contact with vascular tracheids, the

---

[1] FROST, F. H.   Histology of the Wood of Angiosperms, 1.   The Nature of the Pitting between Tracheary and Parenchymatous Elements. *Bul. Torrey Bot. Club,* Vol. 56, pp. 259–264.   1929.

nature of the pitting is similar to that between vessels.   The type and grouping of the pits leading to vasicentric tracheids are illustrated in Text Fig. 39, *F*; the pit aperture may be nearly horizontal or oblique, and the outline of the contiguous vascular tracheid is indicated by the clustering of the pits.   Pits leading to fiber tracheids and libriform fibers are usually in straight, vertical or nearly vertical, uniseriate rows because they must conform to the configuration of these elements.   In some woods, pit pairs are wanting where libriform fibers are in contact with vessel segments.

As stated on page 205, the pit pairs between vessel segments and longitudinal parenchyma may be bordered, half-bordered, or simple. They usually differ from intertracheary pit pairs in that a broader expanse of the pit membrane is exposed and also in being less regular in their groupings.

(3) SPIRAL THICKENING IN VESSEL SEGMENTS.—Spiral thickening characterizes the vessel segments of some hardwoods (Plate XX, Fig. 109; Plate XXI, Fig. 124); this, of course, is localized thickening on the inner surface of the secondary wall.   The spirals may be nearly horizontal or steeply oblique.   They frequently cross the contours of bordered pits but seldom pass through the pit apertures.

In diffuse-porous hardwoods, the vessel segments throughout the ring may be spiraled; in ring-porous woods, on the contrary, the spirals are usually confined to the smaller segments in the summerwood.   Red-gum is peculiar in that the spiraling is restricted to the ligulate tips of the vessel segments.

Spiral thickening in vessel segments is an important diagnostic feature in the identification of porous woods.   It occurs, for example, in *Acer spp.* but is lacking in *Betula spp.*   Tropical hardwoods rarely show thickenings of this sort in the vessels.   The small vessel segments and vascular tracheids of the elms and hackberry are always characterized by its presence.

c. The Inclusions in Vessel Segments.—Water and solutes move through vessel segments while they are a part of the sapwood of a living tree. By this statement is not to be understood that they are necessarily completely filled with liquid; in fact, appreciable amounts of air in the form of bubbles are almost invariably present.   When a tree is felled and worked up into lumber, the wood begins to season.   As soon as the fiber saturation point (see Glossary) is reached and thereafter, there is no free liquid in a vessel segment.   It may be quite empty, or inclusions may be present.

The inclusions that are most frequent in vessel segments fall into two categories.   Tyloses may be present; at other times, the segments may be partly or wholly occluded by amorphous deposits that are gummy or chalky in nature. Rarely, starch grains or crystals are in evidence.

A **tylosis** arises through the proliferation of the protoplast of a living cell through a pit pair into the cavity of a vessel segment. The cause of this phenomenon is undoubtedly the difference in pressure existing between a turgid parenchyma cell with living contents and a dead vessel segment which has ceased or is about to cease to function. The membrane of the pit pair involved in the formation of a tylosis enlarges and arches into the cavity of the vessel segment; a portion of the protoplast then passes into the cavity thus formed.

Since one of the cells responsible for the formation of a tylosis is living, it follows that the tyloses in pores arise only where longitudinal or ray parenchyma is in contact with a vessel segment. In ring-porous woods, the rays in the springwood frequently are forced to bow around the large pores as the latter enlarge greatly in cross-sectional area. Tensions are set up which possibly may explain the formation of tyloses at these points. However, the vessel segments of woods with straight rays are frequently occluded with tyloses.

Tyloses in process of formation and various types of tyloses in transverse and lateral aspects are portrayed in Text Fig. 41. In *C*, tylosic buds are illustrated, arising from living ray cells on the flanks of a pore. A further stage of development is illustrated in *D*. Enlargement in this case has progressed until three tyloses from as many pit pairs have met, completely plugging the pore, and a secondary tylosic bud has formed. It must be understood that the dark line between contiguous tyloses is not composed of intercellular substance; in other words, the condition is quite different from that which exists where cells in a tissue are in contact. *A* and *B*, and *E* and *F*, respectively, illustrate tyloses, in each case in a given but in a different wood, in transverse and in longitudinal aspects. The tylosic mass in *E* and *F* is pseudo-parenchymatous in nature; *i.e.*, it simulates parenchymatous tissue.

Tyloses are usually thin-walled but, on occasion, they may become thick-walled and pitted; in instances of this sort, protoplasmic connections between the protoplasm in contiguous tyloses are established. **Sclerosed tyloses,** *i.e.*, extremely thick-walled tyloses resembling stone cells, feature the wood of certain live oaks in the Southwest (*J*); ramiform pits are frequently in evidence in the walls of tyloses of this nature. In beech (Text Fig. 41, *G*), in red-gum, and in certain other small-pored woods, the tyloses are arranged in a uniseriate row; in such instances, the planes of juncture are directed across the vessel segment and simulate, on casual examination, the end walls of vessel segments.

Tyloses are abundant in some porous woods and sparse or wanting in others; they are also variable in their distribution in samples of the same wood. In those timbers in which they are normally present, they usually develop as the vessel segments are included in the heartwood, although they sometimes form in sapwood, particularly in regions where, for one reason or another, the water content falls below normal. Although they attain their best development in vessels, they are not necessarily confined to these elements but are sometimes in evidence in fibrous cells. They also develop under certain conditions in the longitudinal tracheids of conifers, particularly in the roots.[1]

Profuse tylosic formation inhibits the penetrability of a wood but does not necessarily increase its durability, contrary to widespread opinion. The white oaks normally have a high tylosic content and are used for tight cooperage. The red oaks, in contrast, have few tyloses, so few that it is possible to blow through the wood for some distance along the grain; hence, they are not suited for wine barrels, beer barrels, etc., until after special treatment. Woods with open pores treat best with preservatives. Tyloses are sometimes of diagnostic significance. For fuller information upon inclusions of this nature, see footnote.[2]

Vessel segments frequently contain deposits of gummy material (Text Fig. 41, *H* and *I*).[3] This may occur in irregular lumps on the inner wall, completely occlude the segment, or form false dissepiments (plugs) (*I*) across the vessel at the constricted juncture where two vessel segments meet, thus effectively blocking the vessel at these points. In domestic timbers, the color of the gum is usually some shade of red or brown. In pale yellow woods of the type included in the Rutaceae, it appears yellow by transmitted light. The jet black of genuine ebony (*Diospyros ebenum* Koenig) is due to copious deposits of gummy infiltration of the same color, not only in the vessel segments but in the lumina of the other elements of the wood as well.

The presence or absence of gummy deposits in the vessels of a wood is frequently of value in identification. Honey-locust has abundant deposits of this sort in the heartwood; they are wanting or scanty in the wood of the botanically related coffee-tree, and hence this feature can be used in the separation of these woods.

Chalky deposits occur in the vessels of some woods, although their

---

[1] CHRYSLER, M. A. Tyloses in Tracheids of Conifers. *New Phytol.*, Vol. 7, pp. 198–204. 1908.

[2] GERRY, E. Tyloses: Their Occurrence and Practical Significance in Some American Woods. *Jour. Agr. Res.*, Vol. 1, pp. 445–469. 1914.

ISENBERG, I. Microchemical Studies of Tyloses. *Jour. Forestry*, Vol. 31, pp. 961–967. 1933.

[3] Tyloses may be present at the same time.

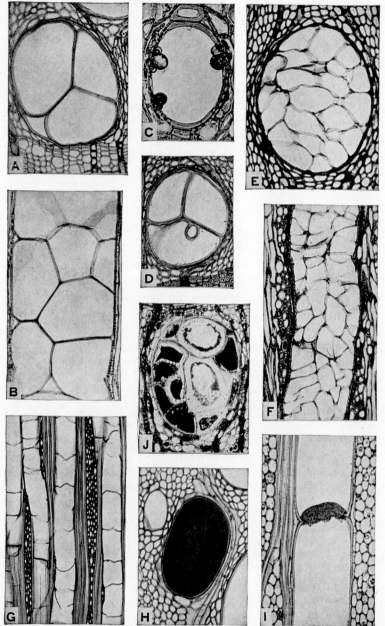

TEXT FIG. 41.—Inclusions in the vessels of hardwoods. (*Photographs A–F, inclusive, by S. Williams.*)

A. Tyloses in a springwood pore of post oak (*Quercus stellata* Wangh.) (walls somewhat thickened) (115 ×).

distribution is too sporadic to serve as a positive aid in their identification. They are usually present in mahogany from the West Indies (*Swietenia mahagoni* Jacq.) and in teak (*Tectona grandis* L. f.) from the Indo-Malayan region. The timbers of *Artocarpus* frequently possess inclusions of this nature, and occasional samples of mulberry are so featured. Little is known about the chemistry of these deposits; those of teak are said to consist of calcium phosphate.

In conclusion, the student should again recall to mind that a vessel segment is but one unit of a larger composite structure known as a vessel. Vessels run in the direction of the grain, *i.e.*, are aligned vertically in the standing tree, and, if of sufficient size, show as lines or grooves on the faces of boards. In the formation of a vessel, immature longitudinal xylary cells in a vertical row or in a diagonal row departing little from the vertical[1] behave synchronously or nearly synchronously,[2] in the manner which was described in paragraph 3, page 197. The openings in the end walls of each two mature vessel segments that are in contact endwise match exactly in the line of the juncture and together constitute the perforation or perforations at that point. Ready communication is thus ensured between consecutive vessel segments which is much more rapid than that taking place through the membrane of pit pairs. Since

---

[1] The length of such a row of cells is undoubtedly several feet, but it cannot be determined with accuracy.

[2] According to Priestley, the reawakening of secondary growth and the development of vessels in hardwoods are initiated in the bud meristems and thence proceed downward in the tree. Such being the case, the growth impetus must be communicated rapidly from segment to segment of the forming vessel, so rapidly that they virtually develop at the same time for appreciable distances along the grain. PRIESTLEY, J. H. Vessel Development in the Angiosperm. *Proc. Leeds Phil. and Lit. Soc. Sci. Sec.*, Vol. 3, Part I, pp. 42–53. 1935.

B. Portion of a springwood vessel segment (*t*) of post oak (*Quercus stellata* Wangh.) showing contiguous tyloses in lateral view (115 ×).

C. Tyloses in the bud stage in a summerwood pore of live oak [*Quercus virginiana* var. *geminata* (Small) Sarg.] (225 ×).

D. Secondary tylosis bud forming on the wall of a tylosis in California blue oak (*Quercus douglasii* Hook. et Arn.) (115 ×).

E. Thin-walled tyloses in a springwood pore of black oak (*Quercus velutina* Lam.) (115 ×).

F. Portion of a springwood vessel (*t*) of black locust (*Robinia pseudoacacia* L.) showing thin-walled tyloses in lateral view (115 ×).

G. Uniseriate rows of tyloses in the vessels of beech (*Fagus grandifolia* Ehrh.); the upper and lower walls (which are in contact) appear as nearly horizontal transverse partitions arranged in a ladderlike series (115 ×).

H. A pore of honey-locust (*Gleditsia triacanthos* L.) occluded with gum (115 ×).

I. A gum-plug at the juncture of two vessel segments in large-leaved mahogany (*Swietenia, macrophylla* King) (115 ×).

J. Sclerosed, pitted tyloses, with dark contents, in a pore in Emory oak (*Quercus emoryi* Torr.) (115 ×).

all the segments composing a vessel become perforate at the same or at nearly the same time, the conduction of liquids can proceed speedily throughout the length of the vessel. A mature vessel is hence a tubular, articulated structure. Each member of the tube is a vessel segment, and the constrictions that are sometimes visible with the naked eye at short

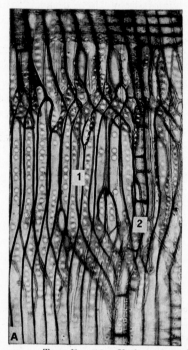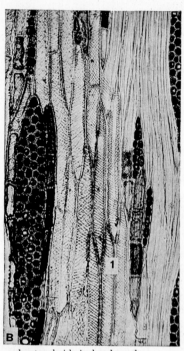

TEXT FIG. 42.—Vasicentric and vascular tracheids in hardwoods.

A. Overlapping vasicentric tracheids with bordered pits (1), and a strand of longitudinal parenchyma (2), in chestnut [*Castanea dentata* (Marsh.) Borkh.] (*r*) (240 ×).

B. Vascular tracheids with spiral thickening (1), which grade into small vessel members elsewhere in the wood. Red elm (*Ulmus fulva* Michx.) (*t*) (160 ×).

or long, and usually at more or less irregular, intervals mark the positions of the perforated junctions where two vessel segments are in contact endwise.

2. Vascular Tracheids (Text Fig. 42, *B*).—Vascular tracheids are arranged in vertical series, like the segments of the small vessels with which they are associated. They are very similar to small vessel segments in shape and size but differ in being imperforate at the ends. A given series may consist entirely of vascular tracheids or of these and small vessel segments, in no regular sequence.

The lateral walls of vascular tracheids are copiously pitted and frequently possess spiral thickening as well. Viewed in tangential aspect, the ends are sloping and dovetail with those of like elements or with small vessel segments above and below. The pit pairs on the end walls are of the same nature as those on the lateral walls. Series of pit pairs of this sort are shown in sectional view at *B*1.

Spiraled vascular tracheids are present in *Ulmus* and *Celtis*. The wavy bands of porous tissue in the summerwood that characterize these woods are largely composed of small vessel segments and of these elements, the former outnumbering the latter. Since vascular tracheids, when cut transversely, appear as pores, they cannot be distinguished from true pores in cross sections of wood.

3. Vasicentric Tracheids (Text Fig. 42, *A*).—Vasicentric tracheids abound in the proximity of the large springwood vessels of ring-porous woods such as oak and chestnut and also in lesser numbers in the flame-shaped areas of porous tissue extending into the summerwood in these timbers; in both instances, they are associated with longitudinal parenchyma the units of which they resemble in cross section. Vasicentric tracheids differ morphologically from vascular tracheids in being different in shape from the vessel segments which they accompany, in not being arranged in definite longitudinal rows, and, usually, in being longer.

The vasicentric tracheids of chestnut, as portrayed in Text Fig. 42, *A*, resemble short coniferous tracheids; those of oak are usually shorter. In each instance, the lateral walls are copiously pitted and the intertracheary pit pairs are bordered. In chestnut, the pits, though smaller, are comparable with those of conifers, even in possessing crassulae (see page 137).

As viewed in cross sections, vasicentric tracheids never exhibit the radial alignment of coniferous tracheids, for they are shoved to one side by the expanding vessel segments. They are usually flattened, for the same reason. Where the pressure is sufficiently great, they frequently become disjoined laterally; they are then called "disjunctive tracheids."

The transition from large springwood vessel segments to neighboring vasicentric tracheids is abrupt; that from the last-named elements to wood fibers, in contrast, is more gradual, often through intermediate cell types. Vasicentric tracheids are to be regarded as transition elements between large springwood vessel segments and typical hardwood fibers.

4. Fiber Tracheids.—As was stated in the description of red-gum, a fiber tracheid is a typically fibrous cell with (1) a relatively thick wall,[1] (2) tapering pointed ends, and (3) small bordered pits. Fiber tracheids have this last feature in common with vascular and vasicentric tracheids.

---

[1] Although the wall of a fiber tracheid is relatively thick, the lumen is not necessarily narrow; in fact, the reverse frequently holds, for the cells of this type often have a greater diameter than libriform fibers (described subsequently).

They differ from these elements, however, in being longer and much more attenuated cells. As fiber tracheids mature following their origin from the fusiform cambial initials that may, on occasion, give rise to vessel segments, vascular tracheids, and vasicentric tracheids, greater elongation ensues lengthwise (along the grain) than takes place in the formation of the other elements mentioned. This is made possible by an increase in the amount of sliding growth which frequently mounts to 300 to 400 per cent; in other words, a mature fiber tracheid is often four to five times longer than the cambial initial from which it was derived.

The bordered pits of fiber tracheids are of the type portrayed in Text Fig. 15, *C*. They may be equally distributed on all the lateral walls but are frequently most abundant on the radial walls. The pit chamber is small, and the inner aperture ranges from lenticular to slitlike and is usually extended. Its orientation is usually vertical or steeply oblique, more commonly the latter. The pit pairs composed of such pits are devoid of a compound torus (see page 80).

Various modifications of the fiber tracheid are encountered in different kinds of wood. As a rule, the inner surface of the secondary wall is smooth (Ex., tulip-poplar); spiral thickening may be present (Ex., holly). Septate fiber tracheids occur in California laurel [*Umbellularia californica* (Hook. & Arn.) Nutt.], in mahogany (*Swietenia spp.*), etc. In such instances, the protoplast apparently segments after the completion of the secondary wall, and cross walls form between the segments. The result is a **septate fiber tracheid** consisting of two or more cells which occupy the original lumen of the fiber. The transverse walls extend only to the inner surface of the lateral secondary walls of the fiber and show as septa, dividing the fiber into a number of compartments. As a rule, the cross walls remain thin and unpitted, but, occasionally, secondary walls are laid down on the flanks of the original cross wall. Fiber tracheids not infrequently are falsely septate. This situation results from the deposition at fairly frequent intervals of transverse plates composed of gummy or resinous material which simulate true septa. The nature of such pseudo-cross walls can be detected by resorting to the proper solvents, to remove the gum or resin. **Gelatinous fiber tracheids** are present in certain woods, although this feature is more frequent in libriform fibers which are subsequently described. In such instances, the innermost layer of the secondary wall appears to be different in nature from the remainder of this wall. It stains differently, is apparently more retentive of moisture, and contracts excessively in drying.

Fiber tracheids grade into libriform fibers on the one hand, and, when septate, into strand parenchyma on the other; cell types intermediate between these two kinds of elements occur in many woods. Fiber

tissue in the summerwood; in
narrow concentric lines of
longitudinal parenchyma is pr
in a characteristic manner ar
shaped areas extending into
species, etc.   In such instance
in transverse sections, is vari
irregular contour, islands, et
general plan frequently persi
which permits of the recognit

As is to be expected, fiber
in diameter, in length (Table
the volume mass entering int
only in different species but
thereof, and even at different

Fibers widely different in
are even contiguous, when f
sufficiently high magnificatio
cells of this nature taper to p
therefore depends upon wher
in a transverse section are cu
in diameter.

In woods with ripple mar
tudinal parenchyma, and the
rays.   In such instances, the
this portion being wholly wi
the original fusiform initial t
tion of the fiber, elongation
ends pushed into the tiers o
from the central portion of t
viewed in transverse sections
without intergrading forms.
ously pitted on the shoulder

Frequently, the last few
are flattened (tabular), and
increment.   For this reason,
clearly defined at low magnifi
be confused with terminal pa
In some woods, the walls of t
the ends.

The volume mass of fib
species often is subject to c

tracheids and libriform fibers may both occur in the same wood, and the transition between them is often so gradual that it is largely an arbitrary matter in assigning a given cell to one or to the other type.   The situation is all the more difficult because the nature of the pits is often not at all obvious.

Woods that the student learns to consider as coarse-fibered, such as tulip-poplar, red-gum, and sourwood, possess fiber trache·ds.   The deduction follows that fiber tracheids usually have a greater diameter than libriform fibers.   Fiber tracheids attain their peak development in what are considered to be the more primitive dicotyledons; such timbers are diffuse porous, are featured by small vessels with steeply oblique, scalariform plates, and possess heterogeneous rays; more or less of a tendency is also manifested toward the retention of the fibrous cells of the wood in radial rows, as viewed in transverse sections, a situation that holds for coniferous woods.

5. Libriform Fibers.—Libriform fibers differ from fiber tracheids in possessing simple pits; not only are the pits simple, but they are usually smaller than those of fiber tracheids.   Libriform fibers are more mechanical in nature than this other type of cell, as is evidenced by their smaller diameter and narrower lumen.   The walls may be thicker than those of fiber tracheids although this does not necessarily follow; frequently they seem to be thicker because the cell lumen is reduced to a mere slit.   The length likewise appears to be greater than that of fiber tracheids; this is because the cells of this sort are generally proportionately narrower in comparison with their length and hence create the illusion of being longer.

The simple pits of libriform fibers require little by way of description. In some woods, they are apparently inherently simple; in others, they have become simple by reduction.   As previously stated, the decision as to whether a pit in a fibrous cell is simple or bordered is often largely an arbitrary matter, for all gradations occur between the two types.   In general, the pits are more abundant on the radial than on the tangential walls.   Hence, it behooves the student seeking this feature to examine radial sections.

Some of the modifications encountered in fiber tracheids also occur in libriform fibers, in fact, may even be more frequent.   For example, gelatinous libriform fibers (Text Fig. 43) are not at all unusual in many woods.   In certain species, they are invariably present; in others, they apparently result from abnormal growing conditions (tension wood), etc. Gelatinous libriform fibers are features of such timbers as black locust, hackberry, mulberry, and certain of the southern oaks [especially overcup oak (*Quercus lyrata* Walt.)]; undoubtedly, they have a bearing on certain properties exhibited by these woods.

Fiber tracheids a[...]
largely[1] or wholly co[...]
or more of a given w[...]

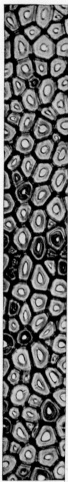

TEXT FIG. 43.—Gelatin[...]
(*Photomicrograph by S. [...]*)

the fibrous mass tha[t...]
facture of paper.

In timbers like[...]
evenly distributed [...]
holds for maple, birc[...]
Fig. 243), in contr[...]

[1] Vasicentric trache[...]

TABLE XIII
AVERAGE LENGTH OF THE VESSEL SEGMENTS AND FIBERS (FIBER TRACHEIDS AND LIBRIFORM FIBERS) OF SOME OF THE HARDWOODS OF THE UNITED STATES, DETERMINED FROM SPECIFIC SAMPLES

(All figures are expressed in millimeters. For significance of "standard deviation," see footnote to Table VII. The data are presented in botanical sequence by genera)

Scientific name	Vessel segments Average length	Vessel segments Standard deviation	Fibers Average length	Fibers Standard deviation	Scientific name	Vessel segments Average length	Vessel segments Standard deviation	Fibers Average length	Fibers Standard deviation
Juglans cinerea	0.36	0.14	1.13	0.17	Celtis occidentalis	0.26	0.03	1.13	0.17
Juglans nigra	0.51	0.08	1.21	0.14	Morus rubra	0.21	0.03	0.91	0.12
Carya tomentosa	0.44	0.06	1.62	0.26	Maclura pomifera	0.18	0.02	1.14	0.16
Carya cordiformis	0.44	0.11	1.38	0.22	Magnolia acuminata	0.72	0.15	1.39	0.28
Carya ovata	0.47	0.09	1.34	0.28	Magnolia grandiflora	0.99	0.14	1.81	0.29
Carya illinoensis	0.41	0.08	1.28	0.20	Liriodendron tulipifera	0.89	0.13	1.74	0.29
Populus grandidentata	0.64	0.09	1.33	0.17	Umbellularia californica	0.37	0.06	0.94	0.14
Populus tremuloides	0.67	0.18	1.32	0.22	Sassafras albidum	0.39	0.06	1.02	0.14
Populus trichocarpa	0.58	0.09	1.38	0.19	Liquidambar styraciflua	1.32	0.30	1.82	0.16
Salix nigra	0.42	0.09	0.85	0.17	Platanus occidentalis	0.63	0.12	1.08	0.17
Carpinus caroliniana	0.42	0.10	1.17	0.18	Prunus serotina	0.39	0.06	1.21	0.20
Ostrya virginiana	0.68	0.11	1.23	0.18	Gymnocladus dioicus	0.27	0.06	1.12	0.15
Betula lenta	0.91	0.12	1.52	0.22	Gleditsia triacanthos	0.19	0.03	1.24	0.11
Betula lutea	0.84	0.16	1.38	0.18	Robinia pseudoacacia	0.18	0.02	1.13	0.16
Betula papyrifera	1.00	0.26	1.35	0.15	Cladrastis lutea	0.23	0.03	0.61	0.14
Betula populifolia	0.74	0.15	1.26	0.14	Ilex opaca	0.88	0.24	1.74	0.27
Alnus rubra	0.85	0.14	1.19	0.18	Acer macrophyllum	0.33	0.05	0.77	0.15
Fagus grandifolia	0.61	0.11	1.28	0.21	Acer rubrum	0.42	0.05	0.92	0.12
Castanea dentata	0.58	0.12	1.22	0.16	Acer saccharinum	0.41	0.07	0.76	0.13
Castanopsis chrysophylla	0.67	0.11	0.87	0.11	Acer saccharum	0.41	0.09	0.92	0.13
Quercus borealis	0.42	0.09	1.32	0.29	Aesculus octandra	0.44	0.08	1.00	0.13
Quercus coccinea	0.43	0.09	1.61	0.26	Tilia americana	0.43	0.09	1.21	0.17
Quercus palustris	0.46	0.09	1.30	0.20	Tilia heterophylla	0.48	0.04	1.34	0.18
Quercus phellos	0.45	0.08	1.38	0.25	Nyssa aquatica	1.11	0.28	1.89	0.33
Quercus shumardi	0.45	0.08	1.44	0.20	Nyssa sylvatica	1.33	0.34	2.30	0.36
Quercus velutina	0.43	0.08	1.44	0.29	Cornus florida	1.04	0.17	1.74	0.29
Quercus alba	0.40	0.09	1.39	0.20	Cornus nuttalli	1.13	0.20	1.64	0.27
Quercus bicolor	0.41	0.07	1.19	0.17	Oxydendrum arboreum	0.47	0.09	1.05	0.16
Quercus lyrata	0.42	0.08	1.35	0.20	Arbutus menziesi	0.53	0.10	0.79	0.14
Quercus macrocarpa	0.35	0.07	1.20	0.19	Diospyros virginiana	0.36	0.04	1.39	0.20
Quercus montana	0.39	0.09	1.34	0.26	Fraxinus americana	0.29	0.03	1.26	0.17
Quercus prinus	0.40	0.09	1.45	0.22	Fraxinus nigra	0.27	0.04	1.27	0.17
Quercus stellata	0.43	0.09	1.35	0.21	Fraxinus oregona	0.23	0.05	1.20	0.16
Lithocarpus densiflorus	0.57	0.11	1.10	0.15	Fraxinus pennsylvanica	0.26	0.03	1.27	0.17
Ulmus americana	0.22	0.04	1.55	0.20	Fraxinus quadrangulata	0.23	0.04	1.03	0.15
Ulmus fulva	0.22	0.03	1.30	0.15	Catalpa speciosa	0.28	0.09	0.64	0.11
Ulmus thomasi	0.25	0.03	1.21	0.16					

quently by variation in the growth rate.   Narrow-ringed wood of ring-porous species contains less fibrous tissue per unit of volume than normal stock produced when the growth rate was faster.   This situation, in turn, has a direct bearing on the strength of the wood, for fibrous tissue in abundant amount bespeaks strength.   The effect of ring width upon strength is discussed at length in Chap. X.

Fibers with serrated or scalloped sides and forked fibers are frequently visible in mounts of macerated wood.   As has been stated previously, among wood elements the maximum elongation takes place in fibrous elements which, in turn, necessitates considerable sliding growth.   As these unusually long cells grow past and push between each other, they sometimes encounter obstacles such as other fibers, and wood rays at right angles.   Considerable pressure is undoubtedly exerted at this time, and the shape of the fiber, particularly toward the ends, is altered to conform to the configuration of neighboring cells at the points of contact.

B. The Longitudinal Parenchymatous Elements of Porous Wood

(Text Fig. 44)

The terms "wood parenchyma" and "xylary parenchyma" are synonymous; when correctly used, they embrace any and all the paren-chymatous cells present in wood.   As contrasted to the wood pros-enchyma of hardwoods which consists of vessels, of various types of tracheids, and of libriform fibers, and whose functions are mainly conduc-tive and mechanical, the wood parenchyma in these timbers is involved primarily in the storage and to a lesser extent in the conduction of carbohydrates.[1]   In further contrast to wood prosenchyma, paren-chymatous xylary cells are usually comparatively short, remain functional for a much longer period (supposedly as long as they are a part of the sapwood and possibly longer), and, as a rule though not always, are provided with simple pits (the prosenchymatous elements of hardwoods have bordered pits, the libriform fibers excepted).

The wood parenchyma of hardwoods, like that of conifers, is of two types: (1) longitudinal, that which is directed along the grain, and (2) transverse, that which extends across the grain.   Cells of the latter type comprise the wood rays which are considered subsequently in the text.   Hence, this type of parenchyma can be properly designated as ray parenchyma.

Hardwoods differ from softwoods, as a group, in possessing much more

[1] Also, where cells of this type enter into the composition of gum canals, undoubt-edly in the production of gums, resins, etc.

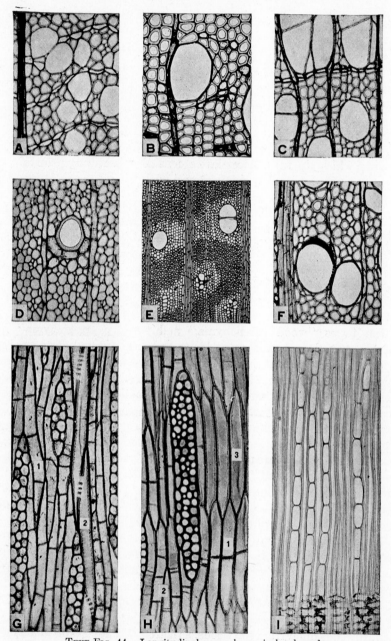

TEXT FIG. 44.—Longitudinal parenchyma in hardwoods.

A. Longitudinal metatracheal (zonate) parenchyma (x) in basswood (*Tilia americana* L*) (150 ×).

B. Longitudinal metatracheal-diffuse parenchyma (dark cells) (x) in yellow birch

wood parenchyma, although there are exceptions to this rule, as, for example, the poplars (*Populus spp.*) and willows (*Salix spp.*). This holds not only for ray parenchyma but for longitudinal parenchyma as well. In some porous woods, the ray parenchyma is present in normal amount, as is evidenced by the size of the wood rays, but longitudinal parenchyma is exceedingly sparse (black cherry, Text Fig. 44, *F*) or wanting altogether. Considerable evidence has been collected to the effect that hardwood trees have a shorter growing season than conifers; growth intensity probably mounts higher in hardwoods. To offset this situation, greater provision to store reserve food is made in hardwood trees, in places (including the parenchyma of the wood) where it will be immediately available when growth gets under way in the spring.

As is indicated in Table XII, there are three types of longitudinal parenchyma: (1) cells of longitudinal (strand) parenchyma, (2) fusiform parenchyma cells, and (3) epithelial cells encircling the cavities of longitudinal gum canals. The manner of the formation of these elements from fusiform initials in the cambium was discussed in explaining Text Fig. 38. The three types of longitudinal parenchyma enumerated above may now be considered to advantage.

1. Longitudinal (Strand) Parenchyma.—The cells of longitudinal (strand) parenchyma, as the term implies, are arranged in rows along the grain (Text Fig. 44, *G*1), for a reason previously stated. To repeat, such a row is formed through the further division of a longitudinal cell arising from a fusiform initial in the cambium. The mature strand has approximately the same shape as the fusiform mother cell from which it was derived; it may have the same length or be somewhat longer, depending upon whether or not sliding growth ensued prior to the formation of cross walls. Strand parenchyma is by far the most common type of longitudinal parenchyma in porous wood.

(*Betula lutea* Michx. f.) (150 ×).

C. Longitudinal terminal parenchyma (x) on the outer margin of an annual ring in cottonwood (*Populus deltoides* Bartram.) (150 ×).

D. Longitudinal paratracheal (vasicentric) parenchyma (x) nearly encircling a summerwood pore in white ash (*Fraxinus americana* L.) (150 ×).

E. Longitudinal paratracheal-confluent parenchyma (x) in honey-locust [*Gleditsia triacanthos* L.] (40 ×).

F. Xylary tissue (x) devoid of longitudinal parenchyma in black cherry (*Prunus serotina* Ehrh.). Longitudinal parenchyma is extremely sparse in this wood. (150 ×).

G. Strands of longitudinal parenchyma (1), and a summerwood vessel (2) with scalariform perforation plates, in lateral, tangential view. Sassafras [*Sassafras albidum* (Nutt.) Nees.] (150 ×).

H. Strands of longitudinal parenchyma composed of two (1) and four (2) units, and fusiform longitudinal parenchyma cells (3), in lateral, tangential view. Black locust (*Robinia pseudoacacia* L.) (150 ×).

I. Portions of a number of strands of longitudinal parenchyma, separated by fibers, in lateral, radial view. Scarlet oak (*Quercus coccinea* Muench.) (150 ×).

The terminal cells in a strand of longitudinal parenchyma have a base at right angles to the long axis of the strand. The ends taper to a point which is sharp as viewed in the tangential plane and more or less blunt as viewed radially; in reality, they are the ends of the original fusiform cell which gave rise to the strand through the formation of cross walls. The cellular units composing the body of the strand are rectangular or approach the rectangular, as viewed in lateral aspect; actually, they are prismatic or cylindrical, depending upon whether the strand is angled or rounded (this can be ascertained in a transverse section). In some woods, particularly when the strands are viewed radially, the cells in the body of the strand are somewhat constricted at the points of contact (Text Fig. 44, *I*), causing the strand to appear linked. Strand parenchyma is best seen in tangential sections, but care should be exercised not to confuse it with the uniseriate rays that are features of many woods. In transverse sections, the cells usually stand out against the remaining tissue because the walls are often thinner and stain differently; traces of gummy infiltration are also frequently visible.

The strands of longitudinal parenchyma are much shorter in hardwoods than in conifers (see page 142). As a rule, it is a comparatively easy matter to determine the number of units comprising the strands in porous wood. The number may vary considerably or be fairly constant within a species. Woods with storied structure usually have strands composed of few units, 2 or 4 being the rule (Text Fig. 44, *H*1 and 2); in unstoried woods, the count usually ranges between 5 and 12, although higher figures are not unusual. In ring-porous woods, the strands tend to be somewhat longer and to consist of more units, as the outer boundary of the growth increment is approached. Those in contact with springwood vessel segments in the timbers of this class are no longer than strands in the same neighborhood that are embedded in other types of cells, but they are usually broader; the cellular units composing such strands then appear to be shorter because of the increased transverse diameter. Strand parenchyma is frequently crystalliferous. This situation is discussed toward the end of this chapter.

The cells of strand parenchyma may have a wall of equal thickness throughout the cell, or certain portions of the wall may remain thin while the remainder thickens; in this second instance, it is usually the radial walls that attain the greater thickness. Where strands of parenchyma are in contact along the grain or a strand is in touch with ray parenchyma, the cells are frequently disjunctive.

The nature of the pitting on the lateral walls of strand parenchyma is contingent upon the types of cells that are in contact with the strand. Where the strand is contiguous to other parenchyma, either longitudinal or transverse (ray parenchyma), the pit pairs are usually simple, are so small as to appear like dots in frontal aspect, and are frequently clustered in thin places in the secondary wall (sieve pitting). The shape of the pits in the pit pairs leading to vessels is usually influenced by the nature of the complementary pits in the vessel wall; the former are often of the same size and shape as the latter, sometimes even to the extent of being linear and scalariformly grouped. Pit pairs may or may not be present where strand parenchyma and fibers are in contact.

As was stated on page 221, strand parenchyma is by far the most common type of longitudinal parenchyma in hardwoods. In some tropical tree species, it frequently comprises an appreciable volume of the wood, at times over 50 per cent; in domestic timbers, volumetrically, it ranges from less than 1 to about 18 per cent. Longitudinal strand parenchyma, when massed in various ways, is often visible on transverse surfaces and in transverse sections at low magnifications. It often stands out against the background of fibrous tissue because the cells, as viewed *en masse*, appear lighter or darker than the surrounding tissue. Various types of distribution characterize different porous woods and are sufficiently uniform to permit of their use in the identification of these timbers. The descriptive terms used in defining strand parenchyma as to location are explained in the next paragraph.

Three general types and a number of subsidiary types of longitudinal strand parenchyma are recognized. When it is situated within the body of a growth increment, is obviously not definitely associated with the vessels,[1] and is arranged in concentric lamellae, it is designated as **metatracheal parenchyma** (Text Fig. 44, *A*); if wholly within a growth increment and aggregated around the vessels, as **paratracheal parenchyma** (*D*); if located on the outer boundary of a growth increment (outer margin of a growth ring), as **terminal parenchyma** (*C*). All three of these general types and various combinations of them may be present in a given wood. If only one type is in evidence, it is usually the paratracheal; but, in certain woods, the longitudinal parenchyma is wholly terminal. Terminal parenchyma on the outer face of an annual ring is held to be indicative of a primitive condition in coniferous woods; in porous woods, on the contrary, its presence in this position is explained as resulting from reduction. This reasoning appears wholly logical since the presence of parenchyma in the body of the ring has become well established among angiospermous woods.

When typically developed, metatracheal parenchyma is arranged in

---

[1] The lines or bands may touch pores here and there, but there is no appreciable widening of the belt of parenchyma to include the pore.

concentric lamellae extending counter to the wood rays.   Narrow bands
of parenchyma of this type characterize such woods as basswood (Text
Fig. 44, *A*), the hickories, certain of the oaks, persimmon, dogwood, and
hop-hornbeam.   If the woods are diffuse porous, there is little variation
in the spacing of the lines throughout the ring.   In ring-porous timbers
such as oak, on the contrary, they usually become more numerous and
are spaced at shorter intervals as the outer margin of the growth ring is
approached; hence, wide rings show this feature to better advantage than
narrow rings.   In certain woods, the lamellae of metatracheal parenchyma exhibit more or less of a tendency to anastomose.   In others, the
lines are narrow and closely and evenly spaced, and form a characteristic
reticulum with the wood rays which extend counter to them (Ex., woods
belonging to the Anonaceae, Sapotaceae, and Ebenaceae).   Broad bands
of metatracheal parenchyma, a dozen or more cells wide, are features of
the woods of such tropical genera as *Ficus, Pongamia, Erythrina, Bauhinia,*
and many others; not infrequently, the zones are as wide as or wider than
the bands of tissue that alternate with them.

In certain woods, the longitudinal parenchyma between the pores
(metatracheal parenchyma) is not present in sufficient amount to form
concentric lines or bands; the cells, as viewed in transverse sections, are
then scattered (diffused) through the tracts of fibrous tissue, or two to
several cells may be contiguous here and there while others are solitary
(Text Fig. 44, *B*); when this distribution prevails, the parenchyma is said
to be **metatracheal-diffuse.**   Whether metatracheal-diffuse parenchyma
results from the reduction (breaking up) of narrow lines of metatracheal
parenchyma, or because such lines failed to form, can only be conjectured.
Possibly it arises in both of these ways.   The birches, red-gum, and many
other domestic woods are characterized by parenchyma of this type.
It follows that metatracheal and metatracheal-diffuse parenchyma
intergrade.

Paratracheal parenchyma, as previously stated, is always associated
with pores; it may be restricted to occasional cells in contact with pores
or occur as a partial (Text Fig. 44, *D*) or complete sheath, one cell in
thickness, around the pore.   At other times, it is present in sufficient
amount to form a narrow or broad aureole, several to many cells in thickness, encircling the pore; the term **vasicentric parenchyma** is used to
denote the last type of arrangement.   If the parenchyma also extends
out from the flanks of the pore, *i.e.,* forms an eyelet with it, it is described
as **aliform parenchyma.**   Not infrequently, the extensions of paratracheal
parenchyma stream out so far laterally that they coalesce.   This arrangement is described as **paratracheal-zonate parenchyma**[1] (Text Fig. 44, *E*).

[1] Also called "paratracheal-confluent parenchyma."

Paratracheal parenchyma and its various modifications characterize many woods. This type of arrangement is especially frequent in leguminaceous timbers.

Terminal parenchyma, when present in woods of the Temperate Zone, serves as a boundary between one annual ring and the next. The term implies that this tissue is produced at the close of the growing season, but some evidence has been offered recently to the effect that it is formed when growth begins in the spring. In woods such as mahogany (*Swietenia spp.*), bands simulating terminal parenchyma occur at fairly regular and frequent intervals; these have been so designated, but in all probability they denote the boundaries of growth increments rather than annual increments. Be this as it may, the expression terminal parenchyma will suffice in both instances, for purposes of description; it is parenchyma confined to the outer (or inner, if it is formed in the spring) face of a growth increment irrespective of whether this is or is not an annual increment.

Terminal parenchyma may be restricted to occasional cells on the outer face of a growth increment or may form a continuous layer one or more cells in thickness. In the willows (*Salix spp.*) and poplars (*Populus spp.*), the line is only one to two cells in thickness (Text Fig. 44, *C*); in tulip-poplar and the magnolias, in contrast, it is appreciably thicker, appearing as a light line visible to the naked eye on the transverse surface of the wood.

The longitudinal parenchyma is strictly terminal in the woods mentioned in the preceding paragraph. In other timbers, it is associated with that of the paratracheal type (*Fraxinus spp.*) or with metatracheal-diffuse parenchyma (*Betula spp.*), etc. The varying distribution of longitudinal strand parenchyma in different hardwoods is a very serviceable tool in their identification, full advantage of which is taken in the Keys for identification that follow Chap. XIII.

2. Fusiform Parenchyma Cells.—The manner of the origin of fusiform parenchyma cells was illustrated in Text Fig. 38, *F3*. They are longitudinal parenchyma cells that develop from fusiform cambial initials without further division and with little or no increase in length. Fusiform parenchyma cells are comparable in function with the cells composing the strands of longitudinal parenchyma in that they possess protoplasts that remain living for some time. In shape, they resemble a short fiber.

In contrast to strand parenchyma, fusiform parenchyma cells are relatively rare in the xylary tissue of trees but are features of the wood of many shrubs. In timber species, they are most frequently encountered in trees with storied cambia. In such instances, the elements of this sort and strands of parenchyma consisting of two and four units, respectively, often occur in close proximity (Text Fig. 44, *H*1, 2, and 3), it appearing to be largely a matter of chance whether or not cross walls happen to form in the developing fusiform xylary cells.

In transverse sections, fusiform parenchyma cannot be distinguished from strand parenchyma. With this, though far in the minority when present, fusiform parenchyma cells constitute the longitudinal parenchyma of wood which is designated according to location as metatracheal, paratracheal, and terminal.

3. Epithelial Cells Encircling the Cavities of Longitudinal Gum Canals.—Longitudinal gum canals are not present as normal structures in any of the woods covered in this text; as stated on page 173, they occur sporadically in red-gum, supposedly as a result of injury. Consequently, longitudinal epithelial cells are wanting in domestic timbers of normal structure. Certain tropical hardwoods, among others those belonging to the Dipterocarpaceae, Anacardiaceae, Burseraceae, and Leguminosae, possess normal gum canals; as a rule, in the woods in which canals occur, they are of either the longitudinal or the transverse type (included in wood rays), the two kinds rarely occurring in the same wood.

The manner of formation of the epithelial cells that encircle the cavities of the gum canals in hardwoods has already been recounted. They arise in the same manner as the units composing strand parenchyma, *i.e.*, through the subdivision by transverse walls of fusiform cells traceable to longitudinal initials in the cambium. A mature epithelial cell in a hardwood differs from its counterpart in strand parenchyma in being broader across the grain. This is occasioned by the fact that the cells of this nature are stretched or grow in the peripheral direction as they mature, to accommodate themselves to the enlarging tubular canal cavity.

The longitudinal epithelial cells of hardwoods may be thin-walled and unpitted or thick-walled, when they are usually provided with simple pits. In the latter instance, they are frequently lignified.

C. The Wood Rays of Porous Wood, Composed of
Transverse Parenchymatous Elements[1]

(Text Fig. 45)

1. The Nature and Origin of Wood Rays Reviewed.—In the discussion of the topic stated above, the procedure is from the gross to the minute. Attention is first focused upon wood rays as structures. Provision is then made to acquaint the student with the types of parenchymatous elements that enter into the composition of these cell aggregates.

[1] In the case of aggregate rays which are subsequently described, of these and longitudinal tracheary elements.

Considerable space has already been devoted in the text to **xylary rays,** *i.e.,* **wood rays.** A certain amount of repetition is in order at this point, however, since it will again afford an opportunity to visualize these structures accurately. Wood rays are sheets or plates of horizontal tissue which extend transversely and radially in the wood of the standing tree, so oriented that the face of the plate is exposed to view when the xylary tissue is sawn, split, or cut in a truly longitudinal plane parallel to a radius of a cross section of a log (Text Fig. 11). A wood ray is only a part of a larger structure in the tree which, in lieu of a better term, may be called a **complete ray.** Such a complete ray consists of a **xylary ray,** *i.e.,* the portion of the ray in the wood, a **phloem ray** which is the portion of the same ray in the phloem, and a **cambial ray** [the place in the cambium where the ray traverses this meristematic layer (Text Fig. 23, *B* and *D*)]. All the growth of a ray can be traced to the division of the cells in its cambial portion. Some of the daughter cells thus arising add to the length of the xylary ray as the cambium moves outward; others become a corporeal part of the phloem ray. The ray mother cells are quite different in shape from the fusiform initials to which the longitudinal elements of wood are traceable. As has already been recounted, there are but two types of mother cells in the cambium of a tree, those which give rise to the longitudinal elements of wood and those which are responsible for the formation of rays.

As in conifers, the xylary rays of hardwoods are confined to the secondary wood. Some of them originate when secondary thickening is first initiated; thereafter, barring injury to the cambium, they are continued as long as the tree lives. These first-formed xylary rays extend completely across the secondary wood. At the inner end, they may terminate blindly opposite the primary xylem; or if the latter no longer forms a ring but consists of patches around the pith,[1] occasional rays appear to enter the pith between the areas of primary wood.[2] This explains the terms **pith rays** and **medullary rays,** which are frequently encountered in the literature on wood; in instances of this sort, the rays seem to consist of the same kind of tissue as the pith or medulla. These terms are unfortunate, and their use should be discouraged.

The rays in a tree diverge as they extend outward in the wood, pass through the cambium, and continue as phloem rays. Hence, the spacing between any two rays increases as they progress outward. When the distance between two such rays has become sufficiently great, a new ray arises in the cambium through the division of a fusiform cambial initial,

[1] This is the situation that is true of timber trees.

[2] The rays that appear to enter the pith have been called "primary rays"; the others, "secondary rays."

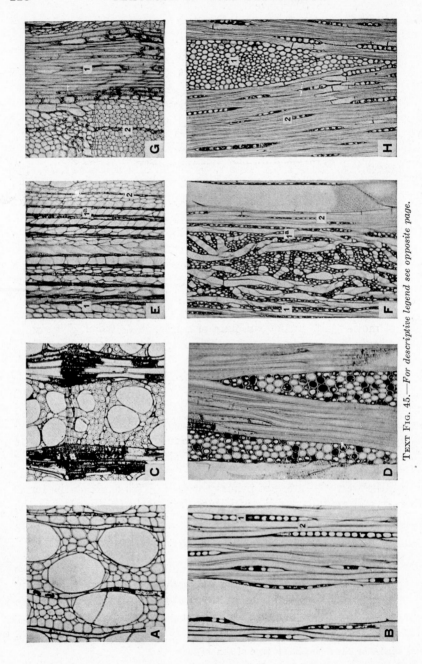

TEXT FIG. 45.—*For descriptive legend see opposite page.*

or a portion thereof, in a manner quite different from that which obtains when a longitudinal xylary element is to be the result.   Transverse walls, or these and vertical walls as well, are formed, and the group of shorter cambial initials thus resulting becomes a cluster of ray mother cells which function as such thereafter.   Once initiated, the cluster of ray mother cells may increase in size in the tangential plane through the addition of further cells, resulting in an increase in the size of the ray in succeeding growth increments.

2. The Size of Wood Rays in Porous Wood.—The length of a wood ray is indeterminate; once formed, barring injury to the cambium, it is continued as long as a tree lives.   The phrase, "size of wood rays," therefore, has reference to the width and the height of these structures. The widths and heights of rays can be indicated in terms either of cells or of linear measurement.

The wood rays of dicotyledonous woods are much more variable in width and in height than those of softwoods.   Uniseriate rays of the sort that feature coniferous woods characterize some domestic hardwoods (Exs., *Salix spp.*, Text Fig. 45, *A* and *B*; *Populus spp.; Aesculus spp.*), but these timbers are greatly in the minority.   The width of such narrow rays is in the neighborhood of 15 to 20 microns.   The biseriate condition is not at all unusual.   Most hardwoods possess multiseriate rays which range from 3- to many-seriate (Text Fig. 45, *C* and *D*).   In the timbers covered by this text, maximum seriation is reached in *Quercus spp.* where the large rays[1] are often 30 or more cells wide (Text Fig. 45, *G* and *H*) and 300 plus microns in width.

Biseriate and multiseriate rays, as viewed tangentially, taper to uniseriate margins above and below.   The body (enlarged portion) of the ray may be uniformly seriate; or two or more several-seriate portions may alternate with portions of lower seriation (these are usually uniseriate but

[1] In the literature, they are described as rays of the oak type.

TEXT FIG. 45.—Ray types in porous woods.   (100 ×.)
A. Uniseriate rays (four) in black willow (*Salix nigra* Marsh.) as seen in a transverse section.
B. Similar rays in black willow (*Salix nigra* Marsh.) as seen in a tangential section; they are composed of procumbent (1) and upright (2) cells, and hence are heterogeneous.
C. Multiseriate rays (two) in sycamore (*Platanus occidentalis* L.) as seen in a transverse section.
D. Portions of two similar rays in sycamore (*Platanus occidentalis* L.) as seen in tangential section; they are composed only of procumbent cells, and hence are homogeneous.
E. Portion of an aggregate ray (1-1*ᵃ*), and one uniseriate ray (2) in red alder (*Alnus rubra* Bong.) as seen in a transverse section.
F. Portions of a similar aggregate ray (1-1*ᵃ*) and uniseriate rays (2) in red alder (*Alnus rubra* Bong.) as seen in a tangential section.
G. Oak-type of ray (1) and one uniseriate ray (2) in scarlet oak (*Quercus coccinea* Muench.) as seen in a transverse section.
H. Portion of a similar oak-type of ray (1), and a number of uniseriate rays (2) in scarlet oak (*Quercus coccinea* Muench.) as seen in a transverse section.

not necessarily so); the ray then seems to consist of several rays which have become confluent along the grain (Plate LXXXI, Fig. 266). Frequently, in woods with ripple marks, such rays extend through two or more stories.

Ray height in hardwoods—in fact, in all woods—is much more variable than ray width. As in conifers, the lowest rays in hardwoods are but one cell and a few microns (about 20) tall. The upper limit is found in the oaks, in red alder (*Alnus rubra* Bong.), and in blue-beech (*Carpinus caroliniana* Walt.) where the large rays frequently extend 2 inches (50,000 microns) or more along the grain. As viewed in a tangential section, the rays of a hardwood are generally quite variable in height, and they usually intergrade in size, possibly indicating the fact that those which arose last in the cambium have yet to attain their maximum height and width. Such varisized rays are usually staggered in the plane in question. Persimmon (*Diospyros virginiana* L.), yellow buckeye (*Aesculus octandra* Marsh.), and many tropical timbers exhibit ripple marks on the tangential surface, occasioned by storied rays or by these and storied longitudinal elements as well. Tiered rays are quite uniform in height, provided that they are restricted to one story. However, in certain storied woods, some of the rays are but one story high, whereas others are much taller and extend through several stories. In such instances ray height is variable, even though the wood exhibits ripple marks.

Oak (Text Fig. 45, *G* and *H*) is peculiar in possessing two kinds of rays between which there are no gradations, large rays hundreds of cells high along the grain (1) and low uniseriate rays (2) which are only a few cells in height. Sycamore, among hardwoods, also has rays that are unusually large (Text Fig. 45, *C* and *D*); these should not be confused with the oak-type rays that are features of *Quercus*. Though most of the rays are large in sycamore, smaller rays are present, and gradations occur between these and the large rays. Multiseriate rays frequently flare where they cross the boundaries of growth rings (Text Fig. 45, *C*). This phenomenon is possibly correlated with changes that took place in the cambium, when it was at this point, incident to the beginning of the dormant season. Depressions occur in the ring boundary on the flanks of the large rays in oak and red alder.

3. The Spacing of Wood Rays in Porous Wood.—The rays of porous woods differ not only in size (width and height) but also in their spacing. Ray spacing in hardwoods can be studied to best advantage on transverse surfaces and in transverse sections. It is computed by noting the number of rays, per millimeter, that cross the boundary of a ring; the upper and lower figures, rather than the average figure, are recorded, as for example, rays six to nine per millimeter, etc.

Table XIV indicates the range of ray spacing encountered in porous woods and gives convenient descriptive terms to record the degree of spacing. In most domestic timbers, the spacing is normal; *i.e.*, the rays average six to nine per millimeter. Red-gum, the species of *Nyssa*, hophornbeam, and buckeye have close rays, so close in fact that often half of the area of a transverse surface of the wood appears to consist of ray tissue. This circumstance is used to advantage in the Key for the identification of woods, based on features visible with the naked eye and hand lens (see page 386).

TABLE XIV

SPACING OF WOOD RAYS IN POROUS WOOD

5 or less rays per mm	Widely spaced
6–9 rays per mm	Normally spaced
10–13 rays per mm	Fairly close
14–20 rays per mm	Close
21 or more	Extremely close

It is well to point out here that the figure of wood, particularly that presented on the radial surface, is affected in no small measure by the size attained by the rays and by their spacing. Some woods possess low, closely spaced, but relatively conspicuous ray flecks (Exs., tulip-poplar, magnolia, maple, dogwood, sourwood). This is due to the fact that the rays are relatively close, as viewed in the tangential plane, and are several-seriate through the central portion; this causes them to register in any given radial plane, even though this is not median, lengthwise, to every ray showing in it. Ray flecks are never conspicuous in willow (*Salix spp.*), poplar (*Populus spp.*), and buckeye, for the rays, though high, are uniseriate and the radial plane does not follow a ray for any distance. In basswood, the flecking is open, and the flecks, though relatively inconspicuous, are usually high. This last condition is occasioned by the fact that the rays in turn are high, but they are too narrow and too widely spaced across the grain to register other than occasionally on the radial surface. Only the large rays of oak are in evidence on the quarter, as flecks; since the large rays of this timber are spaced at fairly wide and irregular intervals across the grain, the flecks of quartered oak are quite widely spaced.

Rays may or may not be visible with the naked eye on the tangential face of wood, depending upon their size. Where they are in evidence, this feature can be used to separate certain woods from others in which the rays are invisible or in which they show but are of a different size or have a different spacing. For example, rays are not visible on the tangential surface of birch but show in maple, a wood that is frequently confused with birch. Maple can be distinguished from beech in that the latter is comparable with oak in possessing unusually large and small rays. Only the large rays show in flat-sawn lumber in beech; they are larger, more conspicuous, and more widely spaced than those of maple. In sycamore, the rays are so closely spaced as to appear like pencil markings on the tangential surface of the wood, in contrast to the figure of beech in this plane which is more open.

4. The Volume of Porous Wood Occupied by Wood Rays.—The ray volumes of porous woods, as well as those of coniferous timbers, undoubtedly exert an important influence on the varying properties exhibited by these woods. This statement holds particularly as regards checking and also, to some extent at least, as regards strength, penetrability with preservatives, etc.

Data on the volume of porous wood occupied by wood rays can be obtained by the method described on page 122 of the text. Reference is again made to the work of J. E. Myer,[1] who also compiled data on the ray volumes of hardwoods; some of the results that he obtained are incorporated in Table XV.

Of the hardwoods studied by Myer, the two *Tilia* species had the lowest ray volumes; the highest was registered in tan-oak [*Lithocarpus densiflorus* (Hook. & Arn.) Rehd.]. The greater number of species possessed ray volumes between 10 and 20 per cent. The average ray volume of all the porous woods examined by Myer was 17.0 per cent; of the conifers that he studied, 7.8 per cent. This substantiates a statement previously made in the text that the parenchyma content of porous woods is much higher than that of conifers; this statement is still valid when the ray parenchyma only is considered.

Ray volume is contingent upon the size attained by the rays and the number (spacing) of rays. It varies not only in different kinds of wood, but also within a species and at different places in the same tree. The variation within a tree is discussed further on page 251, under the caption, Variation in Structure and Specific Gravity of Branch, Trunk, and Root Wood.

According to Myer, the larger variations in the volume of the rays in wood are due to inheritance resulting from long periods of change brought about by diverse ecological conditions. The smaller individual variations are the result of differences in site, climate, temperature, soil, age, the location in the tree, the efficiency of the leaves, and the development of the deciduous habit.

5. The Composition of Wood Rays in Porous Wood.—The composition of wood rays in porous woods depends, of course, upon the kinds of cells entering into their structure. A hardwood ray may consist entirely

[1] See footnote, p. 155.

TABLE XV

AVERAGE RAY VOLUMES OF HARDWOODS OF THE UNITED STATES
(Arranged in Botanical Sequence, by Genera)

Scientific name	Average ray volume, per cent	Variation in samples examined, per cent
Juglans cinerea	8.6	2.0
Juglans nigra	16.8	3.7
Carya cordiformis	16.8	7.8
Carya ovata	19.9	9.4
Populus deltoides	13.7	5.8
Populus grandidentata	11.0	5.6
Populus tremuloides	9.6	4.4
Betula lenta	16.6	6.4
Betula lutea	10.7	0.9
Betula nigra	15.8	3.3
Betula papyrifera	11.0	5.6
Betula populifolia	9.3	2.2
Fagus grandifolia	20.4	5.3
Castanea dentata	11.9	3.3
Quercus borealis	21.2	
Quercus rubra	18.8	
Quercus velutina	31.3	
Quercus alba	27.9	
Quercus bicolor	29.7	
Quercus montana	25.3	
Quercus virginiana	32.2	
Ulmus americana	11.4	7.2
Ulmus fulva	13.0	4.2
Ulmus thomasi	18.6	3.8
Celtis occidentalis	13.3	3.0
Magnolia acuminata	13.8	3.5
Liriodendron tulipifera	14.2	2.5
Liquidambar styraciflua	18.3	1.8
Platanus occidentalis	19.2	3.7
Prunus serotina	17.2	3.4
Gleditsia triacanthos	18.4	3.3
Robinia pseudoacacia	20.9	3.1
Acer macrophyllum	18.4	3.8
Acer rubrum	13.3	2.2
Acer saccharinum	11.9	5.0
Acer saccharum	17.9	5.2
Tilia americana	6.0	3.8
Tilia heterophylla	5.3	2.0
Nyssa sylvatica	17.3	9.7
Fraxinus americana	11.9	4.9
Fraxinus nigra	12.0	7.1
Fraxinus oregona	14.5	4.4
Catalpa speciosa	13.3	2.4

of transverse elements without the inclusion of other tissue or longitudinal xylary elements may be mingled with ray parenchyma (transverse elements) in the ray. Certain hardwoods possess rays with transverse canals. These kinds of rays are discussed separately in the paragraphs that follow.

a. Rays Consisting Entirely of Transverse Elements.—When the rays of hardwoods are composed entirely of transverse elements, these are, except in rare and unimportant exceptions, entirely parenchymatous. There are no cells in the rays of porous woods comparable to the ray tracheids of conifers.

 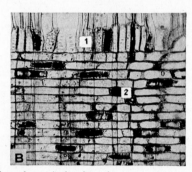

TEXT FIG. 46.—Composition of rays in hardwoods.
A. Homogeneous ray (*r*) in sycamore (*Platanus occidentalis* L.) consisting entirely of "procumbent" cells. (125 ×.) *B.* Heterogeneous ray (*r*) in red-gum (*Liquidambar styraciflua* L.) consisting of marginal upright (1) and of procumbent (2) cells. (125 ×.)

In such wholly parenchymatous rays, the cells are muriform in their arrangement when viewed in radial aspect at sufficiently high magnification; *i.e.*, they appear like bricks in a wall. To continue this analogy further, if the bricks are laid so that the long axis of each is aligned lengthwise of the wall, *i.e.*, horizontally (Text Fig. 46, *A*), the ray is called a **homogeneous ray.** A ray thus constituted consists of horizontally elongated cells which appear to be very much alike. Since the long axes of the cells are horizontal, they are designated as **procumbent cells.** If, on the other hand, some of the bricks are laid as above and others are set on end, *i.e.*, so that their long axes are at right angles to those of the procumbent bricks, then the ray is a **heterogeneous ray** (Text Fig. 46, *B*); it consists of two kinds of cells in terms of shape. The cells that are directed vertically in the standing tree are called **upright cells** (1) in contrast to the procumbent cells (2) which are aligned in the other direction.

The normal position for upright cells is on the upper and lower margins of the ray where they comprise one or more rows. If but one row is present on each margin of the ray, the upright cells composing it tend toward the rectangular (*r*), are directed along the grain, of course, and the exposed end is often rounded (Text Fig. 46, *B*1).   When several rows of upright cells are in evidence, the cells in the upper and lower marginal rows are shaped as described above, but the others in the body of the ray are frequently square or nearly so, as viewed radially.   Additional rows of upright cells, separated from the cells of this nature on the margins of the ray by layers of procumbent cells, characterize the rays of certain woods.   In others, the upright cells are confined to single marginal rows. Some woods contain several-seriate heterogeneous rays with caudate extensions of one to several upright cells (*t*) which are accompanied by uniseriate rays consisting entirely of upright cells [Ex., holly (*Ilex opaca* Ait.)].   In such instances, care must be exercised not to confuse uniseriate rays of this type with strand parenchyma, viewed in the same plane.   When upright cells are situated on the flanks of a multiseriate ray or a portion of such a ray and form a sheath or a partial sheath around some of the procumbent cells, they are called **sheath cells.**[1]

Intergradations between rays which are homogeneous and those which are obviously heterogeneous are frequently encountered in wood.   In such cases, the nature of the rays is of little value diagnostically.   In other cases, woods that might otherwise be confused can be separated by this character alone.   Sassafras is frequently mistaken by students for black ash; the rays in the former range from homogeneous to heterogeneous, while ash possesses rays that are strictly homogeneous.   *Salix spp.* are characterized by rays that are heterogeneous; *Populus spp.* have rays that are essentially homogeneous.   The same holds as between hackberry and the elms.

b. Rays Consisting of Ray Parenchyma (Transverse Elements) and of Included Longitudinal Elements (Tracheary Tissue).—Certain woods are characterized by rays of two kinds: narrow and usually uniseriate rays, which are to all appearances spaced normally as viewed on transverse surfaces or in transverse sections; and congeries, or clusters, of such narrow rays which are closely spaced but between which there is tracheary tissue.   The term "aggregate ray" has been assigned to such a congery of smaller rays.   An **aggregate ray** is a large ray comparable in size to the large rays of oak, but composed of smaller rays and included fibers and sometimes of vessels as well (Text Fig. 45, *E*, 1-1*ᵃ*).   The nature of such a ray is very evident when it is viewed in tangential aspect (*F*, 1-1*ᵃ*).

Aggregate rays are features of such woods as red alder, blue-beech, tan-oak, and some *Quercus spp.*   They may be relatively abundant

---

[1] Heterogeneous rays of peculiar type characterize certain woods, sometimes the woods of an entire plant family.   The description of these does not fall within the province of this text.

(blue-beech) or relatively infrequent when they are often spaced at wide and irregular intervals.   This last is true of red alder (Plate XII, Fig. 70).   Sizable samples of this wood are often devoid of aggregate rays. Provision has been made in the Keys to permit of the identification of such samples.

c. *Rays Composed in Part of Epithelial Cells.*—Transverse canals occur in the rays of some tropical hardwoods; when present, they are generally of the normal type.   The epithelial cells encircling the tubular cavities of such canals fall into the category of parenchyma.   Transverse gum canals are not features of any of the domestic hardwoods discussed in this text.   However, space is allocated to a discussion of these structures here, since it serves to round out the subject matter incorporated in Table XII, Elements of Porous Wood.[1]

As stated previously, transverse canals and longitudinal canals seldom occur in the same porous wood.[2]   When in evidence, transverse canals are invariably confined to rays and are present only in occasional rays, a situation that is true of the conifers.   In hardwoods, if a canal-containing ray is wide, its contour, as seen in tangential sections, is not affected by the presence of the canal.   Narrow rays, on the other hand, are fusiform, as viewed in tangential sections.   Usually, there is only one canal in a ray, but occasionally two or more occur.   The tubular cavity of the canal, as in coniferous woods, is postcambial in its development and arises schizogenously, *i.e.*, by the separation of cells (cells that develop into epithelium), the line of fission taking place in the true middle lamella between cells which prior to this time were contiguous.

6. The Nature of the Transverse Cells Composing the Rays of Porous Woods.—The transverse cells of the rays of porous woods consist entirely of those classified as ray parenchyma, or of these and epithelial cells when transverse gum canals are included in the rays.   The natures of these two kinds of cells are considered separately in the text.

a. *The Nature of Ray Parenchyma and of Its Inclusions.*—Ray paren-

---

[1] In certain specific cases, the rays of hardwood are pierced by a tubular cavity which is of a different nature from that of a transverse canal.   Laticiferous and tanniferous tubes fall into this class; they can be distinguished from transverse canals in that the cavity thus formed is, in reality, a tubular cell which is greatly elongated lengthwise of the ray.   Lysigenous gum cysts, *i.e.*, cavities resulting from the disintegration of the cells, are reported in the rays of woods belonging to the Myrsinaceae. Dry intercellular cavities, apparently comparable to those which arise in the pith in the stems of many plants when growth is unusually rapid, have also been described as characterizing the rays of certain woods; they occur in soft and succulent stems of rapid growth.

[2] They are reported in certain woods of the Indo-Malayan region belonging to the Dipterocarpaceae.

chyma cells vary widely in shape and size,[1] in the thickness of their walls, in the character of their pitting, and in their contents. The end walls may be vertical, oblique, or bowed. In radial aspect, the cells are usually rectangular (brick-shaped), particularly those in the body of the ray, but sometimes they are enlarged near the middle. Marginal upright cells are generally elongated along the grain and are frequently very irregular in form.

The pits of ray parenchyma are generally simple and minute, but occasionally they are bordered and relatively large. The pitting may be equally abundant on all the walls or more abundant on some than on others. Frequently, the lateral walls of the upright cells are copiously and conspicuously pitted (Exs., red-gum, willow), whereas pits are sparse or wanting altogether on the lateral walls of the procumbent cells. Where ray and longitudinal strand parenchyma are in contact, sieve pitting is frequently in evidence. Pits generally lead laterally from ray parenchyma to vessels and the various kinds of tracheids, and their nature is often strongly influenced by the nature of the complementary pit of the pit pair in the wall of the tracheary element. Frequently, pits are wanting between ray parenchyma and libriform fibers. Intercellular spaces are frequent in ray tissue—indeed, they are the general rule. This is indicative of the fact that wood rays are important as avenues of aeration radially in a tree. Blind pits often lead from ray parenchyma to interstitial cavities of this sort.

The cells of ray parenchyma in hardwoods, like those of the longitudinal parenchyma, frequently contain inclusions. These are generally amorphous and gummy in nature, but crystals are sometimes present. In instances like the last, the two kinds of deposits may be set aside in separate cells, or both may occur in the same cell. In certain woods, occasional ray cells develop into oil cysts. Sassafras (Text Fig. 47) is characterized by ray cysts of this kind. The persistent odor of this wood, on freshly exposed surfaces, is traceable to the contents of such cells. It is not at all unusual to find some of the cells of a ray with inclusions while others are quite empty.

All the ray cells or only certain of these may be occluded with gum. At other times, only traces of gum are present; in such instances, the gum may occur as small globules of varying sizes or may form gum plugs at the end of the cells, particularly of the procumbent cells. The pit pairs through the end walls of ray parenchyma are often sharply defined because of the presence of gum in the cavities of the complementary pits.

Traces of gummy deposits are present in the ray parenchyma of

---

[1] They are shorter than the tracheary elements of wood; most of them pass through the screens in the wash water when hardwoods are pulped.

many woods, in fact, in woods that are normally considered to be quite free of deposits of this sort. There is considerable evidence to the effect that amorphous deposits first begin to collect in wood in the ray parenchyma. As they become increasingly copious in amount, they spill over into the longitudinal parenchyma. In certain woods, this, too, eventually becomes completely occluded, and then even the fibrous tissue may serve

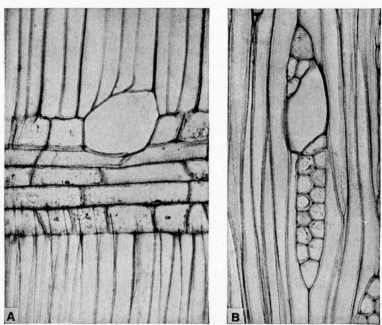

TEXT FIG. 47.—Oil cells in the wood rays of sassafras [*Sassafras albidum* (Nutt.) Nees].
   A. Wood ray in a radial section, showing one oil cell (240 ×). *B.* Wood ray in a tangential section, showing one oil cell (240 ×).

as a repository. Genuine ebony (*Diospyros ebenum* Koenig) is black, not because the substance composing the walls of the xylary cells is black, but because of the presence of dark-colored gummy infiltration which pervades the lumina of all the cells composing the wood. The gummy deposits in vessels sometimes appear to form quite independently of those elsewhere in the wood.

The chemistry of the gummy deposits of wood does not fall within the scope of this manual. They vary greatly in nature, and some of them are exceedingly complex chemically.

The crystal content of xylary parenchyma, which includes ray parenchyma, is discussed in Sec. V of this chapter.

   b. The Nature and Function of Epithelial Cells Encircling the Cavities of Transverse Canals in the Rays.—The epithelial cells of the transverse canals of hardwoods exhibit the same variation as is encountered in those encircling the cavities of longitudinal canals. They arise from the same cambial initials as give rise to the other cells of the ray; the long axis of the cell is, of course, directed lengthwise of the ray. The wall of the cell may be thin, quite evenly thickened throughout, or thinner where the cell margins the cavity of the canal. Thick-walled epithelial cells of rays are usually provided with simple pits and apparently are lignified. This last statement must be tentative until such time as the procedure followed by chemists in the determination of lignin can be applied to cells of this type.

The epithelial cells of the transverse canals of hardwoods function as organs of excretion. The contents of the canals may be fluid or solid; in the latter instance, the deposits range from white or yellow through shades of red and brown to almost black. Fluid deposits often leach out of transverse canals and discolor the surface of the wood. This also holds for longitudinal canals in certain instances where these are present in hardwoods (Exs., species of *Eperua* and *Hardwickia* of the Leguminosae).

IV. NORMAL AND TRAUMATIC GUM CANALS IN POROUS WOODS

Gum canals, as has already been stated, occur in some porous woods. When present, they may be normal to the wood or of traumatic (wound) origin.

Normal gum canals occupy the same positions in porous wood as the resin canals of conifers; they extend with the grain, embedded in longitudinal elements, or across the grain in the wood rays.[1] The two types, however, are seldom present in the same wood, as noted previously; *i.e.*, the canals are usually either longitudinal or transverse in a given wood.

Gum canals are not present as normal structures in any of the domestic woods covered by this text. Normal longitudinal gum canals feature the dipterocarp woods of the Indo-Malayan region and are an important diagnostic feature employed in separating these timbers from those of other plant families. For example, Philippine mahogany, so called, is of dipterocarp origin; it can be distinguished readily from American and African mahogany by the presence of normal longitudinal gum canals which are lacking in the American and African woods. The timbers of certain genera of the Legume Family also are featured by such longitudinal canals.

Normal transverse canals feature the woods of some genera belonging to the Anacardiaceae and Burseraceae. In such instances, they are invariably present while in allied genera of the same family they are wanting. When transverse canals are present, an occasional ray is fusi-

[1] WEBBER, IRMA E. Intercellular Cavities in the Rays of Dicotyledenous Woods. *De Lilloa* [Argentina], II, 465–469. 1938.

form, as viewed in a tangential section, and the gum canal is embedded in it.

The traumatic canals of coniferous woods, as already related, are of schizogenous origin; they result from the separation of cells at the middle lamella and are longitudinal (Text Fig. 36, *A*) or transverse. Those of porous woods, in contrast, may form in one of two ways, or by a combination of these, and are restricted to the longitudinal type. On the one hand, they may arise schizogeneously (schizogenous canals) in the same manner as in conifers. In such cases, they are arranged in a tangential row, rarely in more than one row, as viewed in cross sections (Text Fig. 36, *B*). Or they may result from the actual disintegration (gummosis) of cell walls in which case they are of lysigenous origin (lysigenous canals; Text Fig. 36, *C* and *D*). If a longitudinal gum canal is formed as a result of these two processes, *i.e.*, schizolysigenously, the cavity first develops through cell fission, followed subsequently by the enlargement of the cavity through disintegration (gummosis) of the cells immediately surrounding it. In their final stages of development, longitudinal lysigenous canals cannot be distinguished from those produced schizolysigenously.

For a reason apparent from the preceding paragraph, the traumatic schizogenous canals of porous woods are provided with epithelium; those of lysigenous origin are devoid of such a layer. Since the lysigenous canals result from cell-wall disintegration, they are generally much larger (often ⅛ inch or more in diameter) than schizogenous canals. Lysigenous canals generally are arranged in tangential rows when viewed across the grain, like the longitudinal traumatic canals of conifers, and often are conspicuous to the naked eye because of their size and gummy contents. Along the grain, the cavity may be continuous or the canal may appear as an axial series of cysts separated by tracts of wound tissue.

Traumatic schizogenous gum canals are occasionally encountered in red-gum (Text Fig. 36, *B*). They do not appear elsewhere in the woods covered by this text. Traumatic lysigenous canals are not infrequent in cherry (Text Fig. 36, *D*) in which wood they sometimes form as a result of the work of cambial miners (see page 335). Gummosis resulting in the formation of traumatic lysigenous canals (Text Fig. 36, *C*) is a serious disease of citrous trees in some sections, and much space has been devoted to it in the literature. Traumatic lysigenous canals occur under the stress of unusual conditions in the woods of many plant families among which may be enumerated the Rosaceae, Myrtaceae, Meliaceae, Boraginaceae, Rutaceae, and Sterculiaceae.

As holds for the gummy deposits of wood in general, the chemical nature of the contents of the traumatic schizogenous and lysigenous canals of porous wood does not fall within the sphere of this text. Nor are the canals of this sort of significance diagnostically, for they are too sporadic in their distribution.

V. CRYSTALLIFEROUS XYLARY PARENCHYMA IN POROUS WOODS

The presence and the rarity of crystals in coniferous woods were discussed briefly on page 163. The situation is otherwise in porous woods in which crystals are not at all unusual. This discrepancy in crystal content of hardwoods and softwoods is possibly explained in part by the fact that the growth characteristics of hardwoods are quite different from those of softwoods, in part because porous woods have a much higher percentage of parenchyma that can become crystalliferous.

The xylary parenchyma of porous wood has been discussed previously in this chapter; the term is inclusive and embraces all the parenchymatous cells of the wood. To repeat, some of these are longitudinal, *i.e.*, have their long axes directed along the grain; others, as ray parenchyma, are directed horizontally and radially in the standing tree and constitute the tissue of the wood rays. As recorded on page 221, three kinds of longitudinal parenchyma are recognized: (1) longitudinal (strand) parenchyma, (2) fusiform parenchyma cells, and (3) epithelial cells. The rays of domestic hardwoods consist entirely of ray parenchyma, or of this and longitudinal tracheary elements (aggregate rays).

The xylary parenchyma of porous wood, the epithelial cells excepted, may be crystalliferous (Text Figs. 48 and 49).[1] In such instances the crystals are largely, if not entirely, confined to the strand and to the ray parenchyma. They may be in evidence in both these types of cells or be restricted in a given wood to one or to the other.

When crystals form in longitudinal strand parenchyma, a single cell (unit) of the strand may be transformed into a crystal locule, or two (Text Fig. 48, *B*) or more cells may serve as crystal repositories, the remainder functioning as normal cells. Consequently a strand may be in part crystalliferous and in part devoid of crystals, with the two sorts of cells in no definite order. Since the crystal-bearing cells are usually somewhat enlarged (and contain crystals unless these have been dissolved by the chemical treatment of the wood), they can readily be distinguished from those which are devoid of crystals. Not infrequently, one or more units of a strand of longitudinal parenchyma will divide once or twice, forming two or a longitudinally directed linear tetrad of four crystal locules, respectively. If the last results in two or more consecutive units of a

---

[1] Crystals are not restricted to the xylary parenchyma of porous wood. They sometimes, though rarely, occur in tyloses and separate fibers.

strand, a catenate longitudinal row of crystal locules extending along the grain is the result.

If the rays of a wood are homogeneous, the crystal-bearing ray cells are, of necessity, the type known as procumbent. In such cases, a cell, if it is to become a crystal locule, usually develops into such a structure without further division (Text Fig. 49). Crystalliferous cells may occur sporadically or abundantly in the tissue of homogeneous rays.

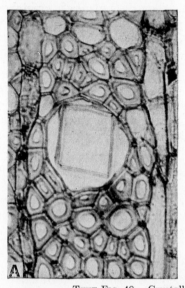 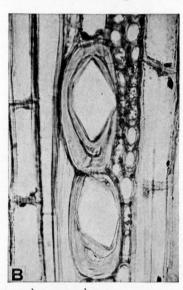

TEXT FIG. 48.—Crystalliferous xylary parenchyma.
  A. Crystal locule in an enlarged cell of longitudinal (strand) parenchyma (x), in bitter-nut hickory [*Carya cordiformis* (Wangh.) K. Koch] (550 ×). The crystal has been dissolved by the acid used in softening the wood. B. Crystal locules in two sclerosed cells of longitudinal (strand) parenchyma (t), in black walnut (*Juglans nigra* L.) (385 ×). As in A, the crystals have been dissolved.

More or less of a tendency is manifested sometimes toward the restriction of crystals to certain of the horizontal rows of procumbent ray cells.

In heterogeneous rays of the type that feature red-gum, crystals, when present, occur more frequently in the upright cells. A cell of this sort may become a crystal locule without undergoing any modification or may divide by a cross wall (usually a horizontal wall) into two locules. Rarely, more than two locules are formed from one upright cell.

In xylary tissue, crystal locules seldom contain more than one crystal. **Rhomboidal crystals** are most frequently encountered (Text Fig. 49). In certain species of *Eugenia* of the Myrtaceae, gravelike deposits of varisized, uniformly shaped crystals are present in the locules. Certain species of *Dillenia* of the Indo-Malayan region have sheathlike bundles

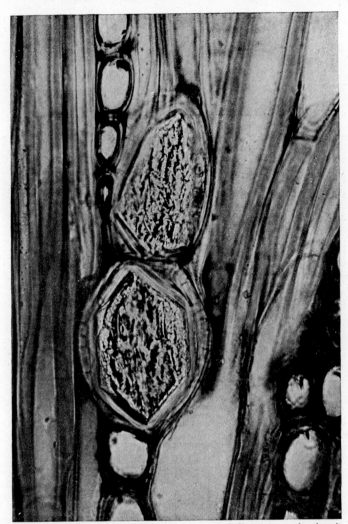

TEXT FIG. 49.—Crystalliferous xylary parenchyma. Solitary crystals, *in situ*, in the ray parenchyma of yellow birch (*Betula lutea* Michx. f.) (590 ×). (*Photomicrograph by Bror L. Grondal.*)

of long acicular crystals known as **raphides** in their xylary parenchyma. Clustered crystals in globose masses called **druses** characterize the phloem parenchyma of many trees but seldom occur in the wood.

The chemical nature of crystals varies widely in plant tissues. Crystals of calcium oxalate are by far the most common (this holds for xylary tissue), but other salts of calcium and of various other inorganic substances also crystallize; likewise many organic substances. Crystals

STUDENT'S NAME: _____

CHART FOR RECORDING ANATOMICAL DATA, HARDWOODS

No.	Scientific name	I Top of wood	II Vessels						III Tracheids		IV Longitudinal parenchyma				V Fibers			VI Wood rays						Remarks
		A B C	A	B	C	D	E	F	A	B	A	B	C	D	A	B	C	A	B	C	D	E	F	
			a								a				a				a	a	a	a		
			b					a		a	b				b		b		b	b	b	b	b	
			c						1	b	c						c		c	c	c	c		
			d						2		d												a	
			e								e												b	
1	*Liquidambar styraciflua*	C	65μ	b	b	b d	b 20–25 thin	a 1			c d	∞*			a	5–8μ	a b c	7–9	a	a	a	a b c	a b	30μ 455μ	Spiral thickening in vessels confined to tips of the vessel segments
2	*Robinia pseudoacacia*	A	410μ	b	b	a c	a a	a 1			a d e		2 and 4	C	b	4–5μ	b	3–7	a	a	a	a b	a b	45μ 280μ	Tyloses completely occluding the pores in the heartwood

* The sign of infinity (∞) is used when the strands are so long that the cells cannot be readily counted in thin longitudinal sections of the wood.

LEGEND FOR CHART ON POROUS WOODS

I. Topography of wood
  A. Ring porous
  B. Semi-ring porous
  C. Diffuse porous

II. Vessels
  A. Arrangement of pores in summerwood
    a. Solitary or in short radial rows of 2-3
    b. In radial rows of 4 or more
    c. In radially aligned, flame-shaped tracts
    d. In wavy tangential bands
    e. In nests of several to many
  B. Size: maximum tangential diameter of largest springwood pores
  C. Spiral thickening (Plate XX, Fig. 109)
    a. Wanting
    b. Present
  D. Shape and arrangement of intervessel pits (intertracheary pits when vessels are not contiguous)
    a. Rounded or polygonal (Plate XX, Fig. 116)
    b. Linear (Plate XXI, Fig. 120)
    c. Spirally arranged (Plate XXI, Fig. 123)
    d. In transverse rows (Plate XXII, Figs. 127 and 128)
  E. Nature of the perforations (Text Fig. 40)
    a. Simple
    b. Scalariform (number and nature of bars)
    c. Reticulate
  F. Inclusions (Text Fig. 41)
    a. Tyloses
      1. Thin-walled
      2. Thick-walled
    b. Gum

III. Tracheids (Text Fig. 42)
  A. Wanting
  B. Present
    a. Vasicentric
    b. Vascular

IV. Longitudinal parenchyma (Text Fig. 44)
  A. Arrangement
    a. Terminal
    b. Metatracheal
    c. Metatracheal-diffuse
    d. Paratracheal
    e. Paratracheal-zonate
  B. Number of cells in wood parenchyma strands
  C. Fusiform parenchyma cells present
  D. Inclusion (crystals) (Text Fig. 49)

V. Fibers
  A. Type
    a. Fiber tracheids
    b. Libriform fibers
  B. Thickness of the walls
  C. Modifications
    a. Septate
    b. Gelatinous (Text Fig. 43)
    c. With spiral thickening

VI. Wood rays (Text Fig. 45)
  A. Number per millimeter tangentially
  B. Kind
    a. Simple
    b. Aggregate
    c. Oak-type
  C. Arrangement
    a. Unstoried
    b. Storied
  D. Seriation
    a. 1-seriate
    b. 2-seriate
    c. 3-seriate or more
  E. Composition (Text Fig. 46)
    a. Homogeneous
    b. Heterogeneous
    c. Oil cells present (Text Fig. 47)
  F. Size
    a. Average width in microns
    b. Average height in microns

form while the protoplast of the cell is still functioning and frequently appear to be enclosed in an angular sac which is attached to the wall of the cell (Text Fig. 48, *A*).   Since crystals are frequently dissolved by the chemical treatment that wood undergoes prior to sectioning, the cavity of such a sac, shaped like the crystal that it originally contained, is frequently mistaken for the crystal itself.   (Compare Text Fig. 48, in which the crystals have been dissolved by the chemical treatment of the wood with Text Fig. 49 showing crystals *in situ*.)

In porous woods no correlation exists between the presence of crystals and plant classification: this is in contrast to the statement already made on page 163 that crystals are restricted to woods of the Pinaceae in the conifers.   In rare instances, the presence or absence of crystals in porous woods is of diagnostic significance; for example, the strand parenchyma of black walnut (*Juglans nigra* L.) contains crystals, whereas they are lacking in this location in butternut (*J. cinerea* L.).

The crystals that occur in porous wood, in fact in any wood and elsewhere in plant tissues, are probably by-products of metabolism, as has already been stated.   When especially abundant, they may have a dulling effect on tools.   This is said to hold for Colombian mahogany (*Cariniana pyriformis* Mier) of Colombia and Venezuela, a wood that otherwise enjoys an excellent reputation.

VI. SUGGESTIONS FOR RECORDING ANATOMICAL DATA ON POROUS WOODS

Following the plan suggested near the end of Chap. VII for recording anatomical data on coniferous woods (see page 163), a chart for hardwoods and the explanatory legend are submitted herewith.   The results of the examination of samples of two porous woods are given in the chart.

A chart of the type submitted can be altered to suit the convenience of the user, in terms of the time available for the study of each sample, the nature and completeness of the data desired, etc.   By examining a number of samples of the same wood and recording the data in the chart, one can accurately estimate the range of anatomical variation that may be expected in a species.   The use of a chart of the type portrayed provides a systematic method of approach to the subject of the comparative anatomy of porous woods.

CHAPTER X

VARIABLE QUALITY OF WOOD WITHIN A TREE-SPECIES

The assertion is sometimes made that no two pieces of wood, even of the same kind, are exactly alike. Long before this, the reader should have grasped the fundamental verity of such a statement. The possible structural departures within the limit of vision that are traceable to fluctuation in cell sorting, cell size, and cell-wall thickness are well-nigh infinite. Add to these the known variation in the physical and chemical composition of cell walls *in situ* that requires special technique for its demonstration, and the variable quality of wood within a tree-species, in fact within one and the same tree, cannot be questioned. Chapter X is concerned with subject matter pertinent to this subject.

I. QUALITY OF A WOOD IN RELATION TO POSITION IN THE TREE

As the reader's acquaintance with wood becomes more intimate, he should be increasingly aware of the existence of wide structural variations in this tissue, not only among species in the same and in different genera but also among different individuals of the same species. In the last instance, some of these variations can undoubtedly be attributed to the influence of site on the rate and the nature of tree growth; others fall within the category of normal anatomical departures from the mean in different individuals of a species; *i.e.*, they are variations that statisticians would include within the limits of a "normal anatomical population." It now remains to determine whether or not the structural and physical characteristics exhibited by a piece of wood are influenced in some measure by its original position in the tree. The discussion that follows is intended to provide an answer to this question; it is based upon information amassed by various investigators.

A. VARIATION IN STRUCTURE, SPECIFIC GRAVITY, AND STRENGTH

1. At a Given Height.—The question of anatomical variation in the wood of a tree trunk in two planes, outward from the pith at a given height and upward, has long been a subject of research. Most investigators have concerned themselves largely with textural variations and, to much lesser degree, with fluctuations, at different heights in the tree, in the percentage of the volume occupied by cells of a given type. Specific information dealing with the variation in the shape, structure, and arrangement of the several xylary elements at different places, horizontally and vertically, in a tree is very meager.

As is to be expected, many of the data collected by different investigators, even from the same species, are contradictory. The reason for this, in addition to differences that can be ascribed to varying technique and the method of interpreting data, is traceable to the fact that, though significant anatomical variations are present throughout the tree, these are easily beclouded or modified by outside (environmental) factors which have a profound effect on tree growth. It follows, therefore, that, unless deductions are drawn from materials that are comparable in every way, they are of little value or significance. This observation becomes all the more pertinent when data from one species are compared with those from another in an attempt to formulate postulations that would be applicable to a group of species. Only those results are presented here that appear to be well substantiated by two or more investigators, working independently. It is convenient to present this information as a series of statements.

a. The wood produced in the trunk in the early stages of its development at any given height differs from that formed subsequently. This discrepancy is occasioned by the rapid increase, at this level, in the size of the cells of each category in successive growth increments from the pith outward. The rate of this increase in cell dimensions and its duration[1] are extremely variable, not only among different species but even among individuals of the same species.[2]

Closely associated with these changes in cell size are variations in the shape and sorting of the cells of the wood. For example, vessel members from the first annual increment may have a quite different shape from those in growth layers farther out from the pith; or the number of vessels per unit of volume of the wood may be different in the regions mentioned.

b. There is some disagreement among investigators as to what happens following the initial period of rapid increase in cell dimensions. One group claims that cell size does not become stabilized at any given tree age; to the contrary, it holds that there is a slow but irregular increase in the lengths of the mature cells of each category through successive xylary increments as the tree ages (150 plus years) after which shortening

---

[1] In the species which have been investigated and on which, therefore, data are available, this period fluctuates between a minimum of 5 to 10 years to a maximum of 50 to 60 years.

[2] The rate of cell-size increase is also different at different heights in the tree.

occurs.[1] Other workers,[2] in contrast, present evidence to the effect that fiber length increases from the earlier rings outward for a period of years, after which it remains constant.

c. But scanty information is available relative to the proportionate volume of the wood, at a given level in the trunk, which is occupied by cells of a given kind (type of wood element). In trees with ring-porous wood, the volume of space occupied by vessels in the earlywood portion of the increment increases at a given height in the tree in successive increments, whereas the reverse holds for the volume of fibrous tissue.[3]

d. At any given height in the trunk of a tree, wood density may fluctuate considerably from the pith outward. This depends largely on the rate and quality of growth which in turn are determined by the environmental factors prevailing when any particular section of the stem is formed.

In coniferous species, the wood nearest the center often has the lowest specific gravity. This is due to the wide rings with a greater proportion of springwood that are formed in the early stages of development of these trees. The specific gravity increases toward the outside as the annual rings become successively narrower, a situation that ensues even when a tree maintains its full vigor. In overmature trees the density of the wood may decrease again in the outer annual rings if a reduction in the rate of growth is accompanied by a decrease in the percentage of summerwood. Fluctuations in the specific gravity of coniferous woods occasioned under circumstances as described above are generally accompanied by corresponding variations in the strength of the wood.

In hardwood trees, in comparison, the evidence is conflicting relative to the specific gravity of the wood along a radius of a cross section. Desch,[4] for example, found in the diffuse porous species that he investigated that the same relationship existed as holds for conifers (see preceding paragraph). Paul,[5] on the other hand, arrived at the conclusion

---

[1] Trees vary widely as to their longevity. It is reasonable to presume that the maximum length of the longitudinal xylary cells is reached sooner in short-lived species than in trees living for a century or more.

[2] BETHEL, JAMES S.   The Effect of Position within the Bole upon Fiber Length of Loblolly Pine (*Pinus taeda* L.), *Jour. Forestry*, Vol. 30, pp. 30–33.   1941.

[3] Since there is little difference in the early stages in the development of the main stem (trunk) of a tree and that of a branch, further insight into the features that distinguish "juvenile" wood from that formed during the ensuing period can be gained by referring to pp. 251 to 255 which deal with the characteristics of branch, trunk, and root wood.

[4] DESCH, H. E.   Anatomical Variations in the Wood of Some Dicotyledonous Trees. *New Phytol.*, Vol. 31, pp. 73–118.   1932.

[5] PAUL, B. H.   The Application of Silviculture in Controlling Specific Gravity. *U.S. Dept. Agr., Tech. Bul.* 168.   1930.

that, in broad-leaved trees, wood of high density may be produced at any period in the life of the tree, depending upon the growing conditions prevailing when that particular portion of the trunk was formed.

2. At Different Heights.—*a.* In a given growth increment in the trunk, in both conifers and hardwoods, the size of each type of xylary element (especially the tracheids of conifers and the fibers of hardwoods) increases until a certain height is reached after which a progressive reduction takes place through the crown of the tree. In conifers, according to the evidence available, the tracheids do not attain their maximum lengths at the same height in successive annual increments; the maximum length is reached in the outer layers of the wood, successively, at higher points above the ground.

b. Rather fragmentary information on the distribution of different types of cells at different heights in the tree-trunk indicates that vessel volume, especially in diffuse-porous woods, tends to increase upward in the stem into the crown of the tree. Myer[1] has reported that the ray volume in hemlock, white pine, and sugar maple reaches a maximum at the top of the merchantable stem; a second peak, slightly smaller than the first, occurs at stump height; the minimum is found at the 16-foot level. Turnbull[2] found that in pines the summerwood in any given ring narrows and the springwood widens in ascent, *i.e.*, from the base of the tree upward.

c. In many instances, the variations in specific gravity along the trunk are so irregular that it is not possible to establish any correlation between wood density and height in the tree. In others, there is considerable evidence to support the contention that the wood in the basal portion of the trunk is heavier than that at higher levels. This seems to hold for many species, particularly for conifers. But even in such cases, the data are so conflicting that it is questionable whether the decrease in wood density follows a regular pattern from the base to the apex of the tree.

The situation is different in certain buttressed trees growing in swamps. In these, the wood of the butt log is much lower in specific gravity than that at higher levels in the trunk, and the transition from the light to the heavier wood is quite abrupt. Above the butt swell in such swamp species, however, there is no apparent correlation between wood density and height in the tree.[3]

---

[1] MYER, J. E.   The Structure and Strength of Four North American Woods as Influenced by Range, Habitat, and Position in the Tree.   *N.Y. State Col. Forestry, Syracuse Univ., Tech. Pub.* 31.   1930.

[2] TURNBULL, J. M.   Variations in Strength of Pine Timbers.   *South African Jour. Sci.*, Vol. 33, pp. 653–682.   1937.

[3] PAUL, B. H., and R. O. MARTS.   Growth, Specific Gravity, and Shrinkage of Twelve Delta Hardwoods.   *Jour. Forestry*, Vol. XXXII, pp. 861–873.   1934.

Summation.—This brief discussion of the structure, specific gravity, and strength of wood in relation to position in the tree trunk should serve to indicate that decided departures in these characteristics, particularly in texture, occur at the same level and at different levels in the main stem. Attention has been focused on the fact that the various wood elements increase rapidly in size, outwardly, in the first few growth increments around the pith (in some trees through the first 5 to 10 layers, in others through as many as 50 to 60). This rapid textural increase may also be accompanied by variations in the shape, proportionate amount of, and sorting of the various cell types. For these reasons, the inner core of wood of a tree trunk is quite different in structure and in its physical properties from that subsequently formed after the tree has attained greater maturity. Or conversely, wood produced after a tree is of some age is more uniform in every way than juvenile wood; such variations as occur in old wood, or in what might even be termed "commercial-run" wood, may be credited largely to varying ring width. Finally, the observation has been recorded that the texture of wood fluctuates up and down the stem. Therefore, if texture is to be used as a means of identification, care must be exercised to see that sufficient discrepancy exists in the texture of the two kinds of wood under comparison to offset minor fluctuations in this character occasioned by height in the tree. In general, in wood identification, it is best to avoid samples taken from near the center of a tree since they would not be typical; the same holds, often to an even greater degree, for branch wood.

B. Variation in Structure and Specific Gravity of Branch, Trunk, and Root Wood

As the title implies, this section is devoted to the comparative anatomy and specific gravity of the wood of the tree members mentioned. The information recorded has been taken largely from a thesis[1] in which is incorporated information on four ring-porous, eight diffuse-porous, and eight coniferous woods. Again, in reciting results, it has proved convenient to present this information as a series of statements.

a. The rate of growth was especially variable in the roots and branches. The widest growth increments were invariably found in the trunk, with the notable exception of swamp species (black spruce, tamarack, northern white cedar, and black ash) in which the widest rings occurred in the roots, followed by the bole and branches, in the order mentioned. The branches, in general, tended to enlarge more slowly in diameter than

[1] Fegel, A. C. A Comparison of the Mechanical and Physical Properties, and the Structural Features of Root-, Stem-, and Branch-wood. Thesis for the doctorate. The New York State College of Forestry, Syracuse, N.Y. 1938.

the roots, though exceptions to this rule were noted, especially in the hardwoods.

The growth rings were generally very eccentric in the branches and roots of all species. In conifers, the greatest eccentricity invariably occurred on the lower side of the branches (see Compression Wood, page 288), whereas the reverse held for hardwoods (see Tension Wood, page 293). In roots, the growth increments were thickest on the upper and lower sides, respectively, ensuring a definite I-beam effect. Other investigators have reported that tree roots are characterized by many incomplete (discontinuous) rings, a condition which existed in the species examined by Fegel.

b. In the hardwoods, the vessel volume was highest in the trunk and lowest in the roots (Text Fig. 50). Vessel volume is contingent on the number of vessels and their size. The vessels were most numerous in the branches and least abundant in the roots. Not only were they the most numerous in the branches, but also they were the smallest; the largest vessels occurred in the roots. In the ring-porous species examined, the root wood tended to approach the diffuse-porous condition, an observation that is well substantiated by the work of other investigators. If the theory is accepted that postulates that roots are the most "conservative" organs of the plant in that they retain ancestral characteristics longest, then the condition approaching diffuse porousness observed in the root wood of ring-porous trees can be cited as evidence to the effect that ring-porous species were evolved from those with diffuse-porous wood as a consequence of the rigorous climate prevailing in the North Temperate Zone. Presumably, evolutionary changes are less rapid in roots than in stems and branches because the former are embedded in the soil and hence do not react fundamentally so much to wide, sudden, or periodic changes in air temperatures as do exposed (aerial) parts.

c. The fibers of the hardwoods and the tracheids of the conifers were of smallest diameter in the branches and widest in the roots.

d. In the hardwoods, the shortest fibers and vessel members were found in the branches, the longest in the trunk. In the conifers, in comparison, the tracheids were invariably shorter in the branches than in the trunk and roots; in the two members last mentioned, the root tracheids were shorter than those of the trunk except in red pine and in the white pines, in which they were longer than those in the trunk and branches. This latter observation tallies well with data collected by Eloise Gerry[1] on white and longleaf pines.

---

[1] Gerry, Eloise. Fiber Measurement Studies. *Science*, Vol. 41, No. 1048, p. 179. 1915.

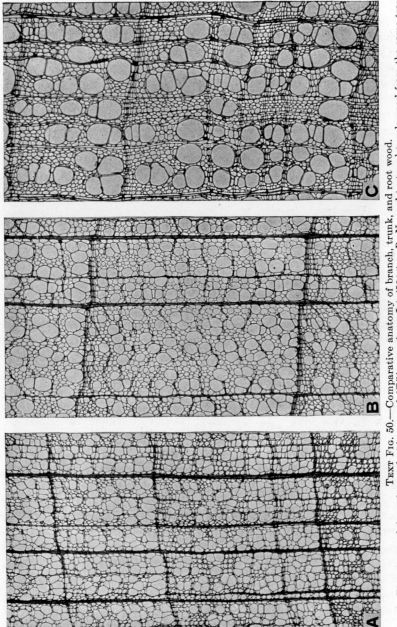

TEXT FIG. 50.—Comparative anatomy of branch, trunk, and root wood.
A. Fine-textured branch wood of basswood (*Tilia americana* L.) (50 ×). *B.* Normal-textured trunk wood from the same tree that produced *A* and *B* (50 ×). *C.* Coarse-textured root wood from the same tree that produced *A* (50 ×).

e. Resin canals in the conifers, if normal in the trunk wood, were also present in the root and branch wood. They were most numerous and smallest in the branches; those in the roots proved to be more numerous than in the trunk, but of about the same size.

f. Wood rays were most numerous in the branches, a circumstance that was equally true of hardwoods and softwoods. In the former, they were least numerous in the trunk; in conifers, on the contrary, in the roots. The greatest ray volume almost invariably occurred in hardwoods in the roots; the ray volumes of the trunk and branches were about equal. There were no significant differences in the ray volumes of the roots, trunk, and branches in conifers.

g. In the hardwoods examined, the wood with the highest specific gravity occurred in the branches, and the roots contained the lightest wood. This last situation was especially evident in the ring-porous species in which the root wood was nearly 20 per cent lighter and the branch wood proved to be 6 per cent heavier than that of the trunk.

In the conifers that were studied, the branch wood was found to be considerably heavier than the trunk wood, averaging 35 per cent heavier for the entire group. The specific gravity of the root wood, however, was found to vary extensively between species, sometimes being higher, at other times, lower, than that of the bole. The normal increase in weight that is to be expected as a logical consequence of a falling growth rate was offset in the root wood of conifers because the tracheids were larger and thinner walled.

Of course, the results cited above were obtained from a relatively small number of tree species and may not hold for all the domestic timber trees covered by this text. To the above comment should be added the observation that some hardwoods possess aggregate rays in the root wood, even though this type of ray is wanting in stem and branches. Examples of this condition have been noted in many oaks and in birch. Proponents of the theory of "conservatism of roots" cite this as an indication that aggregate rays are more primitive than the other types; according to this line of reasoning, aggregate rays gave rise on the one hand to large rays of the oak type (sometimes called "compound rays") through the consolidation of the narrow rays composing them by the elimination of the longitudinal cells (mostly fibers) from the body of the ray, on the other hand to the simple rays that characterize most domestic woods through the spreading, fanwise, of the ray components of the aggregate rays in the older wood. However, there is contrary evidence to the effect that aggregate rays may have been evolved through the progressive reduction and disintegration of rays of the oak type.

Summation.—Careful perusal of the information included in Sec. *B* will serve to indicate that branch and root wood differ considerably from that of the older wood of the stem. These departures in many respects are more significant than the structural variations found in the wood of the stem itself. The differences that are registered between branch and stem wood are not confined to texture only but also include variations in the frequency and arrangement of cells of different types and of portions of xylary tissue (rays). As a rule, branch and root wood differ so materially in general appearance and in gross and minute anatomy from the wood of the mature stem that the identification of wood samples from these regions of the tree is uncertain, especially so when a Key, to be practical, must serve to identify wood from the merchantable part of the tree. It also follows that neither branch wood nor root wood should be used in compiling information on the structure and properties of a commercial wood as known in the trade.

II. QUALITY OF A WOOD IN RELATION TO GROWTH INCREMENTS

It is generally recognized that, within a species, there is a fairly close correlation between the weight (density) of wood and some of its physical properties, especially its strength. Relative density is determined by the amount of cell-wall substance and other materials that are present per unit of volume. The former, in turn, varies directly according to (1) the space occupied by cells of a given kind, (2) the sizes of such cells, (3) the thickness of their respective walls, and (4) the amount of infiltration present in the wood.

From what has been said previously, it should be evident that cell sorting is usually not uniform throughout a given growth increment. This holds particularly for porous woods in which certain elements may be present in the springwood and lacking in the summerwood, or vice versa. Furthermore, if a given kind of cell (element) is present in both regions, it generally undergoes modifications in size and in wall thickness depending upon its position in the growth ring; such differences and the effects thereof become all the more pronounced within a species when unusually wide discrepancies in the rate of growth are registered. It is therefore important in a text of this nature to consider the effect of rate of growth on wood quality, particularly on quality expressed in terms of greater density with a resultant increase in strength. Coniferous trees react differently in this respect from hardwoods, and hence these two classes of woods are considered separately.

A. Effect of Growth Rate on the Quality of a Coniferous Wood

The summerwood of conifers is denser (heavier) than the springwood. This circumstance is explained by the fact that the longitudinal tracheids in the outer portion of the ring are smaller (flatter tangentially) and thicker walled than those formed at the beginning of the growing season; consequently, summerwood contains more cell-wall substance per unit of volume than springwood. The direct correlation between the weight of wood and its strength was cited at the beginning of this section, and this holds, even within the boundaries of growth increments; summerwood is stronger than springwood,[1] provided that it is of the normal type.[2] Forsaith[3] clearly demonstrated this in tests of the strength properties of small beams (matchstick size) of southern yellow pine. By this technique, he was able to prepare test pieces composed wholly of tissue from one growth increment. In some tests, the load was applied to the tangential face of the wood, with the summerwood on the upper side; in others, the springwood was uppermost; edge-grain tests were also run, for purposes of comparison. The denser summerwood was stronger than the springwood, *i.e.,* the wood from the inner portion of an increment failed first.

A piece of coniferous wood, unless very small, consists, of course, of tissue from more than one annual increment. The annual layers making up the piece are organically connected with one another; therefore, the conditions that hold as between summerwood and springwood in a given increment hold also for the whole piece, provided that failures have not taken place in the wood. Coniferous timbers are in large measure strong or weak according to the amount of, and the nature of, the summerwood in the successive rings. If this tissue is dense and is present in appreciable amount, the wood is strong; on the other hand, if the bands of summerwood are narrow in comparison with those of the springwood, or if the summerwood tracheids are not decidedly thicker walled than those of the springwood, or if both conditions exist, the test piece is weak. This explains why the southern yellow pines with broad bands of dense summerwood are structural timbers of great strength whereas the soft pines are comparatively weak.

But growth rings vary in width in conifers, in fact, in all trees. Necessarily correlated with this are changes in the widths of the summerwood and the springwood bands within given rings. Do these portions of the ring vary in width in exact proportion in narrow rings, in normal

[1] The difference in the relative strength values is most striking when the earlywood and latewood are sharply delineated.

[2] The provisional clause in this statement is necessary because compression wood, even though it contains an unusually large amount of summerwood, is weaker than normal wood.

[3] FORSAITH, C. C. The Strength Properties of Small Beams (Match Stick Size) of Southern Yellow Pine. *N.Y. State Col. Forestry, Syracuse Univ., Tech. Pub.* 42. 1933.

rings, and in rings of unusual width? The answer is in the negative. Within reasonable limits of ring width, the denser summerwood consisting of thick-walled tracheids is less affected volumetrically by changes in the width of the growth increments, *i.e.*, by big changes in the growth rate, than is the springwood. But the denser summerwood is stronger. Therefore, under the conditions stated, slow-growth coniferous wood is not only heavier than that produced when a tree is growing more rapidly but also stronger. Or, conversely, coniferous stock with unusually wide rings is usually subnormal in density and hence in strength.

Experimental data compiled on southern pine, Douglas fir, and other softwoods bear out the contention of the preceding paragraph. Not only is wide-ringed stock lower in most strength properties than is normal wood, but also it is characterized by unusually high longitudinal shrinkage which in turn causes excessive crooking and bowing (page 313) as the wood dries. In instances of this sort, it is believed that the inferior quality of fast-grown coniferous lumber is occasioned in part by a reduction in the density due to a volumetric increase in the amount of tissue composed of thin-walled, springwood tracheids (in some cases, accompanied by a reduction in the wall thickness of the latewood tracheids), in part by the greater deviation of the pitch of the fibril helixes (see page 91) of the springwood tracheids from the direction of the grain of the wood. It should be noted, however, that where strength is not an important consideration, lighter wood may actually have certain advantages over slow-grown heavier stock. Numbered among these are lesser weight in handling and shipping, mellowness of stock which is reflected in better machining qualities,[1] lower transverse shrinkage, and lower heat conductivity.

The effect of a reduction in the growth rate below a reasonable limit on the properties of coniferous wood is less definite. In grading rules for certain categories of structural softwood lumber, a more or less arbitrary range is set of not less than 6 or more than 20 rings per inch, to ensure wood of "average run." This stipulation is made on the assumption that, in the rings that are more than ordinarily narrow, the summerwood and the springwood are reduced in amount to approximate degree; therefore, not only are unusually wide rings in conifers responsible for wood of less strength, but the same holds for seasonal increments that are more than ordinarily narrow. The bulk of the available evidence, however, does not support this contention. Lodewick,[2] working

---

[1] This possibly explains why second-grown stock of redwood, etc., is so different in character from that produced by older trees that are frequently overmature.

[2] LODEWICK, J. E. Some Summerwood Percentage Relationships in the Southern Pines. *Jour. Agr. Res.*, Vol. 46, pp. 543–554. 1933.

with southern yellow pine with a rate of growth of 3 to 50 rings per inch, was able to show that the maximum percentage of summerwood, at least in crowded stands, occurred only in the narrowest rings. Hale and Fensom[1] found that the specific gravity of white spruce continued to increase up to the maximum number of rings encountered, which, in the stock they used, was 40 per inch. Alexander[2] has shown that the specific gravity and hence the strength of Douglas fir wood, increase very rapidly as the rings increase from 3 to 12 per inch. Between this last figure and 35 rings per inch, they remain fairly uniform, while in stock produced at a time when growth was even slower (35 to 80 rings per inch), this uniformity was less marked. Nevertheless, no definite downward trend was noticed in this last instance. Rochester,[3] on the other hand, was able to demonstrate by a series of curves that a definite correlation exists between optimum growth expressed in terms of a minimal and a maximal number of growth rings per inch, and the strength of several Canadian softwoods.

In view of the conflicting evidence presented above, only a broad generalization can be made. When strength is a primary consideration in coniferous wood, rapid-grown stock is less likely to prove satisfactory than stock resulting from abnormally slow growth. Coniferous wood of the best quality and of the most uniform strength is produced when the growth rate is average and normal.

In closing this discussion, it is well to bear in mind that, since the density of wood depends in large measure upon the amount of cell-wall substance present per unit of volume, it is quite possible to select pieces of the same kind of wood, with rings of the same or of proximate width, which would vary considerably in density. This last-named discrepancy may be due to (1) variations in the relative proportions of summerwood and springwood, (2) a difference in the thickness of cell walls, (3) a difference in the sizes of the cells, *i.e.*, to wood samples variable in texture, and (4) a combination of all three of these factors. For the reasons stated, it is therefore possible for one piece of wood to contain a higher proportion of summerwood than another of the same species and size and yet to be lighter; in this instance, in the second sample, the cells (tracheids largely) might be smaller, or thicker walled, or both. Such a condition often ensues in stock produced by second-growth trees when it

---

[1] HALE, J. D., and K. G. FENSOM. The Rate of Growth and Density of White Spruce. *Canada Dep. Int., Forest Serv. Cir.* 30. 1931.

[2] ALEXANDER, J. B. The Effect of Rate of Growth upon the Specific Gravity and Strength of Douglas Fir. *Canada Dep. Int., Forest Serv. Cir.* 44. 1935.

[3] ROCHESTER, G. H. The Mechanical Properties of Wood. *Canada Dep. Int., Forest Serv. Bul.* 82. 1931.

is not unusual to find samples with a fairly high proportion of summer-wood which are actually lighter than comparable material from virgin-growth trees; this apparent contradiction can be accounted for, of course, by summerwood tracheids in the first sample which are thinner walled than normal, and by like cells in the second sample which are smaller, or abnormally thick-walled, or both. It is apparent, therefore, that considerable variation may occur in the density and strength of coniferous woods that is nowise connected with ring width. For this reason, in the grading rules for certain types of structural material, a provision is inserted to the effect that not only must the stock fall in the stipulated range of 6 to 20 growth rings per inch, as has been already stated, but at least one-third of its volume must be composed of summerwood.

B. Effect of Growth Rate on the Quality of a Porous Wood

As has been previously explained (page 201), two subgroups of porous woods are recognized: the ring porous and the diffuse porous. The ana-tomical departures that permit of the recognition of these subdivisions have already been enumerated. Since ring-porous woods react dif-ferently to varying ring width than do timbers of the other type, it is advisable to discuss these two classes of woods separately.

1. Ring-porous Hardwoods.—The tissue formed at the beginning of the growing season in a ring-porous hardwood contains large, relatively thin-walled vessels which are usually accompanied by a certain amount of longitudinal parenchyma or by cells of this sort and by tracheids; conse-quently, the springwood in such trees is generally quite porous and is correspondingly light in weight and hence weak. In comparison, the summerwood is much denser; *i.e.*, it contains a higher percentage of cell-wall substance per unit of volume. This is because the vessels are smaller and are usually thicker walled and less numerous. More space, proportionately, is occupied by narrow, thick-walled fibers; and the tissue is therefore heavier. As in conifers, an increase in the weight of the wood signifies greater strength; volume for volume, the summerwood of ring-porous trees is stronger than the springwood.

In conifers, it has been shown that, within reasonable limits, the width of the springwood zone varies according to ring width; the thickness of the layer of denser and stronger summerwood remains more constant. The reverse holds in ring-porous hardwoods; in these, the width of the springwood zone is altered little by fluctuations in the rate of growth; the extent of the formation of summerwood and even its nature, on the other hand, are profoundly affected. Hence, wide-ringed ring-porous wood is usually stronger than slow-grown stock of the same species (Text Fig. 51). This disparity in strength can be readily detected when such

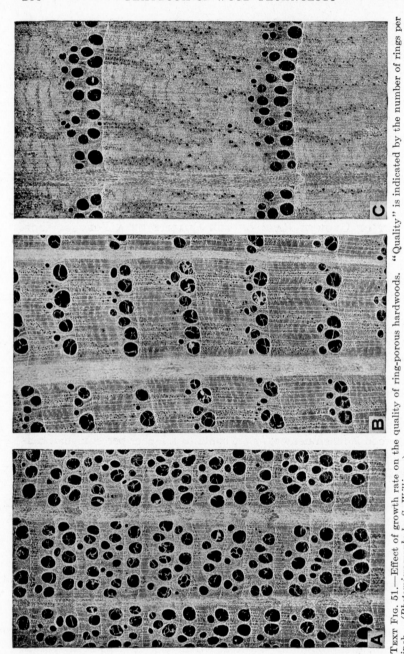

Text Fig. 51.—Effect of growth rate on the quality of ring-porous hardwoods. "Quality" is indicated by the number of rings per inch. *(Photomicrographs by S. Williams.)*

A. A narrow-ringed sample of post oak (*Quercus stellata* Wangh.) with greatly reduced summerwood (10 ✕). *B.* An average-ringed sample of white oak (*Quercus alba* L.) with a normal amount of summerwood (10 ✕). *C.* An unusually wide-ringed sample of white oak (*Quercus alba* L.) with a large amount of summerwood (10 ✕).

samples are compared; the slow-grown specimen will usually prove to be much lighter in weight and visually will be much more porous on the transverse surface because a greater proportion of the area is occupied by large springwood pores. For the reason stated, in selecting hickory stock for ax and hammer handles, etc., that from old, overmature trees or, more specifically, the wood produced in the later years of the life of such trees, should be avoided since it would prove too weak for the purpose intended.

There are numerous exceptions, however, to the rule stated in the preceding paragraph, *viz.*, that slow-growth ring-porous wood is weaker than that possessing wider rings; mention of some of these is in order here. Stock from the butt logs of swamp species often possesses wider rings than that from logs taken at higher elevations and hence contains more summerwood than narrow-ringed stock. But the tissue in such wide rings is generally composed of thinner walled cells, and consequently the wood is lighter in weight and weaker than normal wood. Under normal conditions, the annual rings in the proximity of the pith in a tree are wider than those farther out; in a ring-porous tree the question naturally arises whether the wood toward the pith is therefore stronger, *i.e.*, conforms to the general rule, than that subsequently formed. Paul[1] has contributed some information on this subject. Working with white ash and with pignut and shagbark hickories, he arrived at the conclusion that the rate of growth in these tree-species has little effect on the specific gravity and hence on the strength of wood in the proximity of the pith; irrespective of whether the first few rings were wide or narrow, the quality of the wood remained about the same. His conclusion is borne out by results obtained by Bethal[2] on young chestnut oaks. According to Bethal, growth-ring width is not a good index of either the percentage of summerwood present or of specific gravity and hence the strength of wood.

The validity of the exceptions relative to of effect of ring width on the quality of ring-porous wood recounted in the preceding paragraph cannot be questioned; such exceptions are encountered in wood from near the pith and in young trees. However, in older parts of non-buttressed trees and of buttressed trees above the first log, the rule as originally stated still holds; if the rings are unduly narrow, the xylary tissue is invariably low in specific gravity, weak, and frequently brash (see page 259). Expressing the contradictions of the effect of ring width in a nonbuttressed, ring-porous tree on wood quality in another way,

[1] *Op. cit.*

[2] BETHAL, J. S. Factors Influencing the Specific Gravity of Chestnut-oak Wood. *Jour. Forestry*, Vol. 41, pp. 599–601. 1943.

it matters little whether the rings are narrow or wide when the tree is young. But as it ages, the ring widths play an ever more important role in determining the strength of the wood. In silvicultural practice, it therefore is of little moment whether a tree grows fast or slow in youth, but every effort should be made to promote the production of rings of normal width which in turn bespeaks wood of good quality, as a tree approaches maturity and continues on into old age.

The quality of ring-porous wood also may fluctuate, irrespective of ring width. Wood of low density and inferior in strength is sometimes produced by trees growing on poor upland sites, even though the ring widths are such as to indicate wood of normal strength. Under such conditions, the lowered quality not infrequently is traceable to tracts, in excess of normal, of thin-walled parenchyma or of vasicentric tracheids, to an excessive number of summerwood vessels, or to fibers in the summerwood that are relatively thin-walled. Or one piece of ring-porous wood may be weaker than another of the same rate of growth and density because of local concentrations of summerwood vessels in such a pattern that a definite zone of weakness results.

2. Diffuse-porous Hardwoods.—There is no very close relationship between rate of growth and the quality of the wood in the outer rings (rings at an appreciable distance from the pith) in diffuse-porous hardwoods. This situation apparently results from the diffused arrangement of pores of proximate size; the zone of weakness that is occasioned by larger and frequently more numerous pores at the beginning of the ring in ring-porous woods is lacking. Paul[1] did find, however, if adverse growing conditions prevail for some time, that the narrow rings formed during the period in question contain an abnormal amount of porous tissue, with a corresponding decrease in the specific gravity and hardness of the wood. Tissue of this nature is usually encountered in portions of old and overmature trees in which the increase in diameter was very slow.

The quality of diffuse-porous wood may vary irrespective of ring width, as in ring-porous woods, but generally to lesser degree. As holds for ring-porous wood, this is traceable to variations in the proportions of the different types of wood elements present, in the sorting of these elements, and in the thickness of their walls. The density and, in turn, the strength properties of the wood are materially affected by such departures.

III. QUALITY OF A WOOD AS AFFECTED BY CELL-WALL COMPOSITION

Clarke[2] and others have shown that after all possible allowances are made to account for the variable strength qualities of wood in terms of

---

[1] *Op. cit.*

[2] CLARKE, S. H. Recent Work on the Growth, Structure and Properties of Wood. [Gt. Brit.] *Dept. Sci. and Indus. Res., Forest Prod. Res., Spec. Rpt. 5.* 1939.

growth rate, percentage of summerwood, and specific gravity, a variable still remains that cannot be attributed to these factors, considered singly or in combination.

Among the factors that may possibly account for variations in strength is the composition of the cell wall, *i.e.*, differences in composition of wood substance, variations in the orientation of fibrils, and the nature and thickness of the cell-wall layers. The information on these points is very meager and is confined, to a large extent, to observations made on reaction wood (compression and tension wood).[1]

Clarke[2] presents evidence to the effect that variations in the lignin content of cell-wall substance may be responsible for departures in strength properties. However, his reliance on phloroglucin-stain reactions to indicate the extent of wall lignification opens his work to criticism since but a portion of the lignin complex (mixture) reacts to this stain. Furthermore, Pillow and Luxford[3] have reported that compression wood has a higher lignin content than normal wood, yet is weaker. The results of Bailey[4] and his coworkers are of interest in this connection. Studying the ultramicroscopic structure of cell-wall substance, *i.e.*, the lignocellulosic complex of this substance, they found the cellulose framework to be rigid, while the noncellulosic, amorphous materials (largely lignin) present in this framework afforded planes or regions of weakness.

The fibrillar structure of the primary and secondary cell walls, observable after the cells have been subjected to mechanical or chemical treatment, more particularly, the slope of the fibrils in the secondary wall in relation to the long axis of the cell, has also been suggested as a factor that may be responsible for variations in the strength of wood that cannot be explained on other grounds. Pillow and Luxford, for example, have demonstrated that high fibrillar angle in the cells that feature compression wood in comparison to normal wood contributes to the known weakness of this kind of reaction wood. Granted that a certain amount of fluctuation in fibril canting occurs in normal wood, the question is logical whether a similar relationship may not explain the departures encountered in what passes for normal wood. The deductions of Garland[5] are timely in this connection. This investigator is of the opinion that fibrillar orientation does play some part in determining the strength of normal wood; further, that it does have a bearing on the type

[1] For information on reaction wood, see pp. 287–297.

[2] *Op. cit.*

[3] See footnote 2, p. 288.

[4] BAILEY, I. W. Cell Wall Structure of Higher Plants, *Indus. and Engin. Chem.*, *Indus. Ed.*, Vol. 30, pp. 40–47. 1938.

[5] GARLAND, HEREFORD. A Microscopic Study of Coniferous Wood in Relation to Its Strength Properties. *Ann. Mo. Bot. Gard.*, Vol. 26, pp. 1–94. 1939.

of break that ensues when wood fails under stress. Phillips,[1] on the other hand, found the fibrillar canting from the long axis of the cell to be high near the pith; it decreased rapidly in the next few succeeding rings; thereafter, but minor fluctuations occurred in its mean value. Reasoning from this evidence, he concluded that so far as crushing strength is concerned, no correlation exists between the degree of fibril canting and the strength of the wood. Phillips further suggests that the positive correlation obtained by other workers may have been due "to the inclusion of wood near the pith or compression wood, both of which are characterized by a much higher fibril angle than normal adult wood, but differ also in other respects."

There is some evidence to indicate that variations in the composition of the cell-wall layers, for example, such as those that occur in gelatinous fibers, may account for strength of wood below that of normal. Even in the case of normal wood, Phillips suggests that the composition of the middle zone of the secondary wall (see Text Fig. 21) may play an important role in determining the strength and other properties of wood. To be sure, the effect of such ultramicroscopic variations in the structure of cell walls appears to be quite independent of rate of growth and of the density of wood.

IV. QUALITY OF WOOD FROM OLD AND FROM SECOND-GROWTH TREES

With the passing of climax and virgin forests, a progressively larger share of the timber cut each year in the United States comes from second-growth stands. This statement holds particularly for the eastern half of the United States, but even in the West, second-growth timber of Douglas fir, redwood, and other softwoods is now marketed on a commercial scale. In view of this ever-increasing importance of second-growth wood in the trade, an evaluation of the structural characteristics and properties of such second-growth stock, in comparison to those of wood from virgin stands, is now desirable.

Only fragmentary information on second-grown versus virgin-grown wood is available at this time, and this, for the most part, is based on the study of a few tree-species.[2] Second-growth trees, when converted, are smaller than those of climax forests and, as a rule, exhibit more pronounced taper. Such trees are usually felled before maturity, and hence a larger proportion of the wood is of a type that has been described as juvenile (see page 248). They also possess wider sapwood than more

---

[1] PHILLIPS, E. W. J. The Inclination of Fibrils in the Cell Wall and Its Relation to the Compression of Timber. *Empire Forestry Jour.*, Vol. 20, pp. 74–78. 1941.

[2] KOEHLER, ARTHUR, and B. H. PAUL. Second Growth Problems. *Forest Prod. Lab. Rpt.* R1610–3. 1946.

mature trees, and hence the stock obtained from them consists wholly, or largely of sapwood.

Coniferous wood of second-growth origin is characterized by wider rings than that from mature trees, the springwood is wider, and the summerwood is not so sharply defined; it is also lighter, softer, and lower in strength compared to the wood from older trees. Such stock is also frequently different as regards another feature; it may contain a greater percentage of compression wood since abnormal tissue of this type, when it develops, commonly starts to form in rings not far distant from the pith. As stated on page 292, compression wood shrinks more along the grain than normal wood; stock containing some of it hence shrinks unevenly lengthwise and is therefore prone to warp and twist in drying. Finally, second-growth lumber from scattered trees in the open has more large knots (1 inch and up in diameter) than that from mature trees.

Second-growth hardwood, particularly that from ring-porous trees, frequently is denser than that coming from the outer portions of the trunks of overmature trees. For the reason stated, it is generally heavier, shrinks more in all dimensions, is somewhat stronger, and is reputed to be more refractory under tools.

Second-growth lumber of conifers and hardwoods alike contains fewer defects of the types that are a concomitant of increasing age; numbered among these are heart shakes, heart rot, and decayed and unsound knots. Spiral grain, if present in such stock, is less pronounced because the angle of the slope of this defect generally increases in wood subsequently laid down as a tree ages.

Table XVI presents some interesting data compiled by Davis[1] in a comparative study of old-growth and second-growth white pine with respect to the yields of different grades of lumber that can be obtained from these sources, respectively. His results show clearly that second-growth trees yield but a fraction of the select grades obtainable from old-growth trees, half as much of good common grades, and almost twice as much of the lower common grades. This situation undoubtedly holds for other tree species. One inference is obvious; in the future, wood users will have to become reconciled to the acceptance of more low-grade lumber than at present. This will undoubtedly necessitate changes in current wood-utilization practices that are still based on the availability of lumber of higher grades. The reorientation of utilizational procedures thus entailed, forced by necessity, will in turn result in the speedier adoption in this country of forest-management practices hitherto regarded as economically unsound, practices that not only should stress quantity of

[1] DAVIS, E. M. Lumber from Old-growth versus Lumber from Second-growth in Pinus Strobus. *Jour. Forestry*, Vol. 38, pp. 877–880. 1940.

production attained by a shorter crop rotation of trees but should also strive toward the production of wood reasonably acceptable in quality.

TABLE XVI

COMPARISON OF GRADE YIELDS IN OLD-GROWTH AND
SECOND-GROWTH WHITE PINE, PER CENT

Grades	Old-growth	Second-growth
Selects..........................	10.8	2.4
High–common...................	33.2	16.5
Medium–common................	28.5	22.4
Low–common....................	27.5	58.7
Total......................	100.0	100.0

FIGURE IN WOOD

In a broad sense, any design or distinctive markings that appear on the longitudinal surface of a piece of wood may be described as **figure.** In the trade, however, figure is used in a more or less restricted sense; it signifies only such decorative designs as are prized in the furniture- and cabinetmaking industries. In this text, the broader concept of figure in wood is adopted; for convenience, it is treated under three headings: (1) figure occasioned by growth increments and the nature of woody tissue, (2) figure attributable to the type of grain, and (3) figure caused by the uneven infiltration of coloring materials. Trade designations used in indicating different types of figures are mentioned and briefly discussed in their proper place under the above-mentioned headings.

I. FIGURE OCCASIONED BY GROWTH INCREMENTS AND THE NATURE OF WOODY TISSUE

A. Cause of Such Figure

The surface of a board of practically any tree-species will show some design. Such figure is traceable either to a difference in the nature of the tissue of the springwood and summerwood portions of the growth increments or to the inherent structure of the wood itself. Ring-porous hardwoods and conifers with conspicuous bands of summerwood are especially productive of figures of the first type. On the other hand, the various figures occasioned by wood rays are due to the inherent structure of wood; the aspect in which these ribbon-shaped structures are viewed on the face of a board has a direct bearing on the type of figure produced by them.

It should be clear to the reader by this time that the nature of tree growth is such that the pattern of the design as it appears on sawn products, is greatly influenced by the plane in which the wood is cut and viewed. If a log, for instance, is sawed so that the exposed surface is approximately tangent to the growth increments, *i.e.*, approximately at a right angle to the rays, **plain-** or **flat-sawn** lumber is produced; if the cut is more or less at a right angle to the annual layers, *i.e.*, parallel to the rays, the resulting stock is said to be **quarter-sawn.**[1] It follows that

---

[1] Flat and quartered veneers (for definition of veneer, see Glossary, p. 613) generally are obtained by slicing. In this method of cutting, the veneer flitch (portion

various intermediate types of figure will result if the plane of cut is neither tangential nor at right angles to the growth increments. Furthermore, depending on the place in the log from which the board was taken, one face of a board may exhibit the figure of flat-sawn lumber, whereas the markings on the opposite face may approach those of quarter-sawn stock; likewise, it is not uncommon to find boards in which the central portion is flat-sawn and the margins exhibit more or less of a quartered figure. For the same reason, full-width flat-cut (sliced) veneer stock invariably shows a quartered figure toward the sides of the sheet; the central portion of such stock is usually described as possessing "leaf" pattern.

B. Types of Figure Produced on the Faces of Boards and on Veneers

1. Plain-sawn and Plain-cut Figures (Text Fig. 52, *A*).—As has already been stated, these types of figures are obtained when the surface exposed in sawing or slicing the wood is approximately tangential to the annual layers, thus exposing a relatively broad expanse of each growth increment. Such a figure is characterized through the center of the board by nested angular or parabolic designs, the tips of which are directed toward one end of the board, or by concentric zones of irregular contour, the long diameters of which are directed lengthwise of the board; toward the margins of the board, the figure is edge-grained or approaches that of edge grain.[1]

The distinctive pattern of flat-sawn lumber is traceable to the differences in density existing between springwood and summerwood within the respective growth increments. In ring-porous woods, the springwood is much more porous than that subsequently formed, owing to the presence of large vessels, and hence stands out; the denser summerwood of diffuse-porous and coniferous species, in contrast, is generally darker than the springwood and sets off the growth increments on the faces of

---

of a log) is drawn across a knife that is firmly held in a frame; a thin sheet of veneer is thus sliced off by a diagonal, draw-shave motion. Sliced veneers are either **plain-cut** or **quartered**. Quartered oak veneer is usually obtained by sawing, not slicing, for the latter procedure destroys the effectiveness of the ray fleck to which the figure of quartered oak is traceable; veneers of other species that are thicker than ⅛ inch are usually sawed.

[1] Figures of the first type are more frequent in stock sawed from small logs in which the taper is appreciable; large logs are more prone to yield concentric patterns. Relatively plain-faced boards may be obtained from unusually large logs in which the growth increments are not unduly narrow; the same holds for sheets of half-round sliced and rotary-cut veneer (see p. 271) under the same conditions.

boards.   It follows that no figure is evident in plain-sawn stock of woods in which the seasonal growth increments are poorly defined.

2. Quarter-sawn and Quarter-cut Figures.—The characteristic aspect of quarter-sawn wood with rays of normal size is due to successive growth increments, viewed along the grain in lateral sectional (edge) view, or to interlocked grain (Text Fig. 53, *A*) (see page 274).   In the first instance, the growth layers on surfaces thus exposed appear as parallel stripes, or striae, running lengthwise of the board or veneer sheet.   As was the case

TEXT FIG. 52.—Plain-cut and rotary-cut figures.
A. Plain-cut, matched black walnut (*Juglans nigra* L.).   (*Veneer Association.*)   *B.* Plain-rotary-cut, matched black walnut (*Juglans nigra* L.).   (*American Walnut Mfg. Association.*)

in plain-sawn and plain-cut stock, the various growth increments are delineated either because the springwood in the increment is decidedly more porous than that subsequently formed (ring-porous woods) or because the summerwood is denser and darker than the springwood (diffuse-porous and coniferous woods).   Coniferous woods that are to be used for flooring are frequently quarter-sawn to increase their wearing quality.

Since in quarter-sawing and quarter-slicing the plane of the cut is in the same direction as that in which the rays are directed and of necessity follows some of these for appreciable distances across the growth increments, portions of the rays are exposed in lateral aspect on the surface of the wood.   Under these conditions, if the rays are large, they appear as ribbons extending irregularly across the grain, the length of these ribbons varying according to the distance the plane of section happened to follow given rays.   In species in which some or all of the rays are conspicuous, as in oak and sycamore, a characteristic figure called **ray fleck** is produced (Text Fig. 53, *B*).   In some woods, the ray flecks reflect light

 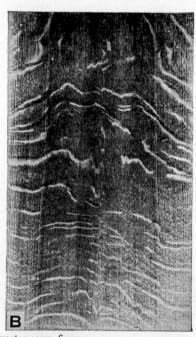

TEXT FIG. 53.—Quarter-sawn figures.
A. Quartered, stripe veneer of African mahogany (*Khaya* sp.); the figure is caused by interlocked grain.   (*Mahogany Association.*)   *B.* Quarter-sawn domestic oak (*Quercus sp.*); the figure is due to large wood rays.   (*Veneer Association.*)

to a greater extent than the surrounding fibrous tissues, *i.e.*, these patches of tissue are more lustrous, and such quartered stock is described as possessing **silver grain.**   If the plane of section is canted to the lateral surface of the rays so that the total height of the ray is not registered on the surface of the board at any one spot, the ray surface exposed crosses the face of the board diagonally.   If two pieces of such stock are matched so that the exposed ray surfaces meet at an angle, a **herringbone figure** results.[1]

---

[1] The term "herringbone figure" is also applied to any prominent diagonal striping that can be matched to produce a distinctive pattern resembling a herringbone.

3. Rotary-cut and Half-round Veneers.—Brief mention should also be made of the figures that are found in rotary-cut and in half-round veneers. **Rotary-cut veneer** is obtained by rotating a log against a knife in such a way that a continuous sheet of veneer is unrolled spirally. Since logs, even those from large trees, usually possess some taper and the growth increments are almost invariably asymmetrical, a sheet of rotary-cut veneer, in a given neighborhood, generally displays portions of several different growth layers. The resulting pattern, therefore, is due largely to the manner in which the various growth increments happen to register; it may assume that of plain-sawn and plain-cut stock or possess bizarre and unpredictable zonation, depending on the angle at which the annual increments are exposed, the number of growth layers that happen to be displayed in the sheet, and, finally, the distinctiveness with which the boundaries of each increment are delimited (Text Fig. 52, *B*).

Most rotary-cut veneer is of the "commercial veneer" type; it is used for the central plies of plywood or for concealed parts in furniture, seldom for exposed surfaces. Such commercial veneers are classified as **plain-rotary-cut veneers.** Rotary-cut veneers that are cut for exposed surfaces (face stock) may be either plain or figured. For example, rotary-cut walnut veneer is classed as "plain rotary" or as "figured rotary," depending on the prominence of the pattern. Outstanding examples of **figured rotary-cut** (face) **veneer** are the bird's-eye, quilted, curly, and blister types, all of which are due to irregularities of grain. These are discussed subsequently in the text.

Half-round veneer is also cut on a lathe.[1] The material to be sliced (usually the split half of a log, a flitch, or a section of a crotch or stump) is mounted on one side of a metal stay-log, which is fastened between two large disks centered on the spindles of a lathe. Adjustments permit of the movement of the stay-log across the faces of the disks through control slots in such a manner as to give controlled eccentricity. A lathe with these adjustments permits of the cutting of sheets of veneer the radius of curvature of which (sweep) is greater than that of the radius of the log.

The section of a log to be cut may also be attached to the stay-log in such a manner that the cutting progresses from the heart toward the outside, *i.e.*, in a direction the reverse of that employed in making rotary-cut veneers.[2] This last method is employed chiefly with black walnut butt logs and crotches, since it produces striking and balanced slant-

---

[1] KNIGHT, E. V., and MEINRAD WULPI. Veneers and Plywood, pp. 157–159. The Ronald Press Company, New York. 1927.

[2] In rotary-cut and half-round veneers, the cutting proceeds from the outside toward the heart of the log.

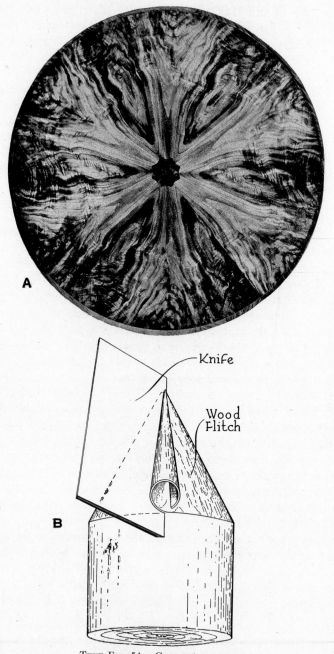

TEXT FIG. 54.—Cone-cut veneer.

A. Table-top made of cone-cut veneer of black walnut (*Juglans nigra* L.), with octagonal inlay at the center. The design is repeated 6 times around the core. (*Mersman Bros. Corporation.*)   *B.* Sketch showing how the knife is set in cutting cone-veneer from a wood flitch.

grain figures which are further accentuated by different degrees of pigmentation. Such veneer is known as **back-cut veneer.**

4. Cone-cut Walnut Veneers.[1]—**Cone-cut veneers** have appeared in the trade. The veneer is shaved from a cylindrical bolt of wood, much as a pencil is sharpened (Text Fig. 54, *B*). The slope of the knife controls the number of revolutions of the bolt necessary to secure a circular sheet and likewise determines the number of times figures proximate in shape occur in such a sheet (Text Fig. 54, *A*). Angular inlays are usually inserted at the center.

II. FIGURE ATTRIBUTABLE TO THE TYPE OF GRAIN

The figures of straight-grained wood that are contingent on the method of cutting were described in the previous section. Attention should now be directed to those figures which result when the grain deviates from the perpendicular in the standing tree and to irregularities of grain occasioned by burls, crotches, and stump swell.

A. Figure Caused by Interlocked Grain

Spiral grain, per se, does not cause striking figure in wood; this is because the light rays that strike the face of a board and are reflected leave the surface at approximately the same angle. Slight spiraling is the rule rather than the exception in most trees. In certain domestic species, such as sycamore and black gum, and in many tropical trees, for some unaccountable reason, reversal of spiral takes place at fairly frequent and even intervals. In such instances, in successive layers of wood along a radius of the trunk or log, the spiral is first right-handed, then left-handed, then right-handed again to proximate degree, etc., each layer including a number of growth increments. In other words, the fibers spiral in a given direction for a number of years; then the direction of pitch is reversed for a comparable period, after which the alignment returns approximately to the original slope. Wood of this type in which the fiber alignment reverses at quite frequent intervals is designated as **interlocked-grained wood** (Text Fig. 55, *A*).

The quarter-sawn surface of interlocked-grain wood exhibits a characteristic striped or ribbon figure, composed of darker and lighter bands running lengthwise of the board (Text Fig. 55, *B*). These are due not to actual variations in the color of the wood but rather to differences in its reflecting qualities in every other zone, so expressed that some bands are dark and the alternating zones are light. By changing the

---

[1] Cone veneers are manufactured by Mersman Bros. Corporation, of Celina, Ohio, and are protected by patents.

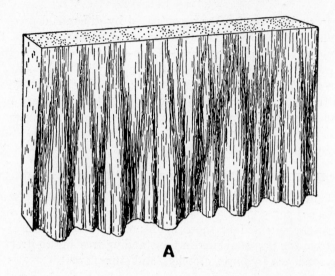

A

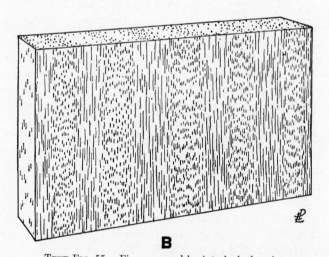

B

TEXT FIG. 55.—Figure caused by interlocked grain.
A. A block of interlocked-grained wood, split radially. The top front edge of the block, where the prying tool was applied, is straight; the lower edge indicates the depth of the interlocking. *B.* The ribbon figure which results when interlocked-grained wood is sawed in a radial direction.

angle of light incidence, it is possible to cause the reversal of the zones, in terms of color. In the trade, the pattern obtained by quarter-sawing interlocked-grained wood is called **ribbon** or **stripe figure.**[1]

---

[1] In some woods, such as black walnut, stripe figure may result from color variation within annual increments. Quartered redwood occasionally exhibits banding of this

In some instances, not only are the fibers aligned in spirals up and down the tree, but undulations occur in the spirals as well. Quartered stock from such trees exhibits tapering stripes which extend for varying distances along the grain. If the stripes are 1 foot or more in length, the figure is termed **broken stripe**; if short, the pattern is designated as **roe figure**.

B. Figure Traceable to Undulations in the Direction of Fiber Alignment[1]

A number of distinctive patterns arise as a result of undulations in the direction of fiber arrangement, even though the slope of the fibers remains

Text Fig. 56.—Figure traceable to undulations in the direction of fiber alignment. Curly grain on the radial face of a block of white ash (*Fraxinus americana* L.) (natural size). (*Material supplied by J. A. Cope.*)

the same in successive layers along the radius of the tree bole or log. Wavy, curly, blister, quilted, and bird's-eye figures belong in this category.

---

sort, due to alternating zones of normal wood and compression wood; in such instances, each zone is composed of a number of increments.

[1] For a discussion of defects arising from deviation in the fiber alignment, see pp. 299 to 301.

1. Wavy and Curly Figure.—This type of figure is due to undulations in the direction of fiber alignment, *i.e.*, to more or less abrupt and repeated right and left deviations from a median axis. The radial-split faces of such a wood are wavy or corrugated (Text Fig. 56); the split tangential surface is smooth but the distortion in fiber alignment is generally evident. When the corrugations are close and abrupt, the resulting pattern is called **fiddleback figure** since such stock, mostly maple and mahogany, has long been used for the backs of violins.

 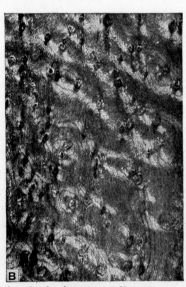

TEXT FIG. 57.—Figures traceable to undulations in the direction of fiber alignment. *A.* Blister figure in veneer of Oregon maple (*Acer macrophyllum* Pursh.) (½ natural size). Oregon maple is also the source of quilted maple (see frontispiece). (*Material supplied by P. J. Landry, Kelso Veneer Co., Kelso, Wash.*) *B.* Bird's-eye figure in veneer of sugar maple (*Acer saccharum*, Marsh.) (½ natural size).

Among domestic woods, wavy and curly figure is most frequent in maple and birch, but it also occurs sporadically in other woods. Curly grain develops locally in the vicinity of knots because the tissues in the main stem are of necessity distorted at these points. It also frequently results through the healing of wounds, this process taking place, of course, while the tree is living.

2. Blister Figure.—This term is used to designate a peculiar type of figure that not infrequently occurs on flat-sawn and rotary-cut surfaces (in which the tangential surface of the wood is exposed). It appears to consist of small, more or less widely spaced, elevated or depressed areas of rounded contour (Text Figure 57, *A*). When stock of this sort is split in the tangential plane, elevations occur on one of the surfaces that form the so-called blister when the wood is cut or sawed. The alignment of the fibers in such patches departs from the vertical, and this change of direction is recorded on the transverse surface of the wood by undulations in the contour of the growth rings. Owing to a difference in their light-reflecting qualities compared to those of normal tissue, such areas stand out on the smooth surface of the wood as seemingly elevated or depressed areas. Blister figure occurs in a number of native species, notably in maple and birch.

3. Quilted Figure.—This expression is employed to designate a characteristic pattern that resembles blister figure in some respects but differs in that the whole tangential surface of the wood is usually involved and also in the size and shape of the blisters; it is obtained from selected stock of Oregon maple (*Acer macrophyllum* Pursh.) (see frontispiece). This figure results from corrugations in the grain which frequently develop in leaning trees and below large limbs. The elevations thus arising and the depressions between them are horizontal in the main, but the latter anastomose at fairly frequent intervals. Consequently, at any height in the tree where convolutions in the grain occur, the contours of the annual rings are undulate because some portions of these are included in the elevations and other parts are situated in the depressions. When such stock is cut on the tangential plane, a striking figure is obtained. Owing to the play of light on the flat surface, the effect is of depressed or elevated areas of varying size and contour, the prevailing direction of which is transverse, delimited by fairly well-defined boundaries.

Quilted maple was discovered and named by P. J. Landry of the Kelso Veneer Company, Kelso, Wash. Mr. Landry states that trees that are quilted throughout the circumference of the stem are rare. He finds that in the majority of cases the convolutions in the grain are confined to one side of the trunk and extend a greater distance along this than circumferentially. In straight logs with eccentric rings, the quilted formation is usually restricted to the side on which growth progressed most rapidly; in curved logs, it is usually limited to the concave side. Where the logs are fluted, the grain of this type is found most frequently on the ridges; the depressions are usually straight-grained.

4. Bird's-eye Figure.—This kind of figure is due to local distortions in fiber alignment that are occasioned by conical indentations in the growth increments. These indentations extend from the surface of the bark inward toward the pith and, once started, continue in successive growth layers for many years, frequently throughout the life of the tree. Conical elevations are usually present on the surface of the inner bark, projecting into the indentations in the wood. When logs with bird's-eye grain are plain-sawn or rotary-cut, the area on the surface of the wood in which the tissue is distorted resembles birds' eyes, hence the name (Text Fig. 57, *B*).

The bird's-eye formation may extend throughout the length of the tree and even into the branches. More frequently, however, the figure is confined to one side of the tree or is restricted to irregular patches, scattered over the trunk, that are separated by normal wood. Considerable variation is also manifested in the size and in the proximity of the eyes on the surface.

Bird's-eye figure is most common and most characteristically developed in hard maple, but a similar figure is also found in soft maple, birch, and white ash. No explanation of the cause of bird's-eye figure that is wholly acceptable has yet been given.

C. Figures Resulting from Twisted Grain

Various figures are produced in wood as a result of twisted grain. Perhaps the most unusual patterns of this kind are obtained from crotches, burls, and stump swells of trees that also produce straight-grained ornamental woods. Because of the twists in the fiber alignment in these parts of the trees, most striking and unpredictable designs are often obtained when such stock is cut into veneer or turned on a lathe. Figured burl, stump, and crotch woods are highly prized for matched veneers. Figured stock, obtained from these specific regions in a tree, usually bears the name of the part from which it comes, with a descriptive adjective and the name of the species, as, for example, walnut feather crotch. The paragraphs that follow are devoted to figures of this type.

1. Crotch Figures.—A crotch is a segment of a stem that forks. Commercial crotches come in sections shaped somewhat like a shallow-throated Y. The length of such a bolt is about twice its diameter at the butt end. In crotches, the fiber alignment follows different courses in closely adjoining parts, as it passes into the forks of the stem. For this reason, a typical crotch figure (Text Figs. 58, *A* and *B*; 59, *C*) has a design resembling either a cluster of feathers or a swirl figure; the first is termed **feather crotch,** and the latter is known as **moonshine crotch. Swirl crotch** is obtained from that section of the tree where the typical crotch figure fades into that of normal stem wood. Among domestic woods, ornamental crotch figures are obtained almost exclusively from black walnut.

2. Burls, or Burrs.—These are large abnormal bulges or excrescences that form on the trunk and limbs of a tree; they may occur on almost any species. The surface of such excrescences may be smooth or corrugated, the latter type being the more common in conifers. The fiber alignment of burls is very irregular, and the burl is more or less gnarled on this account. This irregularity of grain produces very striking figures which are highly prized for veneer and turned articles (Text Fig. 59, *A* and *B*). Among native species, burls of Oregon myrtle, maple, walnut, and redwood are especially renowned for their figure.

In many instances, burls are found to contain numerous but only partly developed buds which, it is believed, have arisen as a result of injury to the tree. Frost, fire, and mechanical injuries fall in this general

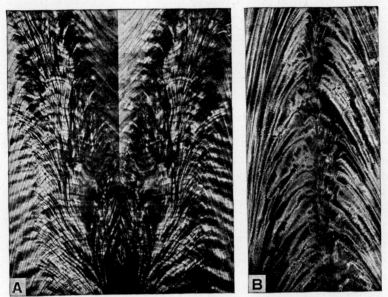

TEXT FIG. 58.—Figures resulting from twisted grain.
A. Feather-crotch figure of black walnut (*Juglans nigra* L.). Two piece, matched. (*American Walnut Mfg. Association.*)
B. Stump-wood figure of mahogany (*Swietenia* sp.). (*Mahogany Association.*)

category. For example, Piccioli[1] reports that he induced the formation of burls in boxwood (*Buxus sempervirens* L.) by placing a close-fitting metal band around the stem; this resulted in the formation of adventitious buds which eventually led to the formation of a swelling. The same investigator also reports that in Algeria during the seventeenth and eighteenth centuries it was common practice to induce the formation of burllike excrescences in African thuja (*Callitris quadrivalis* Vent.) by repeated burning of a part of the stem. The sprouts that developed around the injured area were also burned. As a result, a swelling formed on the trunk on the side opposite the injury. It is believed that burllike

[1] PICCIOLI, L. I Lengi Marezzati. *Ann. R. Ist. Super. Forest. Naz. Firenze*, Vol. 3. 1917–1918.

growths also develop in some cases through irritation of the cambium by fungi and bacteria.

3. Stump-wood Figures.—Stump wood comes from the bell-shaped base of the tree, just above the roots.   To be valuable, stumps must possess irregular grain, the presence of which in the standing tree is generally indicated by fluting at the base of the trunk or by ridges under the bark.   Among native species, figured walnut stumps command an unusually high price.   Such stumps must have a minimum diameter of 21 inches at the top and a length of at least 3 feet.   Those in which the figure extends for at least two-thirds of their length bring the highest prices.   In obtaining stumps for veneering, it is customary to dig down around the roots of a standing tree for 2 to 3 feet and then cut the larger roots; as the tree falls, the merchantable part of the stump swell is pulled out, along with the rest of the trunk.   The above-mentioned method is preferred to that of digging out a stump after a tree has been cut.

At the veneer mills, stumps obtained in the manner described in the preceding paragraph are carefully trimmed and placed in cooking vats where they remain for several days.   After the wood is thoroughly softened, they are debarked and halved vertically through the center. Stump wood is cut into veneer by the half-round method.   Special skill is required in determining the proper angle of cut to ensure the finest figure.   Figured stump wood yields highly varied, right- and left-balanced designs which are admirably suited for ornamental veneers.

D. Figure Caused by the Uneven Infiltration of Coloring Materials

Some woods owe their distinctive figure to the irregular infiltration of coloring materials.   As a result, streaks or patches appear on the surface of wood that are darker than the remaining tissue.[1]   Wood so marked is said to have **pigment figure.**

Pigment figure is quite common in red-gum (Text Fig. 59, *D*).   Stock containing such dark zones is termed **figured red-gum** in the United States and has been marketed abroad as **satin walnut.**   The same type of figure is found in black and "claro" walnut, in Circassian walnut (*Juglans regia* L.), and in various tropical timbers.   Among the latter, zebrawood from the West Coast of Africa is probably the best known to the trade.   It is a handsome timber, characterized by alternating dark and light stripings; hence the common name.

---

[1] The light and dark streaks or patches so formed bear no relationship to the light and dark zones in growth increments occasioned by porous springwood and dense summerwood, respectively.

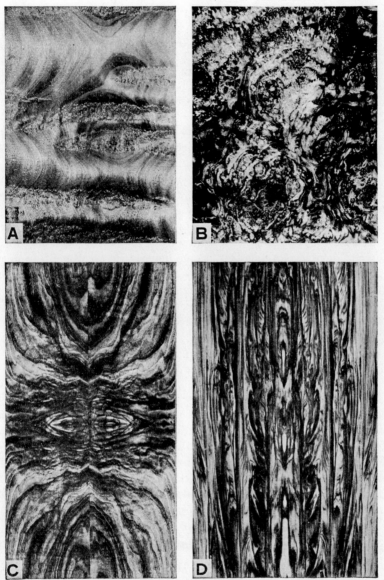

Text Fig. 59.—Figures resulting from twisted grain (*A*, *B* and *C*), and caused by the uneven infiltration of coloring materials (*D*).

A. Burl and swirl in African mahogany (*Khaya sp.*). (*Mahogany Association.*)

B. Small burl of black walnut (*Juglans nigra* L.). (*Walnut Mfg. Association.*)

C. Matched crotch veneer of black walnut (*Juglans nigra* L.). (*Walnut Mfg. Association.*)

D. Pigment-figured red-gum (*Liquidambar styraciflua* L.). (*Veneer Association.*)

CHAPTER XII

DEFECTS IN WOOD

A defect in wood may be defined as any abnormality or irregularity that lowers its commercial value by decreasing its strength, or by affecting adversely its working and finishing qualities or its appearance. No timber is completely free of defects; conversely, the same type of defect frequently occurs in different woods, and some defects are present in all species. Certain imperfections such as knots are unavoidable because of the nature of tree growth; other faults are traceable to unfavorable growing conditions or develop as a consequence of the improper handling of the wood during manufacture. Some defects are contingent on outside forces such as wind and frost, or arise as a result of the inroads of organisms such as fungi, insects, and marine borers.

In this text, for convenience of discussion, the information on defects in wood is incorporated under three main headings: (1) natural defects, (2) defects due to seasoning, and (3) defects due to foreign organisms.

I. NATURAL DEFECTS

In this section are described those abnormalities in the wood of living trees which are due to growth and environment; such faults, because of their very nature, are not subject to direct control by man. The natural defects of wood are distinct from those which develop after the tree has been cut, *i.e.*, from those which come into being as the result of faulty treatment or through the attacks of foreign organisms. Imperfections in the latter category can be avoided or minimized through the application of known methods of control.

A. KNOTS

A knot is a branch base that is embedded in the wood of a tree trunk or of a larger limb or branch (Text Fig. 60); such branch bases are gradually included in the wood of the larger member through addition, year by year, of successive growth increments.

In order to explain the formation of knots in a tree it is first necessary to trace the origin and the development of branches. Twigs originate from buds along the shoot. The terminal bud develops into the leader, while lateral buds give rise to side branches.[1] Each bud, in reality, is a secondary axis capped by a growing point. This secondary axis is provided with a pith and at least rudimentary vascular tissue, and these are organically connected with like tissues to the main stem.[2] As long as the newly formed branch continues to live, it lengthens by primary growth at the apex and thickens by secondary growth, *i.e.*, through

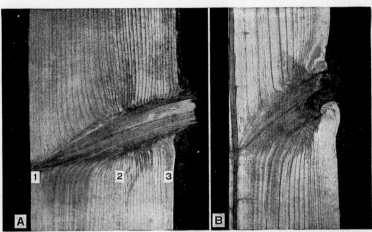

Text Fig. 60.—Natural defects. Knots. (*Photographs by permission of the Forest Products Laboratory.*)
    A. Spike knot with projecting spur, in northern white pine (*Pinus strobus* L.). The branch was living during the period when the series of annual increments between 1 and 2 were added to the main stem; dead between 2 and 3. These zones indicate where the knot is "tight" and "loose" respectively. *B.* Spike knot with partially decayed spur, in western yellow pine (*Pinus ponderosa* Laws.). The knot is in process of being covered by callus.

activity of its cambium throughout its exposed length. Since the cambium of the branch is continuous with that of the larger stem from which it extends, whenever a new increment of wood is laid down in the latter, one forms at the same time in the branch. Therefore, there is no break in the continuity of the tissue between these two component parts of the stem (Text Fig. 60, *A*1 to 2). This is especially noticeable on the underside of a branch, where the continuity of growth is readily observable. On the upper side, the tissue of the larger stem tends to pass around the

---

[1] In most trees producing wood covered by this text, the new twigs formed during a given season remain unbranched. Yellow-poplar (*Liriodendron tulipifera* L.) and sassafras [*Sassafras albidum* (Nutt.) Nees] frequently branch the first year.

[2] Sprouts and sucker shoots may originate from adventitious buds in the inner bark at some distance from the pith. It follows that there will be no continuity between the pith of such shoots and that of the main stem. Abnormal branches formed in this way are relatively unimportant from the standpoint of knot formation.

branch, thus making an imperfect connection with it. The direction of the connective tissue around the living branch is, therefore, approaching a right angle on the upper side and is oblique to the grain on the lower side. The result of this is formation of local cross grain around the living branch. That portion of a branch which is embedded in the bole of a tree, while the branch is still living, causes **intergrown, tight,** or **red knots** in lumber.

When a branch dies, the cambium in the branch ceases to function. No new increments are formed in the branch, although they continue to develop in the living member (limb or bole of the tree to which the branch is attached). From this time on (Text Fig. 60, $A2$ to 3), there is a break in the continuity of the new tissue formed in the larger living stem and the dead tissue of that part of the branch which is incorporated into the living stem. In due time, the branch is cast (see cladoptosis, page 25) or breaks off through a process known as natural pruning, in the second instance usually leaving a projecting stub. This, then, gradually becomes embedded in the wood as successive growth layers are added, year by year. Meanwhile, callus forms at the base of the stub (Text Fig. 60, B), and this wound tissue is pushed outward by continued growth in diameter of the living stem; eventually the end of the stub is covered over by the wound tissue, if growth in the living member continues over a long enough period. When healing is completed, as new layers of wood are formed by the cambium of the tree, clear wood is laid over this point.

The portion of a branch that becomes embedded in the bole of a tree after the branch dies causes a **loose, encased,** or **black knot** in lumber. Since the wood of the tree trunk is not continuous with that of an encased knot, there is less distortion of the grain around it than in the case of intergrown knots.

It is evident from the preceding paragraphs that the shape of the wood of a lateral, living branch, from its apex to the point of the attachment of its pith to that of the main stem, is comparable to that of two cones, the bases of which meet in the plane of the cambium of the main stem. The longer cone is directed outward and, neglecting its appendages, consists of (1) that portion of the branch wood projecting from the outside of the tree, plus (2) the basal portion of this cone which is embedded in the bark of the main stem. The smaller cone is embedded in the wood of the larger member and is directed inward; its apex is, of course, in touch with the pith of the main stem. This smaller cone constitutes the knot, as found in sawed material.

The appearance of knots in lumber depends on the plane in which they are cut. If sawed lengthwise, a **spike knot** results; if the direction of the cut is approximately at right angles to the long axis of the included branch base, the resulting knot is termed a **round knot.** Round knots range from circular to oval, depending in part on the sawing angle, in part on the nature of tree growth.[1] Such knots frequently fall out of lumber on drying, and leave a **knothole.** Loose oval knots are more likely to remain in place although they have no organic connection with the rest of the tissue composing the board. In grading rules, knots are generally classified on the basis of quality, as **sound, unsound, decayed, intergrown** or **encased,** and on the basis of size, as **pin, small, medium (standard)**, and **large.**

The number, size, and type of knots formed in the wood of a tree depend on the number and size of the limbs from which they originate, the rapidity with which the limbs die, and the length of time the dead limb stubs remain on the tree. Variation in the above rests on a number of factors, chief among which are inherent differences in the growth characteristics of different species, site conditions, density and composition of the stand, climate, quality of the wood, etc. For instance, a study of knot formation in pines, conducted at the Forest Products Laboratory,[2] has revealed that northern white pine (*Pinus strobus* L.) retains its dead branches longer than Norway pine (*P. resinosa* Ait.) growing in the same stand, indicating inherent differences in growth characteristics. In both of these species, self-pruning is so slow that if any appreciable volume of clear lumber is to be obtained from the second-growth stands, artificial pruning at an early age seems to be essential. In the southern pines studied, dying and shedding of lateral branches progress rapidly, so rapidly in fact that the need for pruning is much less urgent. In comparison, the difference between the southern and the northern species may be due either to the inherent characteristics of the species or to the climatic conditions favoring more rapid decay of branches in the South. Frequently, especially in conifers, the branches, and hence the knots, are small in the basal portion of the stem. This is due to the fact that crown closure results in the shading of the lower branches and causes their early death while they are small in diameter. In trees in which such branches are tardily cast, numerous, small, loose knots are frequently formed early in the life of the tree.

---

[1] In coniferous trees, the annual increments of the lateral branches are widest on the lower side; in hardwoods, on the upper. Hence, in coniferous lumber, oval knots prevailingly exhibit eccentricity in a direction that was originally downward in the standing tree, the reverse being true for hardwoods. Priestley and Tong ascribe these departures to the effect of gravity upon cambial activity. See PRIESTLEY, S. H., and DOROTHY TONG. The Effect of Gravity upon Cambial Activity in Trees. *Proc. Leeds Phil. and Lit. Soc.*, Vol. 1, Part V, pp. 199–208. 1927.

[2] KOEHLER, ARTHUR. A Method of Studying Knot Formation. *Jour. Forestry*, Vol. 34, pp. 1062–1063. 1936.

In sawing a typical surface-clear log into lumber, the first boards beneath the bark will show at least one clear face and thus will qualify for *Select* or *better grades*.   As the sawing progresses deeper into the log, the first indication of the presence of knots will be signified by slight local irregularities of the grain on the faces which give place to knots as the cuts become ever deeper.   The first boards from the knotty interior will contain large, encased or loose knots, resulting from the inclusion of dead branch stubs in the trunk of the tree.   They are generally graded as *No. 3 Common* or lower.   The boards that follow will contain intergrown knots and grade as *No. 1* or *No. 2 Common* lumber.   The core (heart) of the older trees may again yield poorer grades because of the presence of rot, shakes, and other defects that develop in the center of the stem as a tree ages.

The presence of knots has a distinct bearing on the quality and value of wood.   Knots are the commonest cause for lowering the value (the de-grading) of lumber.[1]   They also affect considerably the working qualities of wood, since they are much more refractory under tools than the wood surrounding them.   Knots are frequently responsible for the twisting and checking of lumber, owing to the presence of local cross grain and greater hardness and density of branch wood.[2]   Their greatest adverse effect, however, is in the lowering of the strength properties of structural timber.   These lower values are due to the distortion of grain resulting from the knots and to the checking that may occur in and around knots in drying; they are not traceable, directly, to any inherent inferiority in quality of sound knot wood.   The reduction in strength is greatest in bending, especially when the knots occur on the tension face of a beam, near the point of greatest tensile stress.   The adverse effect of an intergrown knot on tensile strength is fully as great as that of an encased knot or a knothole of the same size.   This is because the cross grain, and the more extensive checking that accompanies tight knots, more than offset the reduction in strength properties occasioned either by the absence of firm attachment in the case of encased knots or by the lack of substance in a knothole.   The effect of knots on stiffness and horizontal shear is relatively unimportant; hardness and strength in compression perpendicular to the grain, however, are actually somewhat increased by their presence.   The main objection to the knots in the

[1] A notable exception to this rule is No. 2 and No. 3 Common grade of "soft" and ponderosa pine, and western red cedar, for such specialties as knotty panels and knotty interior trim.

[2] Because of the tendency of intergrown knots to check and of encased knots to shrink more than the surrounding wood and, therefore, to loosen, the *Common* soft-wood grades of lumber must be kiln-dried more slowly, using a milder drying schedule than that followed in drying the better grade.

latter instances is nonuniformity of wear and the nonuniform distribution of pressure at contact surfaces.[1]

B. DEFECTS RESULTING FROM GROWTH STRESSES IN WOODY STEMS

The effect of environment on the characteristics of normal wood, *i.e.*, wood formed in the erect boles of trees, is well known (see pages 255 to 262). It is further recognized that environment may be responsible for the formation of wood distinctly abnormal in structure and properties. Abnormal wood of one type is found in leaning trunks and limbs, both in hardwoods and in softwoods.[2] In forestry literature, the woody tissues developed in leaning trunks as they straighten have been designated as **reaction wood.**

There are significant differences in the type, location, and characteristics of the reaction wood that forms in coniferous and in hardwood trees. In conifers the abnormal wood of this sort develops on the underside of leaning trunks and branches and is generally called **compression wood;** in hardwoods, in comparison, it forms on the upper side of these members and is designated as **tension wood.** These terms are sufficiently definitive to suggest that reaction wood in trees is formed as a result of longitudinal stresses in inclined trunks and in limbs.[3] However, the effect of other stimuli, such as light, gravity, and sap-stream tension,[4] on the formation of reaction wood should not be neglected.

In any discussion of reaction wood formed as the result of stresses, the fact should not be overlooked that longitudinal stresses in tree stems are by no means confined to leaning boles; they exist as a normal condition in trunks that are vertical. Jacobs,[5] for instance, removed longitudinal strips consecutively from planks cut diametrically through logs from vertically upright trees of different species and found that the strips so taken varied in length. He concluded,

(*a*) That in the trunks of erect hardwood trees, regardless of size, the outer layers of the wood were in longitudinal tension and the inner layers

[1] More detailed discussion of the effect of knots on strength properties will be found in Vol. II, Part II, of this text. Volume II is in preparation.

[2] Limb wood is abnormal only in the sense that it contains wood of the type associated with leaning stems.

[3] Münch suggests that the terms, compression wood and tension wood, not only should be applied to the abnormal tissue formed under the influence of stresses but should also signify the dynamic stresses acting to cause the formation of such wood. MÜNCH, E. Statik und Dynamik des schraubigen Baues der Zellwand, besonders des Druck-und Zugholzes. *Flora* [Jena], (n.s.), XXXII, pp. 357–424. 1938.

[4] JACOBS, M. R. The Growth Stresses of Woody Stems. *Commonwealth Forestry Bur., Bul.* 28, Canberra, Australia. 1945.

[5] *Op. cit.*

in longitudinal compression; further that the longitudinal compressive force increased progressively toward the pith at which point it attained a peak of at least 100 atmospheres.

(b) That in the trunks of erect coniferous trees, if these were small, the outer layers tended to be in compression and the inner in tension; further, that in larger coniferous trees, the same conditions prevailed as in hardwoods.

The existence of internal forces in living trees, independent of the presence of reaction wood, has also been suggested by Koehler.[1] In observing the frequent occurrence of shakes and cracks in freshly felled trees, he attributed their formation to the presence of tangential and radial stresses in the stems before the trees were felled, these being of sufficient magnitude to produce tissue rupture.

If the presence of stresses is to be recognized as a normal condition in the stems of erect trees, then the stresses in leaning trunks may be regarded simply as such stresses further augmented by inclination of the trunk.

1. Compression Wood.[2]—This term is used to designate reaction wood that forms on the lower side of branches and leaning trunks of coniferous trees. It is generally conceded that compression wood is formed as a result of increased cambial activity locally. There is, however, little direct relationship between the amount of compression wood formed and the extent of recovery of the stem. Jacobs[3] has pointed out that the greater part of the cross-sectional area at the bases of leaning coniferous trees is occupied by compression wood. However, in trees that recover, even though some compression wood is evident, the bulk of the tissue is normal. From this he concludes that "quick recovery of leaning conifers is dependent upon vigorous growth of normal wood as well as compression wood," and that the compression wood "acts like an angle-bracket supporting a shelf. As long as the compression wood maintains its length, recovery of the leaning stem can be brought about by the tension of normal tissue acting against the compression wood."

In logs, compression wood is usually indicated by the presence of eccentric growth rings which appear to contain an abnormally large proportion of summerwood at the point of greatest eccentricity (Text Fig. 61). The main distinguishing characteristics of compression wood in

---

[1] Koehler, Arthur. A New Hypothesis as to the Cause of Shakes and Rift Cracks in Green Lumber. *Jour. Forestry*, Vol. 31, pp. 551–556. 1933.

[2] The information on compression wood that is included here is based mainly on the bulletin by M. Y. Pillow and R. F. Luxford, Structure, Occurrence and Properties of Compression Wood. *U. S. Dept. Agr. Tech. Pub.* 546. January, 1937.

[3] *Op. cit.*

lumber, aside from its color,[1] is its relatively lifeless appearance, which is traceable to the fact that the proportionate amounts of springwood and summerwood are altered appreciably (Text Fig. 62), the contrast

COMPRESSION
WOOD

Text Fig. 61.—Natural defects, compression wood. Cross section of a southern pine log (*Pinus sp.*), with conspicuous compression wood. (*By permission, from "Structure, Occurrence and Properties of Compression Wood," by M. Y. Pillow and R. F. Luxford, U. S. Dept. Agr. Tech. Bul.* 546. 1937.)

between them meanwhile becoming less marked[2] (Text Fig. 63). Typical compression wood is 15 to 40 per cent heavier than normal wood of the same species and of the same rate of growth.

[1] Such tissue is usually redder than normal tissue owing to what appears to be a disproportionate amount of summerwood in the rings at this point; hence the German term, "*Rotholz.*"

[2] A simple device for facilitating the detection of compression wood in lumber has been developed by the Forest Products Laboratory, Madison, Wis. This consists of a box containing an electric light so arranged as to cast its rays through an aperture. When a thin cross section (about $\frac{5}{32}$ inch thick) containing compression wood is placed over the aperture in the box, the summerwood layers of the abnormal wood are more opaque than those of the normal wood.

The structural variations that are features of typical compression wood are largely confined to the summerwood (Text Fig. 64) and can be briefly summarized as follows:

1. The tracheids in the summerwood tend to be circular in transverse sections, in contrast to those of normal wood which are nearly rectangular.

2. Intercellular spaces are visible in the summerwood in transverse sections, at the junction where three or four tracheids meet; such spaces are generally lacking in normal wood.

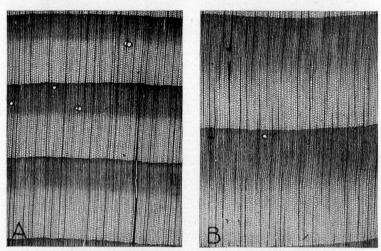

TEXT FIG. 62.—Natural defects, compression wood. Photomicrographs of transverse sections of Douglas fir [*Pseudotsuga taxifolia* (Poir.) Britt.] (18 ×). (*By permission, from* "*Structure, Occurrence, and Properties of Compression Wood,*" *by M. Y. Pillow and R. F. Luxford, U. S. Dept. Agr. Tech. Bul. 546. 1937.*)

A. Normal wood showing relatively sharp contrast between the springwood and the summerwood of the same annual ring.

B. Compression wood in which sharp demarcation between springwood and summerwood is lacking.

3. The slope of the fibrils[1] in the secondary wall of the tracheids in this portion of the increment, in relation to the long axis of the cell, is greater, *i.e.*, approaches more nearly the horizontal in the standing tree, than in normal wood; the secondary walls exhibit spiral checks and striations which are present even in wood taken directly from a living tree and hence cannot be ascribed to shrinkage resulting during the drying of lumber.

4. The thickness of the walls of the tracheids in the summerwood is approximately the same as in the homologous portion of the increment in normal wood; the walls of the springwood tracheids are slightly thicker than those of normal wood.

[1] See Chap. IV.

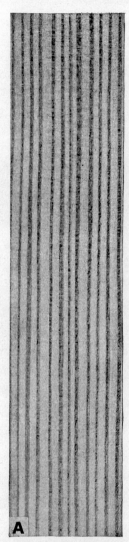 

TEXT FIG. 63.—Natural defects, compression wood. Small pieces of loblolly pine (*Pinus taeda* L.). (*By permission, from "Structure, Occurrence and Properties of Compression Wood," by M. Y. Pillow and R. F. Luxford, U. S. Dept. Agr. Tech. Bul.* 546. 1937.)

  A. Edge-grain view of normal wood, showing clearly delineated growth increments which are of normal width. *B*. Edge-grain view of compression wood, showing abnormally wide growth increments which are not sharply delineated because the springwood merges gradually with the darker summerwood.

5. The tracheids of compression wood are frequently shorter than those from the same portion of the ring in normal wood.

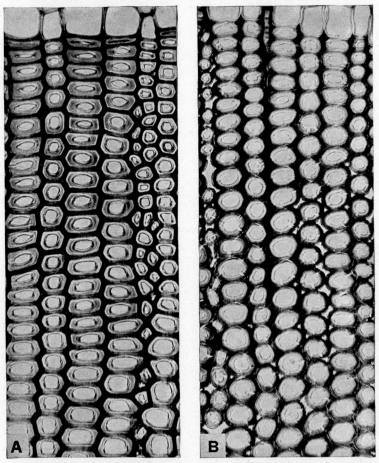

TEXT FIG. 64.—Natural defects, compression wood. Photomicrographs of transverse sections of Douglas fir [*Pseudotsuga taxifolia* (Poir.) Britt.] at high magnification (250 ×) (*By permission, from "Structure, Occurrence and Properties of Compression Wood," by M. Y. Pillow and R. F. Luxford. U. S. Dept. Agr., Tech. Bul. 546.* 1937.)
A. Normal wood. *B.* Compression wood. Note the rounded contours of the summerwood tracheids, the intercellular spaces, and the checks in the secondary walls.

6. In the species investigated, the lignin content of compression wood is slightly higher than that of normal wood of the same species; the reverse holds for the cellulose content.

Compared with normal wood, compression wood is peculiar in exhibiting unusually high and irregular longitudinal shrinkage and shrinkages across the grain that are below normal. It is a principal cause of bowing and twisting in softwood lumber as it dries, is abnormally hard, and is weaker, weight for weight, than normal wood; this last characteristic is apparently due to the fact that, in tissue of this type in the standing tree, the fibrils in the secondary walls of the tracheids in the outer portions of the rings approach more nearly the horizontal plane. Compression wood is therefore considered undesirable where strength and neat appearance are the paramount objectives as in aircraft veneer and plywood.[1]

The possibility of reducing the number of stems containing compression wood by silvicultural practice has been suggested by Pillow and Luxford.[2] The operations should start in the young stands and should consist in removing as many of the inclined, crooked, and twin stems as is consistent with sound managment policies. Care should be exercised, however, to avoid leaving large openings in the canopy that might subject the remaining stems to the action of winds, thus defeating the purpose of the improvement cuttings.

2. Tension Wood.[3]—The reaction wood that forms on the upper side of branches and leaning trunks is known as tension wood (Text Fig. 65). It is generally indicated by the presence of eccentric growth rings[4] in regions of its maximum development. In upper parts of the stem at some distance from the sloping section of the trunk, tension wood may be present on all radii; however, under these conditions it never occurs throughout the same annual ring. Tension wood is not readily distinguishable from normal wood in hardwood trees exhibiting but slight lean, but its influence as a straightening device is nevertheless evident.[5]

In lumber from tree species with dark heartwood, tension wood can be distinguished in the heartwood by its silvery sheen along the grain. This is traceable to tracts of gelationous fibers in the earlywood which

---

[1] ANON. Compression Woods: Importance and Detection in Aircraft Veneer and Plywood. *Forest Prod. Lab., Mimeo. Rpt.* 1586. 1943.

[2] *Op. cit.*

[3] Information on the nature of tension wood and its properties is limited. The most comprehensive studies on this subject, to date, are as follows: CLARK, S. H. The Distribution, Structure and Properties of Tension Wood in Beech (*Fagus silvatica* L.). *Forestry*, Vol. XI, pp. 85–91. 1937; MARRA, A. A. Characteristics of Tension Wood in Hard Maple (*Acer saccharum* Marsh.). Unpublished thesis, Dept. of Wood Technology, The New York State College of Forestry, Syracuse, N.Y. *June*, 1942; CHOW, K. Y. A Comparative Study of the Structure and Chemical Composition of Tension Wood and Normal Wood in Beech (*Fagus sylvatica* L.). *Forestry* Vol. XX pp. 62–77. 1946.

[4] According to Marra, eccentricity in leaning stems of hard maple sometimes develops on the lower (compression) side of the trunk, *i.e.*, opposite the tension wood on the upper side.

[5] JACOBS. *Op. cit.*

cause the abnormal wood to stand out from the duller and generally darker normal wood.[1]   The contrast is much less striking in the sapwood but, in this also, the tension wood can be detected by its more pronounced silvery luster with the proper angle of light.

TEXT FIG. 65.—Natural defects, tension wood. Cross section of a hard maple log (*Acer saccharum*, Marsh.), with tension wood on the upper side. (*Photograph by A. A. Marra.*)

Structurally, the most significant characteristic of tension wood is the presence of fibers with gelatinous walls in the earlywood (Text Fig. 66 *B*). The walls of the fibers toward the outer boundary of the ring appear to be normal.   The fibrils in the nongelatinous portion of the secondary wall of gelatinous fibers are canted at about 45 degrees from the long axis;[2] in the inner gelatinous portion they tend to parallel the long axis.[3]   Münch concluded on the basis of this evidence that this gelatinous layer of the

[1] Hence the German term, "*Weissholz*," *i.e.*, whitewood.
[2] MÜNCH, *Op. cit.*
[3] MARRA, *Op. cit.*

cell wall bears the main tension stress and that it is well adapted mechanically for this purpose.

Chow[1] in studying tension wood in European beech has found that tension-wood fibers in this species are characterized by short, discontinuous, spiral markings in the cell wall. These spiral markings represent

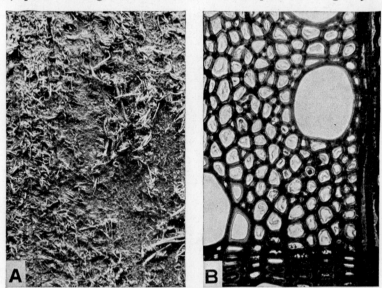

TEXT FIG. 66.—Natural defects, tension wood.
A. Longitudinal sawn surface of hard maple wood (*Acer saccharum* Marsh.) showing woolliness traceable to areas of gelatinous fibers.
B. Cross section of hard maple wood (*Acer saccharum* Marsh.) showing folded gelatinous layer in the springwood fibers (approx. 150 ×). (*From A. A. Marra, "Characteristics of Tension Wood in Hard Maple, Acer saccharum, Marsh." Unpublished thesis, New York State College of Forestry, June, 1942.*)

incipient transverse cracks, resulting from mechanical forces acting on the wood of the standing tree.

Tension wood is slightly lower in lignin content and higher in cellulose and pentosan content than normal wood. The gelatinous layer of the fibers appears to consist largely of alpha cellulose but staining reactions indicate that other, as yet unidentified, substances are also present.[2]

Tension wood shrinks considerably more longitudinally, and somewhat less transversely than normal wood. Chow[3] advances the hypothesis that the abnormal longitudinal shrinkage of tension wood on drying

---

[1] *Op. cit.*

[2] SCHALL, W. M. A Partial Chemical Analysis. Comparison of Normal and Tension Sugar Maple Wood. Graduate problem, University of California, 1942. As reported by Marra. *Op. cit.*

[3] *Op. cit.*

below the fiber saturation point is due mainly to the closing of incipient transverse cracks in the fiber walls.

Tension wood has been found to vary considerably in strength. Marra reports the strength of tension wood in hard maple to be below the average of that of normal wood in static bending; he detected no appreci-

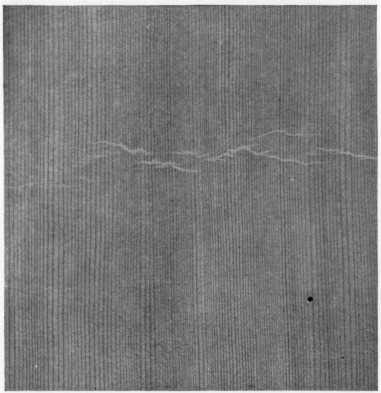

TEXT FIG. 67.—Natural defects, compression failures in wood. Compression failures in edge-grain stock of Sitka spruce, *Picea sitchensis* (Bong.) Carr. (*By permission, from "Detection of Compression Failures in Wood,"* by Eric A. Anderson. *Forest Prod. Lab. Mimeo. Rpt.* 1588. 1944.)

able difference in compression perpendicular and parallel to the grain, although the hardness was more than 13.3 per cent below that of normal wood. Chow attributes the absence of higher tensile strength in this type of reaction wood to the presence of minute transverse cracks in the fiber wall. The results obtained by Clark,[1] on the other hand, are at variance with those of Marra and Chow; in European beech, quoting Clark, "tension wood was found to be exceptionally weak under compression parallel

[1] *Op. cit.*

to the grain; in tensile strength and toughness, however, it was on the average slightly stronger then normal wood of the same density."

Tension wood frequently machines differently than normal wood. For example, Marra found that tension wood in hard maple tended strongly to result in "woolly" surfaces (Text Fig. 66, *A*) traceable to the tracts of gelatinous fibers. The woolliness developed through the tearing of fibers into groups or ribbons by the cutterhead, the fiber masses remaining attached to the surface at one end. In shaping blocks, Marra experienced considerable difficulty in sawing; the saw frequently pinched, making the operation difficult. Clark noted that, when tension wood was worked on a lathe, the tool produced long, unbroken, and rather pliable ribbons of wood while turnings from normal wood, in contrast, came off as short, broken, and brittle chips.

C. COMPRESSION FAILURES

This term denotes localized buckling of the fibers (Text Fig. 67), ranging from well-defined ridges on a longitudinal suface of the wood that are visible with the naked eye to a creasing so slight that it can be detected only under the microscope.[1] Compression failures are indicative of permanent deformation of the walls of cells which results from compression of the wood parallel to the grain beyond its proportional (elastic) limit.[2] They may develop in standing trees when these are bent by severe winds or heavy snow; in felling trees on uneven ground or where they strike other trees, rocks, etc.; from the rough handling of logs and sawed stock; and, finally, from excessive stress in service, such as the overloading of posts and beams.

Compression failures may considerably impair the strength properties of wood, especially its shock resistance in beams, ladder rails, etc.; such timbers then fail in a manner similar to that of a typically brash wood (see below).

D. BRASHNESS

Brashness[3] is an abnormal condition in wood that permits it to break suddenly and completely across the grain, generally at a stress at which

---

[1] When compression failures are suspected but are not clearly visible to the naked eye, they can be made to stand out sharply by the application of carbon tetrachloride to the surface of the wood. See LIMBACH, J. P. Compression Failures in Wood Detected by the Application of Carbon Tetrachloride to the Surface. *Forest Prod. Lab., Mimeo. Rpt.* 1591. 1945.

[2] The proportional, or elastic, limit is that limit beyond which it is impossible to continue the distortion of a body without causing permanent deformation.

[3] FORSAITH, C. C. The Morphology of Wood in Relation to Brashness. *Jour. Forestry*, Vol. 19, pp. 237–249. 1921.

KOEHLER, ARTHUR. Causes of Brashness in Wood. *U.S. Dept. Agr. Tech. Bul.* 342. 1933.

a normal piece of the same wood would not fail (Text Fig. 68). The surfaces exposed by such a break are relatively smooth in comparison to the jagged surfaces resulting from the fracture of normal wood. Brashness is a very objectionable defect in wood, for brash wood gives little warning of failure in advance, especially under shock.

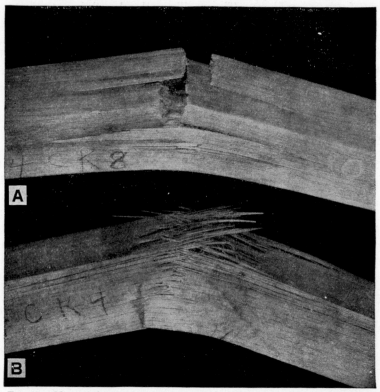

Text Fig. 68.—Natural defects, brashness in wood. Typical fractures in hickory (*Carya sp.*), tested under impact bending. (*By permission from "Causes of Brashness in Wood," by Arthur Koehler. U. S. Dept. Agr., Tech. Bul. 342. 1933.*)

A. Fracture of a brash stick of hickory after an 18-inch drop of the hammer.

B. Fracture of a normal stick of hickory after a 50-inch drop of the same hammer used in A.

Although there is no sharp visual demarcation between brash and normal wood of the same species, brash pieces can usually be detected because they are abnormally low in density; this condition is especially noticeable when such samples are dry. Density is contingent upon the amount of cell-wall substance per unit of volume; wood of low density is often formed, in both softwoods and hardwoods, as a result of unusually slow growth, or in softwoods as a result of unusually wide rings. As stated previously, brash wood is also abnormal in that the fibrils in the walls of the longitudinal elements (see Chap. IV) approach more nearly the horizontal plane than those of normal wood, a feature that is also conducive to a reduction in strength.

In hardwood species such as oak, brashness may be correlated with a decrease in the fiber volume of the wood, coupled with an increase in the number of thin-walled elements such as tracheids and longitudinal parenchyma. Samples so characterized may not necessarily be low in density. Other causes contributing to brashness are compression wood, decay, prolonged exposure to high temperatures, and the presence of compression failures.

E. DEFECTS DUE TO DIRECTION OF THE GRAIN

Whenever the fiber alignment deviates from a direction parallel to the long axis of a piece of wood, *i.e.*, when it runs at an angle to it, the piece is said to be *cross grained*. Although many variations of cross grain are recognized in the trade, such as spiral, diagonal, interlocked, wavy, and curly, only the first two mentioned are held to be important defects. Interlocked, wavy, and curly grained lumber is not generally considered as defective although a certain amount of difficulty may be encountered in the seasoning and machining of such wood.[1]

The degree of cross grain is measured as an angle, expressed as a slope between the direction of fiber alignment and the long axis of the piece. For example, a slope of 1 in 10 inches (recorded as 1:10 in the literature) signifies that the grain deviates 1 inch from the long axis of the piece over a distance of 10 inches. This may be expressed as a fraction, in the case cited as $\frac{1}{10}$ or, in a generalized case, as $1/a$ or $1/b$.

When the grain of a wooden member slopes on two lateral sufaces at right angles, even though these surfaces are not truly radial and truly tangential, respectively, the combined slope $1/x$ can be obtained by substitution in the equation[2]

$$\frac{1}{x} = \sqrt{\left(\frac{1}{a}\right)^2 + \left(\frac{1}{b}\right)^2}$$

in which a is the denominator of one slope and b the denominator of the other.[3] Note should be made of the fact that the combined slope is always steeper than either of the component slopes.

---

[1] See pp. 273 to 276, for a more complete discussion of these types of grain.

[2] This equation may be written as $\dfrac{1}{x} = \dfrac{\sqrt{a^2 + b^2}}{ab}$

[3] For example, if the component slopes are 1 inch in 12 inches and 1 inch in 5 inches, the combined slope is $\dfrac{\sqrt{12^2 + 5^2}}{12 \times 5} = \dfrac{13}{60} = 1$ inch in 4.6 inches.

The best way to determine the direction of the grain in a piece of wood is to split it. In most cases, however, this is not a practical procedure. The direction of the grain may be determined by observing the course of resin canals or vessels. If true tangential and radial surfaces are available, the slope of the grain may be ascertained by noting the direction of seasoning checks on the tangential face and of growth increments on the radial face. Application of a free-flowing ink with a broad pen point or an eye dropper across the grain is also helpful; the fine lines extending from the sides of the ink mark indicate the fiber alignment. Various devices have been suggested for measuring the slope of grain;[1] among these are a plate of clear glass scored with one or more lines indicating slope of grain, machinist's calipers, and specially modified straightedges.

The effect of cross grain is most noticeable in tensile strength where appreciable reduction occurs at a slope of 1 in 25. The effect of cross grain in strength in compression is less marked, the reduction generally not becoming evident until a slope of 1 in 10 is reached. The weakening effect of cross grain in shear is negligible.

The reduction in strength properties occasioned by cross grain is traceable to the wide discrepancies in the strength values of wood along and across the grain. The very nature of cross grain, therefore, tends to accentuate these variables. In addition, cross-grained wood is more prone to check, twist, and warp.

Cross grain, especially diagonal grain occasioned by faulty manufacture, is a serious defect when wood is used for skis, etc. Many pieces of furniture are rendered useless by breakage due to defective stock of this type which could have been eliminated by more rigid inspection.

As stated on page 299, many variations of cross grain are recognized in the trade. Two of these require description here.

1. Spiral Grain.—This term refers to the spiraling of fibers in a tree stem that gives the trunk a twisted appearance after the bark has been removed or falls off (Text Fig. 69). The spiral may be either right- or left-handed, and the direction of the twist as well as the slope may change with the age of the tree.[2] The cause of spiraling in trees has never been explained satisfactorily although there is some evidence that this defect may be hereditary.[3]

---

[1] ANDERSON, E. A., ARTHUR KOEHLER, and R. H. KROME. Instruments for Rapidly Measuring Slope of Grain in Lumber. *Forest Prod. Lab., Mimeo. Rpt.* 1592. June, 1945.

[2] McCARTHY, E. F., and R. J. HOYLE. Knot Zones and Spiral in Adirondack Red Spruce. *Jour. Forestry*, Vol. 16, pp. 777–791. 1918.

[3] CHAMPION, H. G. Contribution toward a Knowledge of Twisted Fiber in Trees. *Indian Forest Rec., New Ser. Silvic.*, Vol. 11, Part 2. 1925.

2. Diagonal Grain.[1]—This type of cross grain may result from care-lessness of the sawyer; the plane of the cut does not follow the growth increments along the grain but, rather, cuts at an angle to them. The most common cause of diagonal grain is the practice of sawing logs parallel

Text Fig. 69.—Natural defects. Base of a tree trunk with a portion of the bark removed, showing spiral grain in surface view.

to the pith rather than to the bark, carelessness in manufacture of wooden articles, and the natural crook present in many logs.

F. Shakes

Shakes result from the actual rupture of the wood. Occasionally, cells are pulled apart by the stresses that are set up, but in most instances the cell walls themselves are ruptured. Shakes arise in standing trees, not in the seasoning of lumber; they frequently are extended farther as logs and sawn stock dry, following the lines of cleavage originally estab-

[1] Although a man-made defect, diagonal grain is discussed under Natural Defects. The logic of this procedure rests on the fact that, after a log is sawed into lumber, the cause of cross grain cannot be determined. In the trade, both spiral and diagonal grain are called "cross grain."

lished.   Two types of shakes are recognized, ring or cup shakes, and heart shakes.

1. Ring or Cup Shakes.—These defects are formed when the breaks occur between annual increments or less frequently within an annual growth layer when they pursue the same direction.   They are very common in eastern hemlock, western larch, cypress, and sycamore and are occasionally found in other species.   Ring shakes are believed to result from the swaying of the tree trunk in the wind and hence are sometimes called **wind shakes**.   Other causes contributing to the formation of ring shakes are thought to be heavy frosts resulting in a shrinkage, followed by a swelling, of the outer layers of the wood, the tilting of a tree with the resultant disturbance to its root system, and possibly the shrinkage of the heartwood in the standing tree.   In 1933, Koehler[1] advanced the hypothesis that shakes in green timber are due to transverse compression and tension stresses resulting largely from growth.   He propounds three reasons why such stresses should be present in green wood, *viz.*, (1) greater circumferential than radial growth, (2) reduction in the turgidity of the older wood in the trunk, (3) chemical shrinkage of the older wood.

2. Heart Shakes.—Heart shakes differ from ring shakes in that the cracks run at right angles to the growth increments, generally following the rays.   Heart shake, also called **heart check** and **rift crack,** occurs in overmature timber, especially in hardwoods such as oak that have broad rays.   The rifts in the tissue may radiate from the pith, when the term **star shake** is applied; or only one crack may form, in which case the defect is called **simple heart shake.**

Heart shakes are generally confined to butt logs.   The initial ruptures usually occur as a result of the shrinkage of the heartwood.   Although such cracks may be relatively small in standing trees, they invariably increase in length along the rays and widen as the lumber from such trees is seasoned.

G. Frost Injuries

Two types of defects develop in the wood of living trees, supposedly as the result of freezing temperatures.   These are known as frost rings and frost cracks.

1. Frost Rings.—Frost rings appear to the naked eye as brownish lines within the boundaries of growth rings which extend in the same direction and simulate false rings.   According to Rhoads,[2] these zones of discolora-

---

[1] Koehler, A.   A New Hypothesis as to the Cause of Shakes and Rift Cracks in Green Lumber.   *Jour. Forestry*, Vol. 31, pp. 551–556.   1933.

[2] Rhoads, A. S.   The Formation and Pathological Anatomy of Frost Rings in Conifers Injured by Late Frosts.   *U.S. Dept. Agr. Dept. Bul.* 1131.   1923.   For

tion result from frost injury to the cambium and to the young xylary cells, which are as yet unlignified, after the cambium has become active in the spring or before it becomes dormant in the autumn.[1]

Examination of frost rings under the microscope reveals a collapsed condition of the partly lignified xylary cells, as well as the presence of an abnormal amount of parenchyma, and wood rays that are wider than normal (Text Fig. 70). The layer of tissue thus resulting constitutes a definite tangential plane of weakness which adversely affects the strength of the wood.

2. Frost Cracks.—Frost cracks develop as radial splits in the bark and wood near the base of a tree. They are found in all species growing in cold climes but are most frequent in hardwoods. Busse[2] states that frost cracks are most frequent in old trees with stout primary roots and broad crowns and are absent in very young trees. He also found that most splits occur shortly before sunrise, at a time when air and soil temperatures are lowest;[3] further, that they always develop between two primary roots or the collars of two such roots.

Frost cracks are usually bridged the following growing season by callus tissue which is formed by the cambium. This, however, is seldom effective in preventing the reopening and even the extension of the crack the following winter. Repeated healing and opening of frost cracks frequently result in the formation of protruding lips of callus along the flanks of the cracks which in turn are rendered more prominent on the trunk of the tree. Such elevations are known as **frost rib.**

Several theories have been advanced to explain the reasons for the development of frost cracks. One claims that the splits form as a result of the low heat conductivity of the wood. According to this hypothesis, the outer annual increments of wood contract as the temperature falls,

---

further information on frost damage, see J. Lequitt. Frost Killing and Hardiness of Plants—A Critical Review. Pp. v + 211 + plates. Burgess Publishing Company, Minneapolis, Minn. 1941.

[1] Trees differ widely in their ability to withstand unseasonable frosts after the cambium has become active, due in part to departures as to the rate at which they shed their outer bark. Species with thin dead bark, and the younger portions of the trunk and limbs of almost all species, are prone to frost injury because they are not sufficiently insulated to prevent damage to delicate cambial cells after growth starts. Beech, for example, is more subject to frost injury than hard maple and yellow birch which grow in association with it.

[2] Busse, W. Frost-, Ring-, und Kernrisse. *Forstwiss. Centbl.*, Band 32, pp 74–84. 1910.

[3] L. P. Plumley, The New York State College of Forestry, Syracuse, N. Y., has uncovered some evidence to the effect that rupture occurs when air temperatures are mounting; *i.e.*, after they have passed the maximum low.

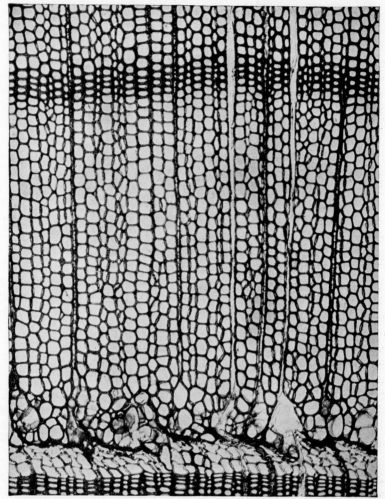

Text Fig. 70.—Natural defects, frost injury.   Abnormal cell production, near the beginning of an annual ring in Jack Pine (*Pinus banksiana* Lamb.) (145 ×).   The wound tissue is similar to that resulting from frost injury and may have been the result of this.   (*The Forest Products Laboratory.*)

before the inner layers are affected by this change.   The tensile stresses thus resulting from this uneven contraction produce failures (cracks) across the grain in a radial direction.   Busse, on the other hand, considers the mechanical action of the wind to be the most important factor in the development of cracks in the first place.   According to this investigator, once they are established, tension stresses resulting from frost would prove sufficient to reopen them.

H. Pitch Defects

A number of defects known as pitch, pitch streaks, and pitch pockets are found in softwoods in which resin canals are normal in the wood, *i.e.*, in spruces, Douglas fir, pines, and larches. The other domestic softwoods are remarkably free of pitch blemishes although they may develop in any coniferous wood as a result of injury to the cambium.

1. Pitch and Pitch Streaks.—These defects develop through the accumulation of resin to excessive amount, in localized tracts in the wood; this fills the cell lumina and permeates the cell walls so that resin-soaked patches or streaks of tissue are present in the wood. If the patches are irregular in shape or poorly defined, they are termed pitch; if sharply delineated, they are called pitch streaks. The reason for the development of such defects is not clearly understood although they undoubtedly result in many cases from the attacks of insects,[1] or from injuries of the type that are inflicted in turpentining southern pines.

2. Pitch Pockets.—Pitch pockets, when viewed on surfaces at right angle to the grain or in edge-grain stock, are planoconvex cavities that are usually wholly within the boundary of a growth increment (Text Fig. 36, *E* to *H*); the flat or nearly flat surface is on the side nearest to the pith. In flat-sawn lumber, such pockets appear as oval or elliptical areas, the long axis of which is parallel to the grain.

As the term implies, pitch pockets usually contain resin in liquid or solid form, but they may be devoid of such contents. At other times, bark inclusions are present. They vary considerably in size; the radial diameter is generally less than ½ inch, but the opening in the grain may extend several inches circumferentially (in the direction of the growth rings) and for an even greater distance vertically in the standing tree.

As held for frost cracks, the reason for the formation of pitch pockets is still obscure. According to Forsaith,[2] " . . . Limited microscopical studies have shown that these cysts are similar to enormous resin centers since their cavities are surrounded by parenchyma-like epithelial tissue. Their confinement to a definite portion of an annual ring reveals that they are formed as a result of cambial activity in which contiguous cambial derivations over a considerable area suddenly cease differentiating as tracheids in order to develop resin epthelium. After several rows of such cells have been formed, the meristematic layer will just as suddenly cease this process and resume the normal development of woody cells. The

[1] SNYDER, T. E.   Defects in Timber Caused by Insects.   *U.S. Dept. Agr. Bul.* 1490.   1927.

[2] FORSAITH, C. C.   The Technology of New York State Timbers.   *N.Y. State Col. Forestry, Syracuse Univ., Tech. Pub.* 18, pp. 263–264.   1926.

cavity itself results from a separation of these resin forming units through-out the central part of its volume, and consequently it is, like the resin canal cavity, post cambial in its development." Forsaith makes no mention of the destruction of the cambium in the formation of pitch

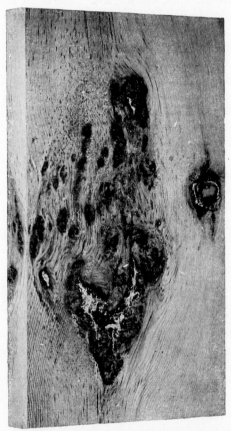

Text Fig. 71.—Natural defects. A bark pocket in western yellow pine (*Pinus ponderosa* Laws.). (*By permission, from "British Columbia Softwoods, Their Decay and Natural Defects," by H. W. Eades. Canadian Forest Serv. Bul.* 80. 1932.)

pockets. Quite recently Frey-Wyssling[1] has presented evidence to support the contention that in larch and other conifers they result from cracks in the cambium; these are formed by wind pressure and subsequently fill with resin. That pitch pockets are due to injury is obvious, but the causal agent is still a matter of debate.

---

[1] Frey-Wyssling, A. Über die Entstehung von Harztaschen. *Schweiz. Ztschr. f. Forstw.*, Band 93, S. 101–106. 1942.

I. Bark Pockets

These are small patches of bark that are embedded in wood (Text Fig. 71). They apparently develop from some injury to the tree, resulting in the death of a small area of the cambium; meanwhile, the surrounding tissue continues to function, and a new cambium forms over the gap in the inner bark, thus embedding a portion of the bark in the wood. Not infrequently, as stated above, portions of bark are found in pitch pockets.

Bark pockets frequently arise as a result of bird pecks (work of sapsuckers, etc.) and from injuries inflicted on the tree by insects (bark beetles, etc.). The shallow tunnels of certain insects may become partly overgrown with bark and subsequently embedded in the wood by the continued activity of the cambium. Bark pockets of this sort, generally containing an appreciable amount of resin, are very common in western hemlock; in this species, this defect is known as **black check**[1] or **black streaks.**

J. Mineral Streaks

This term has been loosely used in the trade to denote stains of various kinds in lumber such as those occasioned by incipient decay and by resin streaks, likewise discoloration caused by wounding.[2] In a more restricted sense, the expression mineral streak or mineral stain should refer only to the olive and greenish-black streaks which are common in otherwise normal wood of hard maple, the hickories, and other hardwoods and which are believed to denote abnormal concentration of mineral matter in the tissue at these points.[3] When such wood is seasoned, cracks frequently form where the discoloration is deepest. Millmen contend that wood containing mineral streaks is harder than normal wood and has a pronounced dulling effect on tools.

A recent investigation by the Division of Forest Pathology, U.S. Department of Agriculture,[4] indicates that mineral streaks in hard maple actually have a higher ash content than the adjoining normal wood, the

---

[1] Burke, H. E. Black Check in Western Hemlock. *U.S. Dept. Agr. Cir.* 61. 1905.

[2] The dark-colored wound tissue in the occluded mines of cambial miners has been confused with mineral streaks (see page 335).

[3] H. E. Wilcox, by spectrographic analysis of the ash obtained from the tissue in the mineral streaks of hickory, has demonstrated, qualitatively, that manganese is present in unusual amount. Wilcox, H. E. The Spectrographic Analysis of White Pine (*Pinus strobus* L.), Master's thesis, The New York State College of Forestry, Syracuse, N. Y. 1940.

[4] Scheffer, T. C. Mineral Stain in Hard Maple and Other Hardwoods. *Jour. Forestry*, Vol. 37, pp. 578–579. 1939.

figures being 5.2 per cent for the former as against 1.2 per cent for the latter. The mineral-stained wood also proved to be somewhat harder than normal wood.

No acceptable explanation has yet been found to account for the development of mineral streaks. There is some evidence, however, to the effect that the mineral discoloration may be initiated by obscure injuries which in some manner interfere with the normal physiological functioning of the cells proximate to these areas; further, that the fungal hyphae which are sometimes present in the stained tissue are not necessarily a contributing factor.

K. Chemical Stains

Stains of this sort are caused by chemical changes which ensue in the materials (foodstuffs, etc.) present in the lumina of xylary cells (see Defects Caused by Wood-staining Fungi, page 331). The exact chemical reactions involved in the production of these nonpathological pigments are as yet unknown. They are believed, however, to be due to the oxidation of certain constituents of the protoplast (cell contents); hence the term **oxidative stains,** which is sometimes used to designate this type of discoloration.

Chemical stains vary considerably in color, ranging through shades of yellow and orange to brown. They develop both in softwoods and in hardwoods, sometimes in logs during storage, but more frequently during the seasoning of lumber. Stains of this nature are superficial in the wood and in no way affect its strength.

The most important chemical stains are the brown discolorations that are especially prevalent in sugar pine and in ponderosa pine. When the stain develops during air seasoning or in storage, it is called **yard brown stain;** if during kiln drying, **kiln brown stain.**

L. White Spots or Streaks ("Floccosoids") in Western Hemlock

Floccosoids is a term coined by Grondal and Mottet[1] for the whitish spots that quite frequently occur in western hemlock [*Tsuga heterophylla* (Raf.) Sarg.]. They are due to whitish deposits in the wood the exact chemical nature of which has not yet been determined (Text Fig. 72, *A*). Floccosoids appear to be of physiological origin.

Floccosoids sometimes resemble the white decay pockets of certain fungi, for example, those of *Fomes pini* (Thore) Lloyd (Text Fig. 72, *C*).

[1] Grondal, B. L., and A. L. Mottet. Characteristics and Significance of White Floccose, Aggregates in the Wood of Western Hemlock. *Univ. Wash., Forest Club Quart.,* Vol. 16, pp. 13–18. 1942.

The wood in a floccosoid, however, is as sound as normal wood; the light color of the tissue is traceable to infiltration in excess of normal (Text Fig. 72, *B*). In decay pockets of the type portrayed, in contrast, the bleaching of the wood is due to a white rot, and the partially decomposed tissue is softer than normal wood. A positive test for floccosoids[1] can

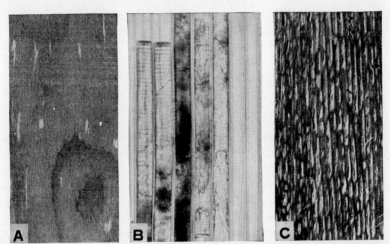

TEXT FIG. 72.—Natural defects. Floccosoids (white specks) in western hemlock [*Tsuga heterophylla* (Raf.) Sarg.]

    A. Floccosoids in rotary-cut veneer.

    B. Floccosoids as seen along the grain through the microscope (approx. 120 ×).

    C. Decay pockets in all stages of development in sliced, edge-grained veneer. Such pockets are sometimes mistaken for floccosoids. (*By permission, from "Western Hemlock 'Floccosoids' (White Spots or Streaks)," by Eloise Gerry, U. S. Forest Prod. Lab. Rpt. 1392.* 1943.)

be made by treating a small, thin, longitudinal section through an involved area with a few drops of caustic alkali (potassium or sodium hydroxide) on a glass slide. A cover glass is then added and the mount is examined under a microscope. If the spot is a floccosoid, it disappears gradually but completely in a relatively short time; a decay pocket remains unchanged.

---

[1] GERRY, ELOISE. Western Hemlock "Floccosoids" (White Spots or Streaks). *Forest Prod. Lab., Rpt.* 1392. March, 1943.

CHAPTER XIII

DEFECTS IN WOOD
(*Continued*)

II. DEFECTS DUE TO SEASONING AND MACHINING

(Text Fig. 73)

As wood comes from the tree, it contains appreciable amounts of water, frequently up to 100 to 200 per cent in terms of its ovendry weight. Wood begins to season as soon as it is exposed; *i.e.*, some or a large part of the moisture is lost through drying.

When green wood dries, the first water to leave it is the free moisture in the cavities (lumina) of the cells. No normal dimensional changes accompany this stage in the drying process. When, however, the drying is continued below the fiber saturation point (the point at which there is no free moisture in cell cavities and before water begins to leave the cell walls), shrinkage takes place. This results in a change in the dimensions of the wood.

Unfortunately, as wood continues to dry below the fiber saturation point, the shrinkage is not equal in all directions. This situation is explained by the fact that xylary tissue is a complex cell aggregate composed of different kinds of cells some of which are aligned vertically in the standing tree, others horizontally and radially. The shrinkage of wood along the grain is negligible;[1] across the grain, it shrinks about twice as much in the tangential direction as radially. This inequality in shrinkage in three directions at right angles sets up strains which are unavoidable and which, if they become too great, cause actual fractures in the tissue. Such failures are described in this text as seasoning defects.[2]

---

[1] Compression and tension woods are an exception to this rule in that they shrink appreciably along the grain.

[2] It follows that most seasoning defects can be avoided if wood is carefully dried over a long period (air seasoning) or under properly controlled conditions during a shorter period (kiln-drying). The technique consists, by manipulation, in minimizing as much as possible the stresses that of necessity arise, *i.e.*, in keeping these below the point at which actual failures would develop. It is even possible, within limits, to correct seasoning defects by further treatment, once they have occurred.

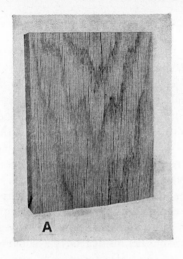
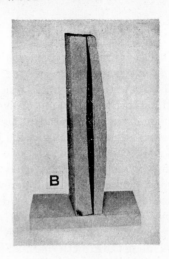
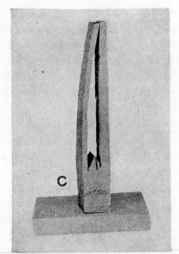
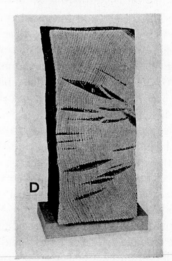

TEXT FIG. 73.—Defects due to seasoning. (*Photographs by permission, from " The Air Seasoning and Kiln Drying of Wood," by Hiram L. Henderson. J. B. Lyon Co., Albany, N.Y.* 1936.)

   A. Surface checking on the face of a board of oak (*Quercus sp.*).

   B. Section of hardwood board, resawn, showing cupping.

   C. Test sample of a hardwood board showing casehardening; at this stage the core of the board was still wetter than the shell and the latter was under tension.

   D. Section of a board of oak (*Quercus sp.*), showing honeycombing.

A. Checks

Checks are ruptures in wood along the grain which, with the exception of heart checks (see Shakes, page 301), develop during seasoning (Text Fig. 73, *A*). Defects of this type arise for two reasons, *viz.*, (1) because of a difference in radial and tangential shrinkage resulting in stresses of sufficient magnitude to cause the failure of the wood along the planes of greatest weakness, usually at the juncture of longitudinal tissue with the rays; (2) because of differences in the shrinkage of the tissue in adjacent portions of the wood, occasioned by varying moisture content; these, as they dry, cause stresses of different magnitude.

Seasoning checks are of two types, **end checks** and **surface checks**. As the terms imply, the former are confined to the ends of the piece; such checks normally follow the rays, although occasionally they may extend along the growth rings. Surface checks result from the separation of the thinner walled springwood cells; they also follow the rays and, therefore, are confined largely to tangential surfaces. Surface checks extend into the wood for varying distances.

As the drying progresses deeper into the wood, many of the checks (especially those of the surface type) close; but, of course, such ruptures are never bridged by wound tissue. In tree species with large rays (oak, beech) the closing of surface checks may lead to honeycombing (see page 319). The formation of surface checks in certain stages of drying may also indicate the presence of drying conditions favorable to the development of casehardening (see page 315). Checks, especially if they are of some magnitude, considerably affect the strength of wood, particularly in shear, because, in a piece, they reduce the areas of the bearing surfaces that can offer resistance to stresses.

In air seasoning, both types of checking can be minimized by following procedures that tend to promote the less rapid but uniform evaporation of moisture. These include reduction of circulation in the lumber pile in the case of surface checking, and shading or painting the ends of boards and timbers with moisture-resistant coatings in the case of end checking.[1] In kiln drying, checking is indicative of uneven or too rapid drying and can be avoided by maintaining adequate circulation and proper temperature and humidity conditions.

Another type of checking frequently develops in wood but cannot be detected except by resorting to a compound microscope; such minute failures are known as **microscopic checks** (Text Fig. 14, *B*). Checking of this sort occurs between the fibrils in the secondary walls; *i.e.*, in the

[1] Anon. Coatings That Prevent End Checks. *Forest Prod. Lab., Tech. Note* 186. 1943.

fault lines that spiral in the cell wall. The slope of such microscopic checks is, therefore, indicative of the alignment of the fibril helixes. **Spiral checking** frequently simulates spiral thickening of the type that characterizes the longitudinal tracheids of Douglas fir (Text Fig. 14, *A*); the slope of such checks is, however, steeper than the helixes formed as a result of spiral thickening.[1]

Spiral checks frequently occur in the dense summerwood of such conifers as southern pine and also in the last-formed tracheids of compression wood. In the latter instance, they are not formed as the result of drying following the conversion of the wood but develop in the living tree.

B. WARPING

In a broad sense, the term "warping" is used to describe any distortion from the true plane that may occur in a piece of wood during seasoning. Several different types of warping are recognized and are easily detected by the appearance of the deformed piece, each arising from a different cause. The principal types of warping are bowing, crooking, cupping, twisting, and diamonding.

1. Bowing is defined as longitudinal curvature, flatwise, from a straight line, drawn from end to end of the piece.

2. Crooking, by comparison, is longitudinal curvature, edgewise, from a straight line, drawn from end to end of the piece.

Both of the above-mentioned types of warping arise as a consequence of differences in longitudinal shrinkage, the first from a discrepancy in the shortening on the faces of a board, the second from a difference in shrinkages on the edges of a board.

Bowing and crooking, for obvious reasons, are very common defects in lumber in which the grain is irregular as, for example, in curly-grained stock or where boards are so sawed that the grain on one side or edge is canted more than on the other. Straight-grained pieces of wood are less subject to these defects although bowing occasionally occurs in what appears to be perfectly straight-grained stock and then invariably toward the bark side.[2] The following reasons have been offered to explain this: (1) tension along the grain which may have existed in the outer portion of the tree producing the timber, (2) greater longitudinal shrinkage in the sapwood than in the heartwood, (3) greater longitudinal shrinkage of the wood toward the periphery of the tree trunk than that of the core,

---

[1] In both instances, a crosshatch pattern may be formed, for the spirals are reversed on different sides of the cell wall, and the lenses of a microscope have depth of focus.

[2] TORGESON, O. W. Seasoning Dimension Stock. *Wood Working Indus.* June, 1932.

explainable by the fact that the former was less dense, and (4) the presence of reaction wood (compression or tension wood). In pieces containing both reaction and normal wood, the excessive longitudinal shrinkage of the former is retarded by the lower longitudinal shrinkage of the latter. This sets up stresses, which frequently are of sufficient magnitude to cause the piece to bow and twist.

3. Cupping signifies the curving of the face of a plank or board so that it assumes a troughlike shape, the edges meanwhile remaining approximately parallel to each other (Text Fig. 73, *B*). There are two primary causes for cupping, *viz.*, (1) the more rapid drying of one face of a board than of the other and (2) the discrepancy between radial and tangential shrinkages which causes one side of the piece to shrink more than the other.

This defect may arise in the first instance when one surface of a board is in contact with, or near the surface of, the ground or is in touch with another object and hence cannot dry at the normal rate; if the other surface is freely exposed to the sun or is merely better aerated, cupping may result on the side that is exposed. Curvatures on lumber of this kind are usually only temporary and tend to correct themselves as the wood becomes uniformly dry.

Cupping, arising as a result of the discrepancy existing between tangential and radial shrinkages across the grain, frequently develops in plain-sawn lumber in which one face of the wood approaches the quarter-sawn condition and the other is flat-grained. The board, of course, shrinks less on the quarter face, causing cupping on the opposite side.

Cupping may also result when casehardened lumber (see page 315) is resawn or is dressed more on one side than on the other. It may likewise occur in resawing lumber that is much wetter in the interior than on the outside; such stock will usually straighten out or even curve in the opposite direction as the exposed interior dries. Finally, any piece of wood which has been painted or varnished on one side and not on the other or which has received a heavier coat of finish on one side, if exposed to sudden changes in atmospheric conditions, may cup. In such instances, the better protected surface loses and gains moisture less quickly than the other face, and cupping may develop on the side that is least protected.

4. Twisting indicates a condition in which one corner of a piece of wood twists out of the plane of the other three; *i.e.*, it denotes a situation in which the four corners of a surface are no longer in the same plane. Twisting is usually a concomitant of cross or irregular grain; but, as in bowing and crooking, it may also develop in a straight-grained piece of wood as a result of uneven drying or because of inherent stresses in the standing tree.

5. Diamonding describes uneven shrinkage, usually developing in squares in which the growth increments extend so diagonally that the faces of the piece are neither flat- nor edge-grained. Such pieces, although square when green, become rhomboidal or diamond-shaped on drying, as viewed facially. The reason for diamonding is, of course, the discrepancy existing between radial and tangential shrinkage.

C. Casehardening

Casehardening is a condition in wood that develops as a result of too rapid drying. It is characterized by the presence of stresses in dry lumber with nearly uniform moisture content[1] resulting from a difference in the "final set" between the interior (core) and the surface portions (shell) of a piece of wood that has dried too rapidly to shrink normally. As a consequence, some of the wood in the interior of the piece is under tension, *i.e.*, partly stretched, while the outer layers are in compression, and as a result internal stresses of considerable magnitude are produced. Casehardening may develop either in kiln-dried or in air-dried stock; it is more common in the former.

The conditions leading to the development of casehardening may be stated briefly as follows. When wood is seasoned, the outer portion of the piece dries below the fiber saturation point first but is restrained from shrinking fully, because the adjacent inner layers, being wetter, lag in shrinking. In consequence, the wood in the surface layers is stretched, *i.e.*, put under tension, while that of the core is compressed. These conditions are normal during the initial stages of drying. When the drying conditions are not too severe, the tensile stresses are relieved as soon as the adjacent inner layers dry and shrink, thus allowing the outer layers to shrink further. On the other hand, if drying proceeds at too rapid a rate, the differences in moisture content and hence in shrinkage, between the shell and the core may become sufficient to cause a "permanent set" of the outer layers, *i.e.*, to allow them to dry in a partly stretched condition, without attaining full shrinkage. If stresses that develop exceed the maximum strength of the wood perpendicular to the grain, surface checks will form at this stage of drying (Text Fig. 73, *A*).

As the drying of such a piece progresses, more moisture is lost from the core, and the tissue composing this tends to shrink further. Since, however, the shell has "set" but is organically connected with the core, it now prevents the normal shrinkage of the core. Hence, the stresses are reversed, *i.e.*, the shell is now in compression and the core is in tension.

[1] The term "casehardening" is sometimes incorrectly applied also to nonuniformly dried lumber, in which the moisture content in the center of a piece is considerably higher than that in the outer layers.

Honeycombing (see page 319), a type of defect in which numerous pockets form in the wood, often develops as a result of the stresses set up during this second and final stage of casehardening.

In addition to surface checking and honeycombing, casehardening may also be responsible for another defect. Casehardened lumber is undesirable because it tends to cup when resawed or dressed (planed) unevenly (see page 314 and Text Fig. 73, *B*). In any case, the stresses that are invariably present often have a cumulative effect in weakening the wood, even though the defects mentioned above are not in evidence.

Casehardening can be relieved by subjecting the lumber to a conditioning treatment (sometimes incorrectly called "steaming") at a temperature of 160°F. or above, and at relative humidities sufficient to even up the moisture content between the core and the shell of each piece.[1] Under such conditioning treatment the wood becomes sufficiently plastic to yield to the stresses, thereby freeing the lumber from casehardening.

D. Reverse Casehardening

Reverse casehardening is a condition that develops in lumber as a result of oversteaming, generally in an attempt to relieve casehardening. If, during conditioning at high humidity, the surface layers are permitted to absorb moisture considerably in excess of that necessary to even up the differences in the moisture content of the shell and of the core, the surface layers tend to swell. This tendency, however, is resisted by the drier interior and results in permanent compression of the outside layers. When, subsequently, the surface layers dry, they shrink more than normal wood, thus producing tension at the surface and compression in the interior of the piece. Reverse casehardening causes outward cupping on resawing; in extreme cases, the initial swelling of the surface layers may also cause honeycombing by developing internal tensile stresses that exceed the maximum tensile strength of the wood perpendicular to the grain.

E. Collapse

Collapse is a defect that sometimes develops when very wet heartwood of certain species is dried. It is usually evidenced by abnormal and irregular shrinkage. Collapse generally appears merely as excessive shrinkage (and is frequently so interpreted). In more severe cases, the sides of the lumber may cave in (Text Fig. 74, *A*), resulting in irregular depressions and elevations on the surfaces of a board and in internal

---

[1] For more detailed information on the method of relieving casehardening, see Detection and Relief of Casehardening. *Forest Prod. Lab., Tech. Note* 213. 1940.

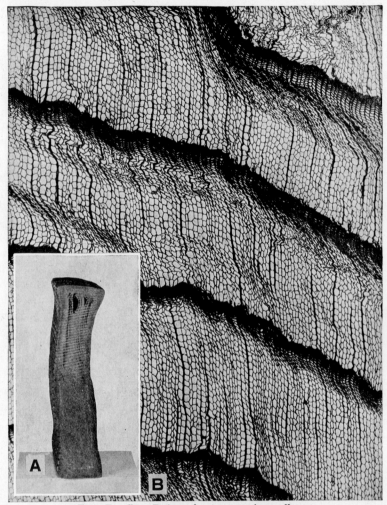

TEXT FIG. **74.**—Defects due to seasoning, collapse.

A. End-grain view of a board of redwood [*Sequoia sempervirens* (D. Don.) Endl.] showing collapse. (*By permission, from " The Air Seasoning and Kiln Drying of Wood," by Hiram L. Henderson. J. B. Lyon Co., Albany, N.Y.* 1936.)

B. Transverse section of the collapsed wood of western red cedar (*Thuja plicata* D. Don.) (20 ×). (*Forest Products Laboratory.*)

honeycombing.[1] Among native species, collapse is most frequent in redwood, western red cedar, bald cypress, red-gum, bottomland oaks, and cottonwood; it also occasionally develops in other domestic woods, such

[1] Collapse may occur, even though there is no visual evidence of its presence; under such conditions, it is frequently misinterpreted as excessive shrinkage. Pieces containing both sapwood and heartwood frequently illustrate this situation; in these, the heartwood appears to shrink more than the sapwood.

as hickory and black walnut.   Certain tropical woods, especially those produced by the Australian genus, *Eucalyptus*, are especially susceptible to this defect.

Unlike other seasoning defects, collapse begins before all the free water has disappeared from cell cavities, *i.e.*, before normal shrinkage starts.   It differs from normal shrinkage in that the latter is caused by the drawing together of the cell-wall particles as the moisture dries out of the walls, while in collapse the walls of the cells are actually pulled together, causing the cells to buckle (collapse) in more or less extensive tracts throughout the wood (Text Fig. 74, *B*).

There are two theories that attempt to explain the cause of collapse.   According to one, it is produced by the hygroscopic tension exerted by water, as it is withdrawn from cell cavities, on wet and plastic cell walls.[1] The tension results from the evaporation of water from completely enclosed fiber cavities (not vessel segments that are perforate), through minute openings in the pit membranes.   Such tension can be set up only when the fiber cavities are completely filled with water.   An air bubble with a diameter exceeding that of the largest opening through which evaporation takes place would tend to relieve the stress on a cell by expanding under tension.   The other theory[2] postulates that collapse occurs when the compressive stresses, developed during drying, exceed the compressive strength of the wood; as a result, the fiber walls collapse into the fiber cavities.

Since the plasticity of wet wood increases with temperature, it follows that collapse is more liable to occur at the higher temperatures that prevail in certain stages of kiln drying.   It is suggested, therefore, that stock exhibiting a tendency to collapse should be dried at a lower temperature, *i.e.*, until it is safely past the fiber saturation point.

Extensive investigations in Australia[3] have led to the development of a method for reconditioning collapsed eucalyptus timber.   It was found that the cells can be restored to their original shape, if the walls have not broken down completely, by remoistening the collapsed wood at a high temperature after which the stock is then redried.   In this procedure, the lumber is first dried to about 10 or 15 per cent of moisture; it is then subjected to a high humidity treatment at about 180° to 200°F. for

[1] TIEMANN, H. D.   Collapse in Wood as Shown by the Microscope.   *Jour. Forestry*, Vol. 39, pp. 271–282.   1941; GREENHILL, W. L.   The Shrinkage of Australian Timbers—Part I.   *Austral. Council Sci. & Indus. Res., Div. Forest Prod., Tech. Paper* 21, *Pamp.* 67.   1936; Part 2, *Tech. Paper* 35, *Pam.* 97.   1940.

[2] STAMM, A. J., and W. K. LOUGHBOROUGH.   Variation in Shrinkage and Swelling of Wood.   *Trans. Amer. Soc. Mech. Engin.*, Vol. 64, pp. 379–386.   1942.

[3] ANON.   Collapse and the Reconditioning of Collapsed Lumber.   *Austral. Council Sci. & Indus. Res., Div. Forest Prod., Trade Cir.* 20.   1934.

several hours, to permit it to reabsorb 2 to 6 per cent of moisture and to return to its original shape. The stock is then redried to its original moisture content, this time without the recurrence of collapse since (1) the redrying process was started below the fiber saturation point, *i.e.*, without water in a free state being present in the wood or at least in a quantity sufficient to fill the cell cavities completely, and (2) the cell walls may have been rendered more pervious.

During the later stages of drying, collapse is frequently accompanied by honeycombing (described below). This occurs when the outer layers (shell) of a stick of wood dry below the fiber saturation point and set. Under these conditions, if the wetter core begins to collapse, internal checks may occur of a type to produce severe honeycombing.[1]

F. Honeycombing

This defect, also called *hollow-horning*, is traceable to internal checking and splitting, generally along the rays, which results in lumber as it dries (Text Fig. 73, *D*). The splits generally do not extend all the way to the surface, although one form of honeycombing develops through the closing of surface checks, the cracks meanwhile deepening and broadening in the interior of the wood. The most common causes of honeycombing are the internal stresses that develop in casehardening and collapse.

G. Raised Grain

According to the American Lumber Standards, *raised grain* denotes the "roughened condition of the surface of dressed lumber in which the hard summerwood is raised above the softer springwood, but not torn loose from it." The surface of the board with this defect has a corrugated feel and appearance. In practice, however, the term, raised grain, is also extended to include the surface fuzzing that is traceable to the breaking or loosening of individual fibers or groups of fibers in sanding operations. Still another type of raised grain, commonly called *loosened grain*, is caused by the loosening and curling of the edges and tips of annual rings.

1. Raised Grain in Dressed Lumber.—In plain-sawn lumber the corrugated appearance of the wood surface is due largely to the crushing of the hard summerwood into the softer springwood beneath by the action of planer knives.[2] Mechanically, compressed wood tends to swell

---

[1] Tiemann, H. D. Lessons in Kiln Drying No. 29—Steaming. *South. Lumberman*, Vol. 155, No. 1957, pp. 47–49. 1937.

[2] Koehler, Arthur. Raised Grain—Its Causes and Prevention. *South. Lumberman*, Vol. 137, p. 210M. 1929; *Idem.* More about Loosened Grain, *South. Lumberman*, Vol. 161, pp. 171–173. 1940.

more than normal wood under the same conditions of moisture. When conditions favor the absorption of moisture, the summerwood in a planed piece rises as the cells in the springwood beneath them gradually resume their original size.

Although raised grain of the type described above occurs in the lumber of all species, it is most common in softwoods such as southern pine and Douglas fir in which the nature of the springwood and the summerwood is quite different. The corrugation of the surface is increased by dull planer knives. It is also affected by the magnitude of the moisture content changes that occur after the lumber is planed. The most distortion takes place in stock planed at a low moisture content and later exposed to damp air; the least, in lumber in which the changes in moisture content subsequent to planing are kept at a minimum.

In quarter-sawn lumber of species with pronounced summerwood, the corrugation of the surface is due to the greater transverse (across the grain) dimensional changes in the summerwood in comparison to those in the springwood. For the reason stated, the extent of the corrugation is in direct proportion to the changes in moisture content that occur after the lumber is dressed. If the lumber is planed while still at a relatively high moisture content and then allowed to dry, the summerwood bands shrink below the level of the springwood; if the opposite is true, *i.e.*, if the quarter-sawn lumber is planed while dry and then permitted to absorb moisture, the summerwood rises above the springwood.

2. Raised Grain Traceable to Surface Fuzzing.—This defect was investigated by Marra and Koehler.[1] They concluded that raised grain of this type occurs as wood cells injured in sanding swell under the action of swelling agents such as stains, or as a result of the atmospheric humidity prevailing.[2] In oak, Marra states that fuzzy surface:

a. May be occasioned by injury to the vessel walls; under the influence of swelling agents the broken and collapsed vessel walls tend to return to their original shape and position, but the broken fragments may assume any position, thus giving a fuzzy appearance to the surface (Text Fig. 75, *A*).

b. May be brought about by the swelling of the wood cells in the ridges between the scratches produced by the abrasives (Text Fig. 75, *B*).

---

[1] MARRA, G. G.   An Analysis of the Factors Responsible for Raised Grain in the Wood of Oak, Following Sanding and Staining. *Trans. Amer. Soc. Mech. Engin.*, Vol. 65, pp. 177–185.   1943.

KOEHLER, ARTHUR.   Some Observations on Raised Grain. *Trans. Amer. Soc. Mech. Engin.*, Vol. 54, pp. 54–59.   1932.

[2] Some kinds of wood also fuzz up under the planer knives when their moisture content is high.

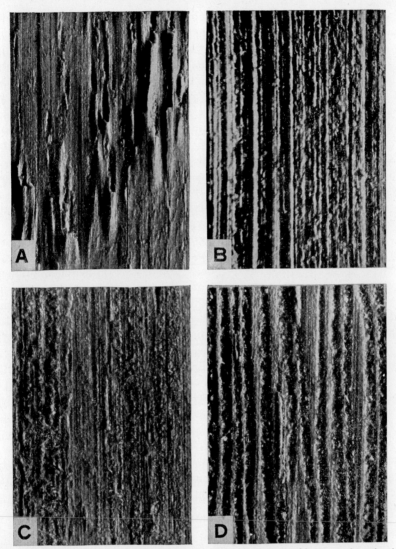

TEXT FIG. 75.—Defects due to machining, raised grain traceable to surface fuzzing.

    A. Raised grain occasioned by injury to cell walls (approx. $4\frac{1}{2}$ ×).

    B. Raised grain associated with scratches (approx. 11 ×).

    C. Raised grain due to fiber separation in the summerwood of oak (approx. 9 ×).

    D. Flat-sawn, straight-grained oak block showing abundant tyloses and lack of collapsed walls (approx. 9 ×).

    (*From "An Analysis of the Factors Responsible for Raised Grain on the Wood of Oak following Sanding and Staining," by G. G. Marra, Trans. A.S.M.E., Vol. 65, pp. 177–185. 1943.*)

c. May result from the fiber separation taking place in the sanding operation; the fibers remain attached at one end (Text Fig. 75, *C*).

In continuation, Marra found that flat-sawn lumber is more subject to raised grain traceable to surface fuzzing than quartersawn lumber. This is explained by the fact that a larger area of springwood is exposed in flat-sawn stock. Marra's experiments also brought out the fact that the angle of the grain, with respect to the surface being sanded, has an important effect on the development of raised grain. Peak development occurs at angles between 3 and 15 degrees, especially if the sand belt travels against the grain. Tyloses, when sufficiently abundant, are effective in restricting the amount of raised grain when this is occasioned by injury of the vessel walls (Text Fig. 75, *D*).

Raised grain, especially when fuzz is present, is objectionable because of the difficulty experienced in arriving at a smooth surface.

3. Loosened Grain.—Loosened grain (Text Fig. 76, *A* and *B*) results in the main, from pressure exerted in planing or in sanding, or in both, sufficient to crush the springwood in one or more growth increments under a layer of summerwood exposed on the face of a board.[1] The crushing of springwood is the initial cause of this defect, but the actual separation of the growth increments near the surface is due to the shrinkage stresses that develop where the summerwood of one increment adjoins the springwood of another. Such stresses arise because summerwood tends to shrink more transversely and less longitudinally than springwood. The curling of the loosened splinters can be attributed to the fact that individual growth increments, were they entirely free, would tend to curve endwise in drying, with the concave side toward the pith.

Loosened grain is objectionable because of the difficulties encountered in machining and painting surfaces with this defect. When wood is in use, its objectionable features likewise at once become evident. For example, softwood floors with slivery surfaces cannot be finished satisfactorily and kept clean by mopping.

H. Weathering of Wood

When wood, unprotected by paint or any other means, is exposed to the weather, it begins to deteriorate; the cumulative effects of such deterioration are termed *weathering*. Generally, the first indication of weathering is the appearance of raised grain, occasioned by the differential shrinkage of springwood and summerwood, or of the outer and inner layers of its exposed face. This is followed by checking, which may eventually develop into large splits, and sometimes by the twisting and warping of the piece. The initial stages of weathering recorded above

---

[1] It could also develop through hard usage.

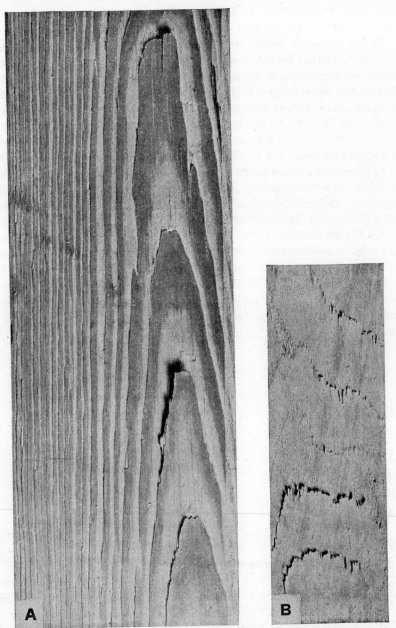

TEXT FIG. 76.—Defects due to seasoning and machining, loosened grain. (*By permission, from "More About Loosened Grain" by A. Koehler, Forest Products Laboratory. South. Lumberman, Vol. 161, pp. 171–173. 1940.*)

A. Loosened grain in southern pine flooring.   B. Loosened grain in soft maple flooring.

that fungous hyphae do not penetrate cell walls mechanically but, rather, grow through such holes formed in advance by enzyme action.[1]

The growth of a wood-inhabiting fungus is contingent upon the fulfillment of four requisites: (1) a favorable temperature, (2) a supply of oxygen, (3) an adequate amount of moisture, and (4) the presence of a suitable food supply. The absence or elimination of any one of these requirements will prevent or greatly inhibit the growth of a fungus. All

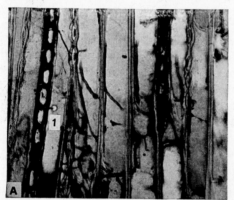

TEXT FIG. 77.—Defects caused by fungi.

A. Highly magnified tangential section of eastern hemlock [*Tsuga canadensis* (L.) Carr.] containing hyphae of *Fomes pinicola* (Swarz) Cook. (260 ×). At 1, a hypha passed through the back wall of a longitudinal tracheid; the opening was subsequently enlarged through further enzyme action.

B. Transverse penetration of wood fibers by a colored zone-line hypha of *Fomes igniarius* (L.) Gill. (750 ×). (*By permission, from "The Formation of Colored Zones by Wood-destroying Fungi in Culture," by Henry Hopp. Phytopathology, Vol. XXVIII, No. 9, p. 604. 1938.*)

the methods for controlling decay are, of necessity, based upon this premise.

In most cases, it is impractical to utilize wood in such a manner that the prevailing temperatures are too low or too high to prevent fungous growth. It is arrested by temperatures approaching the freezing point but not stopped permanently. Wood-destroying fungi can be killed by resorting to elevated temperatures. The actual thermal point at which death ensues varies with the organism, the moisture content of the wood, and the humidity of the atmosphere. Moist heat is more effective than dry heat as a lethal agent. For example Snell,[2] working with five species

---

[1] The hyphae of wood-destroying fungi generally grow directly through cell walls, irrespective of the position of the pits; those of staining fungi usually seek out pits in passing through the walls.

[2] SNELL, WALTER H. The Effect of Heat upon Wood-destroying Fungi in Mills. *Amer. Wood Preservers' Assoc. Proc.*, Vol. 18, pp. 25–29. 1922.

of fungi, found that none withstood a 12-hour exposure to a moist heat of 131°F.; for the same period, a dry heat of 221°F. was required to accomplish the same results.

Temperatures lower than those cited above can be used in killing wood-destroying fungi provided the moisture content of the wood is not permitted to fall below the fiber saturation point. On the other hand, higher temperatures or longer exposures are necessary if the conditions are such that free moisture can escape. In this connection, it is well to bear in mind that the sterilization of wood by elevated temperatures does not guarantee its immunization against fresh fungous attacks.

Retarding fungous growth in wood by excluding oxygen is impractical, even though this condition is sometimes attained in waterlogged pieces and in wood deeply buried in the ground. The best means of control are, therefore, (1) seasoning of the wood, *i.e.*, reducing its moisture content below that essential for the development of fungi,[1] (2) poisoning the wood (the food of the fungus or the medium in which it grows). This consists of introducing toxic substances such as creosote and zinc chloride into it, usually under pressure.

1. Defects Resulting from the Attacks of Wood-destroying Fungi.— Wood-destroying fungi are so numerous and their effects on wood are so variable that only a brief and very general account can be included in this portion of the text. The information in the paragraphs that follow is, therefore, of a very general nature.

Wood becomes fungus-infected in one of two ways: (1) by means of spores produced during the fruiting stage of the fungus, which under favorable conditions germinate on the surface or in cracks in the piece and produce hyphae which invade the tissue; (2) by the direct spread of mycelium from a source of previous infection. In either instance, during the first stage of development, which is called **incipient decay,** the hyphae penetrate and spread through the wood from the initial point of attack, passing from one cell to another either through the pits or directly through cell walls. But slight disintegration of the walls ensues at this stage. Often, the only evidence of infection is a discoloration in the wood which is frequently mistaken for chemical stain (see page 308); many

---

[1] For most fungi, this is about 18 to 20 per cent, reckoned in terms of the oven-dry weight of the wood. The so-called "dry-rot fungi" [*Poria incrassata* (B. & C.) Curt]. (which is especially destructive in coniferous woods) and *Merulius lacrymans* (Wulf.) Fr. (which is prevalent in northern Europe but rare in this country) appear to be exceptions to this rule. They cause considerable damage to buildings and are seemingly able to work in very dry wood. In reality, however, the only point of difference between these dry-rot fungi and others is that the former, once established, are able to transport moisture for a considerable distance by means of rhizomorphs, making it possible for them to grow in wood with a low moisture content.

times, the spread of the fungus goes unnoticed.   Since, at this stage, the general appearance of the wood, the continuity of the grain, and its strength properties are changed but little, its general utility is not undermined, for all practical purposes.

The incipient stage of decay is followed by the **advanced stage of decay,** during which the cell walls exhibit visual evidence of disintegration and the tissue changes definitely in appearance.   Depending on the species of fungus and the manner in which it works, the decayed wood becomes friable, spongy, stringy, pitted, or ring-shaked; its natural color, texture, and resonance are altered, and its strength properties become definitely affected.

No one fungus attacks all species of trees; a given fungus may be restricted to one tree species or grow equally well on a number of related or unrelated species.   Some affect only softwoods, whereas others are confined to hardwoods.   Certain fungi, at least in their initial stages, thrive only on living trees; others seem to be equally at home in dead trees and in wood that has been converted into lumber.   Regional selectivity in the parts attacked in a tree is often manifested.   For example, some of the fungous plants confine their activities to sapwood, whereas others grow only or largely in heartwood; or only definite portions of growth increments may be attacked, as springwood or summerwood, whereas the complementary part is not invaded.   Finally, based on chemical changes taking place in wood, with the resultant change in color accompanying them, wood-destroying fungi can be conveniently divided into those producing **white rots** and those causing **brown rots.**   The former either destroy the lignin or modify it in some way.   Brown-rot fungi, on the other hand, usually concentrate on the destruction of cellulose; the residue in this instance is brown and powdery, with an appreciable lignin content.

One characteristic rot, common to southern cypress and incense cedar, deserves special mention; this defect is known as **peckiness, pecky dry rot,** and **pocket dry rot.**   In incense cedar, peckiness is caused by *Polyporus amarus* Hedg.; the causal organism in cypress is *Fomes geotropus* Cke.[1] Both fungi attack the heartwood of living trees, although *P. amarus* sometimes continues to grow in dead trees that were infected while living. Further development of the fungus is arrested when the trees are felled and converted into lumber.

Peckiness is characterized by finger-sized pockets running with the grain, sometimes for a distance of 6 inches to 1 foot or more (Text Fig. 78).   In the early stages of decay, tracts in the wood are occupied by firm tissue which is only faintly discolored.   As the decay progresses, the

[1] This also causes "blackheart" in evergreen magnolia (*Magnolia grandiflora* L.)

pockets develop; these consist of a dark-brown, friable mass of decayed wood, the tissue between them meanwhile apparently remaining unaffected in both general appearance and strength.   Since all further growth of the fungus causing peckiness ceases after the trees are felled, pecky wood is usable wherever the reduction in strength caused by this defect and its unsightliness are not objectionable.

In general, under the right conditions, the sapwood of all tree species is susceptible to decay.   In some trees, little difference is registered between the sapwood and the heartwood in their ability to resist fungous attack; the heartwood of others, on the other hand, is much more durable.   The

TEXT FIG. 78.—Defects caused by fungi.   Pecky dry rot in California incensecedar (*Libocedrus decurrens* Torr.) caused by the fungus *Polyporus amarus* Hedg. ($\frac{2}{5}$ natural size). Finger-shaped pockets are formed which are directed along the grain and are filled with a brown friable mass of decayed wood.

greater durability of heartwood, where it occurs, is often attributable to some of the extraneous infiltration products deposited in the wood as it passes from sapwood to heartwood; many of these are more or less toxic to fungi and hence prevent the inroads of these organisms.   At other times, heartwood is more durable because of a lower moisture content or for other reasons.   It should be noted at this point that the natural durability of wood is an extremely variable property; in other words, the durability, even within one and the same kind, may exhibit marked diversity, depending on fluctuations in its structural composition, the conditions under which it is utilized, and finally, the type of the invading fungus.

On the basis of voluminous records, the U.S. Forest Products Laboratory has divided most of the common timber species of the United States into classes indicative of the resistance of the heartwood to decay.   Five such classes are recognized (Table XVII).   It must be borne in mind, how-

TABLE XVII
TABLE XVII
RELATIVE DURABILITY OF THE HEARTWOOD OF SOME OF THE COMMON TIMBERS OF THE UNITED STATES WITH RESPECT TO FUNGI*

(Listed alphabetically and not in the order of their relative durability within a class)

Softwoods	*Hardwoods*

Class I. Heartwood Very Durable, Even under Conditions Favoring Decay

Bald cypress	Black locust
Cedar	Black walnut
Alaska yellow	Catalpa
eastern red	Chestnut
northern white	Osage-orange
Port Orford	Red mulberry
southern white	
western red	
Redwood	
Yew	

Class II. Heartwood Durable, in Some Cases Nearly as Durable as That of Species in Class I

Douglas fir (dense)	Honey-locust
Pine, southern yellow† (dense)	White oak

Class III. Heartwood Intermediate in Durability

Douglas fir (unselected)	Chestnut oak
Pine, southern yellow† (unselected)	Red-gum
Tamarack	
Western larch	

Class IV. Heartwood Intermediate in Durability between Classes III and V

Hemlock	Ash, white (commercial)
eastern	Beech
western	Birch
Pine, lodgepole	black
Spruce	yellow
black	Red oak
Engelmann	Sugar maple
red	Sycamore
Sitka	Yellow-poplar
white	

Class V. Heartwood Low in Durability

Firs (true)	Apen
	Basswood
	Cottonwood
	Gum
	black
	tupelo
	Willows

* Adapted from *Wood Handbook*. Prepared by Forest Products Laboratory, U. S. Department of Agriculture. 1935; and HUNT, G. M., and G. A. GARRATT. *Wood Preservation*. McGraw-Hill Book Company, Inc. New York, 1938.

† Includes shortleaf, loblolly, and longleaf pines. There are no adequate records to evaluate the decay resistance of the heartwood of white pines and ponderosa pine, though it is believed that on the whole the heartwood of white pines is more durable.

ever, that all such a classification provides is a means for general comparison of the decay resistance of these woods under average conditions; wide fluctuations from these data are bound to occur.

As has already been indicated, wood-destroying fungi alter the physical and chemical properties of the wood in which they are growing. The most important physical changes arising as a result of their activity are a modification of the color, the development of odors that in some cases are distinctive for the organism causing the decay, and a reduction in the density and strength properties of the wood. In general, the chemical alteration by a given fungus involves the digestion through enzyme action of one of the two principal constituents of the cell wall, *i.e.*, either the lignin or the cellulose. The decomposition of wood substance by fungi materially reduces the yield of products such as sugar, acetic acid, and wood alcohol that are obtained from it by chemical conversion. The same holds when decayed wood is used for pulp; the yield is lower, the pulp is darker, and paper made from it is subnormal in strength.

2. Defects Caused by Wood-staining Fungi.—Wood-staining fungi are responsible for a variety of stains in wood. They are generally confined to sapwood,[1] and the resulting discoloration is hence termed **sap stain.** Sap stain may develop in the sapwood of dead trees, in the log, in lumber, and even in converted wood. The sapwood of dying trees occasionally exhibits blue stain.

Wood-staining fungi fall into two classes: **molds** which grow on the surface of wood and cause only superficial discoloration which can be brushed or planed off, and **true sap-stain fungi** which penetrate the sapwood and cause staining too deep to be easily removed.

a. Discoloration by Molds.—Molds are characterized by cottony or downy growths which vary in color from white through shades of yellow, brown, red, purple, blue, and green to black. Mild temperatures, an abundant supply of moisture, and still air such as results from poor ventilation favor their development. Conditions of this sort frequently prevail when lumber is improperly piled for air seasoning, when green lumber is shipped, in dry kilns when stock is subjected to prolonged treatment at high humidities and low temperatures favorable to fungal growth, and in highly humid buildings.

Molds apparently do not affect the strength properties of wood. They are deleterious in so far as they necessitate the brushing or further planing of stock on which they have developed. Where wood is to be utilized for food containers, molds constitute a serious defect because

---

[1] In rare cases, as in the blue stain in ponderosa pine, the discoloration may also extend into the heartwood.

they are liable to contaminate the comestible product. A further objection to molds is that they impede the circulation of air; severely molded lumber is prone to develop surface checks, for this reason.

In air seasoning, molding can be prevented by adequate circulation of air and by stacking lumber in a place where this trouble has not developed previously. Molds on wood can be destroyed by steaming it at 170°F. and at 100 per cent humidity, for about 1 hour. Dipping freshly cut stock in suitable chemical solutions, such as copper sulphate and sodium carbonate, promises well as a control measure.

b. Discoloration by True Sap-stain Fungi.[1]—Like molds, the sap stains in lumber produced by chromogenic fungi are of various colors depending upon the identity of the causal organism. However, from the standpoint of economic loss ensuing from this type of defect, blue stains outrank all others, in both softwoods and hardwoods. Various species of fungi cause blue stain, the chief of which are species of *Ceratostomella* and *Graphium*.

The main difference between true sap-staining and wood-destroying fungi lies in the fact that the former do not decompose (or only very slightly) the wood substance proper but, rather, derive their nourishment from food materials stored in cells in the sapwood, chiefly in parenchyma. Their hyphae are usually larger than those of a wood-destroying fungus (Text Fig. 79; compare the hyphae visible with those in Text Fig. 77); furthermore, they show a strong predilection, in going from cell to cell, to passing through the pits in the wall, in contrast to those of a wood-decaying fungus. (This holds especially for prosenchymatous elements; the walls of parenchymatous cells are frequently partly destroyed.) The characteristic color of a sap stain results from a relatively heavy concentration of the colored but thin-walled hyphae of the fungus, seen *en masse* on the surface of the wood.[2] Exhaustive tests have indicated that the strength properties of wood are decreased but slightly as a result of sap stain. The economic losses sustained through this defect are due rather to a depreciation in the value of the wood occasioned by the coloration that detracts from its appearance, especially in stock intended for natural finishing.

Sap stain in lumber can be prevented largely by resorting to rapid

---

[1] For a more complete account on sap-stain fungi and their control see Th. C. Scheffer and R. M. Lindgren. Stains of Sapwood and Sapwood Products and Their Control. *U.S. Dept. Agr. Tech. Bul.* 714. 1940; B. M. Lindgren. Temperature, Moisture, and Studies of Wood-Staining Ceratostomellae in Relation to Their Control. *U.S. Dept. Agr. Tech. Bul.* 807. 1942.

[2] Under the microscope, the color of such hyphae is frequently different from that of the sap stain. For example, the hyphae of *Ceratostomella spp.*, causing blue stain in pine, are brown when viewed by transmitted light.

surface drying which diminishes the moisture content of the wood, at least that of the surface layers, to less than 18 to 20 per cent, the minimum amount necessary for the development of fungi of this kind. Another method of controlling stain consists in dipping the wood into chemicals that prevent or retard the development of the fungi until the moisture content of the lumber can be reduced below the critical point. Once the

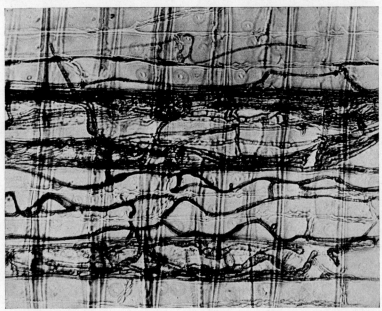

TEXT FIG. 79.—Defects caused by fungi. True sap-stain fungi which cause discoloration. Highly magnified section of loblolly pine (*Pinus taeda* L.) containing hyphae of blue stain [*Ceratostomella pilifera* (Fr.) Wint.] (Radial section showing typical concentration of the threadlike hyphae in one of the wood rays) (370 ×). (*By permission, from "Stains of Sapwood and Sapwood Products and Their Control," by Theodore C. Scheffer and Ralph M. Lindgren. Plate 1, U. S. Dept. Agr. Tech. Bul. 714. 1940.*)

wood is stained, its normal color cannot be restored by any known method. Partial success, however, has been achieved with blue-stained yellow-poplar by bleaching with a solution composed of 50 pounds of sodium phosphate in 60 gallons of water. The restoration of the original color by this method is said to be only temporary.[1]

In general, the pulping of blue-stained wood is also undesirable because the stock thus obtained is dark-colored. Stained pulp, however, can be bleached to the desired whiteness by increasing the amount of bleaching powder that is used.

[1] Although the coloration in stained wood cannot be eliminated permanently, the fungus causing it can be killed by exposing such stock to temperatures of about 130°F. Reinfection may occur unless the wood is kept dry thereafter.

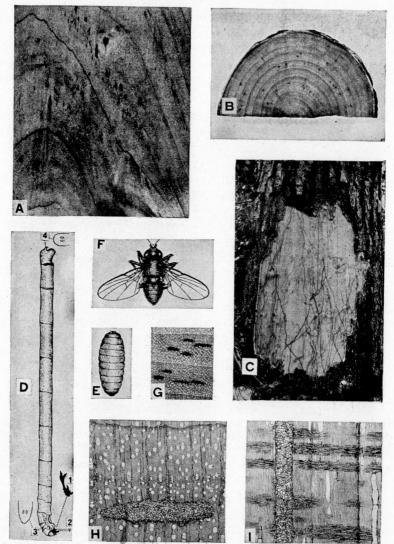

Text Fig. 80.—Insect damage resulting in wood before it is utilized.   Pith flecks in wood.

   A. Pith-fleck streaks on the face of a flat-sawn board of silver maple (*Acer saccharinum* L.) (½ natural size).   (*Photograph by the U. S. Forest Service.*)

   B. Pith flecks on the transverse surface of a limb of river birch (*Betula nigra* L.) (½ natural size.)   (*Photograph by the U. S. Forest Service.*)

   C. Mines caused by the larvae of *Agromyza pruinosa* Coq., under the bark of *Betula nigra* L.; they are occluded with dark wound tissue and are conspicuous on the surface of the wood when the bark is removed.   (*Photograph by the U. S. Forest Service.*)

   D. Cylindrical larva of *Agromyza pruinosa* Coq., showing details of structure (the larva is white except the shiny black mouth parts), shiny mouth parts (1, enlarged) (2, in position); the anterior spiracles (3); the posterior spiracles (4). (3½ ×).   (*U. S. Bureau of Entomology.*)

B. Defects Occasioned by Insect Infestation

The damage to forest products of various kinds by wood-boring insects has been estimated to amount to at least $45,000,000 annually in the United States. This figure does not take into consideration the yearly losses sustained as a result of insect depredations in standing trees; the latter figure is computed at an additional $105,000,000.

From the standpoint of wood utilization, the insects that damage wood can be segregated roughly into those whose depredations are confined to wood before it is utilized and those whose attacks are largely restricted to wood in service. Pith flecks, pinholes, and grub holes result from the activities of insects of the first type; termites and powder-post beetles fall in the category of insects that attack converted wood.

1. Insect Damage Resulting in Wood before It Is Utilized.—*a. Pith Flecks* (Text Fig. 80).—Pith flecks,[1] or medullary spots are confined to hardwoods. On transverse surfaces, they appear as small areas of wound tissue which are usually darker than the surrounding tissue and are wholly within the limits of a growth ring (Text Fig. 80, *B* and *G*). The number of such spots showing on a transverse surface depends, of course, upon the extent of the infestation.

Under a hand lens, in end grain, such spots are seen to possess a definite shape. They are usually either semicircular or lunate (*G*) and so oriented that the long diameter is directed tangentially. This ranges for the most part between $\frac{1}{16}$ and $\frac{1}{8}$ inch although the spots are quite variable in size. Along the grain, pith flecks, when noticeable, appear as dark streaks of varying length (*A*). The degree of prominence of such dark lines varies considerably.

Defects of the type described are produced in wood through injury to the cambium resulting from infestation by the larvae of flies (*F*) belonging to the genus *Agromyza*.[2] The female adult insect perforates the periderm of a young branch with her ovipositor and deposits an egg in the living tissue beneath. This hatches into a filiform larva (*D*)[3] which invades the

---

[1] Brown, H. P. Pith-ray Flecks in Wood. *U.S. Dept. Agr. Cir.* 215. 1913.

[2] Greene, C. T. Cambial Miner in River Birch. *Jour. Agr. Res.*, Vol. 1, pp. 471–474. 1914.

[3] When full-grown, the larva is about 1 inch long.

E. Pupa of *Agromyza pruinosa* Coq. ($3\frac{1}{2}$ ×). (*Courtesy of the U. S. Bureau of Entomology.*)

F. Adult male of *Agromyza pruinosa* Coq. ($5\frac{1}{2}$ ×). (*Courtesy of the U. S. Bureau of Entomology.*)

G. Pith flecks on the transverse surface of gray birch (*Betula populifolia* Marsh.) (3 ×).

H. A pith fleck in red maple (*Acer rubrum* L.) transverse view (10 ×).

I. Occluded tunnel in red maple (*Acer rubrum* L.) made by the larva of a pith-fleck insect. Radial view (10 ×).

cambium while growth is in progress (during the early part of the growing season) and mines downward, leaving a burrow (*C*) about the thickness of a darning needle. Eventually the larva emerges underground and pupates (*E*); but, conditions permitting, it frequently reverses its direction several times near the base of the tree before doing this. For this reason, pith flecks are much more common in butt logs.

Some of the cambial cells, and neighboring phloem and immature xylary cells, are destroyed as the larva travels downward; at the same time, the continuity of the rays through the cambial zone is broken. Healing processes start shortly after the passage of the larva. The living phloem-ray cells on the outside of the tunnel begin to proliferate and soon occlude the tunnel with a mass of parenchymatous cells containing dark contents (*G, H*, and *I*). A short time later the cambium closes in over the mass of wound tissue, and normal wood is produced thereafter. Since the wound tissue occluding the mine resembles that of pith, or medulla, the spots formed as described above have been called "pith flecks" or "medullary spots."

Pith flecks are fairly common in some hardwoods and unusually abundant in others. Birch, maple, basswood, willow, and cherry frequently exhibit these defects; spots of this sort are especially abundant in gray and in river birch. Pith flecks do not materially affect the strength of wood although they do detract from its appearance; the last has a bearing, of course, where the wood is to be given a natural finish.

b. Pinholes.—Pinholes are small, round, and usually unoccluded holes $\frac{1}{100}$ to $\frac{1}{4}$ inch in diameter, which result from the mining of ambrosia beetles and timber worms (Text Fig. 81, *A*). Some of these insects attack only living trees; others infest both living and dead trees and also inflict damage in logs, unseasoned lumber, bolts of wood, and cordwood. Sapwood and heartwood are equally subject to attack, and the same holds for hardwood and softwood trees. Pinholes are especially common in chestnut, possibly because, of late, much of the timber of this species has been obtained from trees killed by chestnut blight; a special "sound wormy" grade of chestnut is recognized which is considered suitable for uses where normal strength and impermeability are not essential.

c. Grub Holes.—Defects of this type are oval, circular, or irregular holes, $\frac{3}{8}$ to 1 inch in diameter (Text Fig. 81, *B*). They are sections of the mines of some adult insects and of the larvae of others, which deposit their eggs in living trees, felled trees, or unseasoned lumber. Grub holes may occur in the wood of any tree species, in either the sapwood or the heartwood, or in both. The future usefulness of the wood depends upon the extent of the damage and the manner in which the stock is to be utilized. Not infrequently, it is necessary to reject such impaired material where strength, impermeability, and appearance are primary considerations; at other times, when less exacting service is required, it is only de-graded.

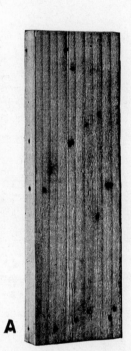

A   **B**

TEXT FIG. 81.—Insect damage appearing in wood before it is utilized. (*Photographs by permission, from "British Columbia Softwoods, Their Decay and Natural Defects," by H. W. Eades. Canadian Forest Serv. Bul.* 80. 1932.)

A. Pinholes in western hemlock [*Tsuga heterophylla* (Raf.) Sarg.] caused by ambrosia beetles (adult stage). The dark linings of the tunnel walls are characteristic of the borings of these insects.

B. A grub hole in western fir (*Abies sp.*), caused by the pine sawyer beetle [*Monochamus sp.*].

d. Black Streak in Western Hemlock.[1]—The black streaks in western hemlock, *Tsuga heterophylla* (Raf.) Sarg. (Text Fig. 82, *A*), also known as black checks, are caused by the maggots of a small black fly (*Chilosia alaskensis* Hunter) which live under the bark and feed at the surface of

---

[1] This information on black streak in western hemlock is based largely on a report by R. F. Luxford, L. W. Wood, and Eloise Gerry. "Black Streak" in Western Hemlock; Its Characteristics and Influence on Strength. *Forest Prod. Lab., Rpt.* 1500. December, 1943.

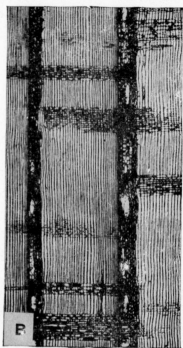

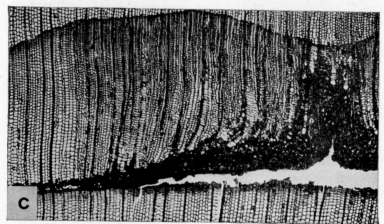

TEXT FIG. 82.—Insect damage occurring in wood before it is utilized. Black streak in western hemlock [*Tsuga heterophylla* (Raf.) Sarg.]

A. Two black streaks in an edge-grained board, with maggot chambers (wider portions of streaks).

B. Two black streaks on edge-grained surface, with resin cysts (approx. 30 ✕).

C. Maggot chamber and black streak with resin cysts, on end-grain (approx. 30 ✕).

(*By permission, from "Black Streak in Western Hemlock; Its Characteristics and Influence on Strength," by R. F. Luxford, L. W. Wood, and Eloise Gerry, U. S. Forest Products Laboratory Rpt. 1500. Dec. 1943.*)

the newly formed wood; the larval stage lasts from 1 to 5 years. As a result of the injury and destruction of portions of the cambium by the growing maggot, a chamber is formed, above and below which a black streak, resembling a pencil line as viewed in edge-grain stock, extends from several inches to as much as 3 feet along the grain. In flat-sawn lumber, the chamber is irregular in shape.

The chamber, formed as described above, may remain open or become considerably narrowed by the subsequent formation of wound tissue. In the latter instance, the traumatic zone is black and not only encircles the chamber but extends along the grain above and below it; it consists of numerous short parenchymatous cells with moderately thick walls and usually with dark resinous contents (Text Fig. 82, *B*). Included within the black streak are numerous, small, traumatic resin canals or short cystlike openings, arranged in a tangential row[1] (Text Fig. 82, *C*).

Mechanical tests on western hemlock wood containing black streak indicate (1) that stock with this defect, except when maggot chambers are present, is suitable for all purposes to which this wood is put, including aircraft parts; (2) that maggot chambers should be graded like pitch and bark pockets but only the wider portion of the streak is to be considered as such, and (3) that the irregular grain that sometimes accompanies maggot chambers should be graded as any other cross grain.

2. Insect Damage Resulting in Wood in Service.—*a. Powder-post Damage.*—This results from the work of beetles in seasoned and unseasoned wood. The small larvae bore through the wood, seeking food and shelter, and leave burrows filled with dry, pulverized, partly digested wood. Pupation takes place in the wood. As the adults emerge on the surface during late spring and late summer, they leave holes $\frac{1}{16}$ to $\frac{1}{12}$ inch in diameter out of which the powder sieves; hence the name "powder-post beetles" (Text Fig. 83). The interior of the wood may be riddled with tunnels, with little visual evidence on the outside of the piece to denote the extent of the infestation.

The most prevalent and destructive powder-post beetles in the United States belong to the genus *Lyctus*. The adults deposit their eggs in the vessels (pores) of hardwoods, and the attack is therefore largely confined to woods the pores of which are sufficiently large to receive the eggs.[2] Powder-post damage is most frequently found in ash, hickory, oak, and California laurel, although cherry, elm, maple, poplar, and black walnut

---

[1] Other types of mechanical and physical injuries to the cambium traceable to sapsuckers, bark beetles, unseasonable frost, lightning, firs, et cetera, may cause similar deformations in eastern and western hemlock, firs, and spruces. They can usually be distinguished from black streak in western hemlock by the absence of color.

[2] Coniferous woods are also attacked by powder-post beetles.

are subject to attack.   Since the principal food of *Lyctus* larvae is starch, the damage is limited for the most part to sapwood, the susceptibility of which is governed by its starch content.   Powder-post injury is practically limited to air-seasoned and kiln-dried stock although cases are known where these beetles have attacked wood containing as much as 40 per cent moisture.   Several generations of larvae may infest the same piece of wood, until it has been rendered quite useless.

TEXT FIG. 83.—Insect damage resulting in wood in service.   Powder-post damage in a board of eastern hemlock [*Tsuga canadensis* (L.) Carr.] caused by an *Anobium sp.* (¾ natural size).   (*Material supplied by the Department of Forest Entomology, New York State College of Forestry.*)

Powder-post damage can be largely prevented by periodic inspection of suspected stock, by avoiding prolonged storage, by proper sanitation requiring the burning of infested wood, and by sterilizing partly damaged stock by exposing it to live steam at not less than 135°F. or by kiln-drying it at 180°F.[1]   Finished products made of wood can be protected against powder-post damage by coating all surfaces with a substance that will seal the pores, thus preventing the adult female insects from depositing their eggs in the wood.   Stock can also be immunized against attack by impregnating it with toxic compounds.

   b. Termite Damage.—Termites, sometimes incorrectly called "white ants," cause an estimated loss in this country of more than $40,000,000 annually.[2]   They differ from true ants in not possessing complete

---

[1] SNYDER, T. E.   Preventing Damage by Lyctus Powder Post Beetles.   *U.S. Dept. Agr. Farmers' Bul.* 147.   1926.

[2] Redwood is said to possess termite-resistant qualities.

metamorphosis. Termites are especially destructive along the Pacific Coast, in the Southwest, and in the South Atlantic and Gulf states. They use wood not only for shelter but also for food. The component of the wood actually used for food is cellulose; this is converted into a digestible form by protozoa that inhabit the intestinal tract of the invading insect.

Text Fig. 84.—Insect damage resulting in wood in service. (*Photograph by A. H. Mac-Andrews.*)

A. Portion of an oak floor board, end grain, showing termite damage.

B. Termite damage in a house sill of eastern hemlock [*Tsuga canadensis* (L.) Carr.] caused by *Reticulitermes flavipes* Kollar. The walls of the galleries are rough on the surface.

There are three major groups of termites in the United States: (1) the subterranean, (2) the dry-wood, and (3) the damp-wood types. Of these, those belonging to the first group are by far the most common and the most destructive.

Subterranean termites live in colonies from which they penetrate wood, destroying the interior but leaving a shell on the outside for protection (Text Fig. 84). This method of attack frequently renders the detection difficult until the damage has arrived at a point where the affected part collapses. Covered runways are constructed out of partly digested particles of wood cemented together by excretions, and these enable the insects, though hidden, to pass over an obstruction or to reach wood that is not in contact with the ground. Subterranean termites infest both sound and decayed wood but require an ample and constant supply of moisture for their existence.

Dry- and damp-wood termites enter the wood directly from the air, at the time of swarming. The latter confine their attacks largely to decaying wood. Dry-wood termites, on the other hand, are able to work in wood that is well air-seasoned, *i.e.*, in wood with a moisture content of only 10 to 12 per cent. Subterranean termites are, of course, unable to exist under these conditions.

C. Defects Resulting from the Activities of Marine Borers

Marine wood borers are animals belonging to the Mollusca (mollusks) and the Crustacea (crustaceans). These organisms live in salt and brack-

A   B

Text Fig. 85.—Defects of wood resulting from the activities of marine borers. (*Photographs by permission, from "Canadian Woods, Their Properties and Uses," by T. A. McElhanney and associates. Forest Products Laboratories of Canada. 1932.*)

A. Transverse section of a sound pile of Douglas fir [*Pseudotsuga taxifolia* (Poir.) Britt.].

B. Transverse section of a similar pile after 9 months' exposure to *Teredo* attack.

ish water and inflict heavy damage on submerged wooden parts or parts exposed at low tide. Untreated piling and other wooden objects, especially those in protected situations such as harbors, are subjected to their attack (Text Fig. 85). In the United States, marine borers are very destructive along the Pacific, South Atlantic, and Gulf coasts; some damage also results as far north as New England, but the greater inroads are made by these organisms in warmer waters.

Three genera of mollusks—*Teredo, Bankia,* and *Martesia*—and a like number of crustacean genera—*Limnoria, Sphaeroma,* and *Chelura*—are represented by species in American waters. Members of the first two genera of mollusks are known as **shipworms,** largely because of the vermiform shape assumed by the adults. Shipworms may attain a length of 1 to 4 feet and a diameter up to 1 inch, although they are generally much smaller. In early life, they are minute and free-swimming but soon become attached at the caudal end to some wooden object. They then proceed to burrow in the wood, meanwhile increasing in length and diameter. The mine is made by the grinding action of a pair of toothed shell valves which develop on the head. Two siphons are situated at the caudal end which can be protruded at will beyond the surface of the wood;

TEXT FIG. 86.—Defects of wood resulting from the activities of marine borers. Untreated piling of Douglas fir [*Pseudotsuga taxifolia* (Poir.) Britt.] destroyed by *Limnoria.* The good piles which show in the photo are replacements. (*By permission, from "Canadian Woods, Their Properties and Uses," by T. A. McElhanney and associates, 1935. Forest Products Laboratories of Canada.*)

one of these is used to suck in water and microscopic organisms which are used for food, the other to eject water and excrement. *Martesia,* the third genus of molluscan borers, consists of forms that are clamlike in appearance; they are generally not more than 2 to 2½ inches in length and about 1 inch in diameter. It is believed that wood-boring mollusks use wood not only for shelter but also for food, at least to some extent.

Crustacean wood borers have segmented bodies ranging from ⅛ to ¼ inch in length in *Limnoria,* to about twice this size in *Sphaeroma.* These organisms are equipped with several pairs of clawed legs by means of which they attach themselves to wood. The boring is done with a pair of toothed mandibles. *Limnoria spp.* are said to utilize wood not only for shelter but also for food (Text Fig. 86); the *Sphaeroma spp.*, on the other hand, apparently make their homes in the wood but obtain their nourishment from other sources. Little is known about the habits of the sand fleas which belong to the genus *Chelura;* they jump like fleas, hence the name. Until recently, sand fleas were considered to be largely tropical and subtropical in their distribution. It appears now, however, that they cause some damage along the Atlantic Coast.

By way of summation, note should be made of the striking difference in the life habits of molluscan wood borers of the shipworm type and the crustacean forms described. The former, upon entering the wood, become attached to and imprisoned in it, extending their tunnels deeper into the core as their bodies elongate. As a result, the interior of infested piling is often thoroughly honeycombed though the wood appears sound on the outside. The crustaceans, on the other hand, are motile throughout their whole life cycle; they can pass in and out of the wood at will, and their burrows seldom extend for any distance into it. Since, however, they attack wood in great numbers, the surface layers are riddled with their mines and are easily dislodged by wave action. The attack of crustacean borers is most severe between the half-tide and ebb-tide levels. In consequence, the cumulative effect of repeated attacks, each resulting in the destruction of the surface layer exposed at a given time, wears away the infested portion of a pile. Eventually, this may become hourglass in shape. The diameter of a pile may be reduced as much as 2 inches in a single year.

Several tropical timbers are famed because the heartwood is unusually resistant to the attacks of marine borers, among others, greenheart [*Ocotea rodiaei* (Schomb.) Mez] of British Guiana. Domestic woods, however, possess no such natural immunity. Many methods of protecting wood against the ravages of marine borers have been tried, with varying success. The most lasting results thus far have been attained by thoroughly impregnating the wood with coal-tar creosote.

CHAPTER XV

NATURAL DURABILITY OF WOOD

Natural durability of wood, as interpreted in this text, signifies its ability to resist the attacks of foreign organisms, especially those of fungi. As has been previously shown (Table XVII), domestic woods exhibit wide departures in their resistance to fungous attack. Although no native wood is immune to the inroads of decay or of insects, a number possess superior durability.

In continuation, the fact should be recognized that the durability of a given kind of wood may fluctuate between wide extremes. Excluding such variables as differences in the conditions under which the wood is utilized and the type of invading organism, other factors have been evaluated to explain this variation. To establish their validity, these are discussed in the pages that follow.

A. DURABILITY OF SAPWOOD AND HEARTWOOD

When conditions prevail that favor the decay of wood or its invasion by insects, the sapwood of all native tree-species is susceptible to deterioration. Under these conditions, the heartwood may be but slightly more durable than the sapwood, or it may be markedly superior in this respect.

The greater durability of heartwood in comparison to sapwood within a species is attributable largely to the presence of extraneous materials in the former. Some of these, such as essential oils, tannins, and phenolic substances, possess toxic properties and are present in amounts sufficient to prevent the disintegration of the wood. The validity of this statement has been tested repeatedly by leaching, with the proper solvents, blocks taken from the heartwood of such durable species as black locust, redwood and western red cedar; invariably the blocks so extracted decayed more rapidly than comparable unleached blocks.[1]

---

[1] In experimenting with western red cedar, Southam and Ehrlich found that, after leaching, the heartwood of this species decays more than the sapwood. One possible explanation of this is that the very low concentration of the toxic substances remaining in the test blocks of heartwood after extraction was sufficient to cause "hormesis," a phenomenon defined as an increase in the growth rate of an organism due to stimulation by subinhibitory concentrations of a toxic substance. For further information, see Chester M. Southam, and John Ehrlich. Decay Resistance and Physical Properties of Wood. *Jour. Forestry*, Vol. 41, pp. 666–673. 1943.

Other factors can be enumerated that also may explain the greater durability of heartwood. Among these are its lower moisture content when this condition holds, its lower rate of water diffusion, and the blocking of cell cavities by gums, resins, and tyloses (vessels) and of intercellular cavities (resin canals) by tylosoids. Any of these might conceivably adversely affect the balance between air and water necessary for the growth of fungi. Insects not infrequently attack sapwood and avoid heartwood because of the presence of reserve food in the parenchymatous cells of the former.

From what has been said, it is obvious that even in a tree-species with relatively durable heartwood, the serviceability of an untreated piece of the wood is determined in no small measure by the amount of sapwood present. The disintegration of the less durable sapwood, especially if it completely surrounds the heartwood as in piles, posts, and mine props, may result in failure, even though the heartwood remains unaffected.

B. Effect of Density and Rate of Growth on Durability

Many heavy woods are highly durable. This is suggestive of the possibility that the density of wood, *i.e.*, its weight per unit of volume, may be used as a criterion in fixing its decay resistance. Reference to Table XVII will quickly dispel this assumption. Light woods such as cedar and redwood are among the most durable; relatively heavy woods such as beech, maple, and black gum, in contrast, are among the least decay-resistant. The superior durability of the lighter woods in this instance is traceable directly to the presence of toxic materials present in the wood; the truth of this statement rests on the fact that no departures have been noted in the decay resistance of extractive-free wood substance irrespective of species.

It now remains to consider the possible effects of wood density within a tree species on durability. Southam and Ehrlich[1] conclude that "For a single species of wood there may be a tendency toward greater initial decay resistance in wood of high specific gravity, but this tendency is nullified and may even be reversed as decay progresses, and so is of little practical value." They support this statement by the following observations:

1. Variations in specific gravity are indicative of variations in the volume of wood substance per unit volume of wood; they are therefore indicative of fluctuations in the volume of the cell-cavity space available for air and water. It follows that light woods and light samples of a given wood possess more cell-cavity space than heavy woods and heavy samples. A fungus requires oxygen (air) and water for growth but only

[1] *Op. cit.*

certain amounts thereof. But the relative proportions of air and of water can fluctuate more widely in light woods and light samples of a given wood than in heavy woods and heavy samples thereof because of the greater cell-cavity space in the former, this without affecting adversely the requirements of a fungus for oxygen and moisture. For the reason stated, it may be assumed that, when the amount of moisture in wood is uncontrolled, the chances of decay are greater in a light wood because of the probability that its air and water content will continue to meet the requirements of the fungus. Even with an unusually low air content and a high water content, or vice versa, the fungus will still be enabled to grow.

2. Since decay is largely a chemical process, the rate of decay varies directly according to the surface area of wood substance subjected to fungous activity. By surface area in this instance is meant the sum of the areas of the surfaces bounding the cavities of the cells. When differences in specific gravity are traceable to differences in the thickness of cell walls, the cells of necessity have smaller lumina and the surface area of the wood as defined is therefore smaller; hence, less surface is exposed to decay. Under such a condition, it is possible that the rate of decay would vary inversely with specific gravity. In other words, a light wood or a light sample of a given wood might decay more rapidly than a heavier piece.

3. It is quite possible that wood substance, to increased amount in heavier woods, might hinder the initial penetration of fungous hyphae.

4. As decay progresses in wood, the space unoccupied by wood substance increases with the digestion of cell walls. This tends to depress the ratio of water to air below the optimum required for the growth of fungi. Given two pieces of the same kind of wood but with different densities, the heavier sample would maintain a more favorable water-to-air ratio than the lighter sample and hence would tend to decay more rapidly.

5. The available food material becomes depleted as decay progresses which, in turn, gradually slows down fungous growth. This retardation in the rate of decay would become evident earlier in a light piece of wood than in a heavy one, tending to compensate any factors favoring the more rapid initial development of decay in a light piece.[1]

[1] When strength is the paramount consideration, another factor requires evaluation; attention was focused on this by Arthur Koehler in an editorial note in commenting on a paper by Stanley Buckman. What Is the Relation between Durability and Specific Gravity of Wood? *Jour. Forestry*, Vol. 32, pp. 725–728. 1934. When two pieces of wood of different densities lose the same percentage of their original weight through decay, the piece with the higher specific gravity will presumably remain the stronger because it will contain the greater amount of wood substance. In any case, weight loss occasioned by decay is a poor index of serviceability since the strength of a piece of wood may be greatly reduced, even though the weight changes little.

The effect of rate of growth, *i.e.*, of ring width, on the quality of wood was discussed in considerable detail in Chap. X of this text. All attempts to correlate growth rate with durability, however, have failed because of the effect of a third inseparable factor, variable density, that prevents fair comparison. Changes in the growth rate of a tree entail structural changes in its wood, among others, variation in the amounts of spring-wood and of summerwood present in a growth increment. These tissues are decidedly different in density, and hence the density of the wood *in toto* fluctuates with the growth rate. The possibility of correlating growth rate with durability is all the more remote because density in itself is no measure of the durability of wood.

C. Effect of Tree Range on Durability

The contention is sometimes advanced that a given kind of wood produced at one place in the geographical range of a tree-species is superior in durability to that coming from elsewhere in the range. The experimental evidence on this subject is meager. Scheffer,[1] in a study of the decay resistance of oak wood, reported that he could detect no significant differences in the durability of white oak (*Quercus alba* L.) from such widely separated areas as the Upper Mississippi River Valley, the Central States and the Northeastern States. On the other hand, he did uncover strong evidence to the effect that, within a given region, the wood varied considerably in its decay resistance. He was unable to ascribe a logical reason for these differences.

D. Effect of Climate on Durability

The effect climate may have on durability is determined largely by the amount of precipitation and by the temperatures and the relative humidities that prevail in a region. In a locality where the moisture is too scanty to promote the growth of fungi and/or the temperatures are unfavorable for their growth, a wood may be durable; elsewhere, where the conditions are different, the reverse may hold. To cite cases in point, the entire eastern United States has a climate favorable for the development of wood-destroying fungi. But in the southern portion of this region, the South, the climate conditions that favor decay persist through a much longer period each year; for the reason stated, under comparable conditions of service, a given kind of wood tends to decay more rapidly in the South. In a northern climate, even when ample

---

[1] Scheffer, Th. C. The Decay Resistance of Oak Wood. *U.S. Dept. Agr., Forest Path. Spec. Release* 13. October, 1943.

moisture is present, fungous decay may proceed very slowly because of adverse temperatures; in an arid region, for example, in the Southwestern States, temperature is not the controlling factor but rather the unusually low moisture content of the wood in service.

E. Effect of Season of Cutting on Durability

The statement is sometimes made that wood from trees felled during the winter months is more durable than that from trees cut at other seasons of the year. So far as is known, however, the season of cutting has no direct effect on the properties of wood, including its durability. Winter felling does offer certain advantages; for example, the climatic conditions prevailing during the colder months are unfavorable for the activities of fungi and insects, thus making less critical the problem of caring for the lumber before it is used. However, winter-cut timber can become as badly decayed or insect-ridden during subsequent warmer periods as that from trees felled during the open months, if it is exposed to conditions favoring such attacks.

Winter logging appears to be advantageous in avoiding infestation by powder-post beetles. Wood dries more slowly during the winter months and this tends to permit of the transformation into other materials of some of the starch in the parenchymatous cells of the sapwood; the starch in these cells provides a food supply for the beetles and, when this is reduced in amount, infestation is discouraged. On the other hand, in timber cut during the open months, the protoplasts of the parenchyma cells in the sapwood die before the starch in the cells disappears; the presence of this starch, therefore, encourages infestation.

F. Relative Durability of Wood from Living and from Dead Trees

Contrary to a rather widely held opinion, wood from a dead tree, if sound, is fully as durable as that from a living tree. The truth of this statement becomes the more apparent when information incorporated previously in this text (page 41) is repeated, *viz.*, that only the parenchymatous cells remain alive in sapwood and that heartwood consists entirely of dead cells. It matters little, therefore, in the case of sapwood, and none at all in the case of heartwood, whether the tree is living or dead at the time of felling; the wood, if sound, can be considered as equally durable for all practical purposes. The important consideration is whether the wood as exposed is free from decay. Rot may be under way in the sapwood or in the heartwood, or in both, of a tree irrespective of whether it is living or dead.

In general, timber from dead trees requires more careful inspection than that from living trees because the likelihood of the presence of decay is greater in the first instance.   This holds especially when wood-destroying fungi were a contributing factor to the death of the tree or where dead trees are left standing long enough to permit of the ingress of wood-destroying agents.

KEYS FOR IDENTIFICATION

USE OF THE KEYS

Three Keys for identification are included in the text: (1) one based on characters visible to the naked eye and with the hand lens (10×), (2) one based on minute characters, and (3) a Key to coniferous woods incorporating both gross and minute features. The experience of the authors has led them to the conclusion that the introduction to wood identification by gross features and by minute features is best made separately. Good results may be achieved in the identification of hardwoods by first using the Key based on gross features and then proceeding to the Key that employs minute features. Coniferous woods are, in general, more difficult to identify with a hand lens. The procedure can well be reversed in this instance. Once a student has become conversant with the minute features of softwoods through use of a key, his accuracy in their hand-lens identification improves because he knows in advance the nature of the character he is seeking to decipher at 10× magnification. This last statement, of course, holds only if the character can be seen with a hand lens (Ex., strand parenchyma in redwood and bald cypress visible because of the dark deposits in the cells).

Both gross and minute features are employed in the third Key, which is for use with coniferous woods only. By resorting to temporary mounts that can be examined with a microscope in the laboratory, the student is enabled to use both gross and minute features in identification. This is desirable because softwoods, in comparison to hardwoods, are much simpler in structure and do not present the array of hand-lens characters that feature porous woods.

The general arrangement of the three Keys is identical. A dichotomous plan has been followed throughout, and the alternatives that deal with the same topic and are coordinate in rank, and hence comparable, are brought together. Ease of manipulation is ensured by indenting the information that has happened to fall under the even numbers. Identifications made by the use of either Key should be checked by reference to Descriptions of Woods by Species, pages 443 to 612.

Botanical relationships are not brought out in the Keys, at least not to their final conclusion. A key works or it does not work, and, in the opinion of the authors, it is best to separate species by using the most reliable characters, even though they do not indicate botanical affinities. In the case of the Key based on gross features, the photomicrographs of transverse sections of the wood on the right-hand page of the text should aid materially in arriving at accurate identification, since they depict the wood across the grain at about the magnification at which it is seen with a hand lens. Plate designations to species are given throughout both Keys.

A word of caution in the use of the Key based on gross features is in order at this time since mistakes in identification in the majority of cases result from inaccurate observation. It is futile to examine the surface of a wood that has been exposed with a dull knife since more or less crushing of the tissue will have resulted. This precludes accurate diagnosis. When the wood is examined, the pocket lens should always be held close to the eye and the object (block of wood) brought up toward the lens until it is in focus. In many timbers the anatomical features, particularly the wood rays, can be brought out by moistening the tissue with water; at other times, the presence of water is a deterrent to accurate observation. It is best to try both ways.

Use of the Keys based wholly or in part on minute characters presupposes access to mounts of wood so made as to render them serviceable for use with a compound microscope.

KEY FOR THE IDENTIFICATION OF THE MORE IMPORTANT COMMERCIAL WOODS OF THE UNITED STATES

Based on Features Discernible to the Naked Eye and with the Hand Lens (10×)

1. Wood nonporous (without vessels); tissue between the rays (x) consisting wholly or largely of tracheids arranged in distinct radial rows; rays indistinct to the naked eye (Figs. 1–29) **2**

1. Wood porous (with vessels); tissue between the rays (x) consisting of pores (vessels) embedded in fibrous (mechanical) and parenchymatous (storage) tissue; rays distinct or indistinct to the naked eye (Figs. 30–96) **33**

  2. Longitudinal and transverse resin canals present; longitudinal canals appearing as small openings or flecks (x) confined for the most part to the outer portion of the growth ring; transverse canals included in the rays, forming radial streaks on the transverse surface (Figs. 1–14) **3**

  2. Longitudinal and transverse resin canals normally absent; longitudinal wound (traumatic) canals occasionally present, aligned in a tangential row (x) (Figs. 15–29) **17**

3. Resin canals numerous, quite evenly distributed in the outer portion of every growth ring, generally visible to the naked eye* as dark- or light-colored dots or as small openings, conspicuous or relatively conspicuous with a hand lens (Figs. 1–7) **4**

3. Resin canals generally sparse, unevenly distributed and sometimes absent in some growth rings (if numerous, 2–many in a tangential row), invisible or barely visible as small dark or white flecks to the naked eye, not conspicuous with a hand lens (Figs. 8–14) **12**

  4. Wood soft, light, quite even-grained; transition from spring- to summerwood gradual (Figs. 1–4) **5**

  4. Wood soft to medium hard or hard, more or less unevengrained; transition from spring- to summerwood more or less abrupt (Figs. 5–7) . . . . : **7**

5. Wood medium- to relatively fine-textured, devoid of sugary exudations; resin canals appearing to the naked eye as light- or dark-colored flecks on the transverse surface **6**

5. Wood relatively coarse-textured, frequently exuding a sugary substance when green; resin canals appearing to the naked eye as minute openings on the transverse surface . . . .
Sugar Pine—*Pinus lambertiana* Dougl.   Plate I, Fig. 1.   Desc. p. 443.

---

* Numerous but relatively inconspicuous in Norway Pine—*Pinus resinosa* Ait.; Jack Pine—*P. banksiana* Lamb.; Lodgepole Pine—*P. contorta* var. *latifolia* S. Wats.; and sometimes in Ponderosa Pine—*P. ponderosa* Laws.

    6. Wood with resinous odor; heartwood varying from creamy white to light brown or reddish brown, turning darker upon exposure; tangential surface (split) not noticeably dimpled.
    Northern White Pine, Eastern White Pine, White Pine—*Pinus strobus* L. Plate I, Fig. 2. Desc. p. 448.
    Idaho White Pine, Western White Pine—*Pinus monticola* Dougl. Plate I, Fig. 3. Desc. p. 445.

    6. Wood without resinous odor; heartwood light pinkish yellow to pale brown with a purplish cast, darkening on exposure to silvery brown with a faint tinge of red; tangential surface (split) frequently noticeably dimpled. . . . .
    Sitka Spruce—*Picea sitchensis* (Bong.) Carr. Plate I, Fig. 4. Desc. p. 470.

7. Tangential surface (split) with numerous depressions which give it a dimpled appearance. **8**

7. Tangential surface (split) not dimpled. **9**

    8. Resin canals small (x), inconspicuous or not visible to the naked eye. . . . .
    Lodgepole Pine—*Pinus contorta* var. *latifolia* S. Wats. Desc. p. 450.

    8. Resin canals comparatively large (x), visible to the naked eye. . . . .
    Ponderosa Pine, Western Yellow Pine—*Pinus ponderosa** Laws. Plate I, Fig. 5. Desc. p. 455.
    Jeffrey Pine—*Pinus jeffreyi* Grev. & Balf. Desc. p. 455.

9. Bands of summerwood usually broad; wood hard, heavy, strong, generally highly resinous. **10**

9. Bands of summerwood usually narrow; wood approaching that of the soft pines, soft to moderately hard, light to moderately heavy. **11**

    10. Bands of summerwood orange-brown to reddish brown. . . . . .
    Southern Pine (Desc. p. 452):
        Longleaf Pine—*Pinus palustris* Mill. Plate I, Fig. 6.
        Shortleaf Pine—*Pinus echinata*† Mill.
        Loblolly Pine—*Pinus taeda* L.
        Slash Pine—*Pinus caribaea* Morelet
        Pitch Pine—*Pinus rigida* Mill.
        Pone Pine—*Pinus rigida* var. *serotina* (Michx.) Loud.
        Etc.

    10. Bands of summerwood pale yellow. . . . .
    Ponderosa Pine, Western Yellow Pine—*Pinus ponderosa** Laws. Plate I, Fig. 5. Desc. p. 455.
    Jeffrey Pine—*Pinus jeffreyi* Grev. & Balf. Desc. p. 455.

---

    * Ponderosa and Jeffrey Pine have been marketed under the trade name of California White Pine.

    † *Pinus echinata* Mill. and *P. taeda* L. are marketed as Arkansas Soft Pine; the woods of these two species and that of *P. virginiana* Mill. are also sold as North Carolina Pine.

Plate I

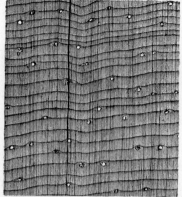

FIG. 1.—*Pinus lambertiana* Dougl.
(x—5 ×)

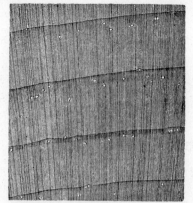

FIG. 2.—*Pinus strobus* L.
(x—5 ×)

FIG. 3.—*Pinus monticola* Dougl.
(x—5 ×)

FIG. 4.—*Picea sitchensis* (Bong.) Carr.
(x—5 ×)

FIG. 5.—*Pinus ponderosa* Laws.
(x—5 ×)

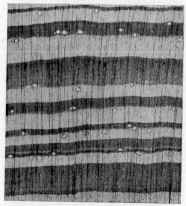

FIG. 6.—*Pinus palustris* Mill.
(x—5 ×)

11. Heartwood with a roseate cast, oily; resin canals small (*x*), generally not distinct without a hand lens.....................
Red Pine, Norway Pine—*Pinus resinosa* Ait.   Plate II, Fig. 7.   Desc. p. 458.
Jack Pine—*Pinus banksiana* Lamb.   Desc. p. 460.

11. Heartwood yellowish, not oily; resin canals comparatively large (*x*), visible to the naked eye.................................
Pondosa Pine, Ponderosa Pine, Western Yellow Pine—*Pinus ponderosa** Laws.   Plate I, Fig. 5.   Desc. p. 455.
Jeffrey Pine—*Pinus jeffreyi* Grev. & Balf.   Desc. p. 455.

> **12.** Transition from spring- to summerwood gradual, the latter not pronounced... **13**
>
> **12.** Transition from spring- to summerwood abrupt,† the latter pronounced.. **14**

13. Heartwood light pinkish yellow to pale brown with a purplish cast, darkening on exposure to silvery brown with a faint tinge of red, dull to somewhat lustrous, medium-textured; tangential, surface (split) frequently noticeably dimpled.................
Sitka Spruce—*Picea sitchensis* (Bong.) Carr.   Plate I, Fig. 4.   Desc. p. 470.

13. Heartwood not distinct; wood nearly white to pale yellowish white or light yellowish brown, lustrous, relatively fine-textured; tangential surface (split) not noticeably dimpled..............
Eastern Spruce (Desc. p. 467):
> **White Spruce**—*Picea glauca* (Moench) Voss.
> **Red Spruce**—*Picea rubens* Sarg.   Plate II, Fig. 8.
> **Black Spruce**—*Picea mariana* (Mill.) B.S.P.

Engelmann Spruce—*Picea engelmanni* (Parry) Engelm.   Plate II, Fig. 9.   Desc. p. 467.

> **14.** Heartwood yellowish or pale reddish yellow to orange-red or deep red, yellowish or reddish brown, dull to somewhat lustrous... **15**
>
> **14.** Heartwood pale yellowish white to pale yellowish brown, lustrous..
> **Engelmann Spruce**—*Picea engelmanni* (Parry) Engelm.   Plate II, Fig. 9.   Desc. p. 467.

15. Wood with characteristic odor on fresh-cut surface, not oily; contour of growth rings frequently wavy; heartwood yellowish or pale reddish yellow to orange-red or deep red (without brownish cast);‡ resin canals frequently in short tangential lines.....
Douglas Fir, Yellow Fir, Red Fir—*Pseudotsuga taxifolia* (Poir.) Britt.   Plate II, Figs. 10, 11, and 12.   Desc. p. 473.

15. Wood without characteristic odor on fresh-cut surface, more or less oily; contour of growth rings seldom wavy; heartwood with brownish cast; resin canals (*x*) not in tangential lines (sometimes in tangential groups of 2–5)........................... **16**

---

* Ponderosa and Jeffrey Pine have been marketed under the trade name of California White Pine.

† In fast-grown Douglas Fir, the transition from spring- to summerwood is frequently more or less gradual.

‡ The color character is generally sufficient to separate Douglas Fir from Tamarack and Western Larch which follow in the Key.   In case of doubt, the first-named wood can be identified by the presence of spiral thickening in the longitudinal tracheids throughout the annual increment; spiral thickening is sometimes present in Tamarack but is confined to the tracheids of the summerwood.   It never occurs in Western Larch.

Plate II

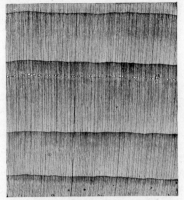

Fig. 7.—*Pinus resinosa* Ait.
(x—5 ×)

Fig. 8.—*Picea rubens* Sarg.
(x—5 ×)

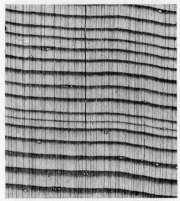

Fig. 9.—*Picea engelmanni* (Parry)
Engelm. (x—5 ×)

Fig. 10.—*Pseudotsuga taxifolia*
(Poir.) Britt. (slow growth)
(x—5 ×)

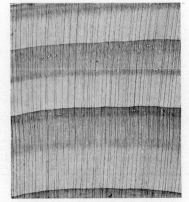

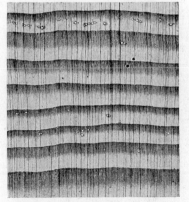

Fig. 11.—*Pseudotsuga taxifolia*
(Poir.) Britt. (second growth)
(x—5 ×)

Fig. 12.—*Pseudotsuga taxifolia*
(Poir.) Britt. (average growth)
(x—5 ×)

16. Wood medium-textured; heartwood yellowish brown (occasionally reddish brown); growth rings generally wide (5–20 per inch), variable in width; band of summerwood usually wide..
Tamarack, Eastern Larch—*Larix laricina* (Du Roi) K. Koch. Plate III, Fig. 13. Desc. p. 462.

16. Wood coarse-textured; heartwood russet or reddish brown; growth rings generally narrow (15–30 plus per inch), quite uniform in width; band of summerwood usually narrow....
Western Larch—*Larix occidentalis* Nutt. Plate III, Fig. 14. Desc. p. 464.

17. Wood fragrant... **18**

17. Wood not fragrant, frequently ill-scented.................... **24**

18. Heartwood purplish or rose-red to dull red, reddish or pinkish brown, or dull brown............................... **19**

18. Heartwood yellowish white to clear yellow, straw-brown, or light brown with a tinge of pink......................... **21**

19. Wood medium- to coarse-textured; heartwood reddish or pinkish brown to dull brown, sometimes with a lavender tinge......... **20**

19. Wood fine-textured; heartwood purplish or rose-red when first exposed, aging to dull red or reddish brown..................
Red Cedar (Desc. p. 405):
   Eastern Red Cedar, Tennessee Red Cedar—*Juniperus virginiana* L. Plate III, Fig. 15.
   Southern Red Cedar—*Juniperus silicicola* (Small) Bailey

20. Wood firm (close-textured), frequently with acrid taste,* often pecky;† springwood and summerwood of about the same hardness‡..
Incense Cedar, Pencil Cedar—*Libocedrus decurrens* Torr. Plate III, Fig. 16. Desc. p. 492.

20. Wood soft (open-textured), without acrid taste, never pecky; summerwood considerably harder than the springwood.‡...
Western Red Cedar, Giant Arbor-vitae—*Thuja plicata* D. Don. Plate III, Fig. 17. Desc. p. 496.

21. Heartwood yellowish white to bright clear yellow or yellowish brown... **22**

21. Heartwood light brown tinged with red or pink (roseate), or straw-brown... **23**

---

* This test is made by placing a thin shaving of the wood on the tongue; a stinging sensation after a brief interval indicates acrid taste.

† Peckiness in Incense Cedar is caused by the fungus, *Polyporus amarus* Hedg. In the final stages, finger-shaped pockets are formed which run with the grain and contain a brown friable mass of decayed wood broken up into sections by transverse cracks. See Text Fig. 78.

‡ Hardness may be tested by indenting the spring- and summerwood zones (*x*) with the thumbnail. The wood dents evenly in Incense Cedar; in Western Red Cedar, the thumbnail penetrates the springwood but slips off the summerwood.

Plate *III*

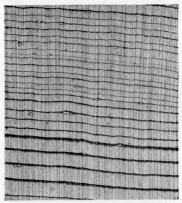

FIG. 13.—*Larix laricina* (Du Roi) K. Koch (x—5 ×)

FIG. 14.—*Larix occidentalis* Nutt. (x—5 ×)

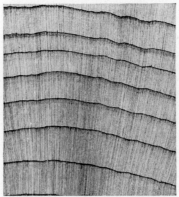

FIG. 15.—*Juniperus virginiana* L. (x—5 ×)

FIG. 16.—*Libocedrus decurrens* Torr. (x—5 ×)

FIG. 17.—*Thuja plicata* D. Don (x—5 ×)

FIG. 18.—*Chamaecyparis lawsoniana* (A. Murr.) Parl. (x—5 ×)

22. Wood with a pungent, gingerlike odor on fresh-cut surface; heartwood yellowish white to pale yellowish brown........
Port Orford Cedar, Port Orford White Cedar—*Chamaecyparis lawsoniana* (A. Murr.) Parl. Plate III, Fig. 18. Desc. p. 499.

22. Wood with an odor resembling that of raw potatoes on fresh-cut surface; heartwood bright clear yellow, darkening somewhat on exposure...................................
Alaska Yellow Cedar, Yellow Cypress—*Chamaecyparis nootkatensis* (Lamb.) Spach. Plate IV, Fig. 19. Desc. p. 500.

23. Wood dry (crumbly when cut across the grain with a knife), with characteristic odor; heartwood uniform straw-brown...........
Northern White Cedar, Eastern Arbor-vitae—*Thuja occidentalis* L. Plate IV, Fig. 20. Desc. p. 494.

23. Wood somewhat oily (rubbery when cut across the grain with a knife), with characteristic odor; heartwood light brown tinged with red or pink......................
Atlantic White Cedar, Southern White Cedar—*Chamaecyparis thyoides* (L.) B.S.P. Plate IV, Fig. 21. Desc. p. 502.

24. Wood more or less oily (greasy), often with rancid odor on fresh surface, frequently pecky;* contour of individual rings frequently irregular.....................
Bald Cypress, Red Cypress, Yellow Cypress,† **Southern Cypress**— *Taxodium distichum* (L.) Rich. Plate IV, Fig. 22. Desc. p. 489.

24. Wood not oily, without rancid odor; contour of individual rings usually quite regular............................. 25

25. Wood whitish or creamy white to buff, clear yellow, or a shade of yellowish brown or light brown, with or without a lavender, roseate, or reddish-brown tinge; heartwood not distinct or, if distinct, clear yellow....................................... 26

25. Sapwood nearly white to light yellow, thin; heartwood bright orange to rose-red, light cherry-red, or deep reddish brown..... 31

26. Wood usually without characteristic odor;‡ heartwood generally wanting, the color whitish or creamy white through shades of pale straw-buff and light brown; spring- and summerwood generally differentiated through discrepancy in color... 27

26. Wood with a characteristic (unpleasant) odor on fresh-cut surface; heartwood distinct, bright clear yellow; spring- and summerwood not conspicuously differentiated through discrepancy in color....................................... 30

---

* Brown rot or peckiness in Bald Cypress, comparable with that in Incense Cedar (see p. 328), results from localized decay in the heartwood occasioned by the inroads of a fungus, *Fomes geotropus* Cke.; the tissue between the pockets is apparently as strong and serviceable as sound wood.

† See Alaska Yellow Cedar, this page.

‡ Firs and hemlocks occasionally have a sour odor, especially when the wood is freshly cut.

Plate IV

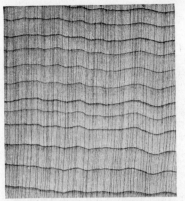

FIG. 19.—*Chamaecyparis nootkatensis*
(Lamb.) Spach   (*x*—5 ×)

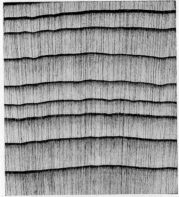

FIG. 20.—*Thuja occidentalis* L.
(*x*—5 ×)

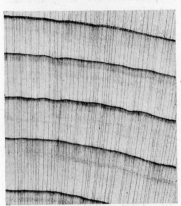

FIG. 21.—*Chamaecyparis thyoides* (L.)
B.S.P.   (*x*—5 ×)

FIG. 22.—*Taxodium distichum* (L.)
Rich.   (*x*—5 ×)

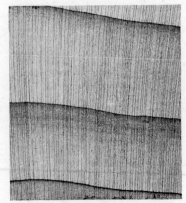

FIG. 23.—*Abies balsamea* (L.) Mill.
(*x*—5 ×)

FIG. 24.—*Abies concolor* (Gord.)
Engelm (*x*—5 ×)

27. Wood light buff to light brown, sometimes with a reddish-brown or pinkish tinge; springwood usually with a reddish tinge, summerwood darker, with a reddish-brown to purplish tinge....... **28**

27. Wood whitish to creamy white or pale brown; springwood whitish passing gradually into darker usually lavender summerwood (color contrasts of spring- and summerwood more pronounced in wider rings)..................................
  Eastern Fir (Desc. p. 481):
    Balsam Fir*—*Abies balsamea* (L.) Mill. Plate IV, Fig. 23.
    Southern Balsam Fir, Fraser Fir—*Abies fraseri* (Pursh) Poir.
  Western Balsam Firs (Desc. p. 483):
    White Fir—*Abies concolor* (Gord.) Hoopes
    Lowland White Fir, Grand Fir—*Abies grandis* Lindl.
    California Red Fir—*Abies magnifica* A. Murr.

28. Wood dry and brittle, moderately hard and harsh under tools, uneven-grained; transition from spring- to summerwood frequently rather abrupt; traumatic longitudinal resin canals generally absent.............................
  Eastern Hemlock, Hemlock, Canada Hemlock—*Tsuga canadensis* (L.) Carr. Plate V, Fig. 25. Desc. p. 476.

28. Wood not very brittle, soft to moderately hard but not harsh under tools, quite even-grained; transition from spring- to summerwood gradual; traumatic resin canals sometimes present.................................... **29**

29. Wood moderately hard; annual rings frequently variable in width...
  West Coast Hemlock, Western Hemlock, Pacific Hemlock†—*Tsuga heterophylla* (Raf.) Sarg. Plate V, Fig. 26. Desc. p. 478.

29. Wood soft; annual rings generally quite uniform in width......
  Noble Fir, Larch—*Abies procera* Rehd.

30. Wood with an odor resembling that of raw potatoes.......
  Alaska Yellow Cedar, Yellow Cypress‡—*Chamaecyparis nootkatensis* (Lamb) Spach. Plate IV, Fig. 19. Desc. p. 500.

30. Wood with a characteristic unpleasant odor (unlike that of raw potatoes)......................................
  California Nutmeg—*Torreya californica* Torr. Plate V, Fig. 29. Desc. p. 508.
  Stinking Cedar—*Torreya taxifolia* Arn.

---

* The wood of Balsam Fir frequently has a somewhat salty taste.

† The characters employed under **29** in the separation of West Coast Hemlock and Noble Fir are not too reliable. Use of a supplemental character is recommended:

1. Springwood tracheids within the same annual ring quite even in size (x)........
  West Coast Hemlock—*Tsuga heterophylla* (Raf.) Sarg.

1. Springwood tracheids within the same annual ring variable in size (x), some rows consisting of very coarse tracheids.....................................
  Noble Fir, Larch—*Abies procera* Rehd.

‡ See Bald Cypress, p. 362.

Plate V

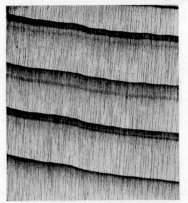

Fig. 25.—*Tsuga canadensis* (L.) Carr.
(x—5 ×)

Fig. 26.—*Tsuga heterophylla* (Raf.)
Sarg. (x—5 ×)

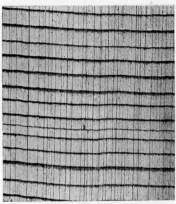

Fig. 27.—*Sequoia sempervirens*
(Lamb.) Endl. (x—5 ×)

Fig. 28.—*Taxus brevifolia* Nutt.
(x—5 ×)

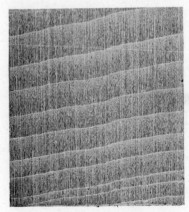

Fig. 29.—*Torreya californica*
Torr. (x—5 ×)

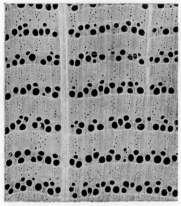

Fig. 30.—*Quercus velutina* Lam.
(x—5 ×)

31. Wood fine-textured, heavy; heartwood bright orange to rose-red, or clear yellow.................................... **32**

31. Wood coarse-textured, moderately light to fairly heavy; heartwood light cherry-red to deep reddish brown.................
Redwood, Coast Redwood—*Sequoia sempervirens* (D. Don) Endl. Plate V, Fig. 27. Desc. p. 486.

    32. Wood heavy; heartwood bright orange to rose-red.........
    Pacific Yew—*Taxus brevifolia* Nutt. Plate V, Fig. 28. Desc. p. 506.

    32. Wood moderately light to moderately heavy; heartwood clear yellow....................................
    California Nutmeg—*Torreya californica* Torr. Plate V, Fig. 29. Desc. p. 508.
    Stinking Cedar—*Torreya taxifolia* Arn.

33. Wood ring porous (springwood zone generally sharply defined); springwood pores conspicuously larger than the summerwood pores, distinct to the naked eye* (Ex., Fig. 30)............... **34**

33. Wood diffuse porous (springwood zone not sharply defined); springwood pores not conspicuously larger than the summerwood pores, not distinct to the naked eye (Ex., Fig. 62)....... **72**

    34. Broad rays present, conspicuous (*x*), often 1 inch or more in height along the grain, forming a broad ray fleck on the radial surface (Ex., Fig. 30)............................ **35**

    34. Broad rays absent (Ex., Fig. 45)........................ **36**

35. Heartwood usually pinkish or pale reddish brown; summerwood pores distinct with a hand lens, not numerous, thick-walled, the orifices plainly visible, rounded; tyloses usually absent or sparse in the springwood pores....................................
Red Oak (Desc. p. 541):
    Northern Red Oak—*Quercus borealis* Michx. f.
    Black Oak—*Quercus velutina* Lam. Plate V, Fig. 30.
    Shumard Oak—*Quercus shumardi* Buckl.
    Scarlet Oak—*Quercus coccinea* Muenchh. Plate VI, Fig. 31.
    Pin Oak—*Quercus palustris* Muenchh.
    Willow Oak—*Quercus phellos* L.
    Other Species of the Erythrobalanus Group.

35. Heartwood rich light brown to dark brown, usually without flesh-colored cast; summerwood pores not distinct with a hand lens, numerous, thin-walled, the orifices scarcely visible, angular; tyloses generally present in the springwood pores (heartwood).
White Oak (Desc. p. 546):
    White Oak—*Quercus alba* L. Plate VI, Fig. 34.
    Bur Oak—*Quercus macrocarpa* Michx.
    Overcup Oak—*Quercus lyrata* Walt.
    Post Oak—*Quercus stellata* Wangenh. Plate VI, Fig. 33.
    Swamp Chestnut Oak, Basket Oak—*Quercus prinus* L.
    Chestnut Oak, Rock Oak—*Quercus montana* Willd.
    Swamp White Oak—*Quercus bicolor* Willd. Plate VI, Fig. 32.
    Other Species of the Leucobalanus Group.

---

* Occluded with tyloses and the contours hence poorly defined in Osage-orange *Maclura pomifera* (Raf.) Schneid.—and Black Locust—*Robinia pseudoacacia* L. See Fig. 50, p. 375.

Plate VI

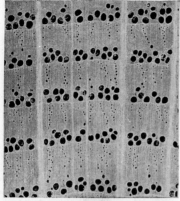

FIG. 31.—*Quercus coccinea* Muenchh.
(*x*—5 ×)

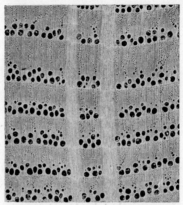

FIG. 32.—*Quercus bicolor* Willd.
(*x*—5 ×)

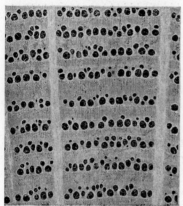

FIG. 33.—*Quercus stellata* Wangenh.
(*x*—5 ×)

FIG. 34.—*Quercus alba* L.
(*t*—natural size)

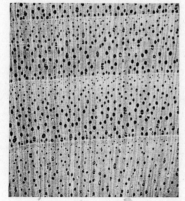

FIG. 35.—*Juglans nigra* L.
(*x*—5 ×)

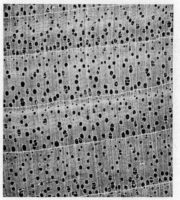

FIG. 36.—*Juglans cinerea* L.
(*x*—5 ×)

36. Transition in size of pores from spring- to summerwood gradual; wood semi-ring porous (Ex., Fig. 35)............ **37**

36. Transition in size of pores from spring- to summerwood abrupt; wood typically ring porous (Ex., Fig. 53)......... **47**

37. Summerwood parenchyma metatracheal (arranged irrespective of the pores), appearing under the lens as fine, numerous, continuous or broken tangential lines or closely and evenly punctate (Ex., Fig. 38).................... **38**

37. Summerwood parenchyma not evident or, if evident, paratracheal (obviously associated with the pores and occasionally connecting the pores in the late summerwood) or terminal..... **41**

38. Heartwood chestnut-brown or chocolate- or purplish brown. **39**

38. Heartwood brown or reddish brown, or the wood creamy white to yellowish, aging to light yellowish or grayish brown. **40**

39. Heartwood rich chocolate- or purplish brown, dull; wood relatively hard, heavy, with a characteristic odor on freshly cut surface.........
Black Walnut, Eastern Black Walnut—*Juglans nigra* L.   Plate VI, Fig. 35.   Desc. p. 510.

39. Heartwood light chestnut-brown, lustrous; wood soft (readily dented with the thumbnail), light, without characteristic odor..
Butternut, White Walnut—*Juglans cinerea* L.   Plate VI, Fig. 36. Desc. p. 509.

    40. Wood with storied rays (forming ripple marks extending across the grain when the wood is viewed on the tangential surface); parenchyma inconspicuous, closely and evenly punctate.........
    Persimmon—*Diospyros virginiana* L.   Plate VII, Fig. 37.   Desc. p. 604.

    40. Wood without storied rays; parenchyma conspicuous, in continuous tangential lines in the summerwood...........
    Hickory (Pecan Hickories) (Desc. p. 513):
        Bitternut Hickory—*Carya cordiformis* (Wangenh.) K. Koch Plate VII, Fig. 38.
        Pecan—*Carya illinoënsis* (Wangenh.) K. Koch
        Water Hickory*—*Carya aquatica* (Michx. f.) Nutt.
        Nutmeg Hickory—*Carya myristicaeformis* (Michx. f.) Nutt.

41. Rays plainly visible to the naked eye; wood red to reddish brown, or with shades of yellow........................... **42**

41. Rays indistinct to the naked eye; wood ranging from whitish through shades of grayish or light chestnut-brown to chocolate-brown and brown.................... **43**

    42. Wood yellow or yellowish streaked with brown; pores appearing thick walled (x) from encircling (paratracheal) parenchyma....................
    Yellowwood—*Cladrastis lutea* (Michx.) K. Koch.   Plate VII, Fig. 39.   Desc. p. 577.

    42. Wood red to reddish brown; pores thin-walled, not encircled by parenchyma....................
    Black Cherry—*Prunus serotina* Ehrh.   Plate VII, Fig. 40.   Desc. p. 572.

---

* Water Hickory differs from the other Pecan Hickories in possessing less clearly defined growth rings and springwood pores which grade more gradually into the summerwood pores, thus approaching diffuse-porous wood in structure.

Plate VII

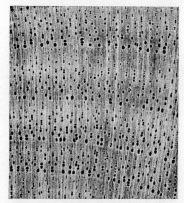

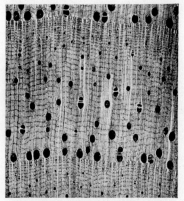

FIG. 37.—*Diospyros virginiana* L.
(x—5 ×)

FIG. 38.—*Carya cordiformis*
(Wangenh.) K. Koch (x—5 ×)

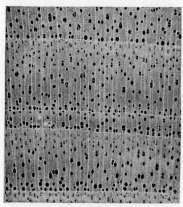

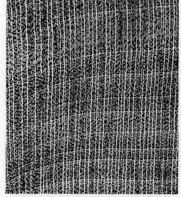

FIG. 39.—*Cladrastis lutea* (Michx.) K.
Koch (x—5 ×)

FIG. 40.—*Prunus serotina* Ehrh.
(x—5 ×)

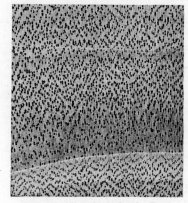

FIG. 41.—*Populus deltoides* Bartr.
(x—5 ×)

FIG. 42.—*Populus grandidentata*
Michx. (x—5 ×)

43. Pores very numerous, usually occupying nearly half the area between the rays (x); parenchyma not evident or, if evident, terminal and barely distinct; rays barely distinct with a hand lens.. **44**

43. Pores scattered, never occupying approximately half the area between the rays (x); parenchyma not evident or, if evident, terminal; rays plainly visible with a hand lens............... **45**

   44. Heartwood grayish white to light grayish brown, pale reddish brown or brown; wood medium-textured (compare Fig. 41 with Fig. 42, p. 369).....................................
   Cottonwood* (Desc. p. 517):
     Eastern Cottonwood, Eastern Poplar—*Populus deltoides* Bartr. Plate VII, Fig. 41.
     Balsam Poplar, Tacamahac Poplar—*Populus tacamahaca* Mill.
     Swamp Cottonwood, Swamp Poplar—*Populus heterophylla* L.
     Northern Black Cottonwood—*Populus trichocarpa var. hastata* Henry
     Etc.
   Willow (Desc. p. 521):
     Black Willow—*Salix nigra* Marsh.   Plate VIII, Fig. 43.
     Etc.

   44. Heartwood pale creamy white; wood fine-textured.........
   Aspen (Desc. p. 519):
     Quaking Aspen, Trembling Aspen—*Populus tremuloides* Michx. Plate XIII, Fig. 74.
     Bigtooth Aspen—*Populus grandidentata* Michx. Plate VII, Fig. 42.

45. Heartwood rich chocolate- or purplish brown; wood relatively hard, heavy, with a characteristic odor on freshly cut surface..
Black Walnut, Eastern Black Walnut—*Juglans nigra* L. Plate VI, Fig. 35. Desc. p. 510.

45. Heartwood grayish brown to light chestnut-brown, occasionally with a lavender tinge; wood soft (readily dented with the thumbnail), light, with a faint characteristic odor or odorless......... **46**

   46. Pores in the late summerwood solitary or in radial rows of 2–several; wood odorless.................................
   Butternut, White Walnut—*Juglans cinerea* L. Plate VI, Fig. 36. Desc. p. 509.

   46. Pores in the late summerwood in interrupted or rarely in continuous tangential bands associated with parenchyma (one or more bands near the outer boundary of the ring occasionally consisting entirely of parenchyma)...........
   Catalpa (Desc. p. 610):
     Northern Catalpa—*Catalpa speciosa* Ward. Plate VIII, Fig. 44.
     Southern Catalpa—*Catalpa bignonioides* Walt.

---

   * Cottonwood, aspen, and willow are usually considered to be diffuse-porous woods.

47. Summerwood figured with wavy, concentric (tangential) bands of pores which are mostly continuous and separated by bands of mechanical tissue (Ex., Fig. 48)........................ **48**

47. Summerwood not figured by wavy, concentric (tangential) bands of pores; groups of pores occasionally confluent in the extreme outer portion of the ring, forming 1–several interrupted or rarely continuous tangential bands (Ex., Fig. 59)........... **54**

   48. Springwood pores in a single, more or less continuous row (Figs. 45, 46)... **49**

   48. Springwood pores in several rows (Figs. 47–50)........... **50**

49. Springwood pores plainly visible without a lens, approximately equal in size and quite evenly spaced in a more or less continuous row; tyloses sparse...
White Elm, American Elm—*Ulmus americana* L.   Plate VIII, Fig. 45. Desc. p. 549.

49. Springwood pores scarcely visible without a lens, variable in size, the larger spaced at more or less irregular intervals in an interrupted row and separated by smaller pores; tyloses abundant...
Hard Elm :* Desc. p. 552.
   Rock Elm, Cork Elm—*Ulmus thomasi* Sarg.   Plate VIII, Fig. 46.
   Cedar Elm—*Ulmus crassifolia* Nutt.
   Winged Elm—*Ulmus alata* Michx.

   50. Springwood pores in the heartwood completely occluded with tyloses, their contours poorly defined (Ex., Fig. 50)... **51**

   50. Springwood pores in the heartwood not completely occluded with tyloses, their contours distinct (Ex., Fig. 47)......... **52**

51. Heartwood golden-yellow to bright orange, darkening upon exposure, often with reddish streaks along the grain; coloring matter readily soluble in water..............................
Osage-orange—*Maclura pomifera* (Raf.) Schneid.   Plate IX, Fig. 49. Desc. p. 558.

51. Heartwood greenish yellow to dark yellowish or golden-brown; coloring matter not readily soluble in water..................
Black Locust—*Robinia pseudoacacia* L.   Plate IX, Fig. 50.   Desc. p. 579.

---

   * The woods of the three hard elms are frequently confused in the trade; the characters employed in the supplemental Key that follows will usually suffice to separate Rock Elm from Southern Hard Elm.

1. Wavy concentric (tangential) bands of pores (x) in the summerwood noticeably narrower than those of mechanical tissue in rings of normal width..............
   Rock Elm—*Ulmus thomasi* Sarg. Plate VIII, Fig. 46.

1. Wavy concentric (tangential) bands of pores (x) and of mechanical tissue (x) of about the same width in rings of normal width...................................
   Cedar Elm—*Ulmus crassifolia* Nutt.
   Winged Elm—*Ulmus alata* Michx.

Plate VIII

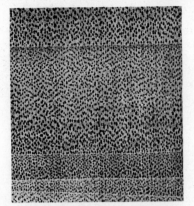

FIG. 43.—*Salix nigra* Marsh.
(x—5 ✕)

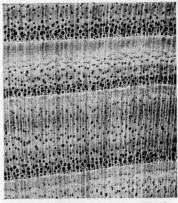

FIG. 44.—*Catalpa speciosa* Ward.
(x—5 ✕)

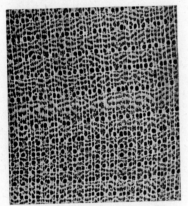

FIG. 45.—*Ulmus americana* L.
(x—5 ✕)

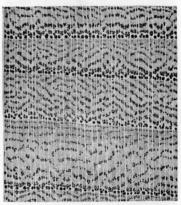

FIG. 46.—*Ulmus thomasi* Sarg.
(x—5 ✕)

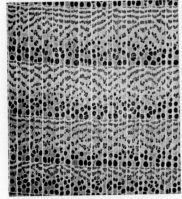

FIG. 47.—*Celtis occidentalis* L.
(x—5 ✕)

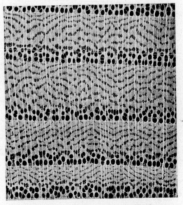

FIG. 48.—*Ulmus fulva* Michx.
(x—5 ✕)

52. Wood pale yellow to grayish or greenish yellow, or orange-yellow to golden-brown and turning dull dark brown on exposure; rays usually distinct without a lens............. **53**

52. Wood light brown to dark reddish brown or brown; rays usually indistinct without a lens...........................
    Red Elm, Slippery Elm*—*Ulmus fulva* Michx.   Plate VIII, Fig. 48. Desc. p. 551.
    White Elm, American Elm—*Ulmus americana* L., from young trees or top logs of old trees.   Desc. p. 549.

53. Wood pale yellow to grayish or greenish yellow, the narrow, imperfectly developed heartwood yellowish gray to light brown streaked with yellow; ray fleck inconspicuous on the radial surface........................
    Hackberry (Desc. p. 554):
    Common Hackberry—*Celtis occidentalis* L.   Plate VIII, Fig. 47.
    Sugar Hackberry—*Celtis laevigata* Willd.

53. Sapwood yellowish, narrow; heartwood orange-yellow to golden-brown and turning dull dark brown on exposure; ray fleck pronounced on the radial surface......................
    Red Mulberry—*Morus rubra* L.   Plate XI, Fig. 61.   Desc. p. 556.

54. Summerwood parenchyma metatracheal (arranged irrespective of the pores), appearing under the lens as fine, numerous, continuous or broken, tangential lines, or closely and evenly punctate (Ex., Fig. 52)..................... **55**

54. Summerwood parenchyma not evident or, if evident, paratracheal (obviously associated with the pores and occasionally connecting the pores in the late summerwood); metatracheal parenchyma, if present, not distinguishable as such......................... **56**

55. Wood with storied rays (forming ripple marks extending across the grain when the wood is viewed on the tangential surface); parenchyma inconspicuous (x), closely and evenly punctate....
    Persimmon—*Diospyros virginiana* L.   Plate VII, Fig. 37.   Desc. p. 604.

55. Wood without storied rays; parenchyma conspicuous (x), in concentric tangential lines in the summerwood...............
    Hickory (True Hickories) (Desc. p. 513):
    Shagbark Hickory—*Carya ovata* (Mill.) K. Koch
    Bigleaf Shagbark Hickory—*Carya laciniosa* (Michx. f.) Loud.
    Pignut Hickory—Carya glabra (Mill.) Sweet
    Oval Pignut Hickory, Red Hickory—*Carya ovalis* (Wangenh.) Sarg.
    Mockernut Hickory—*Carya tomentosa* (Poir.) Nutt.
    Etc.
    Hickory (Pecan Hickories) (Desc. p. 513):
    Bitternut Hickory—*Carya cordiformis* (Wangenh.) K. Koch
    Pecan—*Carya illinoënsis* (Wangenh.) K. Koch
    Nutmeg Hickory—*Carva myristicaeformis* (Michx. f.) Nutt.
    Water Hickory—*Carya aquatica* (Michx. f.) Nutt.
    Etc.

---

* Green wood usually with a characteristic sour odor.

Plate IX

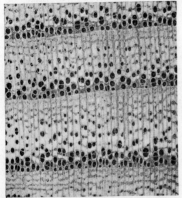

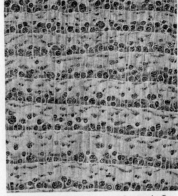

FIG. 49.—*Maclura pomifera* (Raf.) Schn.

FIG. 50.—*Robinia pseudoacacia* L.

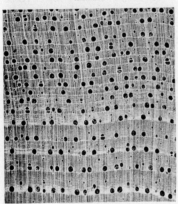

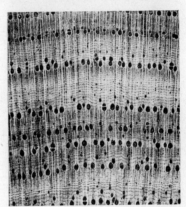

FIG. 51.—*Carya glabra* (Mill.) Sweet
$(x—5 \times)$

FIG. 52.—*Carya ovata* (Mill.) K. Koch
$(x—5 \times)$

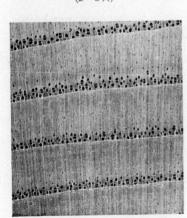

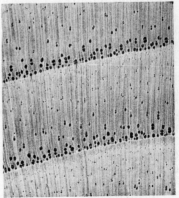

FIG. 53.—*Fraxinus americana* L.
$(x—5 \times)$

FIG. 54.—*Fraxinus oregona* Nutt.
$(x—5 \times)$

56. Springwood pores in the heartwood completely occluded with tyloses, their contours poorly defined................ 57

56. Springwood pores in the heartwood open or partly occluded with tyloses, their contours distinct..................... 58

57. Heartwood golden-yellow to bright orange, darkening upon exposure, often with reddish streaks along the grain; coloring matter readily soluble in water.......................

Osage-orange—*Maclura pomifera* (Raf.) Schneid. Plate IX, Fig. 49. Desc. p. 558.

57. Heartwood greenish yellow to dark yellowish or golden-brown; coloring matter not readily soluble in water..................

Black Locust—*Robinia pseudoacacia* L. Plate IX, Fig. 50. Desc. p. 579.

58. Rays fine to very fine, not distinct on the transverse surface without a hand lens.................................. 59

58. Rays broader, visible to the naked eye on the transverse surface... 64

59. Pores in the summerwood solitary or in radial rows of 2–3 (Ex., Fig. 54), appearing thick-walled from encircling parenchyma or with an aureole of parenchyma.............................. 60

59. Pores in the late summerwood in interrupted or rarely in continuous tangential bands (Fig. 44) or grouped in patches of porous tissue which are obliquely radial (flame-shaped) (Fig. 58), thin-walled................................... 62

60. Wood somewhat lustrous, strong; heartwood light brown or rarely pale yellow streaked with brown...................

White Ash (Desc. p. 606):

White Ash—*Fraxinus americana* L.   Plate IX, Fig. 53.
Red Ash—*Fraxinus pennsylvanica* Marsh.
Green Ash—*Fraxinus pennsylvanica* var. *lanceolata* (Borkh.) Sarg.
Etc.

Oregon Ash—*Fraxinus oregona* Nutt.   Plate IX, Fig. 54.   Desc. p. 606.

60. Wood dull, weak; heartwood grayish brown to orange-brown or dark brown (darker than that of white and Oregon Ash)   61

61. Wood on fresh-cut surface generally with the odor of sassafras; parenchyma forming aureoles around the summerwood pores, frequently uniting the pores in the late summerwood............

Sassafras—*Sassafras albidum* (Nutt.) Nees.   Plate X, Fig. 55.   Desc. p. 566.

61. Wood without the odor of sassafras; parenchyma confined to the walls of the pores, the walls for this reason appearing to be nearly uniform in thickness............................

Black Ash, Brown Ash—*Fraxinus nigra* Marsh.   Plate X, Fig. 56. Desc. p. 608.

62. Springwood pores in several rows........................ 63

62. Springwood pores in one somewhat interrupted row........

Giant Evergreen Chinkapin—*Castanopsis chrysophylla* (Hook.) DC. Plate X, Fig. 57.   Desc. p. 536.

Plate X

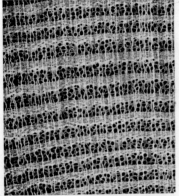

Fig. 55.—*Sassafras albidum* (Nutt.) Nees. (*x*—5×)

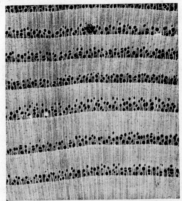

Fig. 56.—*Fraxinus nigra* Marsh. (*x*—5×)

Fig. 57.—*Castanopsis chrysophylla* (Hook.) DC. (*x*—5×)

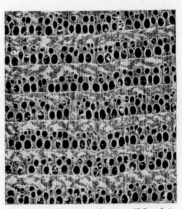

Fig. 58.—*Castanea dentata* (Marsh.) Borkh. (*x*—5×)

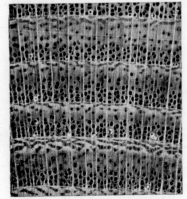

Fig. 59.—*Gleditsia triacanthos* L. (*x*—5×)

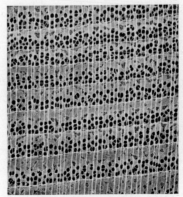

Fig. 60.—*Gymnocladus dioicus* (L.) K. Koch (*x*—5×)

63. Springwood pores large; transition from spring- to summerwood pores abrupt; pores in the summerwood in obliquely radial (flame-shaped) patches of light tissue.........................
Chestnut, American Chestnut—*Castanea dentata* (Marsh). Borkh. Plate X, Fig. 58. Desc. p. 534.

63. Springwood pores small; transition from spring- to summerwood pores somewhat gradual; pores in the late summerwood in interrupted or rarely in continuous tangential bands associated with parenchyma (one or more bands near the outer boundary occasionally consisting entirely of parenchyma)...................
Catalpa (Desc. p. 610):
> **Northern Catalpa**—*Catalpa speciosa* Ward. Plate VIII, Fig. 44.
> **Southern Catalpa**—*Catalpa bignonioides* Walt.

  64. Pores in the early springwood in several rows, the springwood zone plainly visible to the naked eye.............. **65**

  64. Pores in the early springwood in a more or less definite uniseriate row, the springwood zone inconspicuous to the naked eye... **71**

65. Heartwood light red to red or reddish brown (the reddish cast obvious).. **66**

65. Heartwood grayish brown to brown or golden-brown (the reddish cast wanting), rarely light yellow.................... **67**

  66. Pores in the late summerwood solitary, in short radial rows, or in small groups, embedded in short tangential lines of parenchyma; rays conspicuous to the naked eye; gum deposits frequent in the heartwood .... **Honey-locust**—*Gleditsia triacanthos* L. Plate X, Fig. 59. Desc. p. 575.

  66. Pores in the late summerwood in nestlike groups which occasionally coalesce laterally; short bands of parenchyma not evident; rays not very conspicuous to the naked eye; gum deposits infrequent in the heartwood................
Coffee-tree, Kentucky Coffee-tree—*Gymnocladus dioicus* (L.) K. Koch. Plate X, Fig. 60. Desc. p. 574.

67. Pores in the summerwood solitary or in radial rows of 2–3 (Ex., Fig. 54), appearing thick-walled from encircling parenchyma or with an aureole of parenchyma............................ **68**

67. Pores in the late summerwood in nestlike groups, or in interrupted or rarely in continuous tangential bands.............. **70**

  68. Wood somewhat lustrous, strong; heartwood light brown or rarely pale yellow streaked with brown...................
White Ash (Desc. p. 606):
> **White Ash**—*Fraxinus americana* L. Plate IX, Fig. 53.
> **Red Ash**—*Fraxinus pennsylvanica* Marsh.
> **Green Ash**—*Fraxinus pennsylvanica* var. *lanceolata* (Borkh.) Sarg.
> **Etc.**
> **Oregon Ash**—*Fraxinus oregona* Nutt. Plate IX, Fig. 54. Desc. p. 606.

  68. Wood dull, weak; heartwood grayish brown to orange-brown or dark brown (darker than that of White and Oregon Ash) **69**

69. Wood on fresh-cut surface generally with the odor of sassafras; parenchyma forming aureoles around the summerwood pores, frequently uniting the pores in the late summerwood..........
Sassafras—*Sassafras albidum* (Nutt.) Nees.   Plate X, Fig. 55, Desc. p. 566.

69. Wood without the odor of sassafras; parenchyma confined to the walls of the pores, the walls for this reason appearing to be nearly uniform in thickness.................................
Black Ash, Brown Ash—*Fraxinus nigra* Marsh.   Plate X, Fig. 56. Desc. p. 608.

70. Heartwood orange-yellow to golden-brown and turning dull dark brown on exposure; pores in nestlike groups throughout the summerwood; rays conspicuous to the naked eye, forming a pronounced fleck on the radial surface.................
Red Mulberry—*Morus rubra* L.   Plate XI, Fig. 61, Desc. p. 556.

70. Heartwood grayish brown to brown; pores solitary and in short radial rows in the early springwood, grouped in interrupted or rarely in continuous tangential bands in the late summerwood (one or more bands near the outer boundary of the ring occasionally consisting entirely of parenchyma); rays relatively inconspicuous, the ray fleck on the radial surface not pronounced.................................
Catalpa (Desc. p. 610):
  Northern Catalpa—*Catalpa speciosa* Ward.   Plate VIII, Fig. 44.
  Southern Catalpa—*Catalpa bignonioides* Walt.

71. Wood yellow or yellowish streaked with brown; pores appearing thick-walled (x) from encircling (paratracheal) parenchyma....
Yellowwood—*Cladrastis lutea* (Michx.) K. Koch.   Plate VII. Fig. 39. Desc. p. 577.

71. Wood red to reddish brown; pores thin-walled, not encircled by parenchyma...
Black Cherry, Cherry—*Prunus serotina* Ehrh.   Plate VII, Fig. 40, Desc. p. 572.

72. Rays wholly or in part broad, conspicuous or relatively inconspicuous, the broadest fully twice as wide as the largest pores (Figs. 62–70).............................   **73**

72 Rays narrow and nearly uniform in width; if variable in width, the broadest less than twice the width of the largest pores (Figs. 71–96).................................   **78**

73. Large rays (x) sharply delineated (conspicuous), generally numerous and spaced at fairly close intervals (Figs. 62–67)..........   **74**

73. Large rays (x) not sharply delineated (relatively inconspicuous), often sporadic and widely spaced (Figs. 68–70)...............   **77**

74. Rays obviously of two sorts, broad and very narrow; broad rays separated by several of the narrow type (x), plainly visible to the naked eye on the tangential surface as short, staggered lines; grain not interlocked.................   **75**

74. Rays nearly uniform in width, close, appearing to the naked eye on the tangential surface as closely packed, broken lines; grain generally interlocked.........................
Sycamore, Buttonwood, American Plane-tree—*Platanus occidentalis* L.   Plate XI, Figs. 62 and 63.   Desc. p. 570.

Plate XI

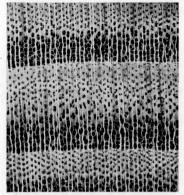

FIG. 61.—*Morus rubra* L.
(*x*—5 ×)

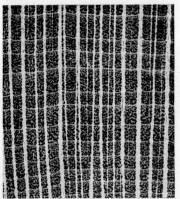

FIG. 62.—*Platanus occidentalis* L.
(*x*—5 ×)

FIG. 63.—*Platanus occidentalis* L.
(*t*—natural size)

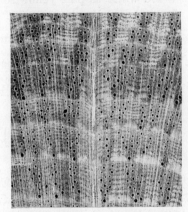

FIG. 64.—*Lithocarpus densiflora* (Hook
& Arn.) Rehd.   (*x*—5 ×)

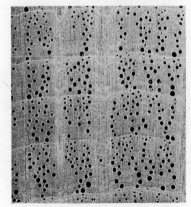

FIG. 65.—*Quercus virginiana* Mill.
(*x*—5 ×)

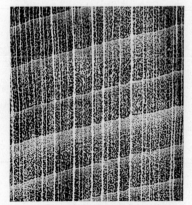

FIG. 66.—*Fagus grandifolia* Ehrh.
(*x*—5 ×)

75. Pores irregularly spaced, arranged in radial, fan-shaped or streamlike groups extending across the rings.................. **76**

75. Pores quite evenly spaced except in the late summerwood, not in radial, fan-shaped, or streamlike groups....................
Beech, American Beech—*Fagus grandifolia* Ehrh. Plate XI, Fig. 66; Plate XII, Fig. 67. Desc. p. 532.

    76. Sapwood reddish brown; heartwood brown tinged with red; zonate parenchyma plainly visible to the naked eye, in more or less continuous, ragged tangential lines................
    Tan-oak—*Lithocarpus densiflora* (Hook. & Arn.) Rehd. Plate XI, Fig. 64. Desc. p. 537.

    76. Sapwood whitish to grayish brown; heartwood dull brown to gray-brown; zonate parenchyma barely visible with a hand lens, appearing closely and evenly punctate..........
    Live Oak—*Quercus virginiana* Mill. Plate XI, Fig. 65. Desc. p. 539.

77. Wood white to pale yellowish or brownish white, hard, heavy; parenchyma in the summerwood in fine, light tangential lines which are generally plainly visible with a hand lens...........
Blue-beech, American Hornbeam—*Carpinus caroliniana* Walt. Plate XII, Fig. 68. Desc. p. 523.

77. Wood flesh colored to light brown tinged with red, light and soft (readily dented with the thumbnail); parenchyma in the summerwood not visible with a hand lens.......................
Red Alder—*Alnus rubra* Bong. Plate XII, Figs. 69 and 70. Desc. p. 530.

    78. Pores in the springwood appreciably larger than those in the summerwood, the transition gradual; wood semidiffuse porous (Ex., Plate VI, Figs. 35 and 36)................. **79**

    78. Pores nearly uniform in size throughout the ring; wood typically diffuse porous (Ex., Fig. 72).................... **91**

79. Pores fairly evenly distributed throughout the ring............ **80**

79. Pores unevenly distributed, inserted in tracts of light-colored tissue in streamlike, radially directed clusters separated by tracts of fibrous tissue devoid of pores............................
Tan-oak—*Lithocarpus densiflora* (Hook. & Arn.) Rehd. Plate XI, Fig. 64. Desc. p. 537.

    80. Summerwood parenchyma metatracheal (arranged irrespective of the pores), appearing under the lens as fine, numerous, continuous or broken tangential lines or closely and evenly punctate (Ex., Fig. 38).................................. **81**

    80. Summerwood parenchyma not evident or, if evident, paratracheal (obviously associated with the pores and occasionally connecting the pores in the late summerwood) or terminal... **84**

81. Heartwood chestnut-brown to chocolate- or purplish brown.... **82**

81. Heartwood brown or yellowish brown, or the wood creamy white to yellowish, aging to light yellowish or grayish brown......... **83**

Plate XII

FIG. 67.—*Fagus grandifolia* Ehrh.
(*t*—natural size)

FIG. 68.—*Carpinus caroliniana* Walt.
(*x*—5 ×)

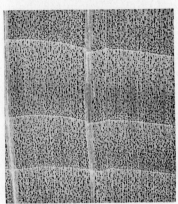

FIG. 69.—*Alnus rubra* Bong.
(*x*—5 ×)

FIG. 70.—*Alnus rubra* Bong.
(*t*—natural size)

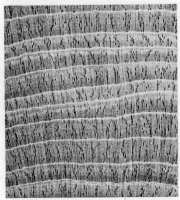

FIG. 71.—*Ostrya virginiana* (Mill.) K.
Koch (*x*—5 ×)

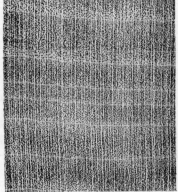

FIG. 72.—*Liquidambar styraciflua* L.
(*x*—5 ×)

82. Heartwood rich chocolate- or purplish brown, dull; wood relatively hard, heavy, with a characteristic odor on fresh-cut surface..
Black Walnut, Eastern Black Walnut—*Juglans nigra* L.   Plate VI, Fig. 35.   Desc. p. 510.

82. Heartwood light chestnut-brown, lustrous; wood soft (readily dented with the thumbnail), light, without characteristic odor..
Butternut, White Walnut—*Juglans cinerea* L.   Plate VI, Fig. 36. Desc. p. 509.

83. Wood with storied rays (forming ripple marks extending across the grain when the wood is viewed on the tangential surface); parenchyma inconspicuous, closely and evenly punctate.......
Persimmon—*Diospyros virginiana* L.   Plate VII, Fig. 37.   Desc. p. 604.

83. Wood without storied rays; parenchyma conspicuous, in continuous tangential lines in the summerwood..................
Water Hickory—*Carya aquatica* (Michx. f.) Nutt.   Desc. p. 513.

84. Rays plainly visible to the naked eye; wood red to reddish brown, or through shades of yellow......................   **85**

84. Rays indistinct to the naked eye; wood ranging from whitish through shades of grayish or light brown to chocolate-brown and brown..   **86**

85. Wood yellow or yellowish streaked with brown; pores appearing thick-walled (*x*) from encircling (paratracheal) parenchyma....
Yellowwood—*Cladrastis lutea* (Michx.) K. Koch.   Plate VII, Fig. 39. Desc. p. 577.

85. Wood red to reddish brown; pores thin-walled, not encircled by parenchyma..
Black Cherry, Cherry—*Prunus serotina* Ehrh.   Plate VII, Fig. 40. Desc. p. 572.

86. Pores very numerous, usually occupying nearly half the area between the rays (*x*); parenchyma not evident or, if evident, terminal and barely distinct; rays barely distinct with a hand lens..   **87**

86. Pores scattered, never occupying half the area between the rays (*x*); parenchyma not evident or, if evident, not terminal; rays plainly visible with a hand lens (Ex., Fig. 36).   **88**

87. Heartwood grayish white to light grayish brown, pale reddish brown or brown; wood medium-textured (compare Fig. 41 with Fig. 42, p. 369)..
Cottonwood (Desc. p. 517):
Eastern Cottonwood, Eastern Poplar—*Populus deltoides* Bartr. Plate VII, Fig. 41.
Balsam Poplar, Tacamahac Poplar—*Populus tacamahaca* Mill.
Swamp Cottonwood, Swamp Poplar—*Populus heterophylla* L.
Northern Black Cottonwood—*Populus trichocarpa* var. *hastata* Henry Etc.
Willow (Desc. p. 521):
Black Willow—*Salix nigra* Marsh.   Plate VIII, Fig. 43.
Etc.

87. Heartwood pale creamy white; wood fine-textured............
Aspen (Desc. p. 519):
Quaking Aspen, Trembling Aspen—*Populus tremuloides* Michx. Plate XIII, Fig. 74.
Bigtooth Aspen—*Populus grandidentata* Michx.   Plate VII, Fig. 42.

88. Heartwood rich chocolate- or purplish brown; wood relatively hard, heavy...
Black Walnut, Eastern Black Walnut—*Juglans nigra* L.   Plate VI, Fig. 35.   Desc. p. 510.

88. Heartwood grayish brown to light chestnut-brown, occasionally with a lavender tinge; wood soft (readily dented with the thumbnail), light.............................. **89**

89. Pores in the late summerwood solitary or in short radial groups of 2–several... **90**

89. Pores in the late summerwood in interrupted or rarely in continuous tangential bands associated with parenchyma (one or more bands near the outer boundary of the ring occasionally consisting entirely of parenchyma).........................
Catalpa (Desc. p. 610):
  Northern Catalpa—*Catalpa speciosa* Ward.   Plate VIII, Fig. 44.
  Southern Catalpa—*Catalpa bignonioides* Walt.

90. Wood usually aromatic on fresh-cut surface; pores encircled by a whitish sheath of parenchyma....................
California Laurel, Oregon Myrtle—*Umbellularia californica* (Hook. & Arn.) Nutt.   Plate XIII, Fig. 77.   Desc. p. 564.

90. Wood not aromatic; pores not encircled by a whitish sheath of parenchyma..
Butternut, White Walnut—*Juglans cinerea* L.   Plate VI, Fig. 36. Desc. p. 509.

91. Summerwood figured with wavy, concentric bands of pores which are mostly continuous and separated by bands of mechanical tissue...
Hard Elm :* Desc. p. 552.
  Rock Elm, Cork Elm—*Ulmus thomasi* Sarg.   Plate VIII, Fig. 46.
  Cedar Elm—*Ulmus crassifolia* Nutt.
  Winged Elm—*Ulmus alata* Michx.

91. Summerwood not figured with wavy, concentric bands of pores **92**

  92. Rays fine to very fine, not distinct on the transverse surface to the naked eye.. **93**

  92. Rays broader, distinct on the transverse surface to the naked eye.. **110**

---

* See footnote, p. 372.

93. Rays very close, seemingly occupying half the area on the transverse surface of the wood* (Figs. 72–76)................. **94**

93. Rays normally spaced, not seemingly occupying half the area on the transverse surface of the wood (Ex., Fig. 78).............. **98**

94. Pores in radial rows which are more or less unevenly distributed and are often further aggregated into flamelike groups; zonate parenchyma generally evident with a hand lens in the outer portion of the ring; ring contours frequently ragged (erose), the late summerwood often specked with white..........
Hop-hornbeam—*Ostrya virginiana* (Mill.) K. Koch. Plate XII, Fig. 71. Desc. p. 525.

94. Pores quite evenly distributed,† not aggregated into flamelike groups; zonate parenchyma wanting or generally not evident in the outer portion of the ring; ring contours, when visible, even or nearly so.............................. **95**

95. Heartwood creamy white or pale yellowish white to greenish or brownish gray.. **96**

95. Heartwood flesh-color or carneous gray to light brown or reddish brown, the darker grades sometimes with darker streaks of pigment figure... **97**

96. Wood light, soft (readily dented with the thumbnail), straight-grained, frequently with darker streaks of sapstain; ripple marks sometimes evident on the tangential surface..
Buckeye (Desc. p. 589):
Yellow Buckeye—*Aesculus octandra* Marsh. Plate XIII, Fig. 73.
Ohio Buckeye—*Aesculus glabra* Willd.
California Buckeye—*Aesculus californica* Nutt.

96. Wood rather light (swollen butt log of *Nyssa aquatica*)‡ to moderately heavy, medium soft to moderately hard, usually interlocked-grained, nearly uniform in color; ripple marks wanting...
Black Gum, Black Tupelo, Pepperidge—*Nyssa sylvatica* Marsh. Plate XIII, Fig. 75. Desc. p. 595.
Swamp Tupelo, Swamp Black Gum—*Nyssa sylvatica* var. *biflora* (Walt.) Sarg.
Tupelo Gum, Water Gum—*Nyssa aquatica* L. Plate XIII, Fig. 76. Desc. p. 595.

---

* The impression gained by casual examination of the wood.

† Sometimes unevenly distributed in the butt log of Tupelo Gum and sparse in portions of the growth ring, the tissue then simulating that of a coniferous wood in structure.

‡ PENFOUND, W. T. Comparative Structure of the Wood and the "Knees," Swollen Bases, and Normal Trunks of the Tupelo Gum (*Nyssa aquatica* L.). *Amer. Jour. Bot.*, Vol. 21, pp. 623–631. 1934.

Plate XIII

FIG. 73.—*Aesculus octandra* Marsh.
(x—5 ×)

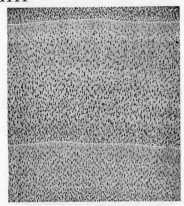

FIG. 74.—*Populus tremuloides* Michx.
(x—5 ×)

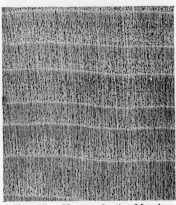

FIG. 75.—*Nyssa sylvatica* Marsh.
(x—5 ×)

FIG. 76.—*Nyssa aquatica* L.
(x—5 ×)

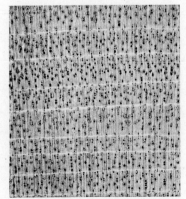

FIG. 77.—*Umbellularia californica*
(Hook. & Arn.) Nutt. (x—5 ×)

FIG. 78.—*Betula lutea* Michx. f.
(x—5 ×)

97. Pores uniform in size throughout the ring, appearing solitary
under the lens...
Red-gum, American Sweet Gum—*Liquidambar styraciflua* L.   Plate
XII, Fig. 72.   Desc. p. 567.

97. Pores usually slightly larger in the springwood, many in radially
aligned pore multiples of 2–several.........................
Red Alder—*Alnus rubra* Bong.

    98. Wood rays plainly visible with a hand lens............... **99**
    98. Wood rays scarcely visible with a hand lens.............. **107**

99. Wood aromatic on fresh-cut surface; pores encircled by a
whitish sheath of parenchyma..............................
California Laurel, Oregon Myrtle—*Umbellularia californica* (Hook. &
Arn.) Nutt.   Plate XIII Fig. 77.   Desc. p. 564.

99. Wood not aromatic on fresh-cut surface; parenchyma not evident around the pores..................................... **100**

    100. Pores in radial rows which are more or less unevenly dis-
tributed and are often further aggregated into flamelike
groups; zonate parenchyma generally evident in the outer
portion of the ring; ring contours frequently ragged
(erose), the late summerwood often specked with white..
Hop-hornbeam—*Ostrya virginiana* (Mill.) K. Koch.   Plate XII,
Fig. 71.   Desc. p. 525.

    100. Pores quite evenly distributed, not grouped as above;
zonate parenchyma wanting or generally not evident in
the outer portion of the ring; ring contours not obviously
ragged.. **101**

101. Pores appearing as white dots to the naked eye, the larger
obviously wider than the rays.............................
Birch (Desc. p. 526):
    Yellow Birch—*Betula lutea* Michx. f.   Plate XIII, Fig. 78;   Plate
    XIV, Fig. 79.
    Sweet Birch, Black Birch, Cherry Birch—*Betula lenta* L.   Plate XIV,
    Fig. 80.
    River Birch, Red Birch—*Betula nigra* L.
    Paper Birch, White Birch—*Betula papyrifera* Marsh.   Plate XIV,
    Fig. 81.
    Gray Birch—*Betula populifolia* Marsh.
    Etc.

101. Pores not visible to the naked eye, not obviously wider than
the rays.. **102**

102. Wood soft (readily dented with the thumbnail), generally with characteristic odor on fresh-cut surface (especially when moistened); ray flecks (r) high, rather distant......
Basswood (Desc. p. 593):
   Basswood—*Tilia americana* L.   Plate XIV, Fig. 82.
   White Basswood—*Tilia heterophylla* Vent.
   Etc.

102. Wood moderately hard to hard, without characteristic odor on fresh-cut surface; ray flecks (r) low, close or indistinct.. **103**

103. Wood very fine-textured; pores small, barely distinct with a hand lens, crowded.. **104**

103. Wood medium fine-textured; pores plainly visible with a hand lens, not crowded.. **105**

  104. Pores in a uniseriate row in the early springwood, elsewhere clustered or banded, the pore bands usually alternating with bands of dense fibrous tissue......................
    Pacific Madrone, Madroña—*Arbutus menziesi* Pursh.   Plate XIV, Fig. 83.   Desc. p. 602.

  104. Pores not in a uniseriate row in the early springwood, evenly distributed throughout the growth ring, solitary for the most part...
    Sourwood—*Oxydendrum arboreum* (L.) DC.   Plate XIV, Fig. 84.   Desc. p. 601.

105. Sapwood yellowish; heartwood yellowish brown tinged with red; ray fleck (r) indistinct.................................
Cascara Buckthorn—*Rhamnus purshiana* DC.   Plate XV, Fig. 85. Desc. p. 591.

105. Sapwood white or reddish; heartwood pale brown with grayish or greenish cast, or pinkish brown; ray fleck (r) distinct...... **106**

  106. Sapwood white; heartwood pale brown, frequently with grayish or greenish cast; pith flecks not infrequent.......
    Soft Maple (Desc. p. 587):
     Red Maple—*Acer rubrum* L.   Plate XV, Fig. 90.
     Silver Maple—*Acer saccharinum* L.   Plate XVI, Fig. 91.

  106. Sapwood reddish white; heartwood pinkish brown; pith flecks rare..
    Oregon Maple—*Acer macrophyllum* Pursh.   Plate XVI, Fig. 92. Desc. p. 585.

107. Heartwood carneous red to varying shades of reddish brown..
Pacific Madrone, Madroña—*Arbutus menziesi* Pursh.   Plate XIV, Fig. 83.   Desc. p. 602.

107. Heartwood creamy white to pale yellowish white, often with darker streaks or grayish white to light grayish brown........ **108**

Plate XIV

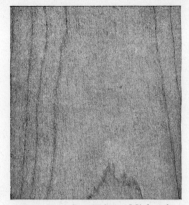

FIG. 79.—*Betula lutea* Michx. f.
(*t*—natural size)

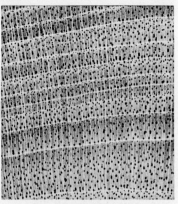

FIG. 80.—*Betula lenta* L.
(*x*—5 ×)

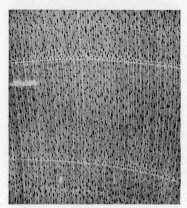

FIG. 81.—*Betula papyrifera* Marsh.
(*x*—5 ×)

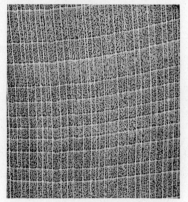

FIG. 82.—*Tilia americana* L.
(*x*—5 ×)

FIG. 83.—*Arbutus menziesi* Pursh
(*x*—5 ×)

FIG. 84.—*Oxydendrum arboreum* (L.)
DC.   (*x*—5 ×)

108. Heartwood grayish white to light grayish brown, pale reddish brown or brown; wood medium textured (compare Fig. 41 with Fig. 42, p. 369, and with Fig. 73, p. 387)....
Cottonwood (Desc. p. 517):
Eastern Cottonwood, Eastern Poplar—*Populus deltoides* Bartr. Plate VII, Fig. 41.
Balsam Poplar, Tacamahac Poplar—*Populus tacamahaca* Mill.
Swamp Cottonwood, Swamp Poplar—*Populus heterophylla* L.
Northern Black Cottonwood—*Populus trichocarpa* var. *hastata* Henry
Etc.
Willow (Desc. p. 521):
Black Willow—*Salix nigra* Marsh. Plate VIII, Fig. 43.
Etc.

108. Heartwood pale creamy white to pale yellowish white; wood fine-textured.................................... **109**

109. Pores diminishing in size toward the outer ring boundary; ripple marks never present.............................
Aspen (Desc. p. 519):
Quaking Aspen, Trembling Aspen—*Populus tremuloides* Michx. Plate XIII, Fig. 74.
Bigtooth Aspen—*Populus grandidentata* Michx. Plate VII, Fig. 42.

109. Pores nearly uniform in size throughout the ring; ripple marks sometimes present..............................
Buckeye (Desc. p. 589):
Yellow Buckeye—*Aesculus octandra* Marsh. Plate XIII, Fig. 73.
Ohio Buckeye—*Aesculus glabra* Willd.
California Buckeye—*Aesculus californica* Nutt.

110. Rays nearly uniform in width (Ex., Fig. 82)........... **111**

110. Rays variable in width, the broader separated by several narrow rays which are scarcely visible with a hand lens (Ex., Fig. 93)....................................... **125**

111. Pores appearing thick-walled from encircling (paratracheal) parenchyma... **112**

111. Pores thin-walled, not encircled by parenchyma............ **113**

112. Wood aromatic on fresh-cut surface; heartwood light rich brown to brown; sheath of parenchyma around the pores wide..
California Laurel, Oregon Myrtle—*Umbellularia californica* (Hook. & Arn.) Nutt. Plate XIII, Fig. 77. Desc. p. 564.

112. Wood not aromatic on fresh-cut surface; heartwood clear yellow, changing upon exposure to light brown or yellow streaked with brown; sheath of parenchyma around the pores narrow......................................
Yellowwood—*Cladrastis lutea* (Michx.) K. Koch. Plate VII, Fig. 39. Desc. p. 577.

113. Outer margin of the growth ring sharply delineated by a narrow light line... **114**

113. Outer margin of the growth ring not delineated by a light line (a dark line of fibrous tissue sometimes present)............. **115**

114. Heartwood variable in color, ranging from clear yellow to dark yellowish, greenish, or pinkish brown, or greenish black (Evergreen Magnolia); ray flecks (*r*) low, close....
Yellow-poplar, Tulip-poplar, Whitewood—*Liriodendron tulipifera* L.   Plate XV, Fig. 86.   Desc. p. 562.
Magnolia (Desc. p. 560):
   Cucumber Magnolia, Cucumber-tree—*Magnolia acuminata* L.   Plate XV, Fig. 87.
   Evergreen Magnolia, Southern Magnolia—*Magnolia grandiflora* L.   Plate XV, Fig. 88.

114. Heartwood creamy white to pale brown; ray flecks (*r*) high, rather distant...
Basswood (Desc. p. 593):
   Basswood—*Tilia americana* L.   Plate XIV, Fig. 82.
   White Basswood—*Tilia heterophylla* Vent.
   Etc.

115. Wood rays very close, seemingly forming half the area on the transverse surface of the wood* (Figs. 71–76).............. **116**

115. Wood rays normally spaced, not seemingly forming half the area on the transverse surface of the wood (Ex., Fig. 91)..... **118**

116. Heartwood carneous gray to varying shades of reddish brown, the darker shades sometimes with darker streaks of pigment figure..................................... **117**

116. Heartwood greenish or brownish gray..................
Black Gum, Black Tupelo, Pepperidge—*Nyssa sylvatica* Marsh. Plate XIII, Fig. 75.   Desc. p. 595.
Swamp Tupelo, Swamp Black Gum—*Nyssa sylvatica* var. *biflora* (Walt.) Sarg.
Tupelo Gum, Water Gum—*Nyssa aquatica* L.

117. Pores crowded between the rays, frequently contiguous.......
Red-gum, American Sweet Gum—*Liquidambar styraciflura* L. Plate XII, Fig. 72.   Desc. p. 567.

117. Pores not crowded between the rays, solitary for the most part
Sourwood—*Oxydendrum arboreum* (L.) DC.   Plate XIV, Fig. 84. Desc. p. 601.

118. Pores in a distinct uniseriate row in the early springwood, crowded.......................................
Black Cherry, Cherry—*Prunus serotina* Ehrh.   Plate VII, Fig. 40.   Desc. p. 572.

118. Pores not in a uniseriate row in the early springwood.... **119**

119. Heartwood ivory-white, frequently with bluish streaks; pores in radial strings extending across the rings; broadest rays obviously wider than the widest pores......................
Holly, American Holly—*Ilex opaca* Ait.   Plate XV, Fig. 89.   Desc. p. 581.

119. Heartwood nearly white to light creamy brown, yellow-brown, light reddish brown, or brown; pores not in radial strings, sometimes in short radial rows of 2–several; broadest rays not obviously wider than the widest pores...................... **120**

---

* The impression gained by casual examination of the wood.

Plate XV

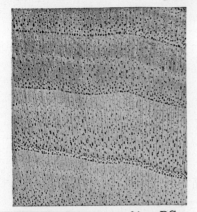

Fig. 85.—*Rhamnus purshiana* DC.
(*x*—5 ×)

Fig. 86.—*Liriodendron tulipifera* L.
(*x*—5 ×)

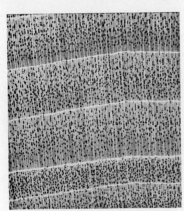

Fig. 87.—*Magnolia acuminata* L.
(*x*—5 ×)

Fig. 88.—*Magnolia grandiflora* L.
(*x*—5 ×)

Fig. 89.—*Ilex opaca* Ait.
(*x*—5 ×)

Fig. 90.—*Acer rubrum* L.
(*x*—5 ×)

120. Largest pores about the width of the broadest rays...... **121**
120. Largest pores obviously wider than the broadest rays....
    Birch (Desc. p. 526):
        Yellow Birch—*Betula lutea* Michx. f. Plate XIII, Fig. 78;
        Plate XIV, Fig. 79.
        Sweet Birch, Black Birch, Cherry Birch—*Betula lenta* L.
        Plate XIV, Fig. 80.
        River Birch, Red Birch—*Betula nigra* L.
        Paper Birch, White Birch—*Betula papyrifera* Marsh. Plate
        XIV, Fig. 81.
        Gray Birch—*Betula populifolia* Marsh.
        Etc.

121. Wood soft (readily dented with the thumbnail), often appearing lacelike under a lens (*x*); rays of the same color as the background on the transverse surface; ray flecks (*r*) high, rather distant......................................
    Basswood (Desc. p. 593):
        Basswood—*Tilia americana* L. Plate XIV, Fig. 82.
        White Basswood—*Tilia heterophylla* Vent.
        Etc.

121. Wood medium hard to hard, not appearing lacelike under a lens (*x*); rays sharply delineated on the transverse surface; ray flecks relatively low, close................................. **122**

    122. Wood very fine-textured; pores very small, solitary for the most part, those in the outer portion of the ring scarcely distinct with a hand lens......................
        Sourwood—*Oxydendrum arboreum* (L.) DC. Plate XIV, Fig. 84. Desc. p. 601.

    122. Wood medium fine-textured; pores solitary and in radial groups of 2–4, those in the outer portion of the ring plainly visible with a hand lens....................... **123**

123. Sapwood yellowish; heartwood yellowish brown tinged with red; ray fleck (*r*) indistinct...............................
    Cascara Buckthorn—*Rhamnus purshiana* DC. Plate XV, Fig. 85. Desc. p. 591.

123. Sapwood white or reddish; heartwood pale brown with grayish or greenish cast, or pinkish brown; ray fleck (*r*) distinct...... **124**

124. Sapwood white; heartwood pale brown, frequently with grayish or greenish cast; pith flecks not infrequent.......
Soft Maple (Desc. p. 587):
  Red Maple—*Acer rubrum* L.   Plate XV, Fig. 90.
  Silver Maple—*Acer saccharinum* L.   Plate XVI, Fig. 91.

124. Sapwood reddish white; heartwood pinkish brown; pith flecks rare...
Oregon Maple, Bigleaf Maple—*Acer macrophyllum* Pursh.   Plate XVI, Fig. 92.   Desc. p. 585.

125. Heartwood ivory-white, frequently with bluish streaks; pores in radial strings extending across the rings.................
Holly—*Ilex opaca* Ait.   Plate XV, Fig. 89.   Desc. p. 581.

125. Heartwood (or wood where heartwood is not visible) darker; pores not in radial strings................................. **126**

126. Sapwood white with a reddish tinge, narrow; heartwood uniform light reddish brown; outer margin of the growth ring usually sharply delineated by a narrow darker line of denser fibrous tissue; wider rays usually quite sharply delineated against the background of pores and fibrous tissue...
Hard Maple (Desc. p. 583):
  Sugar Maple—*Acer saccharum* Marsh.   Plate XVI, Figs. 93 and 94.
  Black Maple—*Acer nigrum* Michx. f.

126. Sapwood carneous to light pinkish brown, very wide; heartwood, when present, dark brown, frequently variegated; outer margin of the growth ring and wider rays not sharply delineated against the background of pores and fibrous tissue......................................
Dogwood (Desc. p. 598):
  Dogwood, Flowering Dogwood—*Cornus florida* L.   Plate XVI, Fig. 95.
  Pacific Dogwood—*Cornus nuttalli* Audub.   Plate XVI, Fig. 96.

Plate XVI

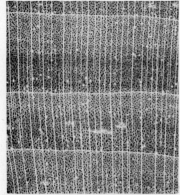

FIG. 91.—*Acer saccharinum* L.
(x—5 ×)

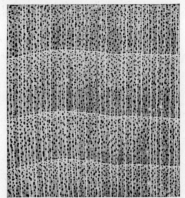

FIG. 92.—*Acer macrophyllum* Pursh.
(x—5 ×)

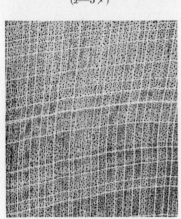

FIG. 93.—*Acer saccharum* Marsh.
(x—5 ×)

FIG. 94.—*Acer saccharum* Marsh.
(t—natural size)

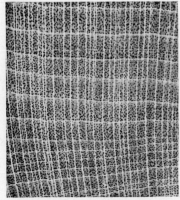

FIG. 95.—*Cornus florida* L.
(x—5 ×)

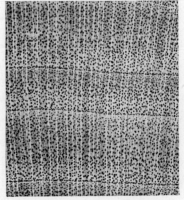

FIG. 96.—*Cornus nuttalli* Audub.
(x—5 ×)

KEY FOR THE IDENTIFICATION OF THE MORE IMPORTANT COMMERCIAL WOODS OF THE UNITED STATES*

BASED ON MINUTE FEATURES

1. Wood without vessels (nonporous)............................ 2
1. Wood with vessels (porous)................................... 35
   2. Longitudinal and transverse resin canals present.......... 3
   2. Longitudinal and transverse resin canals normally absent; traumatic canals† occasionally present, aligned in a tangential row (x)... 18
3. Epithelial cells thin-walled (Text Fig. 35, A and C).......... 4
3. Epithelial cells thick-walled (Text Fig. 35, B and E)......... 14
   4. Ray tracheids dentate (r) (Plate XVII, Figs. 97–99)....... 5
   4. Ray tracheids not dentate (r) (Plate XVII, Fig. 100)...... 12
5. Pits leading from ray parenchyma to longitudinal tracheids large [windowlike (Text Fig. 34, A)], 1–2 per ray crossing......
   Red Pine, Norway Pine—*Pinus resinosa* Ait. Plate XVII, Fig. 97 [pits similar to those in *Pinus strobus* L. (Plate XVII, Fig. 100)]; Plate XXIX, Figs. 141 and 142. Desc. p. 458.
5. Pits leading from ray parenchyma to longitudinal tracheids variable in size and shape [pinoid (Text Fig. 34, B and C)], 1–7 (mostly 2–5) per ray crossing (Plate XVII, Figs. 98 and 99)... 6
   6. Summerwood tracheids forming a band 3–10 cells in width (x).. 7
   6. Summerwood tracheids forming a band 10–many cells in width (x)... 10
7. Outer margin of the growth increment (r) with depressions or sinuses (dimples), the distorted tissue in these areas forming swirls as viewed in the tangential section.................... 8
7. Outer margin of the growth increment (r) not obviously distorted, the grain normal... 9
   8. Longitudinal resin canals with maximum tangential diameter‡ of 230 (av. between 160–185) microns..............
   Ponderosa Pine, Western Yellow Pine—*Pinus ponderosa* Laws. Plate XXVIII, Figs. 139 and 140. Desc. p. 455.
   Jeffrey Pine—*Pinus jeffreyi* Grev. & Balf. Desc. p. 455.
   8. Longitudinal resin canals with maximum tangential diameter of 110 (av. between 80–90) microns...................
   Lodgepole Pine—*Pinus contorta* var. *latifolia* S. Wats. Plate XXVI, Figs. 135 and 136. Desc. p. 450.

---

* Plates XXIII—CII are inserted opposite the Description by Species, pp. 442–612.

† Canals supposedly formed as a result of wounding; as viewed in the transverse section, they resemble normal canals but differ in that they are arranged in a row which frequently extends for some little distance along the growth ring.

‡ The diameter inclusive of the epithelium.

Plate XVII

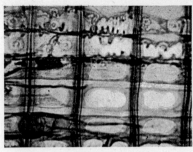
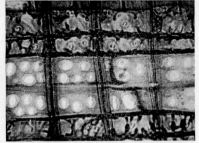

FIG. 97.   FIG. 98.

FIG. 97.—Radial section of the wood of red pine, *Pinus resinosa* Ait., showing portion of a ray composed of two rows of dentate ray tracheids and three complete rows of ray parenchyma with angular, windowlike pits in the ray crossings in the back walls.   (300 ×)

FIG. 98.—Radial section of the wood of Ponderosa Pine, *Pinus ponderosa* Laws., showing portion of a ray composed of three rows of dentate ray tracheids and two complete rows of ray parenchyma with 2-several pits in the ray crossings in the back walls.   (300 ×)

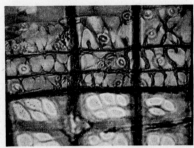
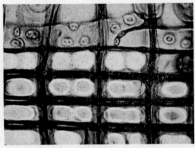

FIG. 99.   FIG. 100.

FIG. 99.—Radial section of the wood of longleaf pine, *Pinus palustris* Mill., showing portion of a ray composed of three rows of dentate ray tracheids and one complete row of ray parenchyma with several pits in the ray crossings in the front walls.   (300 ×)

FIG. 100.—Radial section of the wood of Northern White Pine, *Pinus strobus* L., showing portion of a ray composed of one row of nondentate ray tracheids and three complete rows of ray parenchyma with 1-2 windowlike pits in the ray crossings in the back walls.   (300 ×)

9. Longitudinal resin canals with tangential diameter of 230 (av. between 160–185) microns; dentations in the ray tracheids prominent, frequently extending across the cell (r) forming a reticulate pattern...
Ponderosa Pine, Western Yellow Pine—*Pinus ponderosa* Laws. Plate XXVIII, Figs. 139 and 140. Desc. p. 455.
Jeffrey Pine—*Pinus jeffreyi* Grev. & Balf. Desc. p. 455.
9. Longitudinal resin canals with maximum tangential diameter of 100 (av. between 75–90) microns; dentations in the ray tracheids shallow (not prominent), seldom extending across the cell (r)..
Jack Pine—*Pinus banksiana* Lamb. Plate XXX, Figs. 143 and 144. Desc. p. 460.

10. Outer margin of the growth increment (r) with depressions or sinuses (dimples), the distorted tissue in these areas forming swirls as viewed in the tangential section..............
Lodgepole Pine—*Pinus contorta* var. *latifolia* S. Wats. Plate XXVI, Figs. 135 and 136. Desc. p. 450.
10. Outer margin of the growth increment (r) not obviously distorted, the grain normal............................. **11**

11. Longitudinal resin canals with tangential diameter of 180–230 (av. 90–185) microns; dentations in the ray tracheids prominent, frequently extending across the cell (*r*) forming a reticulate pattern..

Southern Pine (Desc. p. 452):*
    Longleaf Pine—*Pinus palustris* Mill.   Plate XXVII, Figs. 137 and 138.
    Shortleaf Pine—*Pinus echinata* Mill.
    Loblolly Pine—*Pinus taeda* L.
    Slash Pine—*Pinus caribaea* Morelet
    Pitch Pine—*Pinus rigida* Mill.
    Pond Pine—*Pinus rigida* var. *serotina* (Michx.) Loud.
Ponderosa Pine, Western Yellow Pine—*Pinus ponderosa* Laws.   Plate XXVIII, Figs. 139 and 140.   Desc. p. 455.
Jeffrey Pine—*Pinus jeffreyi* Grev. & Balf.   Desc. p. 455

11. Longitudinal resin canals with maximum tangential diameter of 100 (av. between 75–90) microns; dentations in the ray tracheids shallow (not prominent), seldom extending across the cell (*r*)...

Jack Pine—*Pinus banksiana* Lamb.   Plate XXX, Figs. 143 and 144. Desc. p. 460.

---

* The woods of Ponderosa and Jeffrey Pine are frequently confused with those of the Southern Yellow Pines; accuracy of identification is the more certain when a number of features are considered in unison, the majority of which may be diagnostically significant (see the supplemental Key that follows).

1. Summerwood usually forming less than 20 per cent of the annual ring; radial diameter of the lumen of the last-formed summerwood tracheids (*x*) 1–3 times the thickness of the secondary wall; interspersed ray tracheids rare; average number of pits per ray crossing in the springwood less than 2.8; less than 20 per cent of the pits in the ray crossings in the springwood paired vertically....................

Ponderosa Pine, Western Yellow Pine—*Pinus ponderosa* Laws.   Plate XVII, Fig. 98, Plate XXVIII, Figs. 139 and 140.
Jeffrey Pine—*Pinus jeffreyi* Grev. & Balf.

1. Summerwood usually forming more than 20 per cent of the annual ring; radial diameter of the lumen of the last-formed summerwood tracheids (*x*) about equal to the thickness of the secondary wall; interspersed ray tracheids present in one-fourth or more of the rays; average number of pits per ray crossing in the springwood more than 2.8; more than 20 per cent of the pits in the ray crossings in the springwood paired vertically...

Southern Pine:
    Longleaf Pine—*Pinus palustris* Mill.   Plate XVII, Fig. 99; Plate XXVII, Figs. 137 and 138.
    Shortleaf Pine—*Pinus echinata* Mill.
    Loblolly Pine—*Pinus taeda* L.
    Slash Pine—*Pinus caribaea* Morelet
    Pitch Pine—*Pinus rigida* Mill.
    Pond Pine—*Pinus rigida* var. *serotina* (Michx.) Loud.

12. Longitudinal tracheids with average tangential diameter between 35–50 microns;* pits leading from ray parenchyma to springwood longitudinal tracheids rarely if ever superimposed; longitudinal resin canals with maximum tangential diameter† of 200 + (av. between 135–225) microns........ **13**

12. Longitudinal tracheids with average tangential diameter between 25–35 microns; pits leading from ray parenchyma to springwood longitudinal tracheids occasionally superimposed; longitudinal resin canals with maximum tangential diameter of 150 (av. between 90–120) microns............
Northern White Pine, Eastern White Pine, White Pine—*Pinus strobus* L., Plate XXV, Figs. 133 and 134. Desc. p. 448.

13. Pits leading from ray parenchyma to springwood longitudinal tracheids with large, more or less quadrangular orifices, occupying most of the ray crossing; longitudinal resin canals with maximum tangential diameter of 200 (av. between 135–150) microns.......
Idaho White Pine, Western White Pine—*Pinus monticola* Dougl. Plate XXIV, Figs. 131 and 132. Desc. p. 445.

13. Pits leading from ray parenchyma to springwood longitudinal tracheids with smaller, rounded orifices, more or less widely spaced; longitudinal resin canals with maximum tangential diameter of 300 (av. between 175–225) microns..............
Sugar Pine—*Pinus lambertiana* Dougl. Plate XVIII, Fig. 101; Plate XXIII, Figs. 129 and 130. Desc. p. 443.

14. Longitudinal tracheids (spring- and summerwood) with spiral thickening.......................................
Douglas Fir, Yellow Fir, Red Fir—*Pseudotsuga taxifolia* (Poir.) Britt. Plate XXXV, Figs. 155 and 156. Desc. p. 473.

14. Longitudinal tracheids without spiral thickening, or the spirals sporadic (*Larix laricina*) and confined to the summerwood... **15**

15. Summerwood pronounced; transition from spring- to summerwood abrupt; pits leading from ray parenchyma to longitudinal tracheids 1–12 (generally 4–6) per ray crossing, often in a double horizontal row (Plate XVIII, Fig. 102); transverse resin canals (*t*) with 10–12 epithelial cells............................. **16**

15. Summerwood not pronounced; transition from spring- to summerwood usually gradual; pits leading from ray parenchyma to longitudinal tracheids 1–6 (generally 2–4) per ray crossing, generally in a single horizontal row (Plate XVIII, Fig. 103); transverse resin canals (*t*) usually with 7–9 epithelial cells..... **17**

---

* Computed by counting the number of tracheids falling under the calibrated scale of an eyepiece micrometer, using a $10\times$ eyepiece and a 16-mm. objective, *making no allowance* for the wood rays. To obtain an approximate average, five random positions on the section are recommended. A similar procedure should be followed whenever data of this general type are required.

† The diameter inclusive of the epithelium

Plate XVIII

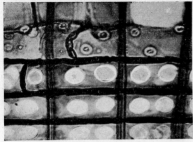

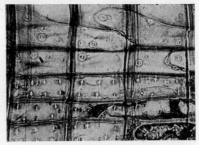

FIG. 101.   FIG. 102.

FIG. 101.—Radial section of the wood of sugar pine, *Pinus lambertiana* Dougl., showing portion of a ray composed of one row of nondentate ray tracheids and two complete rows of ray parenchyma with paired, rounded, windowlike pits in the ray crossings in the back walls.   (300 ×)

FIG. 102.—Radial section of the wood of western larch, *Larix occidentalis* Nutt., showing portion of a ray composed of two rows of nondentate ray tracheids and two complete rows of ray parenchyma with small pits in the ray crossings in the back walls, in part in double horizontal rows.   (300 ×)

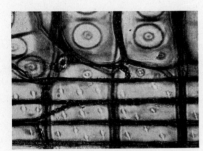

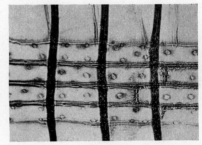

FIG. 103.   FIG. 104.

FIG. 103.—Radial section of the wood of Sitka spruce, *Picea sitchensis* (Bong.) Carr., showing portion of a ray composed of one row of nondentate ray tracheids and three complete rows of ray parenchyma with small pits in the ray crossings in the back walls, for the most part in single horizontal rows.   (300 ×)

FIG. 104.—Radial section of the wood of balsam fir, *Abies balsamea* (L.) Mill., showing portion of a ray composed entirely of ray parenchyma with small pits in the ray crossings in the back walls.   (300 ×)

16. Longitudinal tracheids with average tangential diameter between 30–40 microns;* growth rings generally wide (5–20 per inch).......................................
Tamarack, Eastern Larch—*Larix laricina* (Du Roi.) K. Koch. Plate XXXI, Figs. 145 and 146. Desc. p. 462.

16. Longitudinal tracheids with average tangential diameter between 40–50 microns; growth rings generally narrow (30–60 per inch)....................................
Western Larch—*Larix occidentalis* Nutt. Plate XXXII, Figs. 147 and 148. Desc. p. 464.

17. Ray cells (*t*) oblong to oval; longitudinal tracheids with average tangential diameter between 25–30 microns.................
Eastern Spruce (Desc. p. 467):
    White Spruce—*Picea glauca* (Moench.) Voss.
    Red Spruce—*Picea rubens* Sarg.   Plate XXXIII, Figs. 149 and 150.
    Black Spruce—*Picea mariana* B.S.P.
Engelmann Spruce—*Picea engelmanni* (Parry) Engelm. Plate XXXIII, Figs. 151 and 152.   Desc. p. 467.

17. Ray cells (*t*) orbicular to oval; longitudinal tracheids with average tangential diameter between 35–45 microns...............
Sitka Spruce—*Picea sitchensis* (Bong.) Carr.   Plate XXXIV, Figs. 153 and 154.   Desc. p. 470.

18. Longitudinal tracheids with spiral thickening............. **19**
18. Longitudinal tracheids without spiral thickening.......... **20**

19. Longitudinal tracheids up to 55 (av. 25–35) microns in diameter; bordered pits in 1–2 longitudinal rows (*r*); pits leading to ray parenchyma 2–7 (generally 2–4) per ray crossing.............
California Nutmeg—*Torreya californica* Torr.   Plate L, Figs. 187 and 188.   Desc. p. 508.
Stinking Cedar—*Torreya taxifolia* Arn.

19. Longitudinal tracheids up to 25 (av. 15–20) microns in diameter; bordered pits in one longitudinal row (*r*); pits leading to ray parenchyma 1–4 (generally 1–2) per ray crossing.............
Pacific Yew—*Taxus brevifolia* Nutt.   Plate XLIX, Figs. 185 and 186. Desc. p. 506.

20. Parenchyma fairly abundant to abundant, present in every growth ring... **21**
20. Parenchyma wanting, or very sparse and sporadic (sometimes abundant in a given growth ring but then wanting in neighboring rings).................................. **29**

21. Longitudinal tracheids with average tangential diameter between 20–50 microns;* bordered pits on the radial walls of the tracheids in 1–2 (mostly 1) longitudinal rows......................... **22**
21. Longitudinal tracheids with average tangential diameter between 50–65 microns; bordered pits on the radial walls of the tracheids in 1–4 (mostly 2) longitudinal rows......................... **28**

---

* See first footnote, p. 404.

22. Ray tracheids (r) abundant in the low rays, frequently constituting the entire ray.................................

Alaska Yellow Cedar, Yellow Cypress—*Chamaecyparis nootkatensis*
(Lamb.) Spach.　Plate XIX, Fig. 108; compare with Fig. 107.
Plate XLVI, Figs. 179 and 180.　Desc. p. 500.

22. Ray tracheids (r) absent or extremely sparse.............. **23**

23. Parenchyma metatracheal (x), at least in some rings......... **24**

23. Parenchyma metatracheal-diffuse (x)....................... **27**

24. Springwood longitudinal tracheids with one longitudinal
row of bordered pits (r), up to 40 (av. 20–35) microns in
diameter... **25**

24. Springwood longitudinal tracheids with 1–2 longitudinal
rows of bordered pits (r), up to 50 (av. 35–40) microns in
diameter... **26**

25. Intercellular spaces frequent at the rounded corners of the
tracheids (x), conspicuous; tallest rays less than 250 microns in
height; ray cells (heartwood) occluded with dark-colored
infiltration.....................................

Red Cedar (Desc. p. 504):
　Eastern Red Cedar, Tennessee Red Cedar—*Juniperus virginiana* L.
　Plate XLVIII, Figs. 183 and 184.
　Southern Red Cedar—*Juniperus silicicola* (Small) Bailey

25. Intercellular spaces few or wanting at the corners of the tracheids
(x), if present, inconspicuous; tallest rays more than 250 microns
in height; ray cells empty, or with scanty infiltration..........

Atlantic White Cedar, Southern White Cedar—*Chamaecyparis thyoides*
(L.) B.S.P.　Plate XLVII, Figs. 181 and 182.　Desc. p. 502.

26. Pits leading from ray parenchyma to longitudinal tracheids
taxodioid (Text Fig. 34, *E*); rays strictly uniseriate, the ray
cells in the heartwood with scanty gummy infiltration.....

Western Red Cedar, Giant Arbor-vitae—*Thuja plicata* D. Don.
Plate XLIV, Figs. 175 and 176.　Desc. p. 496.

26. Pits leading from ray parenchyma to longitudinal tracheids
cupressoid (Text Fig. 34, *F*); rays occasionally in part
biseriate, the ray cells in the heartwood with deposits of
dark gum...

Incense Cedar, Pencil Cedar—*Libocedrus decurrens* Torr.　Plate
XLII, Figs. 171 and 172.　Desc. p. 492.

27. Tallest rays less then 300 microns in height; broadest rays
(uniseriate), 7–12 microns wide.............................

Port Orford Cedar, Port Orford White Cedar—*Chamaecyparis lawsoniana* (A. Murr.) Parl.　Plate XLV, Figs. 177 and 178.　Desc. p. 498.

27. Tallest rays more than 300 microns in height; broadest rays
(uniseriate) 15–25 microns wide.............................

Incense Cedar, Pencil Cedar—*Libocedrus decurrens* Torr.　Plate XLII,
Figs. 171 and 172.　Desc. p. 492.

Plate XIX

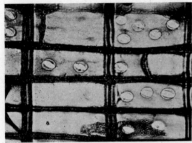 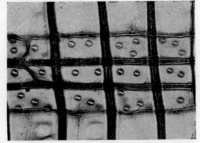

Fɪɢ. 105.   Fɪɢ. 106.

Fɪɢ. 105.—Radial section of the wood of redwood, *Sequoia sempervirens* (Lamb.) Endl., showing position of a ray composed entirely of ray parenchyma with fairly large oval pits in the ray crossings in the back walls.   (300 ×)

Fɪɢ. 106.—Radial section of the wood of Bald Cypress, *Taxodium distichum* (L.) Rich., showing portion of a ray composed entirely of ray parenchyma with small, oval-orbicular pits in the ray crossings in the back walls.   (300 ×)

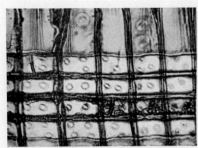 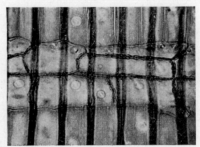

Fɪɢ. 107.   Fɪɢ. 108.

Fɪɢ. 107.—Radial section of the wood of Alaska yellow cedar, *Chamaecyparis nootkatensis* (Lamb.) Spach, showing portion of a ray composed of four rows of ray parenchyma with small pits in the ray crossings in the back walls.   (300 ×)

Fɪɢ. 108.—Same as Fig. 107 except that the ray consists entirely of ray tracheids.   (300 ×)

28. Tallest rays generally less than 600 microns in height;* pits in the ray crossings in the springwood oval for the most part, the long axis of the pit orifice more than 8 microns (Plate XIX, Fig. 105); transverse walls of the longitudinal parenchyma without or with inconspicuous simple pits..........
Redwood, Coast Redwood—*Sequoia sempervirens* (Lamb.) Endl. Plate XL, Figs. 167 and 168. Desc. p. 486.

28. Tallest rays more than 600 microns in height; pits in the ray crossings in the springwood orbicular to oval-orbicular, the long axis of the pit orifice less than 8 microns (Plate XIX, Fig. 106); transverse walls of the longitudinal parenchyma with numerous large pits................................
Bald Cypress, Red Cypress, Yellow Cypress, Southern Cypress— *Taxodium distichum* (L.) Rich. Plate XLI, Figs. 169 and 170. Desc. p. 489.

29. Ray tracheids present (*r*)................................. 30
29. Ray tracheids absent (*r*).................................... 32

30. Ray tracheids fairly abundant, at least in the low rays; rays generally less than 25 cells in height................ 31
30. Ray tracheids sporadic, wanting from many rays; rays frequently 25+ cells in height..........................
Balsam Fir—*Abies balsamea* (L.) Mill. Plate XXXVIII, Figs. 161 and 162.† Desc. p. 481.

31. Ray tracheids usually restricted to one row on the upper and lower margins of the ray, low along the grain................
Eastern Hemlock,‡ Hemlock, Canada Hemlock—*Tsuga canadensis* (L.) Carr. Plate XXXVI, Figs. 157 and 158. Desc. p. 476.
West Coast Hemlock, Western Hemlock, Pacific Hemlock—*Tsuga heterophylla* (Raf.) Sarg. Plate XXXVII, Figs. 159 and 160. Desc. p. 478.

31. Ray tracheids usually wanting in the high rays, abundant in the low rays and frequently constituting the entire ray, short, high along the grain..
Alaska Yellow Cedar, Yellow Cypress—*Chamaecyparis nootkatensis* (Lamb.) Spach. Plate XIX, Fig. 108; compare with Fig. 107. Plate XLVI, Figs. 179 and 180. Desc. p. 500.

---

* Mitchell reports rays with heights in excess of this figure (J. N. Mitchell. The Detailed Structure of Stem Wood of the two Sequoias. *Jour. Forestry*, Vol. 34, pp. 988–993. 1936). I. Isenberg, of the Institute of Paper Chemistry, Appleton, Wis., also states that occasional rays attain heights greater than 600 microns.

† Ray tracheids occasionally occur sporadically on the margins of the rays in Western Red Cedar (*Thuja plicata* D. Don). In such instances, Balsam Fir can readily be separated from Western Red Cedar on the basis of ray height (see descriptions of these woods). Ray tracheids are extremely rare in the Western Balsam Firs.

‡ For separation of Eastern and Western Hemlock, see Remarks under Western Hemlock, p. 480.

32. Tallest rays more than 400 microns in height; end walls of ray cells with abundant local thickenings.............. **33**

32. Tallest rays generally less than 400 microns in height; end walls of ray cells smooth.............................. **34**

33. Ray cells (*t*) oblong.......................................

Eastern Fir (Desc. p. 481):

Balsam Fir—*Abies balsamea* (L.) Mill.   Plate XXXVIII, Figs. 161 and 162.

Southern Balsam Fir, Fraser Fir—*Abies fraseri* (Pursh) Poir.

33. Ray cells (*t*) orbicular to oval............................

Western Balsam Firs (Desc. p. 483):

White Fir—*Abies concolor* (Gord.) Engelm.   Plate XXXIX, Figs. 163 and 164.

Noble Fir, Larch—*Abies procera* Rehd.

Lowland White Fir, Grand Fir—*Abies grandis* Lindl.

California Red Fir—*Abies magnifica* A. Murr.   Plate XXXIX, Figs. 165 and 166.

Southern Balsam Fir, Fraser Fir—*Abies fraseri* (Pursh) Poir.   Desc. p. 481.

34. Tracheids fine, up to 35 (av. 20–30) microns in diameter; bordered pits in one longitudinal row or very rarely paired on the radial walls..

Northern White Cedar, Eastern Arbor-vitae—*Thuja occidentalis* L. Plate XLIII, Figs. 173 and 174.   Desc. p. 494.

34. Tracheids medium coarse, up to 50 (av. 32–38) microns in diameter; bordered pits in 1–2 longitudinal rows on the radial walls..

Western Red Cedar, Giant Arbor-vitae—*Thuja plicata* D. Don. Plate XLIV, Figs. 175 and 176.   Desc. p. 496.

35. Springwood vessels obviously larger (especially at low magnifications) than those in the summerwood (*x*); wood ring porous.. **36**

35. Springwood vessels not larger or but slightly larger than those in the summerwood (*x*); wood diffuse porous................ **69**

36. Broad rays of the oak type present (*Quercus spp.*)......... **37**

36. Broad rays of the oak type absent...................... **38**

37. Summerwood vessels not numerous, thick-walled (thicker walled than the surrounding cells);* tyloses sparse or absent in the springwood vessels in the heartwood....................·....
Red Oak (Desc. p. 541):
  Northern Red Oak—*Quercus borealis* Michx. f.   Plate LXVIII, Figs. 233 and 234.
  Black Oak—*Quercus velutina* Lam.   Plate LXVIII, Figs. 235 and 236.
  Shumard Oak—*Quercus shumardi* Buckl.
  Scarlet Oak—*Quercus coccinea* Muenchh.
  Pin Oak—*Quercus palustris* Muenchh.
  Willow Oak—*Quercus phellos* L.
  Other Species of the Erythrobalanus Group.
37. Summerwood vessels numerous, thin-walled (as thin or thinner walled than the surrounding cells); tyloses abundant in the springwood vessels in the heartwood........................
White Oak (Desc. p. 546):
  White Oak—*Quercus alba* L.   Plate LXIX, Figs. 237 and 238.
  Bur Oak—*Quercus macrocarpa* Michx.
  Overcup Oak—*Quercus lyrata* Walt.
  Post Oak—*Quercus setllata* Wangenh.   Plate LXX, Figs. 241 and 242.
  Swamp Chestnut Oak, Basket Oak—*Quercus prinus* L.
  Chestnut Oak, Rock Oak—*Quercus montana* Willd.   Plate LXIX, Figs. 239 and 240.
  Swamp White Oak—*Quercus bicolor* Willd.
  Other Species of the Leucobalanus Group.

   38. Springwood vessels grading (in size) into those of the sum- merwood; springwood zone not sharply defined the transi- tion from spring- to summerwood more or less gradual; wood semi-ring porous.................................... **39**
   38. Springwood vessels not grading into those of the summer- wood (or if so, the first springwood vessels much larger than those in the outer portion of the ring); springwood zone sharply defined, the transition from spring- to summerwood abrupt; wood typically ring porous...................... **48**
39. Rays 1–6-seriate; parenchyma included in the body of the growth ring, or wanting (*x*).................................. **40**
39. Rays uniseriate; parenchyma terminal (*x*)................... **46**
   40. Parenchyma relatively abundant; vessels without spiral thickening or the spirals restricted to those of the summer- wood; largest vessels more than 100 (ranging from 120–300) microns in diameter†.................................... **41**
   40. Parenchyma extremely sparse or wanting; vessels with spiral thickening (Plate XX, Fig. 109); largest vessels less than 100 (ranging from 60–90) microns in diameter...............
  Black Cherry, Cherry—*Prunus serotina* Ehrh.   Plate LXXXIII, Figs. 269 and 270.   Desc. p. 572.

---

* The pitting on the vessel walls of oak is characteristic; for the nature of the pitting between the vessels and the vasicentric tracheids of oak, see Plate XX, Fig. 114.

† The diameter recorded is always the tangential diameter.

41. Intervessel pits vestured [similar to those of Black Locust, *Robinia pseudoacacia* L. (Text Fig. 16, *E*)]..................
Yellowwood—*Cladrastis lutea* (Michx.) K. Koch. Plate LXXXVI, Figs. 275 and 276. Desc. p. 577.

41. Intervessel pits not vestured.............................. **42**

    42. Summerwood vessels with spiral thickening, those in the outer portion of the growth ring associated with parenchyma forming tangential, several-seriate, more or less continuous bands (one or more bands in the outer portion of the ring occasionally consisting entirely of parenchyma)...........
    Catalpa (Desc. p. 610):
        Northern Catalpa—*Catalpa speciosa* Ward. Plate CII, Figs. 313 and 314.
        Southern Catalpa—*Catalpa bignonioides* Walt.

    42. Summerwood vessels without spiral thickening, solitary or in radial groups of 2–4; metatracheal parenchyma present throughout the growth ring.............................. **43**

43. Rays storied (*t*); intervessel pits minute, 2–several frequently joined laterally (Plate XX, Fig. 110)........................
Persimmon—*Diospyros virginiana* L. Plate XCIX, Figs. 305 and 306. Desc. p. 604.

43. Rays unstoried (*t*); intervessel pits of normal size, rounded or angular, generally not joined laterally (Plate XX, Figs. 111)... **44**

    44. Lines of zonate parenchyma conspicuous, 1–4-seriate; fibers with maximum diameter of less than 25 microns..........
    Hickory (Pecan Hickories) (Desc. p. 513):
        Bitternut Hickory—*Carya cordiformis* (Wangenh.) K. Koch. Plate LIV, Figs. 197 and 198.
        Pecan—*Carya illinoënsis* (Wangenh). K. Koch. Plate LIV, Figs. 199 and 200.
        Water Hickory—*Carya aquatica* (Michx. f.) Nutt.
        Nutmeg Hickory—*Carya myristicaeformis* (Michx. f.) Nutt.

    44. Lines of zonate parenchyma inconspicuous, usually uniseriate; fibers with maximum diameter of more than 25 microns.. **45**

45. Parenchyma frequently crystalliferous; ray cells mostly round (*t*)...
Black Walnut, Eastern Black Walnut—*Juglans nigra* L. Plate LII, Figs. 191 and 192. Desc. p. 510.

45. Parenchyma noncrystalliferous; ray cells mostly elliptical (*t*)...
Butternut, White Walnut—*Juglans cinerea* L. Plate LI, Figs. 189 and 190. Desc. p. 509.

    46. Rays essentially homogeneous (Text Fig. 46, *A*)........... **47**
    46. Rays essentially heterogeneous (Text Fig. 46, *B*).........
    Willow (Desc. p. 521):
        Black Willow—*Salix nigra* Marsh. Plate LVII, Figs. 207 and 208.
        Etc.

Plate XX

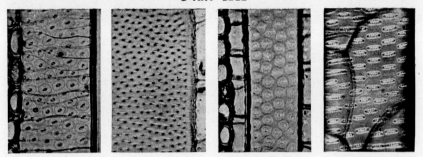

FIG. 109.   FIG. 110.   FIG. 111.   FIG. 112.

FIG. 109.—Portion of the wall of a vessel segment (tangential view) from the wood of black cherry, *Prunus serotina* Ehrh., showing intervessel pitting and spiral thickening. (400 ×)

FIG. 110.—Portion of the wall of a vessel segment (tangential view) from the wood of persimmon, *Diospyros virginiana* L., showing minute intervessel pits with fused apertures. (400 ×)

FIG. 111.—Portion of the wall of a vessel segment (tangential view) from the wood of shagbark hickory, *Carya ovata* (Mill.) K. Koch, showing intervessel pitting. The pits are not vestured; the punctate appearance is caused by artifacts. (400 ×)

FIG. 112.—Portion of the wall of a vessel segment (tangential view) from the wood of black locust, *Robinia pseudoacacia* L., showing vestured intervessel pits. (400 ×)

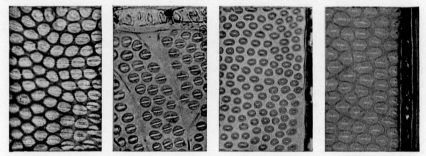

FIG. 113.   FIG. 114.   FIG. 115.   FIG. 116.

FIG. 113.—Portion of the wall of a vessel segment (tangential view) from the wood of osage-orange, *Maclura pomifera* (Raf.) Schn., showing nonvestured intervessel pits with fused orifices. (400 ×)

FIG. 114.—Portions of the walls of three vasicentric tracheids and a wood ray (radial view) from the wood of Shumard red oak, *Quercus shumardi* Buckl., showing intertracheary pitting. The pits are not vestured; the punctate appearance is caused by artifacts. (400 ×)

FIG. 115.—Portion of the wall of a vessel segment (tangential view) from the wood of red alder, *Alnus rubra* Bong., showing widely spaced intervessel pits. (400 ×)

FIG. 116.—Portion of the wall of a vessel segment (tangential view) from the wood of blue-beech, *Carpinus caroliniana* Walt., showing crowded intervessel pits. (400 ×)

415

47. Vessels 30–145 per square millimeter, the largest 75–150 microns
in diameter...
    Cottonwood (Desc. p. 517):
        Eastern Cottonwood, Eastern Poplar—*Populus deltoides* Bartr.
        Plate LV, Figs. 201 and 202.
        Balsam Poplar, Tacamahac Poplar—*Populus tacamahaca* Mill.
        Swamp Cottonwood, Swamp Poplar—*Populus heterophylla* L.
        Northern Black Cottonwood—*Populus trichocarpa* var. *hastata* Henry.
        Plate LV, Figs. 203 and 204.
        Etc.
47. Vessels 85–180 per square millimeter, the largest 50–100 microns
in diameter...
    Aspen (Desc. p. 519):
        Quaking Aspen, Trembling Aspen—*Populus tremuloides* Michx.
        Bigtooth Aspen—*Populus grandidentata* Michx. Plate LVI, Figs.
        205 and 206.

    48. Summerwood figured with concentric, wavy, more or less
        continuous bands of porous tissue composed largely of
        vessels (x)...   **49**
    48. Summerwood without concentric bands of vessels (x) or
        occasionally with interrupted bands in the outer portion of
        the growth ring consisting of vessels and appreciable
        amounts of parenchyma; metatracheal parenchyma some-
        times present...   **53**
49. Large springwood vessels in one row........................   **50**
49. Large springwood vessels in several rows....................   **51**

    50. Large springwood vessels with maximum diameter of over
        200 microns...   **51**
        White Elm,* **American Elm**—*Ulmus americana* L. Plate LXXI,
        Figs. 243 and 244. Desc. p. 549.
    50. Large springwood vessels with maximum diameter of less
        than 200 microns......................................
        Hard Elm:† Desc. p. 552.
            Rock Elm, Cork Elm—*Ulmus thomasi* Sarg. Plate LXXIII,
            Figs. 247 and 248.
            Cedar Elm—*Ulmus crassifolia* Nutt.
            Winged Elm—*Ulmus alata* Michx.

---

    * As seen at low magnifications (10–15×), the springwood, pores of American
Elm appear quite uniform in size and form a conspicuous, more or less continuous row.
Hard Elm, in contrast, is featured by springwood pores which are variable in size,
the largest separated by pores of the smaller type; the larger pores are hence more
widely spaced and the row is described as "interrupted."
    † For the further separation of the three Hard Elms, see the supplemental Key,
footnote, p. 372.

51. Rays 1–6-seriate, essentially homogeneous................... **52**
51. Rays 1–13-seriate, essentially heterogeneous.................
  Hackberry (Desc. p. 554):
  Common Hackberry—*Celtis occidentalis* L.   Plate LXXIV, Figs. 249 and 250.
  Sugar Hackberry—*Celtis laevigata* Willd.

  52. Springwood zone consisting essentially of large pores.......
    Red Elm, Slippery Elm—*Ulmus fulva* Michx.   Plate LXXII, Figs. 245 and 246.   Desc. p. 551.
  52. Springwood zone consisting of large and small pores.......
    White Elm, American Elm—*Ulmus americana* L.   Plate LXXI, Figs. 243 and 244.   Desc. p. 549.

53. Rays uniseriate or rarely in part biseriate................... **54**
53. Rays 1–many seriate..................................... **55**

  54. Springwood vessels usually in one row, the largest 150–200 microns in diameter.......................................
    Giant Evergreen Chinkapin—*Castanopsis chrysophylla* (Hook.) DC.   Plate LXV, Figs. 227 and 228.   Desc. p. 536.
  54. Springwood vessels in several rows, the largest 240–360 microns in diameter.......................................
    Chestnut, American Chestnut—*Castanea dentata* (Marsh.) Borkh. Plate LXIV, Figs. 225 and 226.   Desc. p. 534.

55. Rays 1–4-seriate... **56**
55. Rays 1–5+-seriate....................................... **62**

  56. Parenchyma zonate (*x*), in concentric rows distributed throughout the body of the growth ring.................. **57**
  56. Parenchyma not zonate or, if zonate, the rows restricted to short broken lines in the outer portion of the ring......... **58**

57. Rays storied (*t*); intervessel pits minute, 2–several frequently joined laterally (Plate XX, Fig. 110)......................
57. Rays unstoried (*t*); intervessel pits of normal size, rounded or angular, generally not joined laterally (Plate XX, Fig. 111)....
  Hickory (True Hickories) (Desc. p. 513):
  Shagbark Hickory—*Carya ovata* (Mill.) K. Koch.   Plate LIII, Figs. 195 and 196.
  Bigleaf Shagbark Hickory—*Carya laciniosa* (Michx. f.) Loud.
  Pignut Hickory—*Carya glabra* (Mill.) Sweet
  Oval Pignut Hickory, Red Hickory—*Carya ovalis* (Wangenh.) Sarg.
  Mockernut Hickory—*Carya tomentosa* (Poir.) Nutt.   Plate LIII, Figs. 193 and 194.
  Etc.
  Hickory (Pecan Hickories) (Desc. p. 513):
  Bitternut Hickory—*Carya cordiformis* (Wangenh.) K. Koch.   Plate LIV, Figs. 197 and 198.
  Pecan—*Carya illinoënsis* (Wangenh.) K. Koch.   Plate LIV, Figs. 199 and 200.
  Water Hickory—*Carya aquatica* (Michx. f.) Nutt.
  Nutmeg Hickory—*Carya myristicaeformis* (Michx. f.) Nutt.

  58. Summerwood vessels in part with scalariform perforation plates; rays with oil cells................................
    Sassafras—*Sassafras albidum* (Nutt.) Nees.   Text Fig. 47; Plate LXXX, Figs. 203 and 204.   Desc. p. 566.
  58. Vessels (spring- and summerwood) with simple perforation plates; rays without oil cells............................ **59**

59. Springwood vessels completely occluded with tyloses; tyloses small, appearing cellular *en masse*............................ **60**

59. Springwood vessels open or only partly occluded with tyloses; tyloses large, not appearing cellular *en masse*................. **61**

    60. Intervessel pits vestured (Text Fig. 16, *E*)...............
        Black Locust—*Robinia pseudoacacia* L.   Plate XX, Fig. 112; Plate LXXXVII, Figs. 277 and 278.   Desc. p. 579.

    60. Intervessel pits not vestured (Plate XX, Fig. 113).........
        Osage-orange—*Maclura pomifera* (Raf.) Schneid.   Plate LXXVI, Figs. 253 and 254.   Desc. p. 558.

61. Summerwood vessels with spiral thickening, those in the outer portion of the growth ring associated with parenchyma forming tangential, several-seriate, more or less continuous bands (one or more bands in the outer portion of the ring occasionally consisting entirely of parenchyma); fibers with maximum diameter of more than 25 (ranging from 16–32) microns...............
Catalpa (Desc. p. 610):
    Northern Catalpa—*Catalpa speciosa* Ward.   Plate CII, Figs. 313 and 314.
    Southern Catalpa—*Catalpa bignonioides* Walt.

61. Summerwood vessels without spiral thickening, solitary or in radial rows of 2–several; fibers with maximum diameter of less than 25 (ranging from 12–22) microns.......................
White Ash (Desc. p. 606):
    White Ash—*Fraxinus americana* L.   Plate C, Figs. 307 and 308.
    Red Ash—*Fraxinus pennsylvanica* Marsh.
    Green Ash—*Fraxinus pennsylvanica* var. *lanceolata* (Borkh.) Sarg.
    Etc.
Oregon Ash—*Fraxinus oregona* Nutt.   Plate C, Figs. 309 and 310. Desc. p. 606.
Brown Ash, Black Ash—*Fraxinus nigra* Marsh.   Plate CI, Figs. 311 and 312.   Desc. p. 608.

    62. Parenchyma zonate (*x*), in concentric, 1–4-seriate bands distributed throughout the body of the growth ring (*x*); summerwood vessels solitary or in radial rows of 2–3, without spiral thickening.................................
    Hickory (**True Hickories**) (Desc. p. 513):
        Shagbark Hickory—*Carya ovata* (Mill.) K. Koch.   Plate LIII, Figs. 195 and 196.
        Bigleaf Shagbark Hickory—*Carya laciniosa* (Michx. f.) Loud.
        Pignut Hickory—*Carya glabra* (Mill.) Sweet
        Oval Pignut Hickory, Red Hickory—*Carya ovalis* (Wangenh.) Sarg.
        Mockernut Hickory—*Carya tomentosa* (Poir.) Nutt.   Plate LIII Figs. 193 and 194.
        Etc.
    Hickory (**Pecan Hickories**) (Desc. p. 513):
        Bitternut Hickory—*Carya cordiformis* (Wangenh.) K. Koch. Plate LIV, Figs. 197 and 198.
        Pecan—*Carya illinoënsis* (Wangenh.) K. Koch.   Plate LIV, Figs. 199 and 200.
        Water Hickory—*Carya aquatica* (Michx. f.) Nutt.
        Nutmeg Hickory—*Carya myristicaeformis* (Michx. f.) Nutt.
        Etc.

    62. Parenchyma not zonate (*x*); summerwood vessels solitary, in radial rows, in nests, or in interrupted bands consisting largely of vessels or of vessels and parenchyma, with spiral thickening.. **63**

63. Springwood vessels in one row; intervessel pits vestured [similar to those of Black Locust—*Robinia pseudoacacia* L.—(Text Fig. 16, *E*)]. . . . .
   Yellowwood—*Cladrastis lutea* (Michx.) K. Koch. Plate LXXXVI, Figs. 275 and 276. Desc. p. 577.

63. Springwood vessels in several rows; intervessel pits vestured or not vestured. **64**

    64. Springwood vessels in the heartwood partly or wholly occluded with tyloses, with or without gummy deposits. . . . **65**

    64. Springwood vessels without tyloses or tyloses only occasional, sometimes with gummy deposits. **68**

65. Springwood vessels partly occluded with tyloses; tyloses large, not appearing cellular *en masse*. **66**

65. Springwood vessels completely occluded with tyloses; tyloses small, appearing cellular *en masse*. **67**

    66. Fibers 20–52 microns in diameter, nongelatinous; rays 1–6- (mostly 2–3-) seriate. . . . .
   Catalpa (Desc. p. 610):
   Northern Catalpa—*Catalpa speciosa* Ward. Plate CII, Figs. 313 and 314.
   Southern Catalpa—*Catalpa bignonioides* Walt.

    66. Fibers 18–26 microns in diameter, frequently gelatinous; rays 1–8- (mostly 5–7-) seriate). . . . .
   Red Mulberry—*Morus rubra* L. Plate LXXV, Figs. 251 and 252. Desc. p. 556.

67. Intervessel pits vestured (Text Fig. 16, *E*). . . . .
   Black Locust—*Robinia pseudoacacia* L. Plate XX, Fig. 112. Plate LXXXVII, Figs. 277 and 278. Desc. p. 579.

67. Intervessel pits not vestured (Plate XX, Fig. 113). . . . .
   Osage-orange—*Maclura pomifera* (Raf.) Schneid. Plate LXXVI, Figs. 253 and 254. Desc. p. 558.

    68. Rays 1–14-seriate, the tallest more than 1200 microns in height; porous tissue toward the outer margin of the growth ring consisting of small vessels embedded in short, tangential bands of parenchyma. . . . .
   Honey-locust—*Gleditsia triacanthos* L. Plate LXXXV, Figs. 273 and 274. Desc. p. 575.

    68. Rays 1–7-seriate, the tallest less than 1200 microns in height; porous tissue toward the outer portion of the growth ring consisting for the most part of vessels. . . . .
   Coffee-tree, Kentucky Coffee-tree—*Gymnocladus dioicus* (L.) K. Koch. Plate LXXXIV, Figs. 271 and 272. Desc. p. 574.

69. Springwood vessels somewhat larger than those in the summerwood; wood semidiffuse porous. **70**

69. Vessels (except in the extreme outer portion of the ring in certain species) exhibiting little or no variation in size indicative of seasonal growth; wood typically diffuse porous. **81**

70. Rays 1–many-seriate; parenchyma present in the body of the ring, or wanting.. **71**

70. Rays uniseriate; parenchyma confined to the outer margin of the ring... **79**

71. Longitudinal parenchyma relatively abundant; vessels without spiral thickening or the spirals restricted to those of the summerwood; largest vessels more than 100 (100–320) microns in diameter.. **72**

71. Longitudinal parenchyma extremely sparse or wanting; vessels throughout the ring with spiral thickening (Plate XX, Fig. 109); largest vessels less than 100 (70–90) microns in diameter....... **Black Cherry, Cherry**—*Prunus serotina* Ehrh. Plate LXXXIII, Figs. 269 and 270. Desc. p. 572.

    72. Intervessel pits vestured [similar to those of Black Locust— *Robinia pseudoacacia* L. (Text Fig. 16, *E*)]................ **Yellowwood**—*Cladrastis lutea* (Michx.) K. Koch. Plate LXXXVI, Figs. 275 and 276. Desc. p. 577.

    72. Intervessel pits not vestured............................ **73**

73. Summerwood vessels with spiral thickening, those toward the outer margin of the ring associated with parenchyma forming tangential, several-seriate, more or less continuous bands (one or more bands in the outer portion of the ring occasionally consisting entirely of parenchyma)............................... **Catalpa** (Desc. p. 610):

    Northern Catalpa—*Catalpa speciosa* Ward. Plate CII, Figs. 313 and 314.

    Southern Catalpa—*Catalpa bignonioides* Walt.

73. Summerwood vessels without spiral thickening, solitary or in radial groups of 2–4; zonate parenchyma present, the lines closely spaced throughout the growth ring.......................... **74**

    74. Rays storied (*t*); intervessel pits minute, 2–several frequently joined laterally (Plate XX, Fig. 110).................... **Persimmon**—*Diospyros virginiana* L. Plate XCIX, Figs. 305 and 306. Desc. p. 604.

    74. Rays unstoried (*t*); pits on vessel walls of normal size, generally not joined laterally (Plate XX, Fig. 111)........... **75**

75. Lines of zonate parenchyma conspicuous, 1–4-seriate.......... **76**

75. Lines of zonate parenchyma inconspicuous, usually uniseriate.. **78**

    76. Rays of one type, 1–5-seriate; vessels solitary and in short radial rows (*x*).. **Water Hickory**—*Carya aquatica* (Michx. f.) Nutt. Desc. p. 513.

    76. Rays of two types, uniseriate and broad, the latter sometimes aggregate, up to 50+ cells in width; vessels in streamlike clusters which extend for some distance radially (across several—many rings when these are evident).............. **77**

77. Largest vessels 100–160 microns in diameter; zonate parenchyma in 1–4-seriate lines; most of broad rays distinctly aggregate.... **Tan-oak**—*Lithocarpus densiflora* (Hook & Arn.) Rehd. Plate LXVI, Figs. 229 and 230. Desc. p. 537.

77. Largest vessels 200–280 microns in diameter; zonate parenchyma in 1–2 (mostly 1)-seriate lines; broad rays not distinctly aggregate **Live Oak**—*Quercus virginiana* Mill. Plate LXVII, Figs. 231 and 232. Desc. p. 539.

    78. Parenchyma frequently crystalliferous; ray cells mostly round (*t*)..................................... **Black Walnut, Eastern Black Walnut**—*Juglans nigra* L. Plate LII, Figs. 191 and 192. Desc. p. 510.

    78. Parenchyma noncrystalliferous; ray cells mostly elliptical (*t*)..................................... **Butternut, White Walnut**—*Juglans cinerea* L. Plate LI, Figs. 189 and 190. Desc. p. 509.

79. Rays essentially homogeneous (Text Fig. 46, *A*).............. **80**

79. Rays essentially heterogeneous (Text Fig. 46, *B*)............. **Willow** (Desc. p. 521): **Black Willow**—*Salix nigra* Marsh. Plate LVII, Figs. 207 and 208. Etc.

    80. Vessels 30–145 per square millimeter, the largest 75–150 microns in diameter.................................... **Cottonwood** (Desc. p. 517): **Eastern Cottonwood, Eastern Poplar**—*Populus deltoides* Bartr. Plate LV, Figs. 201 to 202. **Balsam Poplar, Tacamahac Poplar**—*Populus tacamahaca* Mill. **Swamp Cottonwood, Swamp Poplar**—*Populus heterophylla* L. **Northern Black Cottonwood**—*Populus trichocarpa* var. *hastata* Henry. Plate LV, Figs. 203 and 204. Etc.

    80. Vessels 85–180 per square millimeter, the largest 50–100 microns in diameter.................................... **Aspen** (Desc. p. 519): **Quaking Aspen, Trembling Aspen**—*Populus tremuloides* Michx. **Bigtooth Aspen**—*Populus grandidentata* Michx. Plate LVI, Figs. 205 and 206.

81. Widest rays more than 8-seriate........................... **82**

81. Widest rays never more than 8-seriate (aggregate rays, when present, not considered)................................. **83**

    82. Rays of one type, intergrading in size, 1–14 (mostly 3–14)-seriate; intervessel pits not crowded (Plate XXI, Fig. 117). **Sycamore**—*Platanus occidentalis* L. Plate LXXXII, Figs. 267 and 268. Desc. p. 570.

    82. Rays of two types; narrow rays 1–5-seriate; broad rays 15–25 plus-seriate; intervessel pits crowded (Plate XXI, Fig. 118) **Beech, American Beech**—*Fagus grandifolia* Ehrh. Plate LXIII, Figs. 223 and 224. Desc. p. 532.

Plate XXI

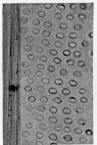 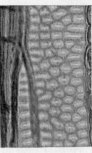 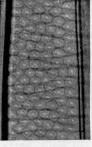 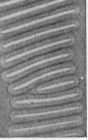

| Fig. 117. | Fig. 118. | Fig. 119. | Fig. 120. |

Fig. 117.—Portion of the wall of a vessel segment (tangential view) from the wood of sycamore, *Platanus occidentalis* L., showing widely spaced intervessel pits. (400×)

Fig. 118.—Portions of the wall of two vessel segments (tangential view) from the wood of beech, *Fagus grandifolia* Ehrh., showing crowded intervessel pits. (400×)

Fig. 119.—Portion of the wall of a vessel segment (tangential view) from the wood of basswood, *Tilia americana* L., showing crowded intervessel pits and spiral thickening. (400×)

Fig. 120.—Portion of the wall of a vessel segment (tangential view) from the wood of cucumber magnolia, *Magnolia acuminata* L., showing scalariform pitting. (400×)

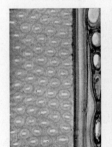 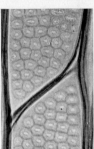 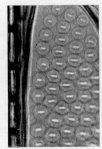 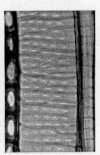

| Fig. 121. | Fig. 122. | Fig. 123. | Fig. 124. |

Fig. 121.—Portion of the wall of a vessel segment (tangential view) from the wood of silver maple, *Acer saccharinum* L., showing intervessel pitting. (400×)

Fig. 122.—Portions of the wall of two vessel segments (tangential view) from the wood of yellow buckeye, *Aesculus octandra* Marsh., showing medium-sized intervessel pits. The pits in the upper right-hand corner are not vestured; the punctate appearance is due to artifacts. (400×)

Fig. 123.—Portion of the wall of a vessel segment (tangential view) from the wood of eastern cottonwood, *Populus deltoides* Bartr., showing large intervessel pits. (400×)

Fig. 124.—Portion of the wall of a vessel segment (tangential view) from the wood of holly, *Ilex opaca* Ait., showing intervessel pitting and spiral thickening; the fibers in holly also possess spiral thickening (see portion of fiber at the right of the figure). (400×)

423

83. Rays of two types (simple and aggregate); aggregate rays not infrequently at wide intervals.............................. **84**

83. Rays of one type (simple)................................... **85**

    84. Simple rays uniseriate or rarely in part biseriate; perforation plates scalariform with 15+ thin bars; intervessel pits not crowded (Plate XX, Fig. 115)........................

        Red Alder—*Alnus rubra* Bong. Plate LXII, Figs. 221 and 222. Desc. p. 530.

    84. Simple rays 1–4 (mostly 1–2)-seriate; perforation plates predominately simple; scalariform perforation plates sporadic, with 3–6 thick bars; intervessel pits crowded (Plate XX, Fig. 116)....................

        Blue-beech—*Carpinus caroliniana* Walt. Plate LVIII, Figs. 209 210. Desc. p. 523.

85. Perforation plates exclusively simple........................ **86**

85. Perforation plates exclusively scalariform, or simple and scalariform, and sometimes reticulate (foraminate)............ **102**

    86. Rays 1–8-seriate....................................... **87**

    86. Rays uniseriate.. **99**

87. Parenchyma absent or extremely sparse...................... **88**

87. Parenchyma fairly abundant to abundant, sometimes restricted to the outer face of the ring.............................. **91**

    88. Vessels solitary and in more or less irregular groups of 2–several which are frequently oblique to the rays, generally more numerous and crowded in the springwood, 100–180 per square millimeter......................................

        Black Cherry, Cherry—*Prunus serotina* Ehrh. Plate LXXXIII, Figs. 269 and 270. Desc. p. 572.

    88. Vessels solitary and in radial rows of 2–5, seldom contiguous in the tangential plane (laterally), quite evenly distributed (the groups) throughout the ring, 20–90 per square millimeter... **89**

89. Rays of two widths, the narrow 1 (rarely 2–3)-seriate and numerous, the broad 3–8 (mostly 5–7)-seriate...............

    Hard Maple (Desc. p. 583):

        Sugar Maple—*Acer saccharum* Marsh. Plate LXXXIX, Figs. 281 and 282.

        Black Maple—*Acer nigrum* Michx. f.

89. Rays intergrading in width, 1–5 (mostly 3–4)-seriate, the uniseriate rays sparse (especially in Oregon Maple).............. **90**

    90. Vessels with maximum diameter of 60–80 microns.........

        Soft Maple (Desc. p. 587):

            Red Maple—*Acer rubrum* L.

            Silver Maple—*Acer saccharinum* L. Plate XCI, Figs. 285 and 286.

    90. Vessels with maximum diameter of 80–120 microns........

        Oregon Maple—*Acer macrophyllum* Pursh. Plate XC, Figs. 283 and 284. Desc. p. 585.

91. Parenchyma in the body of the ring at least in part zonate (metatracheal).. **92**

91. Parenchyma in the body of the ring never zonate.............. **93**

92. Vessels unevenly distributed, frequently in radial rows of 2–6+ (x) which are often further aggregated into flame-shaped groups; rays 1–3-seriate, the tallest less than 1000 microns in height...................................
Hop-hornbeam—*Ostrya virginiana* (Mill.) K. Koch. Plate LIX, Figs. 211 and 212. Desc. p. 525.

92. Vessels quite evenly distributed, the radial grouping not pronounced (x) (Plate XXI, Fig. 119); rays 1–6-seriate, the tallest more than 1000 microns in height.................
Basswood (Desc. p. 593):
Basswood—*Tilia americana* L.
White Basswood—*Tilia heterophylla* Vent. Plate XCIV, Figs. 291 and 292.

93. Intervessel pits vestured [similar to those of Black Locust, *Robinia pseudoacacia* L. (Text Fig. 16, *E*)]....................
Yellowwood—*Cladrastis lutea* (Michx.) K. Koch. Plate LXXXVI, Figs. 275 and 276. Desc. p. 577.

93. Intervessel pits not vestured.............................. **94**

94. Paratracheal parenchyma abundant, forming a 1–3-seriate sheath; rays typically heterogeneous, frequently with oil cells; fibers in part septate...............................
California Laurel, Oregon Myrtle—*Umbellularia californica* (Hook. & Arn.) Nutt. Plate LXXIX, Figs. 261 and 262. Desc. p. 564.

94. Paratracheal parenchyma absent or sparse and then forming a broken uniseriate sheath; rays homogeneous to heterogeneous; fibers nonseptate.................................. **95**

95. Terminal parenchyma absent.............................
Cascara Buckthorn—*Rhamnus purshiana* DC. Plate XCIII, Figs. 289 and 290. Desc. p. 591.

95. Terminal parenchyma absent............................. **96**

96. Terminal parenchyma conspicuous, forming a line 1–several cells in thickness; pitting on the vessel walls generally scalariform, the pits linear, 12–50 microns in diameter (Plate XXI, Fig. 120)..................................
Magnolia (Desc. p. 560):
Cucumber Magnolia, Cucumber-tree—*Magnolia acuminata* L. Plate LXXVII, Figs. 255 and 256.
Evergreen Magnolia, Southern Magnolia—*Magnolia grandiflora* L. Plate LXXVII, Figs. 257 and 258.

96. Terminal parenchyma inconspicuous and restricted to a more or less continuous uniseriate line, or sporadic; pits on the vessel wall orbicular to hexagonal, 4–10 microns in diameter (Plate XXI, Fig. 121).......................... **97**

97. Rays of two widths, the narrow 1(rarely 2–3)-seriate and numerous, the broad 3–8(mostly 5–7)-seriate.................
Hard Maple (Desc. p. 583):
Sugar Maple—*Acer saccharum* Marsh. Plate LXXXIX Figs. 281 and 282.
Black Maple—*Acer nigrum* Michx. f.

97. Rays intergrading in width, 1–5(mostly 3–4)-seriate, the uniseriate rays sparse (especially in Oregon Maple).............. **98**

98. Vessels with maximum diameter of 70–90 microns.........
   Soft Maple (Desc. p. 587):
      Red Maple—*Acer rubrum* L.
      Silver Maple—*Acer saccharinum* L.   Plate XCI, Figs. 285 and
      286.
98. Vessels with maximum diameter of 100–120 microns.......
   Oregon Maple, Bigleaf Maple—*Acer macrophyllum* Pursh.   Plate
      XC, Figs. 283 and 284.   Desc. p. 585.
99. Largest vessels 40–60 microns in diameter, with or without spiral
   thickening; intervessel pits of medium size (Plate XXI, Fig.
   122); parenchyma terminal and paratracheal (restricted to occasional cells); rays and longitudinal elements storied or unstoried
   Buckeye (Desc. p. 589):
      Yellow Buckeye—*Aesculus octandra* Marsh.   Plate XCII, Figs.
      287 and 288.
      Ohio Buckeye—*Aesculus glabra* Willd.
      California Buckeye—*Aesculus californica* Nutt.
99. Largest vessels 60–160 microns in diameter, without spiral
   thickening; intervessel pits large (Plate XXI, Fig. 123); parenchyma strictly terminal; rays and longitudinal elements unstoried **100**
   100. Ray essentially homogeneous (Text Fig. 46, *A*)......... **101**
   100. Rays essentially heterogeneous (Text Fig. 46, *B*)........
      Willow (Desc. p. 521):
         Black Willow—*Salix nigra* Marsh.   Plate LVII, Figs. 207
         and 208.
         Etc.
101. Vessels 30–145 per square millimeter, the largest 75–150
   microns in diameter....................................
   Cottonwood (Desc. p. 517):
      Eastern Cottonwood, Eastern Poplar—*Populus deltoides* Bartr.
      Plate LV, Figs. 201 to 202.
      Balsam Poplar, Tacamahac Poplar—*Populus tacamahaca* Mill.
      Swamp Cottonwood, Swamp Poplar—*Populus heterophylla* L.
      Northern Black Cottonwood—*Populus trichocarpa* var. *hastata*
      Henry.   Plate LV, Figs. 203 and 204.
      Etc.
101. Vessels 85–180 per square millimeter, the largest 50–100
   microns in diameter....................................
   Aspen (Desc. p. 519):
      Quaking Aspen, Trembling Aspen—*Populus tremuloides* Michx.
      Bigtooth Aspen—*Populus grandidentata* Michx.   Plate LVI, Figs.
      205 and 206.
      102. Spiral thickening in the vessels and at least in some fibers **103**
      102. Spiral thickening restricted to the vessels or absent
         (Plate XXI, Fig. 124)............................... **104**

103. Vessels arranged in radial strings or clusters which not infrequently extend across the rings; broader rays high, many 30 or more cells in height..................................
Holly, American Holly—*Ilex opaca* Ait. Plate LXXXVIII, Figs. 279 and 280. Desc. p. 581.

103. Vessels solitary or in multiples of 2–several, frequently further aggregated into tangentially aligned clusters or bands, the zones of pores then alternating with bands of fibrous tissue; broader rays low, under 25 cells in height....................
Pacific Madrone, Madroña—*Arbutus menziesi* Pursh. Plate XCVIII, Figs. 303 and 304. Desc. p. 602.

    104. Rays typically heterogeneous, the upper and lower margins of the broad rays consisting of 1–5+ rows of upright cells; upright cells of the broad rays 30–100 microns in height along the grain............................... **105**

    104. Rays homogeneous to heterogeneous; when heterogeneous, the upper and lower margins of the broad rays generally consisting of 1–several (mostly 1) rows of upright cells; upright cells of the broad rays generally less than 60 microns in height along the grain...................... **108**

105. Rays 1–8-seriate; uniseriate rays usually consisting entirely of upright cells; metatracheal parenchyma relatively abundant.... **106**

105. Rays 1–4-seriate; uniseriate rays consisting of both upright and procumbent cells; metatracheal parenchyma relatively sparse... **107**

    106. Widest rays 3–8-seriate.................................
Dogwood, Flowering Dogwood—*Cornus florida* L. Plate XCVI, Figs. 297 and 298. Desc. p. 598.

    106. Widest rays 3–7 (mostly 3–5)-seriate...................
Pacific Dogwood—*Cornus nuttalli* Audub. Plate XCVI, Figs. 299 and 300. Desc. p. 598.

107. Pits on the vessel walls (*t*) in transverse rows of 1–3, frequently linear through fusion, the pit contour generally rounded (Plate XXII, Fig. 125); interfiber pits conspicuously bordered, large (7–9 microns in diameter); longitudinal traumatic gum canals sometimes present...
Red-gum, American Sweet Gum—*Liquidambar styraciflua* L. Plate LXXXI, Figs. 265 and 266. Desc. p. 567.

107. Pits on the vessel walls (*t*) in transverse rows of 1–5+, seldom linear, the pit contour frequently angular [rectangular (Plate XXII, Fig. 127)]; interfiber pits inconspicuously bordered, small (3–4 microns in diameter); traumatic gum canals absent......
Black Gum, Black Tupelo, Pepperidge—*Nyssa sylvatica* Marsh. Plate XCV, Figs. 295 and 296. Desc. p. 595.
Swamp Tupelo, Swamp Black Gum—*Nyssa sylvatica* var. *biflora* (Walt.) Sarg.
Tupelo Gum, Water Gum—*Nyssa aquatica* L. Plate XCV, Figs. 293 and 294. Desc. p. 595.

108. Pits on the vessel walls orbicular or elliptical to rectangular or linear, medium-sized to large (4–50 microns in diameter).. **109**

108. Pits on the vessel walls orbicular to hexagonal, minute (2–4 microns in diameter) (Plate XXII, Fig. 126).......
Birch (Desc. p. 526):
    Yellow Birch—*Betula lutea* Michx. f.   Plate LX, Figs. 215 and 216.
    Sweet Birch, Black Birch, Cherry Birch—*Betula lenta* L. Plate LX, Figs. 213 and 214.
    River Birch, Red Birth—*Betula nigra* L.   Plate LXI, Figs. 217 and 218.
    Paper Birch, White Birch—*Betula papyrifera* Marsh.   Plate LXI, Figs. 219 and 220.
    Gray Birch—*Betula populifolia* Marsh.
    Etc.

109. Parenchyma paratracheal or metatracheal-diffuse, or both, the cells scattered; scalariform perforation plates with 10–50 bars. **110**

109. Parenchyma terminal, the band 1–several cells in thickness; scalariform perforation plates with 6–10 bars............... **112**

   110. Spiral thickening in the vessels restricted to the tapering ends of the members; perforation plates exclusively scalariform; rays 6–13 per millimeter (*x*)............... **111**

   110. Spiral thickening in the vessels not restricted to the tapering ends of the members; perforation plates simple and scalariform; rays 3–5 per millimeter (*x*)................
    Sourwood—*Oxydendrum arboreum* (L.) DC.   Plate XCVII, Figs. 301 and 302.   Desc. p. 601.

111. Pits on the vessel walls (*t*) in transverse rows of 1–3, frequently linear through fusion, the pit contour generally rounded (Plate XXII, Fig. 125); interfiber pits conspicuously bordered, large (7–9 microns in diameter); longitudinal traumatic gum canals sometimes present.......................................
   Red-gum, American Sweet Gum—*Liquidambar styraciflura* L.   Plate LXXXI, Figs. 265 and 266.   Desc. p. 567.

111. Pits on the vessel walls (*t*) in transverse rows of 1–5+, seldom linear, the pit contour frequently angular (rectangular) (Plate XXII, Fig. 127); interfiber pits inconspicuously bordered, small (3–4 microns in diameter); longitudinal traumatic gum canals absent.......................................
   Black Gum, Black Tupelo, Pepperidge—*Nyssa sylvatica* Marsh.   Plate XCV, Figs. 295 and 296.   Desc. p. 595.
   Swamp Tupelo, Swamp Black Gum—*Nyssa sylvatica* var. *biflora* (Walt.) Sarg.   Desc. p. 595.
   Tupelo Gum, Water Gum—*Nyssa aquatica* L.   Plate XCV, Figs. 293 and 294.   Desc. p. 595.

112. Bars of scalariform perforation plates thick (more than 1 micron); pits on the vessel walls linear, frequently extending across the vessel, 12–50 microns in diameter [similar to those of Cucumber Magnolia, *Magnolia acuminata* L. (Plate XXI, Fig. 120)]. . . . .
Evergreen Magnolia, Southern Magnolia—*Magnolia grandiflora* L. Plate LXXVII, Figs. 257 and 258. Desc. p. 560.

112. Bars of scalariform perforation plates thin (less than 1 micron); pits on the vessel walls orbicular to elliptical or linear, seldom extending across the vessel, 6–40 (usually 6–20) microns in diameter (Plate XXII, Fig. 128). . . . .
Yellow-poplar, Tulip-poplar, Whitewood—*Liriodendron tulipifera* L. Plate LXXVIII, Figs. 259 and 260. Desc. p. 562.

Plate XXII

   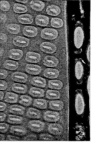

| FIG. 125. | FIG. 126. | FIG. 127. | FIG. 128. |

FIG. 125.—Portion of the wall of a vessel segment (tangential view) from the wood of red-gum, *Liquidambar styraciflua* L., showing oval and linear intervessel pits. (400×)

FIG. 126.—Portion of the wall of a vessel segment (tangential view) from the wood of yellow birch, *Betula lutea* Michx. f., showing small intervessel pits with fused orifices. (400×)

FIG. 127.—Portion of the wall of a vessel segment (tangential view) from the wood of black gum, *Nyssa sylvatica* Marsh., showing opposite pitting. (400×)

FIG. 128.—Portion of the wall of a vessel segment (tangential view) from the wood of yellow-poplar, *Liriodendron tulipifera* L., showing opposite pitting. (400×)

KEY FOR THE IDENTIFICATION OF THE MORE IMPORTANT COMMERCIAL CONIFEROUS WOODS OF THE UNITED STATES

BASED ON GROSS AND MINUTE FEATURES

1. Longitudinal and transverse resin canals present; longitudinal canals appearing as small openings or flecks (*x*) confined for the most part to the outer portion of the growth ring; transverse canals present in some of the rays, forming radial streaks on the transverse surface (Figs. 1–6, p. 357; Figs. 7–12, p. 359; Figs. 13 and 14, p. 361)... **2**

1. Longitudinal and transverse resin canals normally absent; longitudinal wound (traumatic) canals occasionally present, aligned in a tangential row (*x*) (Figs. 15–18, p. 361; Figs. 19–24, p. 363; Figs. 25–29, p. 365)..................................... **18**

    2. Longitudinal resin canals numerous, quite evenly distributed in the outer portion of every growth ring, generally visible to the naked eye* as dark- or light-colored dots or as small openings, conspicuous or relatively conspicuous with a hand lens (Figs. 1–6, p. 357; Fig. 7, p. 359); epithelial cells thin-walled except in *Picea sitchensis* (Bong). Carr. (Fig. 35, p. 158; compare *A* and *C* with *B* and *E*).................... **3**

    2. Longitudinal resin canals generally sparse, unevenly distributed and sometimes absent in portions of some growth rings (if numerous, 2–many in a tangential row), invisible or barely visible as small dark or white flecks to the naked eye, not conspicuous with a hand lens (Figs. 8–12, p. 359; Figs. 13 and 14, p. 361); epithelial cells thick-walled.............. **14**

3. Wood soft, light, quite even-grained; transition from spring- to summerwood gradual (Figs. 1–4, p. 357); ray tracheids not dentate... **4**

3. Wood soft to medium hard or hard, more or less uneven-grained; transition from spring- to summerwood more or less abrupt (Figs. 5–6, p. 357; Fig. 7, p. 359) ray tracheids dentate....... **7**

    4. Wood medium-coarse to relatively coarse-textured; longitudinal tracheids with average tangential diameter of 35–45 microns.. **5**

    4. Wood medium-textured; longitudinal tracheids with average tangential diameter of 25–35 microns....................
    Northern White Pine, Eastern White Pine—*Pinus strobus* L. Fig. 2, p. 357; Fig. 100, p. 401; Plate XXV, Figs. 133 and 134, p. 449. Desc. p. 448.

---

* Numerous but relatively inconspicuous in Red Pine—*Pinus resinosa* Ait.; Jack Pine— *P. banksiana* Lamb.; Lodgepole Pine—*P. contorta* var. *latifolia* S. Wats.; and sometimes in Ponderosa Pine—*P. ponderosa* Laws.

5. Wood with a resinous odor; heartwood cream-colored to light or deep reddish brown; tangential surface (split) not noticeably dimpled; pits leading from ray parenchyma to longitudinal tracheids large [windowlike (Text Fig. 34, *A*)], 1–2 per ray crossing **6**

5. Wood without resinous odor; heartwood light pinkish yellow to pale brown with a purplish cast, darkening on exposure to silvery brown with a faint tinge of red; tangential surface (split) frequently noticeably dimpled; pits leading from ray parenchyma to longitudinal tracheids small [piciform (Text Fig. 34, *D*)], quite uniform in size, 1–4 (generally 2–3) per ray crossing . . . . .
Sitka Spruce—*Picea sitchensis* (Bong.) Carr. Fig. 4 p. 357; Fig. 103, p. 405; Plate XXXIV, Figs. 153 and 154. Desc. p. 470.

    6. Wood with usually prominent dark streaks along the grain (resin canals), frequently exuding a sugary substance when green; seasoned heartwood pale reddish brown; resin canals appearing to the naked eye as minute openings on the transverse surface; windowlike pits leading from ray parenchyma to springwood longitudinal tracheids with rounded or lemon-shaped apertures, not occupying most of the ray crossing, frequently in transverse rows of three or four; longitudinal resin canals with maximum tangential diameter of 300 (av. between 175–225) microns . . . .
    Sugar Pine—*Pinus lambertiana* Dougl. Fig. 1 p. 357; Fig. 101, p. 405; Plate XXIII, Figs. 129 and 130. Desc. p. 443.

    6. Wood without unusually prominent dark streaks along the grain (resin canals), devoid of sugary exudations when green; seasoned heartwood dark reddish brown; resin canals appearing to the naked eye as dark- or light-colored dots; windowlike pits leading from ray parenchyma to springwood longitudinal tracheids with angular orifices, occupying most of the ray crossing, rarely in transverse rows of three; longitudinal resin canals with maximum tangential diameter of 200 (av. between 135–150) microns . . . .
    Idaho White Pine, Western White Pine—*Pinus monticola* Dougl. Fig. 3 p. 357; Plate XXIV, Figs. 131 and 132. Desc. p. 445.

7. Tangential surface (split) with numerous depressions which give it a dimpled appearance; outer margin of the growth increment (*r*) with depressions or sinuses (dimples), the distorted tissue forming swirls as viewed in the tangential section **8**

7. Tangential surface (split) not dimpled; outer margin of the growth increment (*r*) not obviously distorted, the grain normal. **9**

8. Longitudinal resin canals small (x), inconspicuous or not visible with the naked eye, with maximum tangential diameter of 100 (av. between 80–90) microns....................
Lodgepole Pine—*Pinus contorta* var. *latifolia* S. Wats. Plate XXVI, Figs. 135 and 136. Desc. p. 450.
8. Longitudinal resin canals comparatively large (x), plainly visible to the naked eye, with maximum tangential diameter* of 230 (av. between 160–185) microns...............
Ponderosa Pine, Western Yellow Pine—*Pinus ponderosa* Laws. Fig. 5, p. 357; Fig. 98, p. 401; Plate XXVIII, Figs. 139 and 140. Desc. p. 455.
Jeffrey Pine—*Pinus jeffreyi* Grev. & Balf.   Desc. p. 455.

9. Wood hard, heavy, strong, generally highly resinous; bands of summerwood broad; summerwood tracheids forming a band 10–many cells in width (x)................................. **10**

9. Wood approaching that of the soft pines, soft to moderately hard, light to moderately heavy; bands of summerwood usually narrow; summerwood tracheids forming a band 3–10 cells in width (x)... **12**

10. Longitudinal resin canals small (x), inconspicuous or not visible to the naked eye, the majority with a tangential diameter of less than 125 microns; dentations in the ray tracheids shallow (not prominent), seldom extending across the cell (r)... **11**

10. Longitudinal resin canals comparatively large, plainly visible to the naked eye, the majority with a tangential diameter of more than 125 microns; dentations in the ray tracheids prominent, frequently extending across the cell (r) forming a reticulate pattern............................
Southern Pine (Desc. p. 452):†
   Longleaf Pine—*Pinus palustris* Mill.   Fig. 6, p. 357; Fig. 99, page 401; Plate XXVII, Figs. 137 and 138.
   Shortleaf Pine—*Pinus echinata* Mill.
   Loblolly Pine—*Pinus taeda* L.
   Slash Pine—*Pinus caribaea* Morelet
   Pitch Pine— *Pinus rigida* Mill.
   Pond Pine—*Pinus rigida* var. *serotina* (Michx.) Loud.
   Etc.
Ponderosa Pine, Western Yellow Pine—*Pinus ponderosa* Laws.   Fig. 5, p. 357; Fig. 98, p. 401; Plate XXVIII, Figs. 139 and 140. Desc. p. 455.
Jeffrey Pine—*Pinus jeffreyi* Grev. & Balf.   Desc. p. 455.

---

* The diameter inclusive of the epithelium.
† For separation of the woods of Southern Yellow Pine and Ponderosa Pine, see footnote p. 403.

11. Pits leading from ray parenchyma to longitudinal tracheids in the springwood large [windowlike (Text Fig. 34, *A*)], 1–2 per ray crossing ....
Red Pine, Norway Pine—*Pinus resinosa* Ait. Fig. 7, p. 359; Fig. 97, p. 401; Plate XXIX, Figs. 141 and 142. Desc. p. 458.

11. Pits leading from ray parenchyma to longitudinal tracheids in the springwood small [pinoid (Text Fig. 34, *B* and *C*)] and variable in shape, 1–6 (generally 4–6 in two rows) per ray crossing.....
Jack Pine—*Pinus banksiana* Lamb. Plate XXX, Figs. 143 and 144. Desc. p. 460.

    12. Heartwood light red to light brown; resin canals small (*x*), inconspicuous or not visible to the naked eye, the majority with a tangential diameter of less than 125 microns; dentations in the ray tracheids shallow (not) prominent, seldom extending across the cell...............................   **13**

    12. Heartwood yellowish, not oily; resin canals large (*x*), visible to the naked eye, the majority with a tangential diameter of more than 125 microns; dentations in the ray tracheids prominent, frequently extending across the cell (*r*) forming a reticulate pattern...................................
    Ponderosa Pine, Western Yellow Pine—*Pinus ponderosa* Laws. Fig. 5, p. 357; Fig. 98, p. 401; Plate XXVIII, Figs. 139 and 140. Desc. p. 455.
    Jeffrey Pine—*Pinus jeffreyi* Grev. & Balf. Desc. p. 455.

13. Pits leading from ray parenchyma to longitudinal tracheids in the springwood large [windowlike (Text Fig. 34, *A*)], 1–2 per ray crossing ....
Red Pine, Norway Pine—*Pinus resinosa* Ait. Fig. 7, p. 359; Fig. 97, p. 401; Plate XXIX, Figs. 141 and 142. Desc. p. 458.

13. Pits leading from ray parenchyma to longitudinal tracheids in the springwood small [pinoid (Text Fig. 34, *B* and *C*)] and variable in shape, 1–6 (generally 4–6 in two rows) per ray crossing ....
Jack Pine—*Pinus banksiana* Lamb. Plate XXX, Figs. 143 and 144. Desc. p. 460.

    14. Summerwood not pronounced; transition from spring- to summerwood gradual...................................   **15**

    14. Summerwood pronounced (the band of summerwood frequently narrow); transition from spring- to summerwood abrupt*..   **16**

---

* See footnote 2, p. 358.

15. Heartwood light pinkish yellow to pale brown with a purplish cast, darkening on exposure to silvery brown with a faint tinge of red, dull to somewhat lustrous, medium-textured; tangential surface (split) frequently noticeably dimpled; longitudinal tracheids with average tangential diameter between 35–45 microns; ray cells (*t*) orbicular to oval........................

Sitka Spruce—*Picea sitchensis* (Bong.) Carr. Fig. 4, p. 357; Fig. 103, p. 405; Plate XXXIV, Figs. 153 and 154. Desc. p. 470.

15. Heartwood not distinct; wood nearly white to pale yellowish white or light yellowish brown, lustrous, relatively fine-textured; tangential surface (split) not noticeably dimpled; longitudinal tracheids with average tangential diameter between 25–30 microns; ray cells (*t*) oblong to oval........................

Eastern Spruce (Desc. p. 467):

　White Spruce—*Picea glauca* (Moench.) Voss.

　Red Spruce—*Picea rubens* Sarg. Plate XXXIII, Figs. 149 and 150.

　Black Spruce—*Picea mariana* (Mill.) B.S.P.

Engelmann Spruce—*Picea engelmani* (Parry) Engelm. Fig. 9, p. 359; Plate XXXIII, Figs. 151 and 152. Desc. p. 467.

16. Wood with characteristic odor on fresh cut surface, not oily; contour of growth rings frequently wavy; heartwood yellowish or pale reddish yellow to orange-red or deep red (without brownish cast);* longitudinal tracheids (spring- and summerwood) with spiral thickening; longitudinal resin canals (*x*) in short tangential lines; transverse resin canals (*t*) usually with 6 epithelial cells........................

Douglas Fir, Yellow Fir, Red Fir—*Pseudotsuga taxifolia* (Poir.) Britt. Figs. 10, 11, and 12, p. 359; Plate XXXV, Figs. 155 and 156. Desc. p. 473.

16. Wood without characteristic odor on fresh-cut surface, more or less oily; contour of growth rings seldom wavy; heartwood with brownish cast; longitudinal tracheids without spiral thickening or the spirals sporadic (*Larix laricina*) and confined to the summerwood; longitudinal resin canals (*x*) not in tangential lines (sometimes in tangential groups of 2–5); transverse resin canals (*t*) with up to 12 or more epithelial cells...   **17**

---

*See footnote 3, p. 358.

17. Wood medium-textured; heartwood yellowish brown (occasionally reddish brown); growth rings generally wide (5–20 per inch), variable in width; band of summerwood usually wide; longitudinal tracheids with average tangential diameter between 30–40 microns*...

Tamarack, Eastern Larch—*Larix laricina* (Du Roi) K. Koch.   Fig. 13 p. 361; Plate XXXI, Figs. 145 and 146.   Desc. p. 462.

17. Wood coarse-textured; heartwood russet or reddish brown; growth rings generally narrow (15–30 plus per inch), quite uniform in width; band of summerwood usually narrow; longitudinal tracheids with average tangential diameter between 40–50 microns...

Western Larch—*Larix occidentalis* Nutt.   Fig. 14, p. 361; Fig. 102, p. 405; Plate XXXII, Figs. 147 and 148.   Desc. p. 464.

18. Wood fragrant when freshly cut......................... 19

18. Wood not fragrant, sometimes ill-scented when freshly cut.. 25

19. Heartwood purplish or rose-red to dull red, reddish or pinkish brown, or dull brown.................................... 20

19. Heartwood yellowish white to clear yellow, straw-brown, or light brown with a tinge of pink......................... 22

20. Wood medium- to coarse-textured; heartwood reddish to pinkish brown or dull brown, sometimes with a lavender tinge; longitudinal tracheids with average tangential diameter between 30–40 microns; intercellular spaces few or wanting at the corners of the tracheids (*x*), if present, inconspicuous....................................... 21

20. Wood fine-textured; heartwood purplish or rose-red when first exposed, aging to dull brown or reddish brown; longitudinal tracheids with average tangential diameter between 20–30 microns; intercellular spaces frequent at the rounded corners of the tracheids (*x*)....................

Red Cedar (Desc. p. 504):

   Eastern Red Cedar—*Juniperus virginiana* L.   Fig. 15, p. 361; Plate XLVIII, Figs. 183 and 184.

   Southern Red Cedar—*Juniperus silicicola* (Small) Bailey.

---

* See footnote 1, p. 404.

21. Wood firm when cut across grain with a knife, with púngent, spicy (acrid) taste,* often pecky;† spring- and summerwood of about the same hardness;‡ pits leading from ray parenchyma to longitudinal tracheids cupressoid (Text Fig. 34, *F*); rays occasionally in part biseriate, the ray cells in the heartwood with deposits of dark gum.................................
Incense Cedar—*Libocedrus decurrens* Torr.   Fig. 16, p. 361; Plate XLII, Figs. 171 and 172.   Desc. p. 492.

21. Wood crumbly when cut across the grain with a knife, without pungent, spicy (acrid) taste; summerwood considerably harder than the springwood; pits leading from ray parenchyma to longitudinal tracheids taxodioid (Text Fig. 34, *E*); rays strictly uniseriate, the ray cells in the heartwood with scanty, gummy infiltration......................................
Western Red Cedar—*Thuja plicata* D. Don.   Fig. 17, p. 361; Plate XLIV, Figs. 175 and 176.   Desc. p. 496.

22. Heartwood yellowish white to bright clear yellow or yellowish brown...................................... **23**

22. Heartwood light brown tinged with red or pink (roseate), or straw-brown.. **24**

23. Wood with a pungent, gingerlike odor on fresh-cut surface; heartwood yellowish white to pale yellowish brown; annual rings usually averaging 6–15 per inch; rays consisting entirely of ray parenchyma, or very rarely with ray tracheids...............
Port Orford Cedar, Port Orford White Cedar—*Chamaecyparis lawsoniana* (A. Murr.) Parl. Fig. 18, p. 361; Plate XLV, Figs. 177 and 178. Desc. p. 498.

23. Wood with an odor resembling that of raw potatoes on fresh-cut surface; heartwood bright clear yellow, darkening somewhat upon exposure; annual rings usually very narrow, generally averaging 30 to 50 plus per inch; low rays frequently consisting entirely of ray tracheids, the high rays usually composed entirely of ray parenchyma......................................
Alaska Yellow Cedar, Yellow Cypress—*Chamaecyparis nootkatensis* (Lamb.) Spach. Fig. 19, p. 363; Figs. 107 and 108, p. 409; Plate XLVI, Figs. 179 and 180.   Desc. p. 500.

---

* See footnote 1, p. 360.
† See footnote 2, p. 360.
‡ See footnote 3, p. 360.

24. Wood somewhat oily, rubbery when cut across the grain with a knife; heartwood light brown tinged with red or pink; parenchyma fairly abundant to abundant, present in every growth ring; pits leading from ray parenchyma to longitudinal tracheids cupressoid (Text Fig. 34, *F*)............

Atlantic White Cedar, Southern White Cedar—*Chamaecyparis thyoides* (L.) B.S.P. Fig. 21, p. 363; Plate XLVII, Figs. 181 and 182. Desc. p. 502.

24. Wood dry, crumbly when cut across the grain with a knife; heartwood uniformly straw-brown; parenchyma wanting, or very sparse and sporadic (sometimes abundant in a growth ring but then wanting in neighboring rings); pits leading from ray parenchyma to longitudinal tracheids taxodioid (Text Fig. 34, *E*)...................................

Northern White Cedar, Eastern Arbor-vitae—*Thuja occidentalis* L. Fig. 20, p. 363; Plate XLIII, Figs. 173 and 174. Desc. p. 494.

25. Wood very coarse-textured; longitudinal tracheids with average tangential diameter between 45–65 microns; strands of longitudinal parenchyma readily visible along the grain with a hand lens as dark lines (dark gummy infiltration in the cells)........ **26**

25. Wood fine- to medium-coarse textured; longitudinal tracheids with tangential diameter between 15–45 microns; strands of longitudinal parenchyma wanting or, if present, not readily visible along the grain with a hand lens...................... **27**

26. Wood more or less oily (with a greasy feel), often with a rancid odor on fresh-cut surface, frequently pecky;* heartwood very variable in color, ranging from yellowish white to light or dark brown, reddish brown or almost black; contour of individual rings frequently irregular; pits in the ray crossings in the springwood orbicular to oval-orbicular, the long axis of the pit orifice less than 8 microns............

Bald Cypress, Red Cypress, Yellow Cypress, Southern Cypress— *Taxodium distichum* (L.) Rich. Fig. 22, p. 363; Fig. 106, p. 409; Plate XLI, Figs. 169 and 170. Desc. p. 489.

26. Wood dry and brittle, not pecky; heartwood clear light red to deep reddish brown; contour of individual growth rings usually quite regular; pits in the ray crossings in the springwood oval for the most part, the long axis of the pit orifice more than 8 microns...................................

Redwood, Coast Redwood—*Sequoia sempervirens* (Lamb.) Endl. Fig. 27, p. 365; Fig. 105, p. 409; Plate XL, Figs. 167 and 168. Desc. p. 486.

---

* See footnote 1, p. 362.

27. Wood whitish or creamy white to buff, clear yellow or a shade of yellowish brown or light brown, with or without a lavender, roseate, or reddish brown tinge, light to moderately heavy; heartwood not distinct or, if distinct, clear yellow; longitudinal tracheids with average tangential diameter between 25–45 microns*.. **28**

27. Sapwood nearly white to light yellow, thin; heartwood bright orange to rose red; wood heavy; longitudinal tracheids with average tangential diameter between 15–20 microns........... **Pacific Yew**—*Taxus brevifolia* Nutt. Fig. 28, p. 365; Plate XLIX, Figs. 185 and 186. Desc. p. 506.

   28. Wood usually without characteristic odor;† heartwood generally wanting, the color whitish or creamy white through shades of pale straw-buff and light brown; spring- and summerwood generally differentiated through discrepancy in color... **29**

   28. Wood with a characteristic (unpleasant) odor on fresh-cut surface; heartwood distinct, bright clear yellow; spring- and summerwood not conspicuously differentiated through discrepancy in color....................................... **32**

29. Wood light buff to light brown; springwood usually with a reddish tinge; summerwood darker, with a reddish-brown to purplish tinge; pits leading from ray parenchyma to longitudinal tracheids piciform (Text Fig. 34, *D*); ray tracheids present, usually restricted to one row on the upper and lower margins of the ray, lower than the cells of ray parenchyma.............. **30**

29. Wood whitish to creamy white or pale brown; springwood whitish passing gradually into darker, usually lavender summerwood (color contrasts of spring- and summerwood more pronounced in wider rings); pits leading from ray parenchyma to longitudinal tracheids taxodioid (Text Fig. 34, *E*); ray tracheids absent or, if present, sporadic and wanting from many rays... **31**

---

   * Longitudinal tracheids with spiral thickening are indicative that the wood is either Pacific Yew (*Taxus brevifolia* Nutt; see under the second **27**) or a species of *Torreya* (see under the second **32**). These woods are readily distinguishable through color, weight, and texture (see under Descriptions of Woods by Species, p. 506 and 508).

   † See footnote 3, p. 362.

30. Wood dry, brittle, harsh under tools, uneven-grained; transition from spring- to summerwood frequently rather abrupt; longitudinal strands of resin cells and wound canals (termed "bird peck") rarely present....................
Eastern Hemlock, Canada Hemlock—*Tsuga canadensis* (L.) Carr. Fig. 25, p. 365; Plate XXXVI, Figs. 157 and 158. Desc. p. 476.

30. Wood not very brittle, hard but not harsh under tools, quite even-grained; transition from spring- to summerwood gradual; longitudinal strands of resin cells and wound canals (termed "bird peck") frequently present.................
Western Hemlock, West Coast Hemlock, Pacific Hemlock*— *Tsuga heterophylla* (Raf.) Sarg. Fig. 26, p. 365; Plate XXXVII, Figs. 159 and 160. Desc. p. 478.

31. Ray cells (*t*) oblong......................................
Eastern Fir (Desc. p. 483):
Balsam Fir†—*Abies balsamea* (L.) Mill. Fig. 23, p. 363; Fig. 104, p. 405; Plate XXXVIII, Figs. 161 and 162.
Southern Balsam Fir, Fraser Fir—*Abies fraseri* (Pursh) Poir.

31. Ray cells (*t*) orbicular to oval.............................
Western Balsam Firs (Desc. p. 483):
White Fir—*Abies concolor* (Gord.) Engelm. Fig. 24, p. 363; Plate XXXIX, Figs. 163 and 164.
Noble Fir, Larch‡—*Abies procera* Rehd.
Lowland White Fir, Grand Fir—*Abies grandis* Lindl.
California Red Fir—*Abies magnifica* A. Murr. Plate XXXIX, Figs. 165 and 166.

32. Wood with an odor resembling that of raw potatoes; longitudinal tracheids without spiral thickening; ray tracheids (*r*) abundant in the low rays (frequently composing the entire ray), usually wanting in the high rays.............
Alaska Yellow Cedar, Yellow Cypress—*Chamaecyparis nootkatensis* (Lamb.) Spach. Fig. 19, p. 363; Figs. 107 and 108, p. 409; Plate XLVI, Figs. 179 and 180. Desc. p. 500.

32. Wood with characteristic unpleasant odor (unlike that of raw potatoes); longitudinal tracheids without spiral thickening; rays composed entirely of ray parenchyma...............
Stinking Cedar—*Torreya taxifolia* Arn.
California Nutmeg—*Torreya californica* Torr.
Plate L, Figs. 187 and 188. Desc. p. 508.

---

* See footnote 2, p. 364.
† See footnote 1, p. 364.
‡ Noble Fir is sometimes confused with West Coast Hemlock; for the separation of these, see footnote 2, page 364.

DESCRIPTIONS OF WOODS BY SPECIES

SUGAR PINE

Pinus lambertiana Dougl.

Plate I, Fig. 1; Plate XVIII, Fig. 101; Plate XXIII, Figs. 129 and 130

General Characteristics and Properties.—*Sapwood* nearly white to pale yellowish white, narrow to medium wide, *frequently discolored by blue stain; heartwood* light brown to pale reddish brown (never deep reddish brown as in the northern and western white pines), frequently discolored with brown stain; *wood* with a faint, noncharacteristic odor, often exuding a sugary substance when green but without characteristic taste when dry, straight- and even-grained, relatively coarse-textured, light (sp. gr. approx. 0.35 green, 0.38 ovendry), moderately soft (some samples spongy, others quite hard), moderately weak in bending and endwise compression, low in shock resistance, works easily with tools, easy to glue, takes and holds paints well, but the resin in heartwood tends to discolor paint, does not split readily in nailing but is only moderate in nail-holding ability, shrinks very little, stays in place very well when seasoned, seasons easily, low to intermediate in ability to resist decay. *Growth rings* distinct, delineated by a rather narrow band of darker summerwood at the outer margin, narrow to medium wide. Spring-wood zone usually wide, appearing to occupy most of the ring; transition from spring- to summerwood gradual; summerwood as described above, not appreciably more resistant to tools than the springwood. *Parenchyma* not visible. *Rays* very fine (*x*), not visible to the naked eye except where they include a transverse resin canal, forming a fine, close, inconspicuous fleck on the quarter surface. *Resin canals* present, longitudinal and transverse; (*a*) longitudinal canals conspicuous (the orifice visible to the naked eye), numerous, confined largely to the central and outer portions of the ring, solitary or rarely 2–3 contiguous in the tangential plane, appearing as prominent dark streaks along the grain, especially in heartwood, where dark streaks are caused by dust in resin canals (*t*); (*b*) transverse canals less conspicuous than the longitudinal canals, appearing as whitish, rather prominent wood rays spaced at irregular intervals on the transverse surface, visible with a hand lens as brownish specks on the tangential surface.

Minute Anatomy.—*Tracheids* up to 65 (av. 40–50) microns in diameter; bordered pits in 1–2 rows on the radial walls; tangential pitting present in the last few rows of summerwood tracheids; pits leading to ray parenchyma large (windowlike), 1–4 (generally 2 and not infrequently 3) per ray crossing, those in the springwood rounded to elliptical (lemon-shaped) and more or less widely spaced (Fig. 101, page 405), occasionally superimposed. *Longidudinal parenchyma* wanting. *Rays* of two types, uniseriate and fusiform; (*a*) uniseriate rays numerous (*t*), 1–12 plus cells in height; (*b*) fusiform rays scattered, with a transverse

Plate XXIII

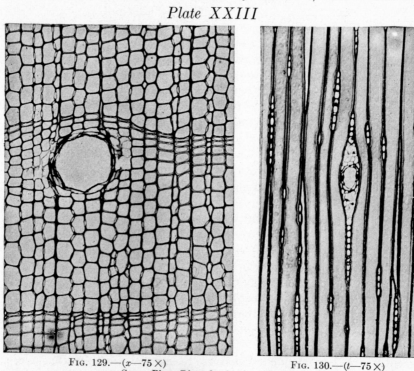

FIG. 129.—(*x*—75 ×)
Sugar Pine, *Pinus lambertiana* Dougl.

FIG. 130.—(*t*—75 ×)

resin canal, 2–4-seriate through the central thickened portion, tapering above and below to uniseriate margins similar to the *a* rays, up to 20 plus cells in height; ray tracheids present in both types of rays, marginal and interspersed, nondentate. *Resin canals* with thin-walled epithelium, frequently occluded with tylosoids in the heartwood; longitudinal canals with maximum diameter of 300 (av. 175–225) microns, the transverse canals much smaller (usually less than 80 microns).

Remarks.—Sometimes confused with northern white pine (*Pinus strobus* L.) and with western white pine (*Pinus monticola* Dougl.), but the heartwood never aging to deep reddish brown as in these species; coarser textured, with more rounded (lemon-shaped) and widely spaced pits in the springwood ray crossings, and with larger longitudinal resin canals resulting in more prominent streaks along the grain.

Uses.—*Boxes* and *crates* (because of light weight and color, nailing properties, and freedom from odor and taste); *millwork* (door, sash, interior and exterior trim, siding, panels, etc.; especially suited for such uses because of ease of working and ability to stay in place and to take and hold paint);[1] lower grades for *building construction* (sheathing, sub-flooring, roofing, etc.); *foundry patterns* for which it is in increasing demand because of the diminishing supply of high-grade northern white pine (standard wood for patterns) and its ability to meet the exacting requirements of this use [light weight, ease of cutting in any direction, minimal shrinkage and swelling, freedom from twisting and warping, ability to receive nails and screws without splitting, ease of gluing, sufficient strength to withstand handling (compression wood should be avoided for this purpose)]; *signs; piano keys* and *organ pipes.*

Selected References

ANON.: Sugar Pine: Its Properties, Uses and Grades. Western Pine Manufacturers Association, Portland, Ore. 1944.

BETTS, H. S.: Sugar Pine—American Woods. Forest Service, U.S. Department of Agriculture. 1945.

LARSEN, L. T., and T. D. WOODBURY: Sugar Pine. *U.S. Dept. Agr., Bul.* 426. 1916.

MATZKE, E. B., and R. L. HULBARY. An Analysis of the Woods of the Three Commercial Species of White Pine. *Bul. Torrey Bot. Club*, Vol. 69, pp. 573–582. 1942.

NEUBRECH, W. LEROY: American Western Pines and Their Uses. *Trade Promotion Series*, No. 180, Forest Products Division, Bureau of Foreign and Domestic Commerce, U.S. Department of Commerce. 1938.

IDAHO WHITE PINE, WESTERN WHITE PINE

Pinus monticola Dougl.

Plate 1, Fig. 3; Plate XXIV, Figs. 131 and 132

General Characteristics and Properties.—*Sapwood* nearly white to pale yellowish white, narrow to medium wide; *heartwood* cream colored to light brown or reddish brown, turning darker on exposure; *wood* with a slightly resinous, noncharacteristic odor, without characteristic taste, straight- and even-grained, medium-coarse to rather coarse-textured, moderately light (sp. gr. approx. 0.36 green, 0.42 ovendry), moderately soft, moderately weak in bending, moderately strong in endwise com-

---

[1] The resin in the heartwood tends to discolor paint.

pression, moderately low in shock resistance, works well with tools, easy to glue, high in ability to hold paint, not splitting readily in nailing but only average in nail-holding ability, shrinks moderately, stays in place well when properly dried, seasons fairly easily, low to intermediate in ability to resist decay. *Growth rings* distinct, delineated by a band of darker summerwood, generally narrow (mature trees). Springwood zone usually wide; transition from spring- to summerwood gradual; summerwood zone usually narrow, not appreciably more resistant to

Plate XXIV

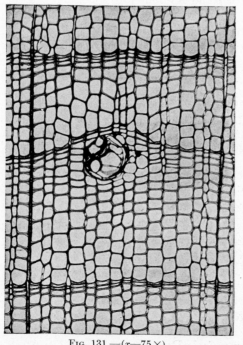
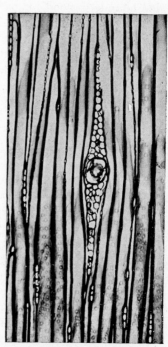

Fig. 131.—(*x*—75 ×)   Fig. 132.—(*t*—75 ×)
Idaho White Pine, Western White Pine, *Pinus monticola* Dougl.

tools than the springwood. *Parenchyma* not visible. *Rays* very fine (*x*), not visible to the naked eye except where they include a transverse resin canal, forming a fine, close, inconspicuous fleck on the quarter surface. *Resin canals* present, longitudinal and transverse; (*a*) longitudinal canals appearing as whitish flecks to the naked eye, numerous, confined largely to the central and outer portions of the ring, solitary or rarely 2–3 contiguous on the tangential plane, forming more or less prominent streaks along the grain (*t*); (*b*) transverse canals less conspicuous than the longitudinal canals, appearing as whitish, rather prominent wood rays spaced at irregular intervals on the transverse surface, scarcely visible with a hand lens on the tangential surface.

Minute Anatomy.—*Tracheids* up to 60 (av. 35–45) microns in diameter; bordered pits in one row (occasionally in two) on the radial walls; tangential pitting present in the last few rows of summerwood tracheids; pits leading to ray parenchyma large (windowlike), 1–4 (mostly 1–2) per ray crossing, occasionally superimposed, those in the springwood more or less angled and occupying most of the back wall. *Longitudinal parenchyma* wanting. *Rays* of two types, uniseriate and fusiform; (*a*) uniseriate rays numerous (*t*), 1–12 plus cells in height; (*b*) fusiform rays scattered, with a transverse resin canal, 2–4-seriate through the central thickened portion, tapering above and below to uniseriate margins similar to the *a* rays, up to 20 plus cells in height; ray tracheids present in both types of rays, marginal and interspersed, nondentate. *Resin canals* with thin-walled epithelium, frequently occluded with tylosoids in the heartwood; longitudinal canals with maximum diameter of 200 (av. 135–150) microns, the transverse canals much smaller (usually less than 80 microns).

Remarks.—Very similar to northern white pine (*Pinus strobus* L.), but usually somewhat coarser textured, with narrower, more uniform rings and with smaller and more angular pits in the springwood ray crossings and larger longitudinal resin canals.

Uses.—*Matches* (principal species); *boxes* and *crates* (very satisfactory because of light weight and color, ability to take nails and screws without splitting, and freedom from odor and taste); *building construction* (lower grades for sheathing, subflooring, roof boards; higher grades for siding, exterior and interior trim, partitions, paneling etc.); *millwork* (such as sash, frames, doors) for which it is very well suited because of the ease of working and its ability to stay in place and hold paint; *patterns; car construction; fixtures; caskets; core stock* for plywood (especially table tops).

Selected References

ANON.: Idaho White Pine: Its Properties, Uses and Grades. Western Pine Manufacturers Association, Portland, Ore. 1942.

ANON.: Facts about Idaho (genuine) White Pine. Western Pine Manufacturers Association, Portland, Ore. No date.

BETTS, H. S.: Western White Pine—American Woods. Forest Service, U.S. Department of Agriculture. 1945.

MAZTKE, E. B., and R. L. HULBARY: An Analysis of the Wood of the Three Commercial Species of White Pine. *Bul. Torrey Bot. Club*, Vol. 69, pp. 573–582. 1942.

NEUBRECH, W. LeROY: American Western Pines and Their Uses. *Trade Promotion Series*, No. 180, Forest Products Division, Bureau of Foreign and Domestic Commerce, U.S. Department of Commerce. 1938.

RAPRAEGER, E. F.: The Use of Idaho White Pine for Matches. *Timberman*, 38 (10): 26–32; (11): 22–28. 1937.

NORTHERN WHITE PINE, EASTERN WHITE PINE, WHITE PINE

Pinus strobus L.

Plate I, Fig. 2; Plate XVII, Fig. 100; Plate XXV, Figs. 133 and 134

General Characteristics and Properties.—*Sapwood* nearly white to pale yellowish white, narrow to medium wide; *heartwood* cream colored to light brown or reddish brown, turning much darker on exposure; *wood* with a slightly resinous, noncharacteristic odor, without characteristic taste, generally straight- and even-grained, medium-textured, light (sp. gr. approx. 0.34 green, 0.37 ovendry), moderately soft, moderately weak in bending and endwise compression, moderately low in shock resistance, works easily with tools, takes glue well, high in ability to hold paint, does not split readily in nailing but average in nail-holding ability, shrinks little, stays in place very well when properly dried, seasons easily, low to intermediate in ability to resist decay. *Growth rings* distinct, delineated by a band of darker summerwood, narrow to wide according to the age and vigor of the tree. Springwood zone usually wide; transition from spring- to summerwood gradual; summerwood zone narrow (wood from mature trees) to wide (second-growth stock), not appreciably more resistant to tools than the springwood. *Parenchyma* not visible. *Rays* very fine (*x*), not visible to the naked eye except where they include a transverse resin canal, forming a fine, close, inconspicuous fleck on the quarter surface. *Resin canals* present, longitudinal and transverse; (*a*) longitudinal canals appearing as whitish flecks to the naked eye, numerous, confined largely to the central and outer portions of the ring, solitary or rarely 2–3 contiguous on the tangential plane, forming more or less prominent streaks along the grain (*t*); (*b*) transverse canals less conspicuous than the longitudinal canals, appearing as whitish, rather prominent wood rays spaced at irregular intervals on the transverse surface, barely visible with a hand lens on the tangential surface.

Minute Anatomy.—*Tracheids* up to 45 (av. 25–35) microns in diameter; bordered pits in one row or occasionally paired on the radial walls; tangential pitting present in the last few rows of summerwood tracheids; pits leading to ray parenchyma large (windowlike), 1–2 (mostly 1) per ray crossing, those in the springwood mostly oblong and occupying most of the back wall (Fig. 100, page 401). *Longitudinal parenchyma* wanting. *Rays* of two types, uniseriate and fusiform; (*a*) uniseriate rays numerous (*t*), 1–8 plus cells in height; (*b*) fusiform rays scattered, with a transverse resin canal, 2–3-seriate through the central thickened portion, tapering above and below to uniseriate margins similar to the *a* rays, up to 12 plus cells in height; ray tracheids present in both types of rays, marginal and interspersed, nondentate. *Resin canals* with thin-walled epithelium, frequently occluded with tylosoids in the heartwood; longitudinal canals with maximum diameter of 150 (av. 90–120) microns, the transverse canals much smaller (usually less than 60 microns).

Remarks.—See Remarks under Idaho White Pine (*Pinus monticola* Dougl., page 447).

Plate XXV

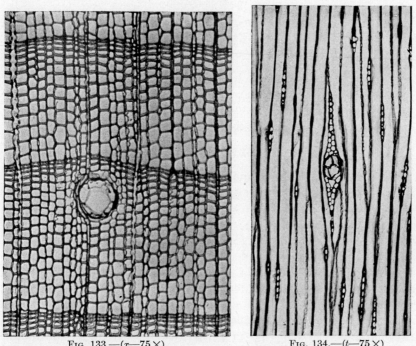

Fig. 133.—(*x*—75 ✕)   Fig. 134.—(*t*—75 ✕)
Northern White Pine, Eastern White Pine, White Pine, *Pinus strobus* L.

Uses.—*Boxes* and *crates* (one of the principal species, second-growth stock being used for the most part), for which it is specially suited because of its light weight, good color for stenciling, and lack of objectionable odor and taste; *patterns* (the standard pattern wood, owing to its uniform texture, ease of cutting in any direction, minimal shrinkage and swelling, ability to stay in place, ease of gluing, freedom from resin, and strength to withstand rough handling); *millwork* (principally sash and doors); *toys; woodenware* and *novelties; signs; caskets; building construction* (formerly widely used for practically every part of a house, but now infrequently because of the scarcity of suitable stock); *matches* (formerly the leading wood, now largely replaced by western white pine and aspen); *shade* and *map rollers; Venetian blinds; dairy* and *poultry supplies; boot* and *shoe findings.*

Selected References

BETTS, H. S.: Eastern White Pine—American Woods.   Forest Service, U.S. Department of Agriculture.   1945.

DAVIS, C. M.: Lumber from Old-growth versus Lumber from Second-growth in Pinus strobus. *Jour. Forestry*, Vol. 38, pp. 877–880.   1940.

FINDLAY, W. P. K.: Resistance to Decay of *Pinus strobus*.   *Empire Forestry Jour.*, Vol. 21, p. 134.   1942.

MATZKE, E. B., and R. L. HULBARY: An Analysis of the Wood of the Three Commercial Species of White Pine.   *Bul. Torrey Bot. Club*, Vol. 69, pp. 573–582.   1942.

SPALDING, V. M. (revised by B. E. FERNOW): The White Pine.   *U.S. Dept. Agr., Div. Forestry, Bul.* 22.   1899.

LODGEPOLE PINE

Pinus contorta var. *latifolia* S. Wats.

Plate XXVI, Figs. 135 and 136

General Characteristics and Properties.—*Sapwood* nearly white to pale yellow, narrow; *heartwood* light yellow to pale yellowish brown, often scarcely darker than the heartwood and not clearly distinct; *wood* with a distinct, noncharacteristic, resinous odor (especially when green), without characteristic taste, generally straight- but somewhat uneven-grained, medium fine-textured, prominently dimpled on the tangential surface (split), moderately light (sp. gr. approx. 0.38 green, 0.43 ovendry), moderately soft, moderately weak in bending and endwise compression, moderately low in shock resistance, easy to work, glues well, average in paint-holding ability, holds nails and screws poorly, shrinks appreciably, stays in place very well when properly dried, seasons easily, not durable under conditions favorable to decay.   *Growth rings* distinct, not so conspicuous as in many of the other hard pines, delineated by a band of darker summerwood.   Springwood zone wide or narrow (outer rings of mature trees); transition from spring- to summerwood more or less abrupt; summerwood zone narrow but distinct, not appreciably more resistant to tools than the springwood.   *Parenchyma* not visible.   *Rays* very fine (*x*), not visible to the naked eye, appearing whitish or brownish with a lens where they contain a transverse resin canal, forming a fine, close, inconspicuous fleck on the quarter surface.   *Resin canals* present, longitudinal and transverse; (*a*) longitudinal canals relatively inconspicuous or not visible to the naked eye, numerous, confined largely to the central and outer portions of the ring, solitary for the most part, forming fairly conspicuous, brownish streaks along the grain (*t*); (*b*) transverse canals less conspicuous than the longitudinal canals, appearing as brownish radial lines spaced at irregular intervals on the transverse surface, barely visible with a hand lens on the tangential surface.

Minute Anatomy.—*Tracheids* up to 55 (av. 35–45) microns in diameter, those in the dimpled areas swirled as viewed in the tangential section; bordered pits in one row or occasionally paired on the radial

Plate XXVI

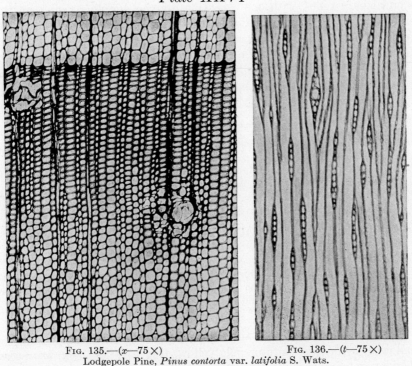

FIG. 135.—(*x*—75 X)   FIG. 136.—(*t*—75 X)
Lodgepole Pine, *Pinus contorta* var. *latifolia* S. Wats.

walls; tangential pitting wanting in the last few rows of summerwood tracheids (sometimes appearing to be present owing to a twist in the tracheids); pits leading to ray parenchyma pinoid, variable in size and shape, 1–6 (generally 2–4) per ray crossing. *Longitudinal parenchyma* wanting. *Rays* of two types, uniseriate or in part biseriate, and fusiform; (*a*) uniseriate rays numerous (*t*), 1–8 plus cells in height; biseriate rays frequent in the areas of swirled tissue; (*b*) fusiform rays scattered or rarely 2–3 confluent along the grain in the swirled areas, with a transverse resin canal, 2–3-seriate through the central thickened portion, tapering above and below to uniseriate margins similar to the *a* rays, up to 10 plus cells in height; ray tracheids present in both types of rays, marginal and interspersed, prominently dentate [with teeth frequently extending across the cell forming a reticulate pattern (r)]; marginal tracheids often in several rows; low rays frequently consisting entirely of ray tracheids; ray parenchyma thin-walled. *Resin canals* with thin-walled epithelium, frequently occluded with tylosoids in the heartwood; longitudinal canals with maximum diameter of 110 (av. 80–90) microns, the transverse canals much smaller (usually less than 50 microns).

Remarks.—Lodgepole pine can be separated from the other commercial hard pines, with one exception, by the dimpling visible on the split tangential surface. Ponderosa pine frequently exhibits this feature, but this species has much larger longitudinal resin canals (see Remarks under Ponderosa Pine, page 457).

Uses.—*Mine timbers; railroad ties; poles; posts; fuel wood; rough construction* (locally); *planing-mill products* (locally) such as siding, finish, flooring.

Selected References

BETTS, H. S.: Lodgepole Pine—American Woods. Forest Service, U.S. Department of Agriculture. 1945.

MASON, D. T.: Utilization and Management of Lodgepole Pine in the Rocky Mountains. *U.S. Dept. Agr., Bul.* **234.** 1915.

SOUTHERN PINE

Longleaf Pine (*Pinus palustris* Mill.), Plate I, Fig. 6; Plate XVII, Fig. 99; Plate XXVII, Figs. 137 and 138
Shortleaf Pine (*Pinus echinata* Mill.)
Loblolly Pine (*Pinus taeda* L.)
Slash Pine (*Pinus caribaea* Morelet)
Pitch Pine (*Pinus rigida* Mill.)
Pond Pine [*Pinus rigida* var. *serotina* (Michx.) Loud.]
Etc.

General Characteristics and Properties.—*Sapwood* nearly white to yellowish or orange-white or pale yellow, thin to very thick; *heartwood* distinct, ranging through shades of yellow and orange to reddish brown or light brown, resinous;[1] *wood* with a distinct, noncharacteristic, resinous odor, without characteristic taste, generally straight- but uneven-grained, medium-textured, moderately heavy to very heavy (av. sp. gr. 0.45–0.56 green, 0.52–0.66 ovendry),[2] moderately hard to hard, moderately strong

[1] In longleaf pine the sapwood contains about 2 per cent resin, while the average for the heartwood is 7 to 10 per cent. The average resin content for the heartwood in butt logs may be 15 per cent and that in the stump 25 per cent.

[2] In order to assist in selection of wood suitable for structural purposes, the grading rules for southern yellow pine contain the *density rule* provision. To qualify under this provision, structural timber must show on one end of the piece an average of not less than 6 rings per inch and one-third summerwood.

to very strong in bending and endwise compression, moderately stiff to very stiff, moderately high to high in shock resistance (in general, longleaf and slash pines are harder, stronger, and stiffer than other southern pines), refractory under tools, glues well, low in ability to take and hold paint, holds nails and screws well, with moderately low to moderately high shrinkage, seasons easily, intermediate (lighter wood) to fairly durable (denser wood) under conditions favorable to decay. *Growth*

Plate *XXVII*

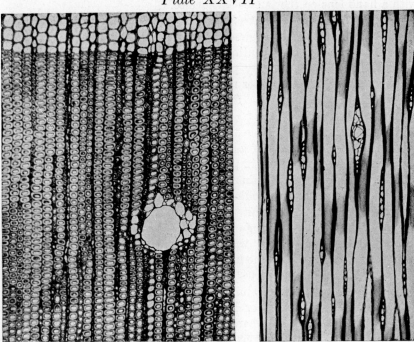

FIG. 137.—(x—75 ✕) FIG. 138.—(t—75 ✕)

Longleaf Pine, *Pinus palustris* Mill.

rings distinct, delineated by a pronounced band of darker summerwood. Springwood zone varying from wide or very wide (slash pine, loblolly pine) to narrow (slow-growth shortleaf pine, etc.); transition from spring- to summerwood abrupt, the contrast frequently very striking; summerwood zone ranging from broad to narrow, varying greatly in width and density according to age of the tree, conditions of growth, and within general limits according to species. *Parenchyma* not visible. *Rays* very fine (x), not visible to the naked eye except where they include a transverse resin canal, forming a fine, close, inconspicuous fleck on the quarter surface. *Resin canals* present, longitudinal and transverse; (*a*) longitudinal canals appearing as whitish or brownish flecks which are conspicuous or relatively conspicuous to the naked eye, plainly distinct with a hand lens, numerous, confined largely to the central and outer portions of the ring, solitary or rarely 2–3 contiguous in the tangential plane, generally visible as relatively inconspicuous streaks along the grain (*t*); (*b*) transverse canals less conspicuous than the longitudinal canals, appearing as whitish, relatively inconspicuous wood rays spaced at irregular intervals on the transverse surface, not visible or barely visible with a hand lens on the tangential surface.

Minute Anatomy.—*Tracheids* up to 60 (av. 35–45) microns in diameter; bordered pits in one row or not infrequently paired on the radial walls; tangential pitting wanting on the last few rows of summerwood tracheids; pits leading to ray parenchyma pinoid, variable in size and shape, 1–6 (generally 2–5) per ray crossing (Fig. 99, page 401). *Longitudinal parenchyma* wanting. *Rays* of two types, uniseriate and fusiform; (*a*) uniseriate rays numerous (*t*), 1–8 plus cells in height; (*b*) fusiform rays scattered, with a transverse resin canal, 2–4-seriate through the central thickened portion, tapering above and below to uniseriate margins similar to the *a* rays, up to 12 plus cells in height; ray tracheids present in both types of rays, marginal and interspersed, prominently dentate [the teeth frequently extending across the cell forming a reticulate pattern (*r*)]; marginal and interspersed tracheids often in several rows; low rays frequently consisting entirely of ray tracheids; ray parenchyma thin-walled. *Resin canals* with thin-walled epithelium, frequently occluded with tylosoids in the heartwood; longitudinal canals with maximum diameter of 180 (av. 90–150) microns, the transverse canals much smaller (usually less than 70 microns).

Remarks.—The yellow or hard pines of southeastern and eastern United States cannot be separated on the basis of wood structure; in the trade, southern pine is usually marketed according to density.

Uses.—*Pulpwood* (converted largely by the sulphate process for use in the manufacture of kraft paper and pulpboard); *poles; mine timbers; piling; railroad ties; slack cooperage* (shortleaf and loblolly); *veneer; excelsior; structural timbers* (such as stringers, beams, and joists in bridge, trestle, warehouse, and factory construction, for which it is highly suited because of its strength, stiffness, and hardness); *building construction* (joists, rafters, studdings, and building lumber);[1] *boxes; baskets* and *crates* (boards and veneer); *planing-mill products* and *millwork* (because of hard-

---

[1] Longleaf and slash pines are used for heavy construction such as for factories, warehouses, bridges, and docks, whereas loblolly and shortleaf pines are used principally for such building materials as interior finish, frame and sash, wainscoting, joists, and subflooring.

ness and good wearing qualities); *railroad-car construction; agricultural implements; ship-* and *boatbuilding; paving blocks; tanks* and *silos; woodenware* and *novelties; destructive distillation* (mostly heartwood from the stumps and tops of longleaf pine).

Selected References

BETTS, H. S.: The Southern Pines—American Woods. Forest Service, U.S. Department of Agriculture. 1945.

BOADLE, A. E., E. M. FERREE, and P. A. HAYWARD: American Pitch Pine and Its Uses. *Trade Prom. Ser.*, No. 119, Bureau of Foreign and Domestic Commerce, U.S. Department of Commerce. 1931.

DAVIS, E. M.: Shortleaf Pine: The Lumber Making Qualities of Second Growth and Virgin Growth Timber. Reprinted from *South. Lumberman.* Dec. 15, 1929.

ILLICK, J. S., and J. E. AUGHANBAUGH: Pitch Pine in Pennsylvania. *Pa. Dept. Forests and Waters, Res. Bul.* 2, Harrisburg, Pa. 1930.

MATTOON, W. R.: Longleaf Pine. *U.S. Dept. Agr. Bul.* 1061. 1925.

————: Shortleaf Pine. *U.S. Dept. Agr. Farmers' Bul.* 1671. 1931. Revised, 1940.

————: Slash Pine. *U.S. Dept. Agr. Farmers' Bul.* 1256. Revised, June 1939.

————: Loblolly Pine Primer. *U.S. Dept. Agr. Farmers' Bul.* 1517. 1926.

PAUL, B. H.: Variation in the Specific Gravity of the Springwood and Summerwood of Four Species of Southern Pines. *Jour. Forestry*, Vol. 37, pp. 478–482. 1939.

TEESDALE, L. V.: The Kiln Drying of Southern Yellow Pine Lumber. *U.S. Dept. Agr. Tech. Bul.* 165. 1930.

WAHLENBERG, W. G.: Longleaf Pine. Charles Lothrop Pack Forestry Foundation (in cooperation with the Forest Service, U.S. Department of Agriculture). 1946.

PONDEROSA PINE AND JEFFREY PINE

Ponderosa Pine, Western Yellow Pine (*Pinus ponderosa* Laws.), Plate I, Fig. 5; Plate XVII, Fig. 98; Plate XXVIII, Figs. 139 and 140 **Jeffrey Pine** (*Pinus jeffreyi* Grev. & Balf.)

General Characteristics and Properties—*Sapwood* nearly white to pale yellowish, wide (often composed of 80 or more rings); *heartwood* of ponderosa pine yellowish to light reddish or orange-brown, that of Jeffrey pine sometimes with a pinkish cast; *wood* of ponderosa pine with distinct, noncharacteristic, resinous odor, that of Jeffrey pine sweet (applelike) when first exposed; woods of both species without characteristic taste, generally straight- and quite even- to very uneven-grained, medium coarse-textured, frequently dimpled on the tangential surface (split) but the dimples less conspicuous than in lodgepole pine, moderately light (sp. gr. approx. 0.38 green, 0.42 ovendry), moderately soft, moderately weak in bending and endwise compression, moderately low in shock resistance,[1] easy to work, glues well, average in paint-holding ability, does not split readily in nailing but only average in nail-holding ability, moderately low in shrinkage, stays in place well when properly dried, seasons very easily, not durable under conditions favorable to decay. *Growth rings* distinct, inconspicuous to conspicuous, delineated by a band of darker summerwood. Springwood zone narrow to wide (wide-ringed stock); transition from spring- to summerwood abrupt;

Plate XXVIII

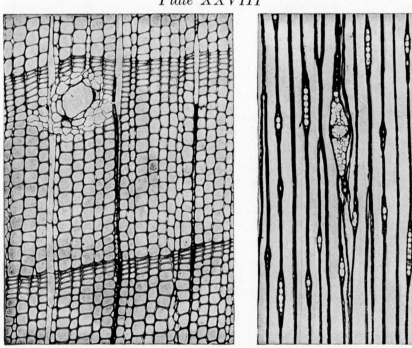

Fig. 139.—(x—75×)   Fig. 140.—(t—75×)
Ponderosa Pine, Western Yellow Pine, *Pinus ponderosa* Laws.

summerwood zone broad and conspicuous in wide rings, in narrow rings much reduced and often appearing as a narrow line which is not visible without magnification, the wood then resembling soft pine. *Parenchyma* not visible. *Rays* very fine (x), not visible to the naked eye except where they include a transverse resin canal, forming a fine, close, inconspicuous fleck on the quarter surface. *Resin canals* present, longitudinal and transverse; (a) longitudinal canals conspicuous (the orifice generally visible to the naked eye), numerous, confined largely to the central and

---

[1] The wood from the outer portions of saw logs is, on the average, somewhat lighter, softer, and less strong than that from the inner zone of such logs or from young trees.

outer portions of the ring, solitary or rarely 2–3 contiguous in the tangential plane, appearing as relatively prominent dark streaks along the grain (*t*); (*b*) transverse canals less conspicuous than the longitudinal canals, appearing as whitish, relatively inconspicuous wood rays spaced at irregular intervals on the transverse surface, barely visible with a hand lens as brownish specks on the tangential surface.

Minute Anatomy.—*Tracheids* up to 60 (av. 35–45) microns in diameter; bordered pits in one row (occasionally in two) on the radial walls; tangential pitting wanting in the last few rows of summerwood tracheids; pits leading to ray parenchyma pinoid, variable in shape and size, 1–7 (generally 4–5) per ray crossing (Fig. 98, page 401). *Longitudinal parenchyma* wanting. *Rays* of two types, uniseriate and fusiform; (*a*) uniseriate rays numerous (*t*), 1–12 plus cells in height; (*b*) fusiform rays scattered, with a transverse resin canal, 3–5-seriate through the central thickened portion, tapering above and below to uniseriate margins similar to the *a* rays, up to 16 plus cells in height; ray tracheids present in both types of rays, marginal and occasionally interspersed, prominently dentate [the teeth frequently extending across the cell forming a reticulate pattern (*r*)]; marginal tracheids often in several rows; low rays frequently consisting entirely of ray tracheids; ray parenchyma thin-walled. *Resin canals* with thin-walled epithelium, frequently occluded with tylosoids in the heartwood; longitudinal canals with maximum diameter of 230 (av. 160–185) microns, the transverse canals much smaller (usually less than 70 microns).

Remarks.—Since ponderosa pine and Jeffrey pine cannot be separated on the basis of wood structure, other characteristics must be used in attempting to distinguish them. The heartwood of Jeffrey pine is generally softer than that of ponderosa pine and frequently has a pinkish cast which is lacking in ponderosa pine; the odor of fresh-cut Jeffrey pine is sweet (hence the term "apple pine") in contrast to the resinous odor of ponderosa pine. Dimpled ponderosa pine is sometimes confused with lodgepole pine in which dimpling is a prominent feature, but differs in possessing darker heartwood and larger longitudinal resin canals [ponderosa pine—230 (av. 160–185) microns; lodgepole pine—110 (av. 80–90) microns].

Uses.—*Boxes* and *crates*, usually lower grades (for which it is well suited because of its light weight and color, ability to take nails and screws without splitting, strength to withstand rough handling, and freedom from objectionable odors and taste); *millwork* (the softer grades), especially for sash, doors, and screens (because of its softness and uniformity of grain which permit of accurate machining, and its moderately low shrinkage, ability to stay in place, resistance to abrasion, and attractive clear color); *planing-mill products* [interior finish, trim, siding, paneling, including knotty grade (the difference between the color of the heart- and sapwood is accentuated upon exposure, necessitating care in matching the wood for interiors)]; *building construction* (the heavier, wider ringed, more resinous wood), as joists, rafters, studdings, sills, and sheathing; *turned work* (porch columns, posts, balusters, stair rails); *caskets* and *coffins; furniture; shade* and *map rollers; patterns* (not considered equal to the white pines); *trunks* and *valises; toys; piling; poles; posts; mine timbers; veneer.*

Selected References

Anon.: Ponderosa Pine: Its Properties, Uses and Grades. Western Pine Manufacturers Association, Portland, Ore. 1942.

Anon.: Facts about Ponderosa Pine. Western Pine Manufacturers Association, Portland, Ore. Undated.

Betts, H. S.: Ponderosa Pine—American Woods. Forest Service, U.S. Department of Agriculture. 1945.

Cockrell, R. A.: Shrinkage and Density of Ponderosa Pine Wood. *Jour. Forestry,* Vol. 42, pp. 288–290. 1944.

Munger, R. R.: Western Yellow Pine in Oregon. *U.S. Dept. Agr. Bul.* 418. 1917.

Neubrech, W. LeRoy: American Western Pines and Their Uses. *Trade Prom. Ser.,* No. 180, Forest Products Division, Bureau of Foreign and Domestic Commerce, U.S. Department of Commerce. 1938.

RED PINE, NORWAY PINE

Pinus resinosa Ait.

Plate II, Fig. 7; Plate XVII, Fig. 97; Plate XXIX, Figs. 141 and 142

General Characteristics and Properties.—*Sapwood* nearly white to yellowish, narrow to medium wide; *heartwood* light red to orange-brown or reddish brown; *wood* somewhat oily, with a fairly strong, resinous, noncharacteristic odor, without characteristic taste, usually straight and quite even-grained, medium-textured, moderately heavy (sp. gr. approx. 0.44 green, 0.51 ovendry), moderately soft, moderately strong in bending, strong in endwise compression, stiff, moderately high in shock resistance, works easily with tools, glues well, below average in ability to hold paint, average in nail-holding ability, with moderately low to moderately high shrinkage, seasons easily, not durable when subjected to conditions favorable to decay. *Growth rings* distinct, delineated by a band of darker summerwood, narrow to wide. Springwood zone generally wide; transition from spring- to summerwood more or less abrupt; summerwood zone narrow to fairly wide (in wide rings), darker and appreciably denser than the springwood zone. *Parenchyma* not visible. *Rays* very fine (x), not visible with the naked eye, appearing whitish with a lens where they contain a transverse resin canal, forming a fine, close, inconspicuous fleck on the quarter surface. *Resin canals* present, longitudinal and transverse; (a) longitudinal canals relatively inconspicuous to the naked eye, appearing as minute, brownish flecks,

Plate XXIX

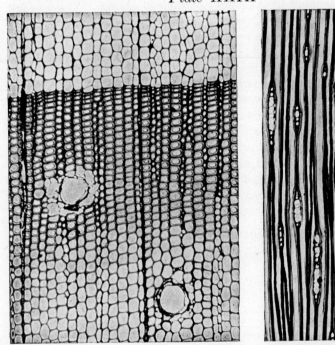

Fig. 141.—(x—75 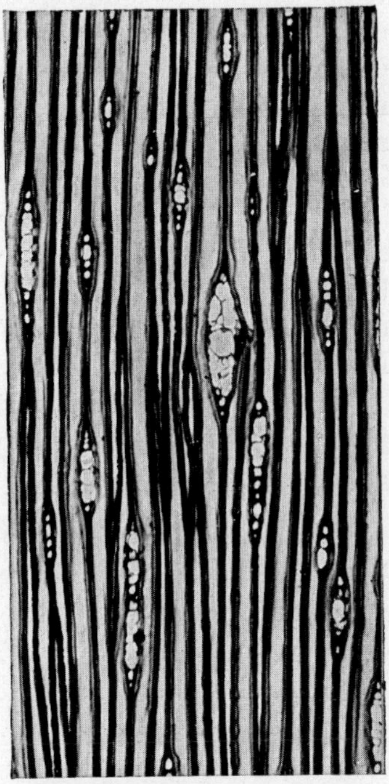 ×) Fig. 142.—(t—75 ×)
Red Pine, Norway Pine, *Pinus resinosa* Ait.

relatively conspicuous with a hand lens, numerous, confined largely to the central and outer portions of the ring, solitary or rarely 2–3 contiguous in the tangential plane, not visible or forming relatively inconspicuous streaks along the grain (t); (b) transverse canals less conspicuous than the longitudinal canals, appearing as whitish, radial lines spaced at irregular intervals on the transverse surface, not visible with a hand lens on the tangential surface.

Minute Anatomy.—*Tracheids* up to 45 (av. 30–40) microns in diameter; bordered pits in one row or occasionally paired on the radial walls; tangential pitting wanting or very sporadic in the last few rows of summerwood tracheids; pits leading to ray parenchyma large (window-like), 1–2 (mostly 1) per ray crossing (Plate XVII, Fig. 97). *Longitudinal parenchyma* wanting. *Rays* of two types, uniseriate and fusiform; (*a*) uniseriate rays numerous (*t*), 1–8 plus cells in height; (*b*) fusiform rays scattered, with a transverse resin canal, 2–3 seriate through the central thickened portion, tapering more or less abruptly above and below to uniseriate margins, up to 10 plus cells in height; ray tracheids present in both types of rays, marginal and interspersed, shallowly dentate (the teeth seldom extending to the center of the cell cavity). *Resin canals* smaller than in most pines, with thin-walled epithelium, frequently occluded with tylosoids in the heartwood; longitudinal canals with maximum diameter of 120 (av. 80–110) microns, the transverse canals much smaller (usually less than 50 microns).

Remarks.—Norway pine is sometimes confused with the soft pines but can readily be separated by the more or less abrupt transition between spring- and summerwood and the presence of dentate ray tracheids (nondentate in the soft pines). The windowlike pits that feature the ray crossings are similar to those of the soft pines and serve to distinguish Norway pine from all other domestic hard pines.

Uses.—*Pulpwood* (converted by sulphate process); *railroad ties; poles; posts; ties; building construction* (locally); *boxes* and *crates; planing-mill products* (sash, doors, blinds, interior and exterior finish).

Selected References

Betts, H. S.: Red Pine—American Woods. Forest Service, U.S. Department of Agriculture. 1945.
Woolsey, T. S., Jr., and H. H. Chapman: Norway Pine in the Lake States. *U.S. Dept. Agr., Bul.* 139. 1914.

JACK PINE

Pinus banksiana Lamb.

Plate XXX, Figs. 143 and 144

General Characteristics and Properties.—*Sapwood* nearly white, wide; *heartwood* formation frequently delayed until trees reach the age of 40 to 50 years, light orange to light brown, somewhat resinous; *wood* with a distinct, noncharacteristic, resinous odor, without characteristic taste, generally straight but somewhat uneven-grained, medium-textured, moderately heavy (sp. gr. approx. 0.40 green, 0.46 ovendry), moderately soft, moderately weak in bending, moderately strong in endwise compression, not stiff, moderately low in shock resistance, somewhat refractory under tools, with moderately low shrinkage, average in paint- and nail-holding ability but prone to split, shows tendency to warping and checking in drying, intermediate under conditions favorable to decay. *Growth rings* distinct, delineated by a band of darker summerwood. Springwood zone variable in width; transition from spring- to summerwood abrupt; summerwood zone narrow to fairly wide, darker and appreciably denser than the springwood zone. *Parenchyma* not visible.

Plate XXX

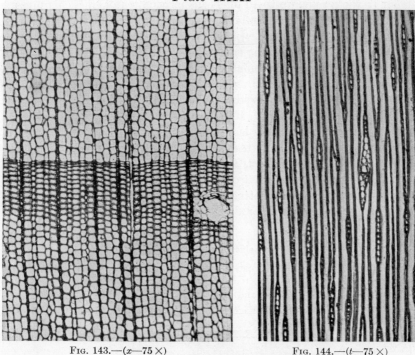

Fig. 143.—(x—75 ×) Fig. 144.—(t—75 ×)

Jack Pine, *Pinus banksiana* Lamb.

Rays very fine (x), not visible to the naked eye, appearing whitish with a lens where they contain a transverse resin canal, forming a fine, close, inconspicuous fleck on the quarter surface. *Resin canals* present, longitudinal and transverse; (*a*) longitudinal canals relatively inconspicuous to the naked eye, numerous, confined for the most part to the central and outer portions of the ring, mostly solitary, forming inconspicuous, brownish streaks along the grain (*t*); (*b*) transverse canals inconspicuous, appearing with a hand lens as whitish, radial lines spaced at irregular intervals on the transverse surface, barely visible with a hand lens on the tangential surface.

Minute Anatomy.—*Tracheids* up to 45 (av. 27–37) microns in diameter; bordered pits in one row or occasionally paired on the radial walls; tangential pitting wanting in the last few rows of summerwood tracheids; pits leading to ray parenchyma pinoid, variable in size and shape, 1–6 (generally 4–6 in two rows) per ray crossing. *Longitudinal parenchyma* wanting. *Rays* of two types, uniseriate and fusiform; (*a*) uniseriate rays numerous (*t*), 1–8 plus cells in height; (*b*) fusiform rays scattered, with a transverse resin canal, 2–3-seriate through the central thickened portion, tapering more or less abruptly above to uniseriate margins similar to the *a* rays, up to 10 plus cells in height; ray tracheids present in both types of rays, shallowly dentate [the teeth seldom extending to the center of the cell cavity (*r*)]; marginal tracheids often in several rows; low rays frequently consisting entirely of ray tracheids; ray parenchyma thin-walled. *Resin canals* smaller than in most pines (comparable in size to those of lodgepole and red pine), with thin-walled epithelium, frequently occluded with tylosoids in the heartwood; longitudinal canals with maximum diameter of 100 (av. 75–90) microns, the transverse canals much smaller (usually less than 45 microns).

Uses.—*Pulpwood* (converted usually by sulphate process); *railway ties; poles; posts; mine timbers; fuel.* Lumber generally knotty and considered less desirable than that of red pine, used principally for *boxes* and *crates; rough construction;* better grades generally marketed as red pine and used for *planing-mill products* (sash, doors, interior and exterior finish).

Selected References

BETTS, H. S.: Jack Pine—American Woods. Forest Service, U.S. Department of Agriculture. 1945.

CHIDESTER, G. H., M. W. BRAY, and C. E. CURRAN: Growth Factors Influencing the Value of Jack Pine for Kraft and Sulphite Pulps. *Paper Trade Jour.*, Vol. 109(13), pp. 36–42. 1939.

STERRETT, W. D.: Jack Pine. *U.S. Dept. Agr. Bul.* 820. 1920.

TAMARACK, EASTERN LARCH

Larix laricina (Du Roi) K. Koch

Plate III, Fig. 13; Plate XXXI, Figs. 145 and 146

General Characteristics and Properties.—*Sapwood* whitish, narrow; *heartwood* yellowish to russet brown or occasionally reddish brown (fast-grown stock); *wood* generally without characteristic odor or taste, more or less oily and with somewhat greasy feel, frequently spiral-grained, medium fine-textured, moderately heavy (sp. gr. approx. 0.49 green, 0.53 ovendry), moderately hard, moderately strong in bending, strong in endwise compression, moderately high in shock resistance, brittle, with moderate shrinkage, intermediate in durability when exposed to conditions favorable to decay. *Growth rings* distinct, delineated by a pronounced band of darker summerwood, generally moderately wide to

Plate XXXI

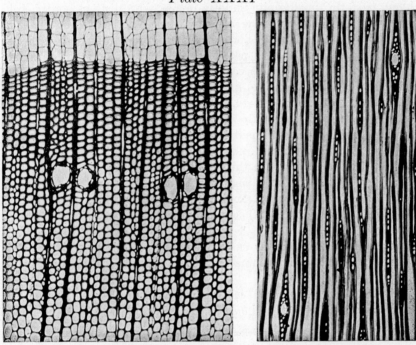

Fig. 145.—(x—75 ×)　　　　Fig. 146.—(t—75 ×)

Tamarack, Eastern Larch, *Larix laricina* (Du Roi) K. Koch

wide (8–20 per inch) and variable in width. Springwood zone usually occupying three-fourths or more of the ring; transition from spring- to summerwood abrupt; summerwood zone narrow to wide, conspicuous to the naked eye. *Parenchyma* not visible. *Rays* very fine (x), not distinct to the naked eye, forming a fine, close, inconspicuous fleck on the quarter surface. *Resin canals* present, longitudinal and transverse; (*a*) longitudinal canals small, inconspicuous, not visible to the naked eye or appearing as whitish or dark flecks, sparse, confined largely to the central and outer portions of the ring, solitary or 2–several contiguous in the tangential plane, occasionally in a tangential line extending for some distance along the ring; (b) transverse canals smaller than the longitudinal canals, appearing with a hand lens as somewhat broader, whitish rays spaced at irregular intervals on the transverse surface, not visible or barely visible with a hand lens on the tangential surface.

Minute Anatomy.—*Tracheids* up to 45 (av. 28–35) microns in diameter, those in the summerwood occasionally with spiral thickening; bordered pits in 1–2 rows on the radial walls; tangential pits present in the last few rows of summerwood tracheids; pits leading to ray parenchyma piciform, small, quite uniform in size, with distinct border, 1–12 (generally 4–6) per ray crossing, often in a double horizontal row. *Longitudinal parenchyma* terminal and very sparse, or wanting. *Rays* of two types, uniseriate or rarely in part biseriate, and fusiform; (a) uniseriate rays numerous (t), 1–16 plus cells in height; biseriate rays very sparse and scattered, or wanting; (b) fusiform rays scattered, with a transverse resin canal, 2–3-seriate through the central thickened portion, tapering above and below to uniseriate margins similar to the a rays, up to 16 plus cells in height; ray tracheids present in both types of rays, marginal and very rarely interspersed, nondentate; marginal tracheids usually in one row. *Resin canals* with thick-walled epithelium, occasionally with tylosoids in the heartwood; longitudinal canals with maximum diameter of 110 (av. 60–90) microns; transverse canals much smaller (usually less than 25 microns), the duct (t) commonly encircled by 12 or more epithelial cells.

Remarks.—Tamarack or eastern larch is sometimes confused with western larch; for distinguishing characters, see Remarks under Western Larch, page 466.

Uses.—Locally for *rough construction; posts; poles; ties; boxes* and *crates; wooden pipe; pails* and *buckets; pulpwood.*

Selected Reference

BETTS, H. S.: Tamarack—American Woods. Forest Service, U.S. Department of Agriculture. 1945.

WESTERN LARCH

Larix occidentalis Nutt.

Plate III, Fig. 14; Plate XVIII, Fig. 102; Plate XXXII, Figs. 147 and 148

General Characteristics and Properties.—*Sapwood* whitish to pale straw-brown, narrow (rarely over 1 inch in width); *heartwood* russet or reddish brown; *wood* without characteristic odor or taste, with characteristic oily appearance and greasy feel, straight-grained, coarse-textured, moderately heavy (sp. gr. approx. 0.48 green, 0.59 ovendry),[1] moderately hard, moderately strong in endwise compression, stiff, moderately high in shock resistance, splits easily, subject to ring shake, difficult to work with tools, moderately high in nail-holding capacity (because of tendency to split, blunt-pointed nails are recommended), easy to glue, low in ability

Plate XXXII

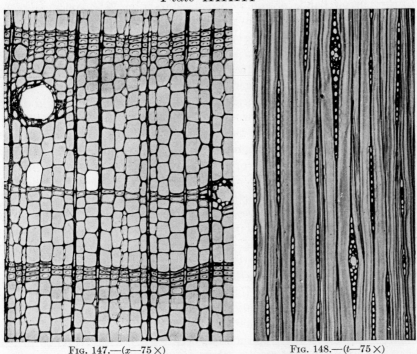

FIG. 147.—(*x*—75 ×)   FIG. 148.—(*t*—75 ×)
Western Larch, *Larix occidentalis* Nutt.

to hold paint but takes stains readily and finishes well in its natural color, shrinks moderately to considerably, dries satisfactorily but tends to split (wide boards), intermediate in durability when exposed to conditions favorable to decay. *Growth rings* distinct, delineated by a pronounced band of darker summerwood, generally very narrow (30–60 per inch) and quite uniform in width. Springwood zone usually occupying two-thirds or more of the ring, appearing porous with a hand lens (large

---

[1] According to Betts (see Selected References) the butt logs of western larch frequently contain large quantities of a gum (galactan), which increases their weight and darkens the color of the wood. Such logs are often left in the woods because they are either too heavy to float or contain too much shake.

tracheids); transition from spring- to summerwood very abrupt; summer-wood zone generally very narrow, sharply delineated and conspicuous to the naked eye. *Parenchyma* not visible. *Rays* very fine (x), not distinct to the naked eye, forming a fine, close, inconspicuous fleck on the quarter surface. *Resin canals* present, longitudinal and transverse; (*a*) longitudinal canals small, inconspicuous, not visible to the naked eye or appearing as whitish or dark flecks, sparse, confined for the most part to the narrow bands of summerwood, solitary or 2–several contiguous in the tangential plane, not visible or forming inconspicuous streaks along the grain; (*b*) transverse canals smaller than the longitudinal canals, appearing with a hand lens as somewhat broader, whitish rays spaced at irregular intervals on the transverse surface, not visible or barely visible with a hand lens on the tangential surface.

Minute Anatomy.—*Tracheids* up to 60 (av. 38–50) microns in diameter, those in the summerwood occasionally with spiral thickening; bordered pits in 1–2 rows on the radial walls; tangential pitting present on the last few rows of summerwood tracheids; pits leading to ray parenchyma piciform, small, quite uniform in size, with distinct border, 1–10 (generally 4–6) per ray crossing, often in a double horizontal row (Fig. 102, page 405). *Longitudinal parenchyma* terminal and very sparse, or wanting. *Rays* of two types, uniseriate or rarely in part biseriate, and fusiform; (*a*) uniseriate rays numerous (*t*), 1–20 plus cells in height; biseriate rays very sparse and scattered, or wanting; (*b*) fusiform rays scattered, with one or very rarely two transverse resin canals, 2–3-seriate through the central thickened portion, tapering above and below to uniseriate margins similar to the *a* rays, up to 20 plus cells in height; ray tracheids present in both types of rays, marginal and very rarely interspersed, nondentate; marginal tracheids usually in one row. *Resin canals* with thick-walled epithelium, occasionally with tylosoids in the heartwood; longitudinal canals with maximum diameter of 135 (av. 60–90) microns; transverse canals much smaller (usually less than 25 microns), the duct (*t*) commonly encircled by 12 or more epithelial cells.

Remarks.—For differences between western larch and Douglas fir, see Remarks under Douglas Fir, page 475. Western larch is sometimes confused with tamarack or eastern larch but can be separated by the following characters: the heartwood of eastern larch is generally yellowish brown in contrast to the russet- or reddish-brown heartwood of western larch; the annual rings in the eastern species are usually much wider and less uniform in width, the grain is not so straight, and the texture is finer [tracheids with maximum diameter of 45 (av. 30–40) microns].

Uses.—*Ties; poles; fuel wood* (rated high in fuel value compared with other woods of the Inland Empire); *building construction* (principal use) in the form of small timbers, planks, boards, rough-dimension stock; *planing-mill products*, especially for edge-grained flooring (for which it is very satisfactory because of hardness resulting from narrow rings with large percentage of summerwood; flat-grained flooring tends to separate along the annual increments), also for interior finish (for which there is a growing demand because of the distinctive figure and the ease with which it can be finished in the natural color); *boxes* and *crates* (shows a tendency to split if large, pointed nails are used); *car construction; electrical machinery* and *apparatus*. Western larch wood (especially butt logs), contains considerable quantities of a water-soluble gum (galactan), which can be easily extracted and oxidized into mucic acid, used in making baking soda.

Selected References

ANON.: Larch: Its Properties, Uses and Grades. Western Pine Manufacturers Association, Portland, Ore. 1931.

BETTS, H. S.: Western Larch—American Woods. Forest Service, U.S. Department of Agriculture. 1945.

Goss, O. P. M.: Mechanical Properties of Western Larch. *U.S. Dept. Agr. Bul.* 122. 1913.

JOHNSON, R. P. A., and M. I. BRADNER: Properties of Western Larch and Their Relation to Uses of the Wood. *U.S. Dept. Agr. Tech. Bul.* 285. 1932.

EASTERN SPRUCE AND ENGELMANN SPRUCE

Eastern Spruce:
  White Spruce [*Picea glauca* (Moench.) Voss.]
  Red Spruce (*Picea rubens* Sarg.), Plate II, Fig. 8; Plate XXXIII, Figs. 149 and 150

Black Spruce [*Picea mariana* (Mill.) B.S.P.]
Engelmann Spruce [*Picea engelmanni* (Parry) Engelm.], Plate II, Fig. 9; Plate XXXIII, Figs. 151 and 152

General Characteristics and Properties.—*Wood* nearly white to pale yellowish brown (*heartwood* not distinct), lustrous, without characteristic odor or taste, even- and usually straight-grained, medium- to fine-textured, light (Engelmann spruce, av. sp. gr. approx. 0.31 green, 0.35 ovendry) to moderately light (eastern spruces, av. sp. gr. approx. 0.37 green, 0.41–0.45 ovendry), soft to moderately soft, weak to moderately weak in bending and endwise compression, limber to moderately stiff, low to moderately low in shock resistance (in general, Engelmann spruce is softer and weaker than the eastern species), easy to work, glues well, average in paint-holding ability, with little tendency to split, low to very low in ability to hold nails, shrinks moderately, stays in place well

Plate XXXIII

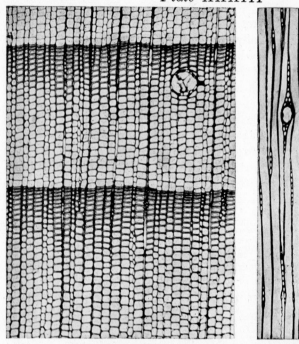

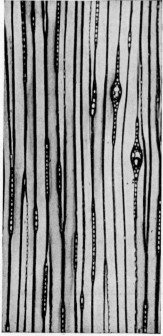

FIG. 149.—(x—75 ✕)

FIG. 150.—(t—75 ✕)

Red Spruce, *Picea rubens* Sarg.

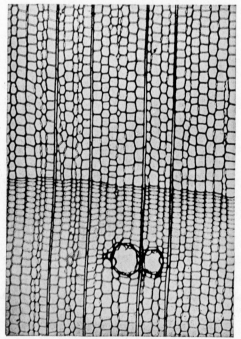

FIG. 151.—(x—75 ✕)

FIG. 152.—(t—75 ✕)

Engelmann Spruce, *Picea engelmanni* (Parry) Engelm.

when seasoned, easy to kiln-dry, not durable when exposed to conditions favorable to decay. *Growth rings* distinct, delineated by the contrast between the summerwood and the springwood of the succeeding ring, narrow to wide. Springwood zone usually a number of times wider than the summerwood, grading into the summerwood; summerwood zone distinct to the naked eye but usually not pronounced, somewhat darker than the springwood, generally narrow. *Parenchyma* not visible. *Rays* very fine (*x*), not distinct to the naked eye or barely visible where they include a transverse resin canal, forming a fine, close, inconspicuous fleck on the quarter surface. *Resin canals* present, longitudinal and transverse; (*a*) longitudinal canals small, generally not visible to the naked eye, appearing as white flecks with a hand lens, solitary or 2–several contiguous in the tangential plane or not infrequently grouped in a tangential line extending for some distance along the ring, often irregularly distributed and wanting entirely from portions of some rings, not visible or barely visible along the grain; (*b*) transverse canals smaller than the longitudinal canals, visible with a hand lens and occasionally to the naked eye as somewhat broader, whitish rays spaced at irregular intervals on the transverse surface, not visible or indistinct with a hand lens on the tangential surface.

Minute Anatomy.—*Tracheids* up to 35 (av. 25–30) microns in diameter; bordered pits in one row or very rarely paired on the radial walls; tangential pitting present in the last few rows of summerwood tracheids; pits leading to ray parenchyma piciform, small, quite uniform in size, with distinct border, 1–6 (generally 2–4) per ray crossing, generally in a single horizontal row. *Longitudinal parenchyma* wanting. *Rays* of two types, uniseriate or rarely in part biseriate, and fusiform; (*a*) uniseriate rays numerous (*t*), 1–16 plus cells in height; biseriate rays very sparse and scattered, or wanting; (*b*) fusiform rays scattered, with one or rarely two transverse resin canals, 2–3-seriate through the central thickened portion, tapering above and below to uniseriate margins similar to the *a* rays, up to 16 plus cells in height; ray tracheids present in both types of rays, usually restricted to one row on the upper and lower margins, nondentate. *Resin canals* with thick-walled epithelium, occasionally with tylosoids in the heartwood; longitudinal canals with maximum diameter of 135 (av. 50–90) microns; transverse canals much smaller (usually less than 30 microns), the duct (*t*) usually encircled by 7–9 epithelial cells.

Remarks.—The woods of white, red, black, and Engelmann spruce cannot be separated with certainty by either gross characteristics or minute anatomy. These timbers are sometimes confused with those of the true firs (*Abies spp.*, pages 481–486) but can readily be separated in that resin canals of the normal type do not occur in the latter. Eastern spruce is usually slightly heavier and stronger than Engelmann spruce; in some samples of Engelmann spruce the transition from spring- to summerwood is more abrupt than in eastern spruce, and the summerwood is then usually appreciably denser than the springwood.

Uses.—*Pulpwood* (most important use), reduced principally by the sulphite and the mechanical processes and manufactured into a wide range of papers (from newsprints to high-grade writing paper); *cooperage* (mostly tight staves and heading). Lumber used for *boxes* and *crates* (very satisfactory in every respect except when high nail-holding ability is required); *refrigerators; general building purposes* (boards, planks, dimension stock, joists); *planing-mill products* (door, sash, casing, dimension stock); *musical instruments,* especially for sounding boards (long a favorite because of its high resonant qualities); *car construction* and *repairs; ship-* and *boatbuilding; furniture* and *kitchen cabinets; woodenware* and *novelties; ladder rails; paddles* and *oars* (because of its lightness combined with the required stiffness and strength).

Selected References

BETTS, H. S.: Eastern Spruce—American Woods. Forest Service, U.S. Department of Agriculture. 1945.

————: Engelmann Spruce—American Woods. Forest Service, U.S. Department of Agriculture. 1945.

HALE, J. D., and K. G. FENSOM: The Rate of Growth and Density of the Wood of White Spruce. *Canada Dep. Int., Forest Serv. Cir.* 30. 1931.

———— and J. B. PRICE: Density and Rate of Growth in Spruce and Balsam Fir of Eastern Canada. *Canada Dept. Mines and Resources, Dominion Forest Serv., Bul.* 94. 1940.

HODSON, E. R., and J. H. FOSTER: Engelmann Spruce in the Rocky Mountains. *U.S. Dept. Agr. Forest Serv. Cir.* 170. 1910.

MURPHY, LOUIS S.: The Red Spruce: Its Growth and Management. *U.S. Dept. Agr. Bul.* 544. 1917.

SPARHAWK, W. N.: Supplies and Production of Aircraft Woods. *Rept.* 67, National Advisory Committee for Aeronautics. 1919.

SITKA SPRUCE

Picea sitchensis (Bong.) Carr.

Plate I, Fig. 4; Text Fig. 35, *C* and *E*; Plate XVIII, Fig. 103; Plate XXXIV, Figs. 153 and 154

General Characteristics and Properties.—*Sapwood* creamy white to light yellow, grading into the darker heartwood, wide; *heartwood* light pinkish yellow to pale brown with purplish cast, darkening on exposure to silvery brown with a faint tinge of red; *wood* more or less lustrous, without characteristic odor or taste, generally straight- and even-grained and frequently dimpled on the tangential surface, medium-textured, moderately light (sp. gr. approx. 0.37 green, 0.42 ovendry), moderately soft, moderately weak in bending, moderately strong in endwise compression, moderately stiff, moderately low in shock resistance, works easily under tools (inclined to be more or less woolly-fibered), very easy to

Plate XXXIV

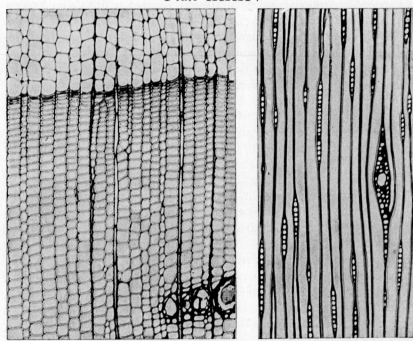

Fig. 153.—(*x*—75 ×)   Fig. 154.—(*t*—75 ×)
Sitka Spruce, *Picea sitchensis* (Bong.) Carr.

glue, average in paint-holding ability, shrinks moderately, stays in place well when seasoned, very easy to kiln-dry, not durable when exposed to conditions favorable to decay. *Growth rings* distinct, delineated by a band of darker summerwood, narrow to medium wide. Springwood zone usually occupying one-half to two-thirds of the ring; transition from spring- to summerwood gradual; summerwood zone somewhat darker and denser than the band of springwood. *Parenchyma* not visible. *Rays* very fine (*x*), not visible to the naked eye except where they include a transverse resin canal, darker than the background (infiltration) and forming a fine, rather conspicuous fleck on the quarter surface. *Resin canals* present, longitudinal and transverse; (*a*) longitudinal canals fairly large, appearing as white flecks in the dark heartwood to the naked eye, sparse to fairly numerous, solitary or 2–several contiguous in the tangential plane or rarely in longer tangential lines, more or less regularly distributed and often wanting entirely from portions of some rings, appearing as scattered streaks along the grain; (*b*) transverse canals smaller than the longitudinal canals, visible against the dark background of heartwood on the transverse surface as somewhat broader whitish rays spaced at irregular intervals, usually distinct with a hand lens on the tangential surface.

Minute Anatomy.—*Tracheids* up to 55 (av. 35–45) microns in diameter; bordered pits in one row or rarely paired on the radial walls; tangential pitting present in the last few rows of summerwood tracheids; pits leading to ray parenchyma piciform, small, quite uniform in size, with distinct border, 1–4 (generally 2–3) per ray crossing, generally in a single horizontal row (Fig. 103, page 405). *Longitudinal parenchyma* wanting. *Rays* of two types, uniseriate and fusiform; (*a*) uniseriate rays numerous (*t*), 1–16 plus cells in height; (*b*) fusiform rays scattered, with a transverse resin canal, 3–5-seriate through the central portion, tapering above and below to uniseriate margins similar to the *a* rays, up to 16 plus cells in height; ray tracheids present in both types of rays, usually restricted to one row on the upper and lower margins, nondentate; ray parenchyma in the heartwood generally with gummy infiltration. *Resin canals* with thick-walled epithelium, occasionally with tylosoids in the heartwood; longitudinal canals with maximum diameter of 135 (av. 60–90) microns; transverse canals much smaller (usually less than 35 microns), the duct (*t*) usually encircled by 7–9 epithelial cells.

Remarks.—Distinct from the eastern spruces and Engelmann spruce in color and texture (coarser textured and more or less wooly-fibered). Sometimes confused with northern white pine (*Pinus strobus* L.) because of its dark-colored heartwood and unusually large resin canals but readily separated through the absence of resinous odor and windowlike pits in the ray crossings, and by its thick-walled epithelium.

Uses.—*Pulpwood* (reduced by the sulphite and mechanical processes). Lumber used for *boxes* and *crates; general construction; planing-mill products* and *millwork* (flooring, siding, ceiling, sash, doors, blinds); *aircraft construction* (formerly widely used because of its high strength properties on the basis of weight, availability in clear pieces of large sizes, uniform texture, and freedom from hidden defects); *musical instruments*, especially sounding boards (slow-growing material preferred because of high resonant qualities); *refrigerators* and *kitchen cabinets; shipbuilding; car construction* and *repair; furniture* (hidden parts); *woodenware* and *novelties; cooperage* (mostly staves and headings for slack barrels); *ladder rails.*

Selected References

ANON.: Sitka Spruce. West Coast Lumber Trade Extension Bureau. Seattle. 1927.

BETTS, H. S.: Sitka Spruce—American Woods. Forest Service, U.S. Department of Agriculture. 1945.

BROWN, L. L.: Canadian Sitka Spruce: Its Mechanical and Physical Properties. *Canada Dep. Int., Forestry Branch Bul.* 71. 1921.

CARY, N. L.: Sitka Spruce: Its Uses, Growth and Management. *U.S. Dept. Agr. Bul.* 1060. 1922.

FINLAYSON, E. H.: Sitka Spruce. *Canada Dep. Int., Forest Serv., Tree Pam.* 12. 1926.

HAUSBROUGH, J. R., and G. H. ENGLERTH: The Significance of the Discolorations in Aircraft Lumber: Sitka Spruce. *Forest Prod. Lab., Forest Path., Spec. Release* 21, pp. 12. 1944.

DOUGLAS FIR, YELLOW FIR, RED FIR

Pseudotsuga taxifolia (Poir.) Britt.

Plate II, Figs. 10, 11, and 12; Text Fig. 14, *A*; Plate XXXV, Figs 155 and 156

General Characteristics and Properties.—*Sapwood* whitish to pale yellowish or reddish white, narrow (Rocky Mountain type) to several inches in width (Pacific Coast type); *heartwood* ranging from yellowish or pale reddish yellow (slow-grown stock) to orange-red or deep red (fast-grown stock), the color varying greatly in different samples; *wood* with a characteristic resinous odor when fresh (different from that of pine), without characteristic taste, usually straight- and even- or uneven-grained, medium- to fairly coarse-textured, moderately light (sp. gr. approx. 0.40 green, 0.45 ovendry—Rocky Mountain type) to moderately heavy (sp. gr. approx. 0.45 green, 0.51 ovendry—Pacific Coast type), moderately hard, moderately strong in bending, moderately strong (Rocky Mountain type) to very strong (Pacific Coast type) in endwise compression, moderately stiff and moderately low in shock resistance (Rocky Mountain type) to stiff and moderately high in shock resistance (Pacific Coast type), difficult to work with hand tools, machines satisfactorily, splits easily, glues satisfactorily, takes and holds paint poorly, difficult to treat with preservatives (material to be treated is usually incised to allow better penetration of preservatives), shrinks moderately (Rocky Mountain type shrinks the least), easy to kiln-dry if proper methods are used, moderately durable to durable (dense stock) when exposed to conditions favorable to decay. *Growth rings* very distinct, frequently wavy, delineated by a pronounced band of darker summerwood, narrow (yellow fir) to very wide (red fir); growth increments (striae) usually less conspicuous than in pine on the radial surface. Springwood zone usually several times wider than the band of summerwood; transition from spring- to summerwood generally abrupt (in wide rings sometimes more or less gradual); summerwood zone pronounced,

Plate XXXV

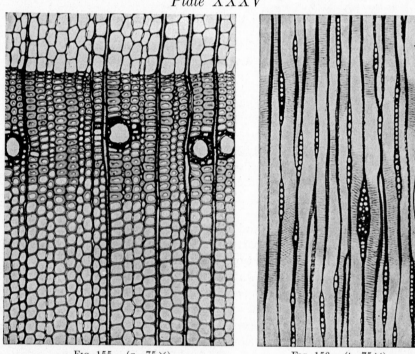

Fig. 155.—(x—75 ×)　　　　　　Fig. 156.—(t—75 ×)

Douglas Fir, Yellow Fir, Red Fir, *Pseudotsuga taxifolia* (Poir.) Britt.

very narrow in slow-grown stock to very wide and dense in wide rings. *Parenchyma* not visible. *Rays* very fine (x), not visible to the naked eye, forming a fine, close, inconspicuous fleck on the quarter surface. *Resin canals* present, longitudinal and transverse; (a) longitudinal canals small, barely visible or indistinct to the naked eye, plainly visible with a hand lens as dark spots or openings, confined largely to the outer half of the ring, sparse and scattered or numerous and exhibiting more or less a tendency (especially in certain rings) toward alignment in tangential rows of 2–30 plus, not visible or forming relatively inconspicuous streaks along the grain (t); (b) transverse canals smaller than the longitudinal canals, appearing with a hand lens as somewhat broader rays spaced at irregular intervals on the transverse surface, not visible or barely visible with a hand lens on the tangential surface.

Minute Anatomy.—*Tracheids* up to 55 (av. 35–45) microns in diameter, characterized (in spring- and summerwood) by fine, close bands of spiral thickening; bordered pits in one row or occasionally paired on the radial walls; tangential pitting present in the last few rows of summerwood tracheids; pits leading to ray parenchyma piciform, small, quite uniform in size, with distinct border, 1–6 (generally 4) per ray crossing. *Longitudinal parenchyma* terminal and very sparse, or wanting. *Rays* of two types, uniseriate or rarely in part biseriate, and fusiform; (*a*) uniseriate rays numerous (*t*), 1–12 plus cells in height; biseriate rays very sparse and scattered, or wanting; (*b*) fusiform rays scattered, with one or very rarely two transverse resin canals, 3–5-seriate through the central thickened portion, tapering above and below to uniseriate margins similar to the *a* rays, up to 16 plus cells in height; ray tracheids present in both types of rays, marginal and very rarely interspersed, nondentate, occasionally with spiral thickening; marginal tracheids usually in one row. *Resin canals* with thick-walled epithelium, constricted at intervals and occasionally with tylosoids in the heartwood; longitudinal canals with maximum diameter of 150 (av. 60–90) microns; transverse canals much smaller (usually less than 25 microns), the duct (*t*) usually encircled by 4–6 epithelial cells.

Remarks.—Very variable in color, ring width, strength, and working qualities, and hence graded and sold in the trade as yellow fir and red fir. Yellow fir is narrow-ringed, fine-grained, quite uniform-textured, moderately soft and easily worked, and yellow or pale reddish yellow; hence the name. Red fir, in contrast, is characterized by wide rings with a wide band of dense, reddish summerwood which is responsible for its orange-red or deep-red color; it is coarser grained and more uneventextured than yellow fir, also stronger and more refractory under tools than that timber. Red and yellow fir are sold abroad as Oregon pine; in Australia merely as "Oregon." Douglas fir is sometimes confused with southern pine and western larch. It can usually be separated from the former on the basis of color and distinctive odor; the smaller resin canals of Douglas fir, which show a tendency toward alignment in tangential rows of 2–20 plus, and the bands of spiral thickening in the tracheids in this species permit of certain identification. The heartwood of western larch, in contrast to that of Douglas fir, has a distinct brownish cast and the springwood tracheids are devoid of spiral thickening.

Uses.—*Building* and *construction*, in the form of lumber, timbers, piling, and plywood (an excellent structural material because of its strength and the availability of high-grade stock in large sizes); *veneer* (leading veneer wood) converted largely into plywood and widely used in building and construction; *railroad ties* (usually incised and pressure-treated with creosote); *cooperage; mine timbers; pulp* (sulphate process). Principal uses of lumber, in addition to general construction, are *planing-mill products* (sash, doors, flooring, blinds, and general millwork); *car construction; boxes* and *crates; silos* and *tanks; containers* for corrosive chemicals; *ship-* and *boatbuilding* (Douglas fir is the species generally used for ship knees on the Pacific Coast); *furniture; motion-picture* and *theatrical scenery.*

Selected References

ANON.: American Douglas Fir and Its Uses. *Trade Prom. Ser.*, No. 87, U.S. Department of Commerce. 1929.

BETTS, H. S.: Douglas Fir—American Woods. Forest Service, U.S. Department of Agriculture. 1945.

CLINE, McGARVEY, and J. B. KNAPP: Properties and Uses of Douglas Fir. *U.S. Dept. Agr. Forest Serv. Bul.* No. 88. 1911.

HAYWARD, P. A., *et al.*: American Douglas Fir Plywood and Its Uses. *Trade Prom. Ser.*, No. 167, Forest Products Division, Bureau of Foreign and Domestic Commerce, U.S. Department of Commerce. 1937.

HOGUE, C. J., *et al.*: Douglas Fir Use Book, Structural Data and Design Tables. West Coast Lumbermen's Association, Seattle. 1936.

EASTERN HEMLOCK, HEMLOCK, CANADA HEMLOCK

Tsuga canadensis (L.) Carr.

Plate V, Fig. 25; Plate XXXVI, Figs. 157 and 158

General Characteristics and Properties.—*Wood* buff to light brown, the summerwood portion of the ring frequently with a roseate or reddish-brown tinge (*heartwood* not distinct, but the last few rings near the bark usually somewhat lighter in color), odorless or with a sour odor when fresh, without characteristic taste, uneven- and frequently spiral-grained, coarse- to medium-textured, moderately light (sp. gr. approx. 0.38 green, 0.43 ovendry), moderately hard, moderately weak in bending, moderately strong in endwise compression, moderately low in shock resistance, low in splitting resistance, dry and brittle (harsh and splintery under tools), subject to ring shake, low to average in nail-holding capacity, glues easily, takes and holds paint moderately well, shrinks moderately, not durable when exposed to conditions favorable to decay. *Growth rings* distinct, delineated by a pronounced band of darker summerwood, narrow to wide (proximate rings not infrequently very variable in thickness; individual rings often variable in thickness and hence more or less sinuate in contour). Springwood zone usually occupying two-thirds or more of the ring; transition from spring- to summerwood gradual to abrupt; summerwood zone distinct to the naked eye, decidedly darker (roseate or reddish brown) and denser than the springwood, variable in thickness in different rings and often in a given ring. *Parenchyma* not visible. *Rays* very fine (x), not

Plate XXXVI

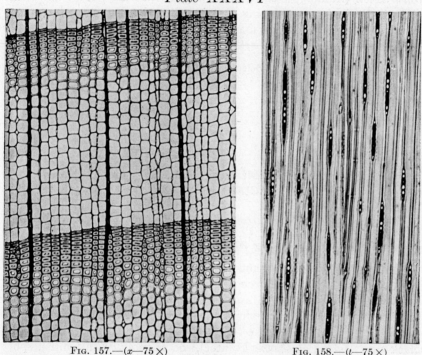

FIG. 157.—(x—75 ×)   FIG. 158.—(t—75 ×)
Eastern Hemlock, Hemlock, Canada Hemlock, *Tsuga canadensis* (L.) Carr.

distinct to the naked eye, forming a fine, close, inconspicuous fleck on the quarter surface. Normal *resin canals* wanting; traumatic canals very rare.

Minute Anatomy.—*Tracheids* up to 45 (av. 28–40) microns in diameter; bordered pits in 1–2 (mostly 1) rows on the radial walls; tangential pitting present in the last few rows of summerwood tracheids; pits leading to ray parenchyma generally cupressoid, small, quite uniform in size, with distinct border, 1–5 (generally 3–4) per ray crossing. *Longitudinal parenchyma* terminal and very sparse, or wanting. *Rays* uniseriate, 1–12 plus cells in height; ray tracheids present, usually restricted to one row on the upper and lower margins of the ray.

Remarks.—For differences between eastern and western hemlock, see Remarks under Western Hemlock. Eastern hemlock differs from the spruces (*Picea spp.*) in the absence of normal resin canals and from the firs (*Abies spp.*) in possessing ray tracheids (ray tracheids sporadic in *A. balsamea* Mill., wanting in other North American species of *Abies*).

Uses.—*Pulpwood* (converted largely by the sulphite process); *generul construction* (framing, sheathing, roofing, subflooring); *boxes* and *crates* (principally for heavy shipping containers); *sash* and *doors; car construction; kitchen cabinets; refrigerators; trunks.* The bark contains 10–13 per cent of tannin and is an important domestic source of this product.

Selected References

BETTS, H. S.: Eastern Hemlock—American Woods. Forest Service, U.S. Department of Agriculture. 1945.

FROTHINGHAM, E. H.: The Eastern Hemlock. *U.S. Dept. Agr. Bul.* 152. 1915.

WEST COAST HEMLOCK, WESTERN HEMLOCK, PACIFIC HEMLOCK

Tsuga heterophylla (Raf.) Sarg.

Plate V, Fig. 26; Text Fig. 36, *A*; Plate XXXVII, Figs. 159 and 160

General Characteristics and Properties.—*Wood* whitish to light yellowish brown, the summerwood portion of the ring frequently with a roseate, purplish, or reddish-brown tinge (*heartwood* not distinct, but the last few rings near the bark almost white), frequently with dark streaks (termed "bird pecks" in the trade) caused by the maggots of a small black fly (*Chilosia alaskensis* Hunter),[1] occasionally with whitish spots (floccosoids),[2] odorless or with a sour odor when fresh, without characteristic taste, generally straight and quite even-grained, medium- to fine-textured, moderately light (sp. gr. approx. 0.38 green, 0.44 ovendry), moderately hard, moderately weak to moderately strong in bending and endwise compression, moderately low in shock resistance, comparatively free from ring shakes, less splintery than eastern hemlock, machines satisfactorily, average in nail-holding capacity, glues easily, takes and

---

[1] See p. 337.

[2] The floccosoids are produced by whitish deposits within the wood cells. The origin or the chemical composition of these deposits is not known. For further detail see R. F. Luxford, L. W. Wood, and Eloise Gerry, under Selected References.

holds paint moderately well, shrinks moderately, easy to kiln-dry, not durable when in situations favorable to decay. *Growth rings* distinct, delineated by a band of darker summerwood, narrow to wide but generally narrower and more uniform in width than in the eastern hemlock; individual rings frequently variable in thickness and hence more or less sinuate in contour. Springwood zone usually occupying two-thirds or more of the ring; transition from spring- to summerwood more or less

Plate XXXVII

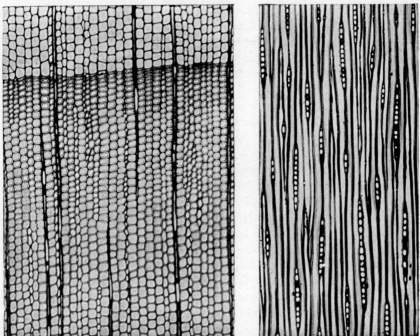

Fig. 159.—(x—75 ×)   Fig. 160.—(t—75 ×)

West Coast Hemlock, Western Hemlock, Pacific Hemlock, *Tsuga heterophylla* (Raf.) Sarg.

gradual; summerwood zone distinct to the naked eye, darker and denser than the springwood (the contrast between spring- and summerwood less accentuated than in the eastern hemlock). *Parenchyma* not visible. *Rays* very fine (x), not distinct to the naked eye, forming a fine, close, inconspicuous fleck on the quarter surface. Normal *resin canals* wanting; longitudinal strands of traumatic resinous cells or wound canals sometimes present, the latter sporadic and often in widely separated rings, arranged in a tangential row (x), appearing as dark streaks along the grain.

Minute Anatomy.—*Tracheids* up to 50 (av. 30–40) microns in diameter; bordered pits in 1–2 (mostly 1) rows on the radial walls; tangential pitting present in the last few rows of summerwood tracheids; pits leading to ray parenchyma generally cupressoid, small, quite uniform in size, with distinct border, 1–4 (generally 2–3) per ray crossing. *Longitudinal parenchyma* very sparse and terminal, or wanting. *Rays* uniseriate or very rarely with paired cells, 1–16 plus cells in height; ray tracheids present, usually restricted to one row on the upper and lower margins of the ray.

Remarks.—West coast hemlock is sometimes confused with western fir; for distinguishing characters, see Remarks under Western Fir. West coast hemlock cannot always be separated with certainty from eastern hemlock, but the following characters will serve to distinguish these woods in most instances: roseate cast less pronounced than in the eastern species; straighter grained and less harsh under tools; springwood somewhat finer textured; rings generally narrower and more uniform in width; transition from spring- to summerwood more gradual and the latter less accentuated; longitudinal strands of resin cells and wound canals, termed "bird pecks" in the trade, not infrequent (rare in eastern hemlock).

Uses.—*Pulpwood* (principal source in the Pacific Northwest; converted by the sulphite and mechanical processes); *general construction* (all but the heaviest type); *planing-mill products* (such as siding, ceiling, flooring, shiplap, and finish); *boxes* and *crates* (generally in the type requiring rather thick boards because of the tendency to split in nailing); *car construction; refrigerators; slack cooperage*, especially for sugar and flour barrels (because of freedom from resinous materials and the absence of taste, and its clear color); *ladder rails*, for which purpose it competes with spruce. The bark contains 12–22 per cent of tannin and may become an important domestic source of this product.

Selected References

ANON.: West Coast Hemlock. West Coast Lumber Trade Extension Bureau, Seattle. 1927.

BETTS, H. S.: Western Hemlock—American Woods. Forest Service, U.S. Department of Agriculture. 1945.

EADES, H. W.: Investigation of Brown Streak in Western Hemlock Used for Aircraft Purposes. *Forest Prod. Labs.* (Vancouver). 1943.

ENGLERTH, G. H., and J. R. HANBROUGH: The Significance of the Discolorations in Aircraft Lumber: Noble Fir and Western Hemlock. *Forest Prod. Lab., Forest Path., Spec. Release* No. 24. 1945.

GOSS, O. P. M.: Mechanical Properties of Western Hemlock. *U.S. Dept. Agr. Bul.* 115. 1913.

GRONDAL, B. L., and A. L. MOTTET: Characteristics and Significance of White Floccose Aggregates in the Wood of Western Hemlock. *Univ. Wash. Forest Club Quart.*, Vol. 16, pp. 13–18. 1942–1943.

JOHNSON, R. P. A., and W. H. GIBBONS: Properties of Western Hemlock and Their Relation to Uses of the Wood. *U.S. Dept. Agr. Tech. Bul.* 139. 1929.

LUXFORD, R. F., L. W. WOOD, and ELOISE GERRY: Black Streaks in Western Hemlock. *Forest Prod. Lab., Mimeo.* 1509. 1943.

SMOOT, CHARLES C., and R. W. FREY: Western Hemlock Bark, an Important Potential Tanning Material. *U.S. Dept. Agr. Tech. Bul.* 566. 1937.

EASTERN FIR

Balsam Fir [*Abies balsamea* (L.) Mill.]. Plate IV, Fig. 23; Plate XVIII, Fig, 104; Plate XXXVIII, Figs. 161 and 162

Southern Balsam Fir, Fraser Fir [*Abies fraseri* (Pursh) Poir.]

General Characteristics and Properties.—*Wood* whitish to creamy white or pale brown (especially the springwood), the summerwood portion of the ring frequently with a lavender tinge (*heartwood* not distinct), without characteristic odor, tasteless or with a slight salty tang, straight- and even-grained, medium-textured, light (sp. gr. approx. 0.34 green, 0.41 ovendry), soft, weak in bending, moderately weak in endwise compression, low in shock resistance, average to below average in paint-holding ability, low in nail-holding ability, works well under tools, shrinks moderately, easy to kiln-dry, not durable when exposed to conditions favorable to decay. *Growth rings* distinct, delineated by the contrast between the somewhat denser summerwood and the springwood of the succeeding ring, medium wide to wide or narrow in the outer portion of mature trees. Springwood zone usually occupying two-thirds or more of the ring; transition from spring- to summerwood very gradual; summerwood zone distinct to the naked eye, somewhat darker than the springwood, generally narrow. *Parenchyma* not visible. *Rays* very fine (*x*), not distinct to the naked eye, forming a fine, close, inconspicuous fleck on the quarter surface. Normal *resin canals* wanting; longitudinal wound (traumatic) canals sometimes present, sporadic and often in widely separated rings, arranged in a tangential row (*x*) which frequently extends for some distance along the ring, appearing as dark streaks along the grain.

Minute Anatomy.—*Tracheids* up to 50 (av. 30–40) microns in diameter; bordered pits in one row or very rarely paired on the radial walls; tangential pitting present in the last few rows of summerwood tracheids; pits leading to ray parenchyma taxodioid, small, quite uniform in size, with distinct border, 1–3 (generally 2–3) per ray crossing (Fig. 104, page 405). *Longitudinal parenchyma* wanting. *Rays* uniseriate, very variable in height (1–30 plus cells and up to 400 plus microns), consisting wholly of ray parenchyma or rarely with a row of ray tracheids on the upper and lower margins [*Abies balsamea* (L.) Mill.].

Remarks.—Lighter, softer, and weaker than spruce. Frequently confused with eastern spruce but readily separated in that ray tracheids [*A. balsamea* (L.) Mill. excepted] and normal resin canals do not occur in the true firs (*Abies spp.*). The longitudinal wound (traumatic) canals,

Plate XXXVIII

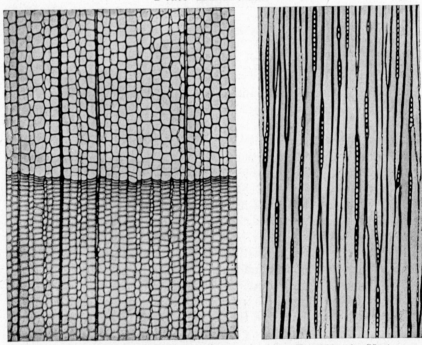

Fig. 161.—(*x*—75 ×)   Fig. 162.—(*t*—75 ×)

Balsam Fir, *Abies balsamea* (L.) Mill.

which are occasionally present, sometimes resemble normal canals; in case of doubt, examine a tangential section of the wood and note the absence (true fir) or presence (spruce) of transverse resin canals in the wood rays.

Uses.—*Pulp* (in admixture with eastern spruce); *cooperage* (sugar and butter tubs, because of the absence of objectionable taste and resinous materials that might taint). Lumber used for *boxes* and *crates* (especially cheeseboxes); *millwork* (siding, molding); *general construction; novelties* and *woodenware;* bark on young trees and branches contains blisters filled with an *oleoresin* (Canada balsam), used in cementing glass and mounting specimens for observation with a microscope.

Selected References

BETTS, H. S.: Balsam Fir—American Woods. Forest Service, U.S. Department of Agriculture. 1945.

HALE, J. D., and J. B. PRICE: Density and Rate of Growth in the Spruce and Balsam Fir of Eastern Canada. *Canada Dept. Mines and Resources. Dominion Forest Serv., Bul.* 94. 1940.

ZON, RAPHAEL: Balsam Fir. *U.S. Dept. Agr., Bul.* 55. 1914.

WESTERN BALSAM FIRS

White Fir [*Abies concolor* (Gord.) Engelm.], Plate IV, Fig. 24; Plate XXXIX, Figs. 163 and 164

Lowland White Fir, Grand Fir (*Abies grandis* Lindl.)

California Red Fir (*Abies magnifica* A. Murr.), Plate XXXIX, Figs. 165 and 166

Noble Fir, Larch (*Abies procera* Rehd.)

General Characteristics and Properties.—*Wood* whitish or light buff to yellowish brown or light brown, the summerwood portion of the ring frequently with a roseate, reddish-brown, or lavender tinge (*heartwood* not distinct), without characteristic odor (sometimes with a slight disagreeable odor when green), tasteless, generally straight- and quite even-grained, medium- to somewhat coarse-textured, light (sp. gr. approx. 0.35–0.37 green, 0.40–0.42 ovendry), moderately soft, moderately weak in bending, moderately strong in endwise compression, moderately stiff, moderately low in shock resistance, easy to cut, saw, or shape, glues readily, takes and holds paint moderately well, low in nail-holding capacity, shrinks moderately, easy to kiln-dry but subject to surface checking if dried too rapidly, not durable when exposed to conditions favorable to decay. *Growth rings* distinct, delineated by a band of darker summerwood, medium wide to wide (3–4 per inch) or narrow in the outer portion of mature trees. Springwood zone usually occupying one-half or more of the ring; transition from spring- to summerwood very gradual; summerwood zone distinct to the naked eye, variable in depth of color and density according to conditions of growth, ranging from broad in wide rings to very narrow. *Parenchyma* not visible. *Rays* very fine (*x*), not distinct to the naked eye, forming a fine, close, inconspicuous fleck on the quarter surface. Normal *resin canals* wanting; longitudinal wound (traumatic) canals sometimes present, sporadic and often in widely separated rings, arranged in a tangential row (*x*) which frequently extends some distance along the ring, appearing as dark streaks along the grain.

Plate XXXIX

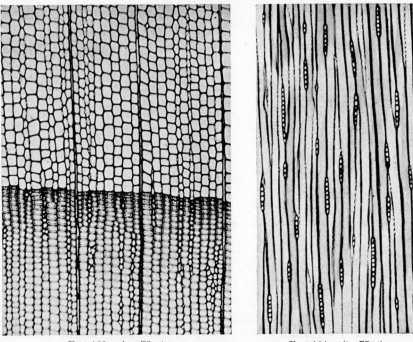

FIG. 163.—(*x*—75 ×)   FIG. 164.—(*t*—75 ×)

White Fir, *Abies concolor* (Gord.) Engelm.

FIG. 165.—(*x*—75 ×)   FIG. 166.—(*t*—75 ×)

California Red Fir, *Abies magnifica* A. Murr.

Minute Anatomy.—*Tracheids* up to 60 (av. 35–45) microns in diameter; bordered pits in one row or occasionally biseriate on the radial walls; tangential pitting present in the last few rows of summerwood tracheids; pits leading to ray parenchyma taxodioid, small, quite uniform in size, with distinct border, 1–4 (generally 2–4) per ray crossing. *Longitudinal parenchyma* terminal and very sparse, or wanting.[1] *Rays* uniseriate (or occasionally in part biseriate in *Abies magnifica* A. Murr.), very variable in height (1–30 plus cells and 400 plus microns), consisting wholly of ray parenchyma.

Remarks.—The timber of noble fir (*A. procera* Rehd.) resembles that of west coast hemlock [*Tsuga heterophylla* (Raf.) Sarg.] but can be separated as follows: the wood of west coast hemlock is drier, more brittle, and harsher under tools; the rings are generally narrower (tolerant tree) and more uniform in width than those of the noble fir, and the springwood is finer and more even-textured (springwood coarse and somewhat variable in texture in noble fir); marginal ray tracheids are invariably found in the wood rays of hemlock and are generally wanting in the western firs. The woods of the other western balsam firs resemble eastern balsam fir [*A. balsamea* (L.) Mill.] in color, ranging from white and creamy white to pale brown with lavender, reddish, or reddish-brown bands of summerwood. The true firs (*Abies spp.*) cannot be separated on the basis of wood anatomy.

Uses.—*General construction* (rough and dressed boards, dimension timbers); *boxes* and *crates* (because of its light weight, clean appearance, freedom from odors and stains, and relatively low cost); *refrigerators* (for which it is well suited because of the above-mentioned properties combined with ease of working and high thermal insulating value); *planing-mill products* (especially sash, doors, and trim); *pulpwood* (used in manufacture of printing paper and high-grade wrapping paper).

Selected References

ANON.: The Uses, Sizes and Grades of White Fir (*Abies concolor* and *Abies grandis*). *West. Pine Assoc., Pam.* 8. pp. 81. 1940.

BETTS, H. S.: White Fir—American Woods. Forest Service, U.S. Department of Agriculture. 1945.

————: Noble Fir—American Woods. Forest Service, U.S. Department of Agriculture. 1945.

ENGLERTH, G. H., and J. R. HANBROUGH: The Significance of the Discolorations in Aircraft Lumber: Noble Fir and Western Hemlock. *Forest Prod. Lab., Forest Path., Spec. Release* No. 24, pp. 10. 1945.

[1] The strands of traumatic resinous cells, forming black streaks and termed "bird pecks," that are sometimes found in the body of the ring as a transitional stage in the formation of longitudinal wound canals, are not interpreted here as true longitudinal parenchyma.

JOHNSON, H. M.: Recovery of Aircraft Lumber from Noble Fir Logs. *Timberman*, 45 (2): 38, 40, 42. 1943–1944.

JOHNSON, R. P. A., and M. R. BRUNDAGE: Properties of White Fir and Their Relation to the Manufacture and Uses of the Wood. *U.S. Dept. Agr. Tech. Bul.* 408. 1934.

REDWOOD, COAST REDWOOD

Sequoia sempervirens (D. Don) Endl.

Plate V, Fig. 27; Plate XIX, Fig. 105; Plate XL, Figs. 167 and 168

General Characteristics and Properties.—*Sapwood* nearly white, narrow; *heartwood* clear light red to deep reddish brown; *wood* without characteristic odor or taste, generally straight- and even- (slow growth- or uneven- (second growth) grained (rarely wavy grained), coarse) textured, light to moderately light (sp. gr. 0.28–0.38 green, 0.31–0.42 ovendry), soft to moderately heavy, moderately strong in bending, strong in endwise compression, moderately stiff, moderately low in shock resistance (these strength values are for typical virgin redwood; second-growth stock is said to be harder and stronger), works with tools moderately well, glues and holds paint exceptionally well, intermediate in nail-holding ability, shrinks very little, stays in place well when seasoned, subject to collapse when kiln-dried too rapidly (especially sinker stock from butt logs) but can be seasoned satisfactorily with proper methods, fire resistant, very durable under conditions favorable to decay (however, since the durability is attributable to extractives in the wood, it varies considerably, depending on the amount of extractive materials present), said to be very resistant to termite attack. *Growth rings* distinct, delineated by a band of darker summerwood, very narrow (sometimes only 2–3 tracheids in width and not infrequently discontinuous in old trees) to very wide (coppice-grown stock). Springwood zone porous (the openings of the tracheids readily visible with a hand lens), narrow to wide; transition from spring- to summerwood generally abrupt; summerwood zone distinct to the naked eye, darker and denser than the springwood, narrow or wide in broad rings. *Parenchyma* abundant, present in every growth ring; cells scattered, readily visible in the sapwood with a lens and sometimes to the naked eye because of their dark resinous contents, inconspicuous in the dark-colored heartwood; strands of parenchyma visible along the grain (split) as dark lines. *Rays* coarse (x) for a coniferous wood, lighter than the background in the heartwood and hence generally visible to the naked eye, forming a fine, close, relatively conspicuous fleck on the quarter surface. Normal *resin canals* wanting; longitudinal wound (traumatic) canals sometimes present, sporadic and often in widely separated rings, arranged in a tangential row (x), appearing as dark streaks along the grain.

Minute Anatomy.—*Tracheids* up to 80 (av. 50–65) microns in diameter; bordered pits in 1–3 (generally 2) rows on the radial walls; tangential pitting present in the last few rows of summerwood tracheids;

Plate XL

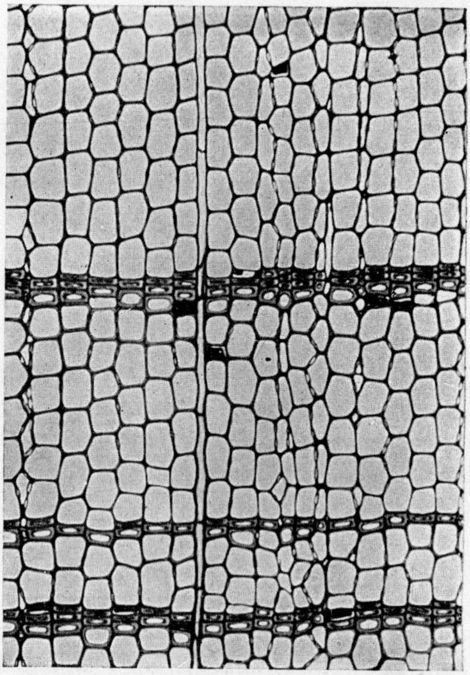

FIG. 167.—(x—75 ×)

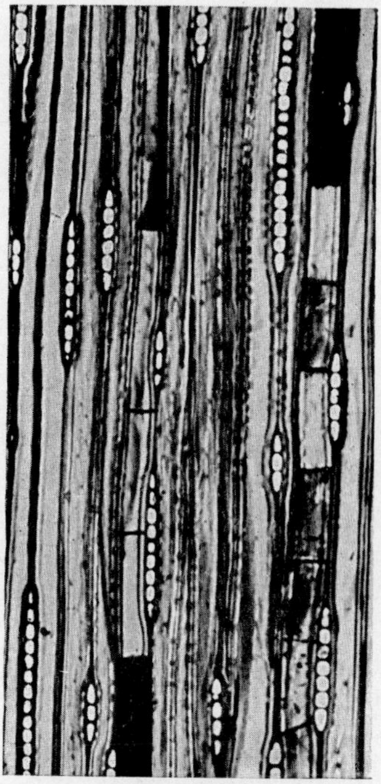

FIG. 168.—(t—75 ×)

Redwood, Coast Redwood, *Sequoia sempervirens* (Lamb.) Endl.

pits leading to ray parenchyma taxodioid, fairly large, quite uniform in size, oval for the most part (the long axis of the pit orifice more than 8 microns), 1–4 (generally 2–3) per ray crossing (Fig. 105, page 409). Longitudinal parenchyma metatracheal-diffuse (the cells solitary or occasionally 2–several contiguous in the tangential plane, conspicuous because of their dark resinous contents). *Rays* uniseriate or not infrequently in part biseriate, consisting entirely of ray parenchyma or rarely with marginal or isolated ray tracheids,[1] the tallest up to 40 (mostly

[1] GORDON, M. Ray Tracheids in *Sequoia sempervirens*. *New Phytol.*, Vol. 11, pp. 1–7. 1912.

10–15) cells and generally less than 600 (rarely up to 1100) microns in height.

Remarks.—Unique among domestic coniferous woods because of its distinctive characteristics (straightness of grain, coarseness of texture, freedom from oily materials that characterize some coniferous woods, etc.). Resembles some of the cedars in color but much coarser textured, without characteristic odor, and with more conspicuous parenchyma. Readily separated from bald cypress by its color, lack of greasiness, and the nature of the pits in the ray crossings (compare Figs. 105 and 106, page 409). Some samples of redwood are peculiar in exhibiting even-width zones of compression wood composed of a number of annual increments which alternate at regular intervals with bands of normal wood.

Sierra redwood is the product of an allied tree, the Big tree or giant sequoia of the high Sierra, *Sequoia gigantea* (Lindl.) Decne. [*Sequoiadendron giganteum* (Lindl.) Buchholz]; it is occasionally used for fence posts, vineyard stakes, shakes, shingles, and for lumber but the supply is becoming more limited as the groves of this species are incorporated into parks. Formerly employed for siding but generally too light and too soft for this purpose.

The wood of Sierra redwood closely resembles that of Coast redwood. The following characters will usually suffice to separate these two timbers: Sierra redwood generally softer and more brittle; heartwood darker, often with a purplish cast; bands of summerwood generally narrower (1–4 tracheids in width); rays less conspicuous and less abundant, and biserate rays less frequent.

Uses.—*General* and *building construction* (timbers, sills, joists, building lumber), because of its durability combined with strength and availability in large sizes; *planing-mill products* and *millwork* (especially sash, doors, and blinds, also siding, ceiling, and general millwork); *boxes* and *crates; caskets* and *coffins* (because of high natural durability); *tanks* and *vats* (because of durability, high resistance to action of chemicals, low shrinkage, and freedom from twisting and warping); *cigar-, tobacco-,* and *candy-boxes; conduits* such as pipes and flumes (because of durability, low cost, smoothness of surface, and ability to withstand extremes of temperature); *garden furniture; dairy, poultry,* and *apiary supplies; electrical equipment; signs; stadium seats; ship-* and *boatbuilding; laundry appliances; greenhouses; woodenware* and *novelties; shingles* and *shakes* (sawed and hand-split); wood from *burls* used for turned and carved articles and occasionally for table tops; *shredded bark* converted into woollike insulating sorptive material.

Selected References

ANON.: Redwood Information Series. California Redwood Association, San Francisco.

ANON.: Redwood. A Report of Fundamental Investigation and Related Application Studies for the Pacific Lumber Company, 1937–1945. Institute of Paper Chemistry, Appleton, Wis. 1945.

BAILEY, I. W., and ANNA F. FAULL: The Cambium and Its Derivative Tissues, No. IX. Structural Variability in the Redwood, *Sequoia sempervirens*, and Its Significance in Identification of Fossil Woods. *Jour. Arnold Arboretum*, Vol. 15, pp. 233–254. 1934.

BETTS, H. S.: Redwood—American Woods. Forest Service, U.S. Department of Agriculture. 1945.

LUXFORD, R. F., and L. J. MARKWARDT: The Strength and Related Properties of Redwood. *U.S. Dept. Agr. Tech. Bul.* 305. 1932.

MITCHELL, J. N.: The Detailed Structure of Stem Wood of the Two Sequoias. *Jour. Forestry*, Vol. 34, pp. 988–993. 1936.

NEUBRECH, W. LeROY: California Redwood and Its Uses. *Trade Prom. Ser.*, No. 171, Bureau of Foreign and Domestic Commerce, U S. Department of Commerce. 1937.

SHERRARD, C. E., and E. F. KURTZ: Distribution of Extractives in Redwood, *Indus. and Engin. Chem.*, Vol. 25, pp. 300–302. 1933.

BALD CYPRESS, RED CYPRESS, YELLOW CYPRESS, SOUTHERN CYPRESS

Taxodium distichum (L.) Rich.

Text Fig. 33, *C*; Plate IV, Fig. 22; Plate XIX, Fig. 106; Plate XLI, Figs. 169 and 170

General Characteristics and Properties.—*Sapwood* pale yellowish white, merging more or less gradually into the heartwood, usually 1 inch or more in width; *heartwood* very variable in color, ranging from yellowish to light or dark brown, reddish brown, or almost black (in the Gulf Coast and South Atlantic regions, the color averages darker than farther North); *wood* with greasy feel (especially along the grain), often with a rancid odor (light-colored stock sometimes odorless),[1] generally straight- and even- or uneven-grained, coarse-textured, moderately heavy (sp. gr. approx. 0.42 green, 0.48 ovendry), moderately hard, moderately strong in bending, strong in endwise compression, moderately stiff, moderately low in shock resistance, somewhat difficult to work with tools, holds paint very well, reputed to be difficult to kiln-dry, shrinks considerably, stays in place well when seasoned, exceptionally resistant to decay, said to be very resistant to termite attack. *Growth rings* distinct, delineated by a band of darker summerwood, narrow and occasionally discontinuous

---

[1] In spite of the presence of an oil that is responsible for the greasy feel and rancid odor, cypress wood does not impart taste, odor or color to food products that come into contact with it.

in old, overmature trees, or wide (proximate rings not infrequently variable in thickness; individual rings often variable in thickness and the rings then sinuate in contour). Springwood zone narrow to wide, usually several times wider than the summerwood; transition from spring- to summerwood more or less abrupt; summerwood zone conspicuous (in the darker grades) or inconspicuous (lighter stock), narrow or broad in wide rings. *Parenchyma* abundant, present in every growth ring; cells

Plate XLI

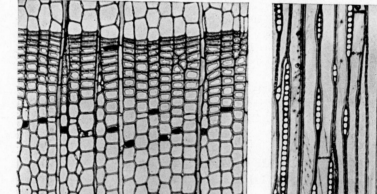

FIG. 169.—(*x*—75 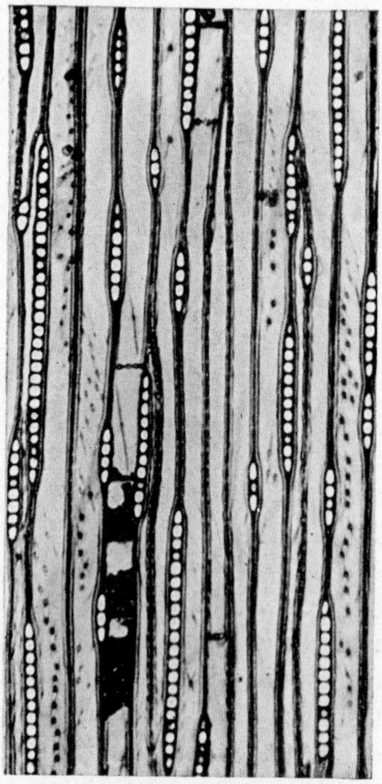 ×)   FIG. 170.—(*t*—75 ×)

Bald Cypress, Red Cypress, Yellow Cypress, Southern Cypress, *Taxodium distichum* (L.) Rich.

scattered, readily visible in the lighter colored grades with a hand lens and sometimes to the naked eye because of their dark resinous contents; strands of parenchyma visible along the grain as dark lines. *Rays* rather coarse (*x*) for a coniferous wood, forming a fine, relatively conspicuous fleck on the quarter surface. *Resin canals* wanting. Finger-shaped pockets extending along the grain and containing a brown friable mass of decayed wood, frequently present; this defect, known as brown rot or peckiness, is caused by the fungus *Fomes geotropus* Cke.

Minute Anatomy.—*Tracheids* up to 70 (av. 45–60) microns in diameter; bordered pits in 1–4 (frequently 3) rows on the radial walls; tangential pitting present in the last few rows of summerwood tracheids; pits leading to ray parenchyma taxodioid or cupressoid, fairly large, quite uniform in size, orbicular for the most part (the long axis of the pit orifice less than 8 microns), 1–6 (generally 4) per ray crossing (Fig. 106, page 409). *Longitudinal parenchyma* metatracheal-diffuse (the cells solitary or occasionally 2–several contiguous in the tangential plane, conspicuous because of their dark resinous contents). *Rays* uniseriate or rarely in part biseriate, consisting entirely of ray parenchyma, the tallest more than 15 (up to 60) cells and over 600 microns in height.

Remarks.—Bald cypress is one of the most variable woods in the United States in color, weight, and durability, and various grades such as red cypress, tidewater red cypress, yellow cypress, and white cypress are recognized by the trade; red cypress is usually slightly heavier and more durable than the yellow or white grades. The term "yellow cypress" is also applied to the wood of Alaska yellow cedar [*Chamaecyparis nootkatensis* (D. Don) Spach]. A second species of *Taxodium, T. ascendens* Brongniart, occurs on the coastal plain in southeastern United States, but the wood is not distinguished from that of bald cypress.

Uses.—Most of the major uses of this wood depend on its extreme durability when exposed to conditions favorable to decay: *construction,* especially parts exposed to the weather (such as siding, beams, posts, timbers in docks and bridges); *caskets* and *coffins; millwork* (especially doors, sash, and blinds, also interior trim and paneling); *tanks, vats,* and *silos; containers* for corrosive chemicals; *laundry appliances; refrigerators* and *kitchen cabinets; greenhouses; machine parts; ship-* and *boat-building; patterns* and *flasks; fixtures; stadium seats; boxes* and *crates* (considerable quantities, but mostly low-grade stock). In forms other than lumber, cypress is used extensively for *railway ties* and in limited quantities for *poles, piling, fence posts,* and *cooperage.*

Selected References

ANON.: American Cypress and Its Uses. *Trade Prom. Ser.,* No. 141, Bureau of Foreign and Domestic Commerce, U.S. Department of Commerce. 1932.

————: The Southern Hardwoods. Southern Hardwood Producers, Inc., Memphis, Tenn. 1941.

BETTS, H. S.: Baldcypress—American Woods. Forest Service, U.S. Department of Agriculture. 1945.

MATTOON, W. R.: The Southern Cypress. *U.S. Dept. Agr. Forest Ser. Bul.* 272. 1915.

VON SCHRENK, HERMANN: The American Bald Cypress. The Southern Cypress Manufacturers' Association, Jacksonville, Fla. 1931.

INCENSE CEDAR, PENCIL CEDAR

Libocedrus decurrens Torr.

Plate III, Fig. 16; Plate XLII, Figs. 171 and 172

General Characteristics and Properties.—*Sapwood* nearly white, thin; *heartwood* reddish brown to dull brown, sometimes with a lavender tinge;

Plate XLII

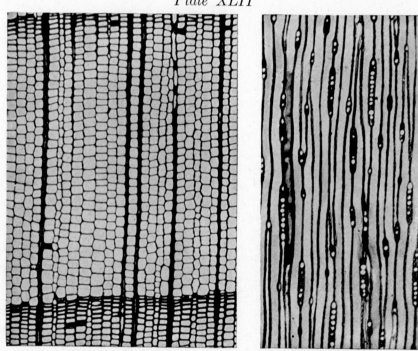

Fig. 171.—(x—75 X)   Fig. 172.—(t—75 X)
Incense Cedar, Pencil Cedar, *Libocedrus decurrens* Torr.

wood with characteristic pungent odor and spicy acrid taste, straight- and even-grained, medium-textured, light (sp. gr. approx. 0.35 green, 0.37 ovendry), moderately soft, moderately weak in bending, moderately strong in endwise compression, not stiff, low in shock resistance, splits readily and evenly, works well with tools, finishes smoothly, takes and holds paint very well (classed with woods that hold paint the longest), shrinks little, easy to kiln-dry, stays in place well after seasoning, very resistant to decay. *Growth rings distinct*, delineated by a band of darker summerwood, quite uniform in width, medium broad to broad (av. 9–12 per inch). Springwood zone usually broad, occupying most of the ring;

transition from spring- to summerwood gradual; summerwood zone fairly conspicuous, narrow. *Parenchyma* very abundant, (*a*) metatracheal-diffuse and not visible or barely visible with a hand lens in the spring-wood, (*b*) not infrequently metatracheal in 1–2 dark bands in the summerwood which are visible with a hand lens and often to the naked eye. *Rays* fine (*x*), plainly visible with a hand lens, forming a fine, close fleck on the quarter surface. *Resin canals* wanting. Finger-shaped pockets extending along the grain and containing a brown mass of decayed wood, frequently present; this defect, known as "peckiness," is caused by the fungus *Polyporus amarus* Hedg.

Minute Anatomy.—*Tracheids* up to 50 (av. 35–40) microns in diameter; bordered pits in 1–2 rows on the radial walls; tangential pitting present in the last few rows of summerwood tracheids; pits leading to ray parenchyma cupressoid, small, oval, quite uniform in size, with distinct border and lenticular orifice, 1–4 (generally 1–2) per ray crossing. Cells of *longitudinal parenchyma* solitary or 2–several contiguous in the tangential plane, with dark gummy contents. *Rays* uniseriate or not infrequently in part biseriate, low for the most part (tallest rays 15 plus cells and 300 plus microns in height), consisting entirely of ray parenchyma or with occasional ray tracheids; broadest rays (uniseriate) 15–25 microns wide; ray cells in the heartwood with deposits of dark gum.

Remarks.—Sometimes confused with western red cedar (*Thuja plicata* D. Don). For distinguishing characteristics of these two woods, see Remarks under Western Red Cedar, page 497.

Uses.—*Fence posts* (because of its durability and ease of splitting); *ties* (very satisfactory as to durability but so soft that it requires tie plates). Lumber used for *pencil slats* (principal species), for which purpose it is especially suited because of the ease with which it may be whittled owing to the evenness of the grain (spring- and summerwood of approximately the same hardness), its uniformity of texture, and its relative firmness; *Venetian blinds* (owing to its uniformity of texture, excellent painting characteristics and ability to stay in place); *woodenware* and *novelties; millwork* (interior finish, outside trim, doors, and sash); *mothproof chests* and *closets; furniture.*

Selected References

BANNAN, M. W.: Wood Structure of *Libocedrus decurrens. Amer. Jour. Bot.,* Vol. 31, pp. 346–351. 1944.

BETTS, H. S.: California Incense-cedar—American Woods. Forest Service, U.S. Department of Agriculture. 1945.

GRAVEM, ROY: Utilization of California Incense Cedar. *Jour. Forestry,* Vol. 38, pp. 285–287. 1940.

MITCHELL, J. A.: Incense Cedar. *U.S. Dept. Agr. Bul.* 604. 1918.

NORTHERN WHITE CEDAR, EASTERN ARBOR-VITAE

Thuja occidentalis L.

Plate IV, Fig. 20; Plate XLIII, Figs. 173 and 174

General Characteristics and Properties.—*Sapwood* nearly white, narrow; *heartwood* uniformly straw-brown; *wood* with characteristic

Plate XLIII

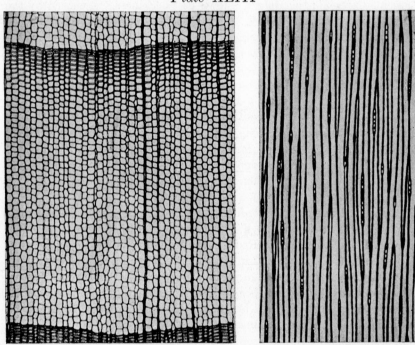

FIG. 173.—(*x*—75 ×)   FIG. 174.—(*t*—75 ×)
Northern White Cedar, Eastern Arbor-vitae, *Thuja occidentalis* L.

cedary odor [distinct from that of southern white cedar (*Chamaecyparis thyoides* (L.) B.S.P.)], with faint bitter taste, usually straight- and even-grained, fine-textured, very light (sp. gr. approx. 0.29 green, 0.32 oven-dry), soft, weak in bending, very weak in endwise compression, low in shock resistance, brittle, has tendency to separate along the growth increments (frequently develops ring shakes), reputed to be harsh under tools, but can be worked to a smooth finish, holds paint well, shrinks very little, easy to kiln-dry, stays in place well after seasoning, very resistant to decay. *Growth rings* distinct, delineated by a darker band of summerwood, usually narrow. Springwood zone occupying most of the ring; transition from spring- to summerwood more or less gradual; summerwood zone somewhat denser than the springwood, narrow. *Parenchyma* not visible. *Rays* very fine (*x*), forming a fine, close, inconspicuous fleck on the quarter surface. *Resin canals* wanting.

Minute Anatomy.—*Tracheids* fine [up to 35 (av. 20–30) microns in diameter]; bordered pits in one row or very rarely paired on the radial walls; tangential pitting present in the last few rows of summerwood tracheids; pits leading to ray parenchyma taxodioid, small, orbicular or nearly so, quite uniform in size, with distinct border and lenticular orifice, 1–4 per ray crossing. *Longitudinal parenchyma* variable in distribution, (*a*) sparse (metatracheal-diffuse) and often apparently wanting, or (*b*) abundant and metatracheal in a given growth ring and then often wanting in neighboring rings; cells solitary or 2–several contiguous in the tangential plane, especially where the parenchyma is metatracheal. *Rays* uniseriate, 1–8 plus cells and generally less than 400 microns in height, consisting entirely of ray parenchyma or sometimes with an occasional ray tracheid; ray cells empty or with scanty infiltration.

Remarks.—Comparable to western red cedar (*Thuja plicata* D. Don), but lighter in color, finer textured, and generally with less prominent growth rings. Sometimes confused with southern white cedar [*Chamaecyparis thyoides* (L.) B.S.P.], and most readily separated by gross features: drier (less oily) and more brittle; heartwood straw-brown in contrast to the roseate-tinted heartwood of southern white cedar; with a characteristic odor that is different from that of the last-named species. Structurally, these two woods are very similar, but the parenchyma is much more abundant and more evenly distributed in southern white cedar (see description of parenchyma under each species).

Uses.—Principally for *poles* and *posts* (because of its durability when in contact with the ground); *cabins; ties* (so soft that it requires tie plates); *pails* and *tubs; rustic furniture; shingles.* Lumber used for *tanks; ship-* and *boatbuilding* (especially canoe ribs); *fish-net floats* and *imitation minnows* (because of the extreme lightness of the wood); *woodenware* and *novelties.*

Selected References

BANNAN, M. W.: Wood Structure of *Thuja occidentalis. Bot. Gaz.,* Vol. 103, pp. 295–309. 1941.

BETTS, H. S.: Northern White-cedar—American Woods. Forest Service, U.S. Department of Agriculture. 1945.

WESTERN RED CEDAR, GIANT ARBOR-VITAE

Thuja plicata D. Don

Plate III, Fig. 17; Plate XLIV, Figs. 175 and 176

General Characteristics and Properties.—*Sapwood* nearly white, narrow; *heartwood* reddish or pinkish brown to dull brown; *wood* with a

Plate XLIV

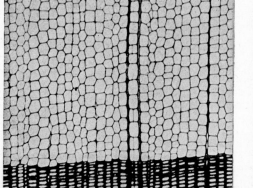
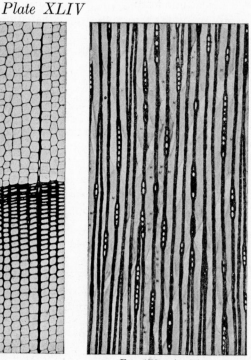

Fig. 175.—(*x*—75 ×)   Fig. 176.—(*t*—75 ×)
Western Red Cedar, Giant Arbor-vitae, *Thuja plicata* D. Don

characteristic sweet, fragrant (cedary) odor and faint bitter taste, straight- and quite even-grained, medium- to somewhat coarse-textured, light (sp. gr. approx. 0.31 green, 0.34 ovendry), moderately soft, moderately weak in bending and endwise compression, low in shock resistance (darker colored heartwood is lower in specific gravity, softer, less tough, and weaker in compression than the normal light-colored heartwood),[1]

---

[1] According to W. P. K. Findlay and C. D. Pettifor (see Selected References), since fungous mycelium is almost invariably present in the darker wood (probably *Poria weiri* Murr.) and absent in the lighter wood, it appears that the dark coloration, lower specific gravity, and reduced strength properties are brought about by fungous attacks.

splits readily, low in nail-holding ability, easily worked with tools, shrinks very little, easy (material from upper logs) to difficult (stock from butt logs that develops collapse) to kiln-dry, glues well, excellent in paint-holding ability, very resistant to decay. *Growth rings* distinct and generally quite conspicuous, delineated by a darker band of summerwood, narrow to fairly wide. Springwood zone occupying most of the ring, soft under tools; transition from spring- to summerwood more or less abrupt; summerwood zone narrow, hard. *Parenchyma* not visible or barely distinct with a hand lens as a narrow line in the summerwood. *Rays* fine (*x*), forming a fine, close, inconspicuous fleck on the quarter surface. Resin canals wanting.

Minute Anatomy.—*Tracheids* medium coarse [up to 45 (av. 30–40) microns in diameter]; bordered pits in 1–2 rows on the radial walls; tangential pitting present in the last few rows of summerwood tracheids; pits leading to ray parenchyma taxodioid, small, orbicular or nearly so, quite uniform in size, with distinct border and lenticular orifice, 1–4 per ray crossing. Lines of metatracheal *parenchyma* very variable in distribution, (*a*) present in every ring in some samples, (*b*) in other instances sporadic in distant rings, the wood then often apparently without parenchyma. *Rays* uniseriate, 1–12 plus cells and generally less than 400 microns in height, consisting entirely of ray parenchyma or rarely with a more or less continuous or interrupted row of ray tracheids on the upper and low margins; ray cells with scanty gummy infiltration.

Remarks.—Similar in color to, and hence often confused with, incense cedar (*Libocedrus decurrens* Torr.); softer,[1] more brittle (drier), and less firm under tools than this species, without the relatively high infiltration content and acrid taste that are features of this wood; parenchyma generally much less abundant; rays strictly uniseriate (those of incense cedar not infrequently in part biseriate). For differences between *Thuja plicata* D. Don and *T. occidentalis* L., see Remarks under the latter, page 495.

Uses.—*Shingles* (more than 95 per cent of all shingles manufactured in the United States), for which purpose its durability, ease of working, and lightness make this the premier wood; *poles* (because of the good form of the tree, large sizes available, and its durability; shipped to all parts of the United States); *posts; piling* (has a tendency to crush in driving); *boxes* and *crates*. The lumber is used for all purposes where durability and ease of working are of first importance [especially for caskets and coffins, siding, tank stock, porch columns, hothouse construction, boatbuilding (planking of racing shells)], also for interior finish.

[1] See footnote **3**, p. 360.

Selected References

Anon.: Western Red Cedar.   West Coast Lumber Trade Extension Bureau, Portland.
    Ore. 1927.
Betts, H. S.: Western Redcedar—American Woods.   Forest Service, U.S. Depart-
    ment of Agriculture. 1945.
Eades, H. W., and J. B. Alexander: Western Red Cedar: Significance of Its Heart-
    wood Coloration.   *Forest Serv. Cir.* 41, Forest Products Laboratories of Canada,
    Ottawa. 1934.
Findlay, W. P. K., and C. D. Pettifor: Dark Coloration in Western Red Cedar in
    Relation to Certain Mechanical Properties.   *Empire Forestry Jour.*, Vol. 20,
    pp. 64–71. 1941.
Knapp, J. B., and A. C. Jackson: Characteristics and Utilization of Western Red
    Cedar.   *West Coast Lumberman*, Vol. 25 (296), pp. 34–35; (298) pp. 62–64, 66–70,
    73–74, 76–78. 1918.
Southam, C. M., and J. Ehrlich: Decay Resistance and Physical Characteristics of
    Wood (*Thuja plicata*).   *Jour. Forestry*, Vol. 41, pp. 666–673. 1943.

PORT ORFORD CEDAR, PORT ORFORD WHITE CEDAR

Chamaecyparis lawsoniana (A. Murr.) Parl.

Plate III, Fig. 18; Plate XLV, Figs. 177 and 178

General Characteristics and Properties.—*Sapwood* nearly white to pale yellowish white, frequently not clearly distinguishable from the heartwood, narrow to fairly wide (1–3 inches); *heartwood* yellowish white to pale yellowish brown; *wood* with a characteristic pungent, gingerlike odor when freshly cut,[1] with bitter, somewhat spicy taste, straight- and even-grained, medium- to somewhat coarse-textured, moderately light (sp. gr. approx. 0.40 green, 0.44 ovendry), moderately soft, moderately strong in bending, strong in endwise compression, stiff, moderately high in shock resistance, works easily under tools, capable of high polish, holds paint well, shrinks moderately, easy to kiln-dry, stays in place well after seasoning, acid-resistant, very resistant to decay.   *Growth rings* distinct but not conspicuous, delineated by a band of somewhat darker summerwood, narrow to fairly wide (usually of medium width).   Springwood zone generally broad, occupying most of the ring; transition from spring- to summerwood more or less gradual; summerwood zone only slightly denser than the springwood, narrow.   *Parenchyma* abundant, not distinct

---

[1] This odor is due to a volatile oil, which, if inhaled continuously for a long time, may cause kidney complications.   Men working at the sawmills cutting Port Orford cedar use masks as a protection against the oil and the fine dust resulting from sawing this wood.

or barely visible with a hand lens. *Rays* narrow (x), appearing fine with a hand lens, forming a close, low, inconspicuous fleck on the quarter surface. *Resin canals* wanting.

· **Minute Anatomy.**—*Tracheids* up to 50 (av. 35–45) microns in diameter; bordered pits in one row or occasionally in part biseriate on the radial walls; tangential pitting present on the last few rows of summer-

Plate XLV

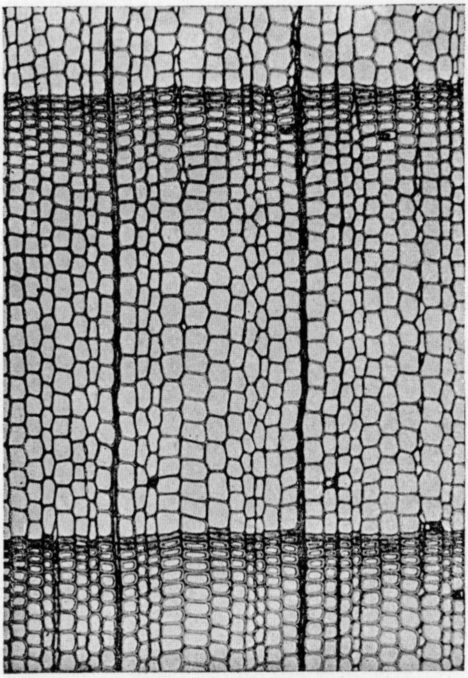

Fig. 177.—(x—75 ×)

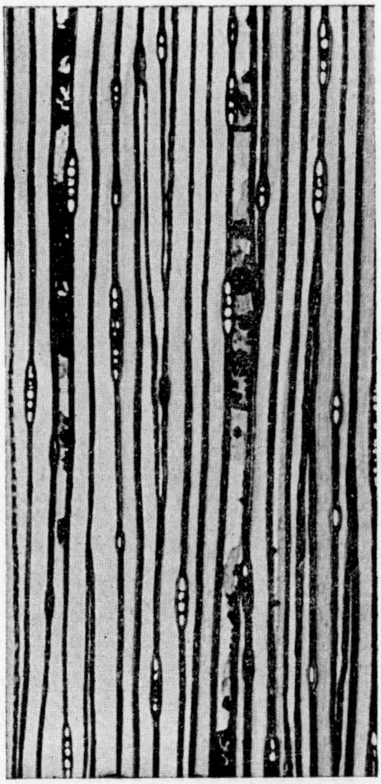

Fig. 178.—(t—75 ×)

Port Orford Cedar, Port Orford White Cedar, *Chamaecyparis lawsoniana* (A. Murr.) Parl.

wood tracheids; pits leading to ray parenchyma cupressoid, small, orbicular or nearly so, quite uniform in size, with distinct border and lenticular orifice, 1–4 per ray crossing. *Longitudinal parenchyma* metatracheal-diffuse or occasionally exhibiting more or less a tendency toward zonation; cells usually conspicuous on account of their gummy contents, solitary or 2–several contiguous in the tangential plane. *Rays* uniseriate or rarely with paired cells, low (1–6 plus cells and less than 300 microns in height), narrow (7–12 microns), consisting entirely of ray parenchyma or very rarely with ray tracheids; gummy infiltration fairly abundant in the ray cells in the heartwood.

Remarks.—Distinctive among North American coniferous woods because of its pungent, gingerlike odor. Comparable to Alaska yellow cedar [*Chamaecyparis nootkatensis* (Lamb.) Spach] but without the pronounced yellow cast that is a feature of this wood, with a different odor, with broader rings, somewhat coarser textured, and seldom with ray tracheids.

Uses.—*Storage-battery separators* (the principal wood for this purpose because of its electrical resistance and high resistance to the action of acids); *slats* for *Venetian blinds* (because of good working qualities, moderate shrinkage, lightness, ability to stay in place, and good paint-holding properties); *millwork* (sash, doors, interior finish); *lining* for *mothproof boxes* and *closets* (because of its reputed moth-repellent qualities; closets should be aired when new, as otherwise the volatile oil from the wood condenses on hardware, buttons, and glass); *woodenware* and *novelties; boat construction*, especially *decking; match blocks* for sulphur matches (because of its uniform texture, good machining properties, lightness, and ability to dry quickly after wetting); *general construction; tanks; planking; ties; mine timbers* (lower grades).

Selected References

BETTS, H. S.: Port Orford White-cedar—American Woods. Forest Service, U.S. Department of Agriculture. 1945.

SMITH, H. H.: Uses of Port Orford Cedar. *Hardwood Rec.*, Vol. 37, p. 4. 1913.

ALASKA YELLOW CEDAR, YELLOW CYPRESS

Chamaecyparis nootkatensis (Lamb.) Spach

Plate IV, Fig. 19; Plate XIX, Figs. 107 and 108; Plate XLVI, Figs. 179 and 180

General Characteristics and Properties.—*Sapwood* nearly white to yellowish white, very narrow; *heartwood* bright clear yellow, darkening upon exposure; *wood* with a characteristic odor which in some samples resembles that of raw potatoes, with a faint bitter, somewhat spicy taste, straight- and even-grained, fine- to medium-textured, moderately heavy (sp. gr. approx. 0.42 green, 0.46 ovendry), moderately hard, moderately strong in bending and endwise compression, moderately high in shock resistance, easy to work with tools, capable of high polish, takes glue readily, shrinks little, easy to kiln-dry, stays in place well after seasoning, rather low in nail-holding ability, very resistant to decay. *Growth rings* not visible or barely visible to the naked eye, generally plainly visible with a hand lens, delineated by a darker band of summerwood, narrow to very narrow (50–90 per inch), quite uniform in width. Springwood zone occupying most of the ring; transition from spring- to summerwood more or less abrupt; summerwood zone appreciably denser than the springwood, narrow, not conspicuously differentiated from the springwood through discrepancy in color. *Parenchyma* not distinct at low magnifications. *Rays* fine (x), appearing fine with a hand lens,

Plate XLVI

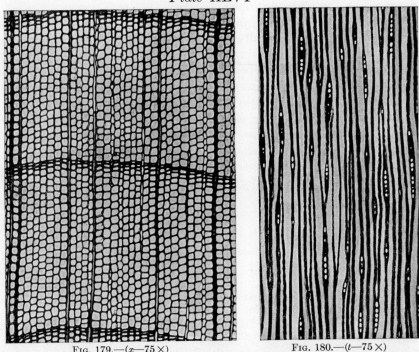

Fig. 179.—(x—75 ×) Fig. 180.—(t—75 ×)

Alaska Yellow Cedar, Yellow Cypress, *Chamaecyparis nootkatensis* (Lamb.) Spach.

forming a fine, low, inconspicuous fleck on the quarter surface. *Resin canals* wanting.

Minute Anatomy.—*Tracheids* up to 40 (av. 25–35) microns in diameter; bordered pits in one row or rarely paired on the radial walls; tangential pitting present on the last few rows of summerwood tracheids; pits leading to ray parenchyma cupressoid, small, orbicular or nearly so, quite uniform in size, with distinct border and lenticular orifice, 1–3 per ray crossing (Fig. 107, page 409). *Longitudinal parenchyma* sparse, or not infrequently wanting altogether, to abundant; cells metatracheal-diffuse, usually distinguishable on account of their gummy contents, solitary or 2–several contiguous in the tangential plane. *Rays* uniseriate or rarely with paired cells, 1–20 plus (the majority less than 12) cells in height; low rays with ray tracheids, these frequently constituting the entire ray (Fig. 108, page 409); ray tracheids (*r*) short and high (along the grain); gummy infiltration fairly abundant in some of the ray cells.

Remarks.—Comparable to Port Orford cedar [*Chamaecyparis lawsoniana* (A. Murr.) Parl.]; for distinguishing characters, see Remarks under this species, page 500. Not to be confused with yellow cypress produced by *Taxodium distichum* (L.) Rich.

Uses.—Locally for *poles, interior finish, furniture, cabinetwork, novelties, caskets,* and *hulls* of small boats; valuable for patterns (because of its good working qualities, low shrinkage, and ability to stay in place); *canoe paddles* (long preferred by the Alaska Indians); *oars; piling* and *marine buoys* (because of its resistance to marine borers); *greenhouse* and *conservatory* construction (because of its resistance to decay); *acid tanks* and *chemical containers* (because of its acid resistance); *sounding boards* of musical instruments (because of its uniform density, straightness and evenness of grain, low shrinkage, and ability to stay in place); *battery separators* [because of its electrical resistance and resistance to sulphuric acid (comparable to Port Orford cedar in these respects)]. A few logs are shipped to Japan where the wood is used in temple buildings and other important structures, because of its purported resistance to termite attack.

Selected References

BETTS, H. S.: Alaska Yellow-cedar—American Woods. Forest Service, U.S. Department of Agriculture. 1945.

MARKWARDT, L. J.: The Distribution and the Mechanical Properties of Alaska Woods. *U.S. Dept. Agr. Tech. Bul.* 266. 1931.

PERRY, R. S.: Yellow Cedar—Its Characteristics, Properties and Uses. Forest Products Laboratories of Canada, Vancouver Laboratory, Vancouver. 1938.

ATLANTIC WHITE CEDAR, SOUTHERN WHITE CEDAR

Chamaecyparis thyoides (L.) B.S.P.

Plate IV, Fig. 21; Plate XLVII, Figs. 181 and 182

General Characteristics and Properties.—*Sapwood* whitish, narrow; *heartwood* light brown tinged with red or pink (roseate); *wood* somewhat oily, with a characteristic cedary odor [distinct from that of northern white cedar (*Thuja occidentalis* L.)] and faint bitter taste, usually straight- and even-grained, fine-textured, light (sp. gr. 0.31 green, 0.35 ovendry), moderately soft, weak in bending, weak in endwise compression, low in shock resistance, splits easily, works readily under tools, finishes smooth, holds paint well, shrinks little, very resistant to decay. *Growth rings* distinct but not conspicuous, delineated by a darker band of summerwood, usually fairly wide. Springwood zone occupying most of the ring; transition from spring- to summerwood more or less gradual; summerwood zone somewhat denser than the springwood, narrow. *Parenchyma* fairly

Plate XLVII

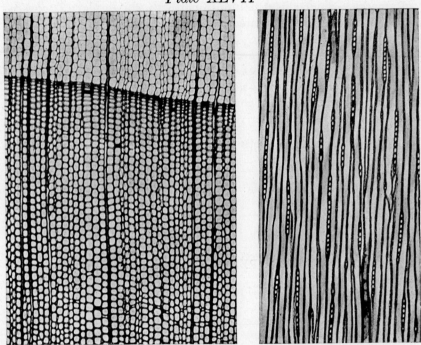

Fig. 181.—(x—75 ×)   Fig. 182.—(t—75 ×)
Atlantic White Cedar, Southern White Cedar, *Chamaecyparis thyoides* (L.) B.S.P.

abundant to abundant (present in every growth ring), metatracheal and metatracheal-diffuse, in the former instance appearing as darker concentric lines which are visible with a hand lens and not infrequently to the naked eye. *Rays* very fine (x), forming a fine, close, inconspicuous fleck on the quarter surface. *Resin canals* wanting.

Minute Anatomy.—*Tracheids* fine [up to 40 (av. 25–35) microns in diameter], without or with few intercellular spaces at the corners; bordered pits in one row or very rarely paired on the radial walls; tangential pitting present in the last few rows of summerwood tracheids; pits leading to ray parenchyma cupressoid, small, orbicular or nearly so, quite uniform in size, with distinct border and lenticular orifice, 1–4 per ray crossing. Cells of *longitudinal parenchyma* solitary and often scattered, or 2–several contiguous in the tangential plane (especially in the bands of zonate parenchyma), generally distinguishable in the transverse section by their contents. *Rays* uniseriate or rarely with paired cells, 1–12 plus cells and over 250 plus microns in height, consisting entirely of ray parenchyma or with an occasional ray tracheid; ray cells empty or with scanty infiltration.

Remarks.—Similar in structure to northern white cedar (*T. occidentalis* L.); for distinguishing characters see Remarks under Northern White Cedar, page 495.

Uses.—Principally for *poles, shingles, woodenware* (tubs and pails), and *lumber* (with many defects, particularly knots and wind shakes). Lumber used for *planing-mill* products (such as siding, porch lumber); *water tanks* (because of its lightness and durability); *boat construction; boxes* and *crates* (especially for vegetables and small fruits); *fencing.*

Selected References

Betts, H. S.: Atlantic White-cedar—American Woods.   Forest Service, U.S. Department of Agriculture.   1945.

Korstian, C. F., and W. D. Brush: Southern White Cedar.   *U.S. Dept. Agr. Tech. Bul.* 251.   1931.

RED CEDAR

Eastern Red Cedar, Tennessee Red Cedar (*Juniperus virginiana* L.), Plate III, Fig. 15; Plate XLVIII, Figs. 183 and 184

Southern Red Cedar [*Juniperus silicicola* (Small) Bailey]

General Characteristics and Properties.—Usually available only in small sizes and generally knotty; *sapwood* nearly white, thin; *heartwood* purplish or rose-red when first exposed, aging to dull red or reddish brown, sometimes with lighter streaks of included sapwood; *wood* with mild characteristic "pencil-cedar" odor and taste, straight- (except near knots) and even-grained, fine-textured, moderately heavy (sp. gr. approx. 0.44 green, 0.49 ovendry), hard, moderately weak in bending, moderately strong in endwise compression, high in shock resistance, works easily under tools, excellent for whittling, shrinks very little on drying, stays in place well after seasoning, very resistant to decay. *Growth rings* distinct, delineated by a band of darker summerwood, narrow to wide (a given ring often variable in width and the rings hence sinuate in contour), not infrequently eccentric; false rings occasioned by 2–3 bands of summerwood sometimes present. Springwood zone usually broad, occupying most of the ring; transition from spring- to summerwood gradual to rather abrupt; summerwood zone conspicuous, much darker than the springwood, narrow. *Parenchyma* very abundant, metatracheal, in 1–several (usually 1–2) dark bands which are visible with a hand lens and often to the naked eye (especially in the sapwood). *Rays* very fine

Plate XLVIII

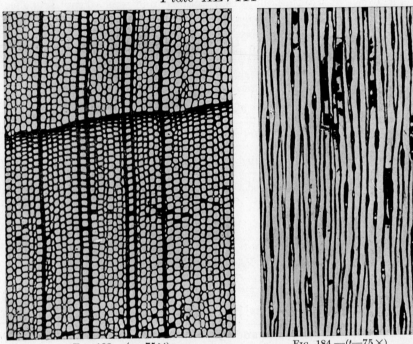

FIG. 183.—(*x*—75 ×)
FIG. 184.—(*t*—75 ×)
Eastern Red Cedar, Tennessee Red Cedar, *Juniperus virginiana* L.

(*x*), darker than the background and forming a fine, low fleck on the quarter surface. *Resin canals* wanting.

Minute Anatomy.—*Tracheids* fine [up to 35 (av. 20–30) microns in diameter], often with intercellular spaces at the corners (*x*); bordered pits in one row or very rarely paired on the radial walls; tangential pitting present in the last few rows of summerwood tracheids; pits leading to ray parenchyma cupressoid, small, orbicular or nearly so, quite uniform in size, with distinct border and lenticular orifice, 1–4 per ray crossing. Cells in the bands of *longitudinal parenchyma* solitary or 2–3 contiguous in the tangential plane, with dark gummy contents. *Rays* uniseriate, low (1–6 plus cells and less than 250 microns in height), consisting entirely of ray parenchyma; ray cells in the heartwood with copious deposits of dark gum.

Remarks.—Distinctive among North American coniferous woods because of the color of the heartwood. The two species producing this timber cannot be separated on the basis of wood structure.

Uses.—*Fence posts* (principal use from the standpoint of quantity). Lumber used for *chests, wardrobes,* and *closet linings* (because of its color, excellent working qualities, fragrance, and reputed moth-repellent properties); *millwork* (sash, doors, interior finish); *pencil slats* (formerly the most important use; today, because of the scarcity of suitable material, composing less than 10 per cent of the output); *woodenware* and *novelties; water buckets.*

Selected References

BANNAN, M. W.: Wood Structure of the Native Ontario Species of *Juniperus. Amer. Jour. Bot.,* Vol. 29, pp. 245–252. 1942.

BETTS, H. S.: Eastern Red Cedar—American Woods. Forest Service, U.S. Department of Agriculture. 1945.

MOHR, CHARLES: Notes on the Red Cedar. *U.S. Dept. Agr., Div. Forestry, Bul.* 31. 1901.

WHITE, L. L.: Production of Red Cedar for Pencil Wood. *U.S. Dept. Agr. Forest Serv. Cir.* 102. 1907.

PACIFIC YEW

Taxus brevifolia Nutt.

Plate V, Fig. 28; Plate XLIX, Figs. 185 and 186

General Characteristics and Properties.—*Sapwood* light yellow, thin; *heartwood* bright orange to rose-red; *wood* without characteristic odor or taste, even-grained, very fine-textured, heavy (sp. gr. approx. 0.60 green, 0.67 ovendry), very hard, very strong in bending and endwise compression, not stiff, very high in shock resistance, refractory under tools, finishes smoothly, very durable when exposed to conditions favorable to decay. *Growth rings* distinct, delineated by a band of darker summerwood, narrow to medium wide or broad. Springwood zone usually occupying about one-half of the ring; transition from spring- to summerwood very gradual; summerwood very dense. *Parenchyma* not visible. *Rays* very fine (x), not distinct to the naked eye, forming a fine, close, inconspicuous fleck on the quarter surface. Normal and wound (traumatic) *resin canals* wanting.

Minute Anatomy.—*Tracheids* fine [up to 25 (av. 15–20) microns in diameter], more or less rounded, featured by fine, close bands of spiral thickening; bordered pits in one row on the radial walls; tangential pitting present in the last few rows of summerwood tracheids; pits leading to ray parenchyma cupressoid, small, orbicular or nearly so, quite uniform in size, with distinct border and lenticular orifice, 1–4 (generally

Plate XLIX

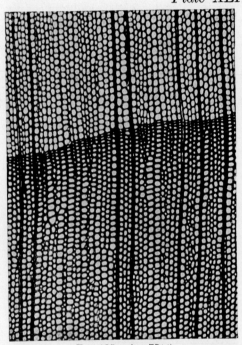 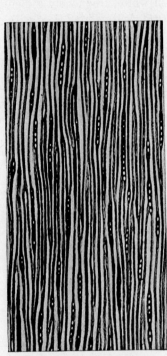

Fig. 185.—(*x*—75 ×) Fig. 186.—(*t*—75 ×)

Pacific Yew, *Taxus brevifolia* Nutt.

1–2) per ray crossing. *Longitudinal parenchyma* wanting. *Rays* uniseriate or very rarely with paired cells, 1–25 plus cells in height, consisting entirely of ray parenchyma.

Remarks.—Of limited commercial importance because of its scarcity and small size.

Uses.—*Poles, bows, canoe paddles, small turned articles,* and *carvings.*

CALIFORNIA NUTMEG AND STINKING CEDAR

California Nutmeg (*Torreya californica* Torr.), Plate V, Fig. 29; Plate L, Figs. 187 and 188   **Stinking Cedar** (*Torreya taxifolia* Arn.)

General Characteristics and Properties.—*Sapwood* whitish to yellowish white, frequently difficult to distinguish from the heartwood; *heartwood* clear yellow; *wood* with a characteristic odor (strong and unpleasant

Plate L

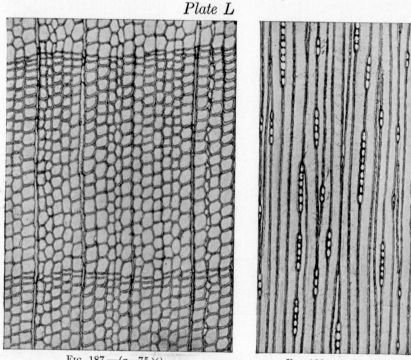

Fig. 187.—(x—75×)   Fig. 188.—(t—75×)

California Nutmeg, *Torreya californica* Torr.

in *T. taxifolia*), with a mild, characteristic, bitterish taste, even-grained, medium- to somewhat coarse-textured, moderately light to moderately heavy (av. sp. gr. approx. 0.48 green), soft to moderately hard. *Growth rings* fairly distinct but not prominent, delineated by a band of darker summerwood. Springwood occupying most of the ring; transition from spring- to summerwood very gradual; summerwood dense. *Parenchyma* not visible. *Rays* very fine (x), not distinct to the naked eye, forming a fine, close, inconspicuous fleck on the quarter surface. Normal and wound (traumatic) *resin canals* wanting.

Minute Anatomy.—*Tracheids* fine [up to 55 (av. 25–35) microns in diameter], featured by fine, widely spaced bands of spiral thickening; bordered pits in 1–2 rows on the radial walls; tangential pitting sparse, usually confined to the summerwood tracheids; pits leading to ray parenchyma cupressoid, small, orbicular or nearly so, 2–7 (generally 2–4) per ray crossing. *Longitudinal parenchyma* wanting. *Rays* uniseriate, 1–12 plus cells in height, consisting entirely of ray parenchyma.

Uses.—Of no commercial importance; used locally for *fence posts, cabinets, models, novelties,* and *patterns.*

BUTTERNUT, WHITE WALNUT

Juglans cinerea L.

Plate VI, Fig. 36; Plate LI, Figs. 189 and 190

General Characteristics and Properties.—*Sapwood* white to light grayish brown, rarely more than 1 inch wide; *heartwood* light chestnut-brown, frequently variegated with pigment figure, lustrous; *wood* without characteristic odor or taste, straight-grained, moderately light (sp. gr. approx. 0.36 green, 0.46 ovendry), moderately soft, moderately weak in bending and endwise compression, moderately high in shock resistance, works well, takes stain well, can be finished to resemble black walnut (*J. nigra* L.), shrinks moderately, not very durable. *Growth rings* distinct, delineated through an abrupt difference in size between the pores of the late summerwood and those in the springwood of the succeeding ring. *Pores* scattered (never approximating half the area between the rays), those in the springwood readily visible to the naked eye, decreasing gradually in size toward the outer margin of the ring (wood semi-ring porous), solitary and in multiples of 2–several; tyloses fairly abundant. *Parenchyma* visible with a hand lens (especially in the outer portion of the ring), arranged in fine, numerous, more or less continuous, tangential lines. *Rays* fine, indistinct without a hand lens.

Minute Anatomy.—*Vessels* 6–12 per square millimeter, the largest 160–260 microns in diameter; perforation plates simple; intervessel pits orbicular to oval or angular through crowding, large (10–16 microns in diameter). *Parenchyma* metatracheal and metatracheal-diffuse, non-crystalliferous; lines of zonate parenchyma mostly uniseriate. *Fibers* thin-walled, 20–45 microns in diameter. *Rays* unstoried, 1–4-seriate, homogeneous to heterogeneous.

Uses.—*Furniture; cabinetwork; instrument cases; boxes* and *crates; millwork* (such as interior trim, sash, and doors); *woodenware, toys,* and *novelties.*

Plate LI

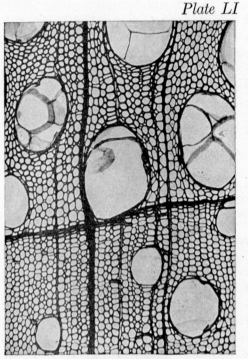 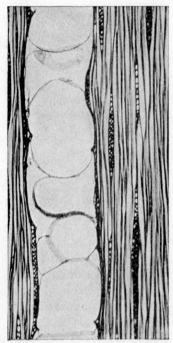

Fig. 189.—(x—75×)   Fig. 190.—(t—75×)
Butternut, White Walnut, *Juglans cinerea* L.

Selected References

Betts, H. S.: Butternut—American Woods. Forest Service, U.S. Department of Agriculture. 1945.

Heimsch, C., and R. H. Wetmore: The Significance of Wood Anatomy in the Taxonomy of the Juglandaceae. *Amer. Jour. Bot.,* Vol. 26, pp. 651–660. 1939.

BLACK WALNUT, EASTERN BLACK WALNUT

Juglans nigra L.

Plate VI, Fig. 35; Plate LII, Figs. 191 and 192

General Characteristics and Properties.—*Sapwood* whitish to yellowish brown (in the trade commonly darkened by steaming or staining to match the heartwood); *heartwood* light brown to rich chocolate- or purplish brown (the lighter shades from trees grown in the open), dull; *wood* with mild characteristic odor when worked, tasteless, straight- or irregular-grained (the wavy, curly, and mottled figures for which this wood is famous are obtained from burls, crotches, and stumpwood; quartersawn wood frequently shows alternate stripes due to uneven pigmentation), heavy (sp. gr. approx. 0.51 green, 0.56 ovendry), hard, strong in bending, very strong in endwise compression, stiff, high in shock resistance, works

Plate LII

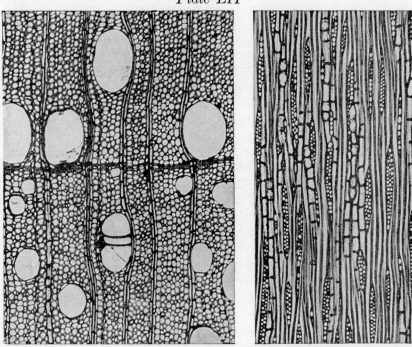

Fig. 191.—(*x*—75 ✕)   Fig. 192.—(*t*—75 ✕)
Black Walnut, Eastern Black Walnut, *Juglans nigra* L.

easily with tools, finishes very smoothly, takes and holds stains well, glues readily, shrinks moderately, stays in place well after seasoning, very durable under conditions favorable to decay. *Growth rings* distinct, delineated through an abrupt difference in size between the pores of the late summerwood and those in the springwood of the succeeding ring. *Pores* scattered (never approximating half the area between the rays), those in the springwood readily visible to the naked eye, decreasing gradually in size toward the outer margin of the ring (wood semi-ring porous), solitary and in multiples of 2–several; tyloses fairly abundant. *Parenchyma* barely visible with a hand lens, arranged in fine, numerous, continuous, or broken tangential lines. *Rays* fine, indistinct without a hand lens.

Minute Anatomy.—*Vessels* 4–13 per square millimeter, the largest 180–260 microns in diameter; perforation plates simple; intervessel pits orbicular to oval or angular through crowding, large (10–16 microns in diameter). *Parenchyma* metatracheal and metatracheal-diffuse, frequently crystalliferous; lines of zonate parenchyma mostly uniseriate. *Fibers* thin- to moderately thick-walled, 16–32 microns in diameter. *Rays* 1–5-seriate, homogeneous to heterogeneous.

Remarks.—Unique among the woods of the United States in the color of its heartwood, and hence easily identified. Unquestionably our finest domestic cabinet wood.   The Claro walnut of the trade is obtained from *Juglans hindsi* Jepson, a tree native to California; the heartwood is tan-brown, with prominent dark stripes and spots.

Uses.—*Veneer* (largely sliced, rotary-cut to a limited extent), used extensively for plywood faces in the manufacture of furniture, in cabinet-work, and in interior paneling; *gunstocks* (leading wood because of sufficient strength, shock resistance, and hardness, ability to stay in place, and good machining and finishing properties combined with sufficient coarseness of texture to permit of a good grip on the gun); low-grade stock used locally for *railway ties, fence posts* (formerly for fence rails), *fuel wood*.   Lumber used principally for *furniture*, especially for dining-room tables (because of its ability to stand hard usage), chairs, bedroom, and living-room suites, and, more recently, office furniture; *fixtures; caskets* and *coffins* (because of good working qualities and pleasing appearance, combined with durability); *radio* and *phonograph cabinets; piano cases; millwork* (such as doors, sash, frames, and interior finish); *sewing machines; woodenware* and *novelties.*

Selected References

BETTS, H. S.: Black Walnut—American Woods.   Forest Service, U.S. Department of Agriculture.   1945.

BRUSH, W. D.: Utilization of Black Walnut.   *U.S. Dept. Agr. Bul.* 909.   1921.

———: Selling Black Walnut Timber.   *U.S. Dept. Agr. Farmers' Bul.* 1459.   1933 (revised).

GREEN, BURDETT, and B. C. JAKWAY: The Story of American Walnut, 8th ed., American Walnut Manufacturers Association, Chicago.   1936.

HEIMSCH, C., and R. H. WETMORE: The Significance of Wood Anatomy in the Taxonomy of the Juglandaceae.   *Amer. Jour. Bot.*, Vol. 26, pp. 651–660.   1939.

MATTOON, W. R., and C. A. REED: Black Walnut for Timber and Nuts.   *U.S. Dept. Agr. Farmers' Bul.* 1392.   1933 (revised).

NEUBRECH, W. LeRoy: American Hardwoods and Their Uses.   *Trade Prom. Ser.,* No. 178, Bureau of Foreign and Domestic Commerce, U.S. Department of Commerce.   1938.

PAUL, B. H.: Black Walnut for Gunstocks.   *South. Lumberman,* Vol. 166(2089), pp. 32–36.   1943.

HICKORY

True Hickories

Shagbark Hickory [*Carya ovata* (Mill.) K. Koch], Plate IX, Fig. 52; Plate XX, Fig. 111; Plate LIII, Figs. 195 and 196

Bigleaf Shagbark Hickory [*Carya laciniosa* (Michx. f.) Loud.]

Pignut Hickory [*Carya glabra* (Mill.) Sweet], Plate IX, Fig. 51

Oval Pignut Hickory, Red Hickory [*Carya ovalis* (Wangenh.) Sudw.]

Mockernut Hickory [*Carya tomentosa* (Poir.) Nutt.], Plate LIII, Figs. 193 and 194

Pecan Hickories

Bitternut Hickory [*Carya cordiformis* (Wangenh.) K. Koch] Plate VII, Fig. 38; Plate LIV, Figs. 197 and 198

Pecan [*Carya illinoënsis* (Wangenh.) K. Koch], Plate LIV, Figs. 199 and 200

Nutmeg Hickory [*Carya myristicaeformis* (Michx. f.) Nutt.]

Water Hickory [*Carya aquatica* (Michx. f.) Nutt.]

General Characteristics and Properties.—*Sapwood* whitish to pale brown; *heartwood* pale brown to brown, or reddish brown (heartwood of pecan rich reddish brown, sometimes containing streaks of a slightly darker hue); *wood* without characteristic odor or taste, straight-grained, heavy to very heavy (sp. gr. 0.56–0.66 green, 0.62–0.78 ovendry), very hard, strong to exceedingly strong in bending and endwise compression, high to exceedingly high in shock resistance (although there is a prejudice against "red" hickory, this is unfounded; tests have shown conclusively that at the same moisture content, the strength of the wood varies directly with its density, irrespective of color due to heartwood), machines satisfactorily, finishes well, below average in gluing properties, splits readily in nailing but has a good nail-holding capacity, shrinks appreciably, low in ability to stay in place, subject to attack by boring insects, not durable when exposed to conditions favoring decay. *Growth rings* distinct (wood ring porous or semi-ring porous). *Springwood pores* large, visible to the naked eye; transition from spring- to summerwood abrupt (true hickories) or more or less gradual (pecan hickories); *summerwood pores* small, visible with a hand lens, solitary and in multiples of 2–3. *Parenchyma* conspicuous with a hand lens, in fine, continuous, tangential lines which are arranged irrespective of the pores. *Rays* indistinct without a hand lens.

Minute Anatomy.—*Vessels* 2–11 per square millimeter; largest springwood vessels 160–320 microns in diameter; perforation plates simple; intervessel pits orbicular to oval or angular through crowding (Fig. 111, page 415), 6–8 microns in diameter. *Parenchyma* metatracheal, metatracheal-diffuse, and terminal; lines of zonate parenchyma 1–4-seriate. *Fibers* thin- to thick-walled, frequently gelatinous, 12–20 microns in diameter. *Rays* 1–5-seriate, homogeneous to heterogeneous.

Plate LIII

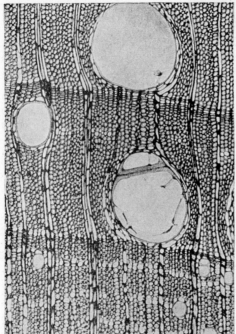

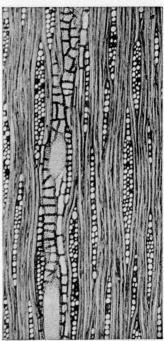

FIG. 193.—(x—75 ×)   FIG. 194.—(t—75 ×)
Mockernut Hickory, *Carya tomentosa* (Poir.) Nutt.

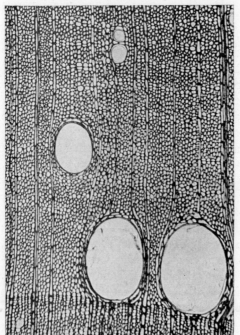

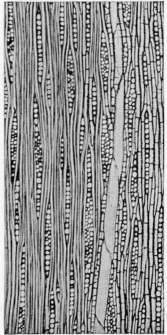

FIG. 195.—(x—75 ×)   FIG. 196.—(t—75 ×)
Shagbark Hickory, *Carya ovata* (Mill.) K. Koch

Plate LIV

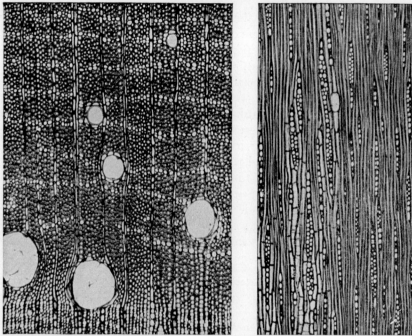

FIG. 197.—(x—75 ×)   FIG. 198.—(t—75 ×)
Bitternut Hickory, *Carya cordiformis* (Wangenh.) K. Koch

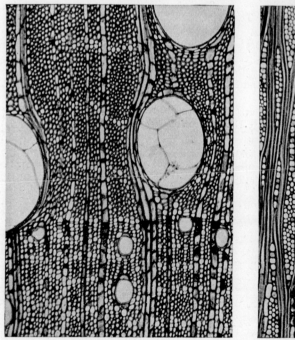
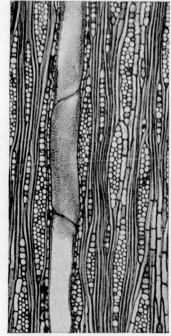

FIG. 199.—(x—75 ×)   FIG. 200.—(t—75 ×)
Pecan, *Carya illinoënsis* (Wangenh.) K. Koch

Remarks.—The woods of the pecan hickories differ from those of the true hickories in possessing less clearly defined annual rings owing to the tendency of the springwood pores to grade into those of the summerwood (wood semi-ring porous).[1]

Uses.—*Tool handles* (especially for "impact" tools such as hammers, axes, picks, and sledges) for which use hickory is unsurpassed because of its inherent qualities of hardness, strength, toughness, and resiliency; *motor* and other *vehicles* (in recent years, the use of wire spokes and disk wheels has resulted in the virtual elimination of wooden spokes for which quantities of this wood were utilized); *ladders; furniture; sporting goods* (such as skis, gymnastic bars, golf-club shafts); *agricultural implements; flooring* (only pecan); *woodenware* and *novelties; special products* requiring a strong, tough, elastic wood (such as sucker rods—long straight-grained strips used in boring wells, picker sticks in cotton and silk mills, dowel pins, skewers); for *smoking meats; fuel wood* because of its high caloric value.

Selected References

ANON.: The Southern Hardwoods.   Southern Hardwood Producers, Inc., Memphis, Tenn.   1941.

BETTS, H. S.: Hickory—American Woods.   Forest Service, U.S. Department of Agriculture.   1945.

————: Pecan—American Woods.   Forest Service, U.S. Department of Agriculture. 1945.

BOISEN, A. T., and J. A. NEWLIN: The Commercial Hickories.   *U.S. Forest Serv. Bul.* 80.   1920.

HATCH, CHARLES F.: Manufacture and Utilization of Hickory.   *U.S. Forest Serv. Cir.* 187.   1911.

NEUBRECH, W. LeRoy: American Hardwoods and Their Uses.   *Trade Prom. Ser.*, No. 178, Bureau of Foreign and Domestic Commerce, U.S. Department of Commerce.   1938.

————: American Hickory Handles.   *Trade Prom. Ser.*, No. 203, Bureau of Foreign and Domestic Commerce, U.S. Department of Commerce.   1939.

---

[1] Some progress has been made of late in the separation of the woods of *Carya spp.* by color reactions.   For further information, see I. H. Isenberg, and M. A. Buchanan. A Color Reaction of Wood with Methanol-hydrochloric Acid.   *Jour. Forestry*, Vol. 43, pp. 888–890.   1945.

COTTONWOOD

Eastern Cottonwood, Eastern Poplar
(*Populus deltoides* Bartr.), Plate VII,
Fig. 41; Plate XXI, Fig. 123; Plate LV,
Figs. 201 and 202
Balsam Poplar, Tacamahac Poplar
(*Populus tacamahaca* Mill.)

Swamp Cottonwood, Swamp Poplar
(*Populus heterophylla* L.)
Northern Black Cottonwood (*Populus
trichocarpa* var. *hastata* Henry), Plate
LV, Figs. 203 and 204
Etc.

General Characteristics and Properties.—*Sapwood* whitish, frequently merging into the heartwood and hence not clearly defined, thin or thick; *heartwood* grayish white to light grayish brown (sometimes dull brown in *P. heterophylla* L.); *wood* odorless or with a characteristic disagreeable odor when moist, without characteristic taste, usually straight-grained, medium light to light (sp. gr. 0.32–0.37 green, 0.37–0.43 ovendry), moderately soft to soft, moderately weak in bending, weak in endwise compression, low in shock resistance, easy to moderately hard to work with tools (inclined to produce chipped and fuzzy grain), easy to glue, takes paint moderately well, low in nail-holding ability but excellent in resistance to splitting, has tendency to warp in seasoning, shrinks considerably, below average in ability to stay in place, very low in durability. *Growth rings* distinct but inconspicuous, narrow to very wide. *Pores* numerous, small, the largest barely visible to the naked eye in the springwood, more crowded in the early springwood, decreasing gradually in size through the summerwood (wood semi-ring to diffuse-porous), solitary and in multiples of 2–several. *Parenchyma* terminal, the narrow, light-colored line more or less distinct. *Rays* very fine, scarcely visible with a hand lens.

Minute Anatomy.—*Vessels* 30–145 per square millimeter, the largest 75–150 microns in diameter; perforation plates simple; intervessel pits orbicular to oval or angular through crowding (Fig. 123, page 423), large (9–13 microns in diameter). *Parenchyma* terminal, forming a narrow, continuous or interrupted line. *Fibers* thin- to medium thick-walled, occasionally gelatinous, 23–40 microns in diameter. *Rays* unstoried, uniseriate, essentially homogeneous; pits leading to vessels confined to the marginal cells or occurring in occasional rows in the body of the ray as well.

Remarks.—The heartwood of *Populus heterophylla* L. is somewhat darker than that of the other species. The aspens are similar in structure to the cottonwoods but finer textured. For differences between the woods of *Salix* and *Populus*, see Remarks under Willow, page 522.

Uses.—*Pulp* (manufactured by the soda process) for high-grade book and magazine paper; *excelsior* (the aspens and cottonwoods are the principal excelsior woods for which purpose they are especially well

Plate LV

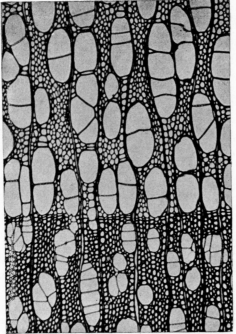

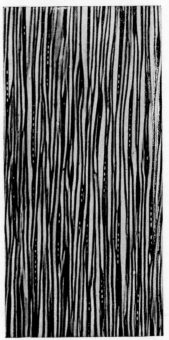

Fig. 201.—(x—75 ×)

Fig. 202.—(t—75 ×)

Eastern Cottonwood, Eastern Poplars, *Populus deltoides* Bartr.

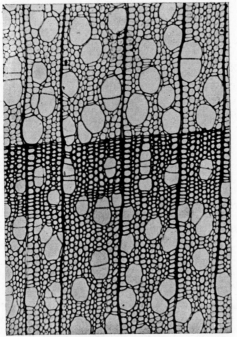

Fig. 203.—(x—75 ×)

Fig. 204.—(t—75 ×)

Northern Black Cottonwood, *Populus trichocarpa* var. *hastata* Henry

suited because of freedom from staining materials, light color, light weight, and uniformity of texture and straightness of grain which permit of easy shredding into soft but strong and resilient strands); *veneer* for the manufacture of plywood for furniture (mostly as core and cross-bending stock), musical instruments, containers (such as berry boxes). Lumber (it is estimated that 85 per cent of the lumber classified as "cottonwood" is cottonwood and balsam poplar, and the remainder aspen) used for *boxes* and *crates* (about two-thirds to three-fourths of all "cottonwood" lumber) for which it is especially well suited because of light weight, ease of nailing without splitting, and good color for stenciling; *furniture* (concealed parts); *dairy, poultry,* and *apiary supplies* (especially poultry coops and brooders); *laundry appliances* (such as ironing and washboards); *tubs* and *pails* for butter, lard, jelly, and other food products.

Selected References

ANON.: The Southern Hardwoods. Southern Hardwood Producers, Inc., Memphis, Tenn. 1941.

BETTS, H. S.: Cottonwood—American Woods. Forest Service, U.S. Department of Agriculture. 1945.

————: Balsam Poplar—American Woods. Forest Service, U.S. Department of Agriculture. 1945.

NEUBRECH, W. LEROY: American Hardwoods and Their Uses. *Trade Prom. Ser.,* No. 178, Bureau of Foreign and Domestic Commerce, U.S. Department of Commerce. 1938.

ASPEN

Quaking Aspen, Trembling Aspen (*Populus tremuloides* Michx.), Plate XIII, Fig. 74

Bigtooth Aspen (*Populus grandidentata* Michx.), Plate VII, Fig. 42; Plate LVI, Figs. 205 and 206

General Characteristics and Properties.—*Sapwood* whitish to creamy colored, generally merging gradually into heartwood and hence not clearly defined, wide; *heartwood* whitish, creamy to light grayish brown; *wood* with a characteristic disagreeable odor when wet, odorless when dry, without characteristic taste, with a pronounced silky luster, usually straight-grained, medium light (sp. gr. approx. 0.36 green, 0.40 ovendry), soft, moderately weak in bending and endwise compression, moderately low to moderately high in shock resistance, low in stiffness, moderately hard to work with tools (inclined to produce chipped and fuzzy grain), easy to glue, takes enamel and paints satisfactorily, low in nail-holding ability but does not split in nailing, has tendency to warp in seasoning, but can be satisfactorily kiln-dried if proper methods are used, shrinks considerably, very low in durability. *Growth rings* distinct because of darker summerwood but not conspicuous, wide. Pores numerous, small, not visible without a hand lens, more crowded in the early springwood, decreasing gradually in size through the summerwood, solitary or in multiples of 2–several. *Parenchyma* terminal, indistinct. *Rays* very fine, scarcely visible with a hand lens.

Plate LVI

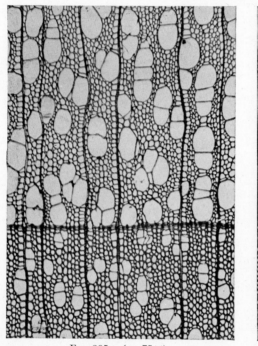 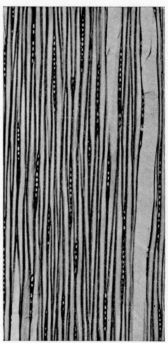

Fig. 205.—(x—75 ×)   Fig. 206.—(t—75 ×)
Bigtooth Aspen, *Populus grandidentata* Michx.

Minute Anatomy.—Vessels 85–180 per square millimeter, the largest 50–100 microns in diameter; perforation plates simple; intervessel pits orbicular to oval or angular through crowding, large (8–12 microns in diameter). *Parenchyma* terminal, forming a narrow, continuous, or interrupted line. *Fibers* thin- to medium thick-walled, occasionally gelatinous, 23–33 microns in diameter. *Rays* unstoried, uniseriate, essentially homogeneous; pits leading to vessels confined to the marginal cells or occurring in occasional rows in the body of the ray as well.

Remarks.—The woods of the two aspens are quite similar in appearance and properties and cannot be separated from each other. The woods of the cottonwoods are also quite similar to aspen, but coarser in texture, somewhat darker in color (never creamy) and devoid of luster.

Uses.—*Pulp* (manufactured by the soda process for high-grade book and magazine paper, or in admixture with spruce and balsam for sulphite pulp); *excelsior* (the aspen and cottonwoods are the principal excelsior woods) for which purpose they are especially well suited because of freedom from staining materials, light color, light weight, and uniformity of texture and straightness of grain which permit of easy shredding into soft but strong and resilient strands; logs are used for *cabin construction* and, when kept away from the ground, give satisfactory service; *matches* (veneer-cut by the rotary method). Lumber used for *boxes* and *crates; core stock* in plywood panels; *laundry appliances; dairy, poultry,* and *apiary* supplies; *tubs* and *pails* for food products; *clothespins; rough construction* (locally).

Selected References

ANON.: Canadian Aspen. *Wood Inform. Ser.,* Trade Commission for Eastern Canada (London). 1939.

BAKER, F. S.: ASPEN in the Central Rocky Mountain Region. *U.S. Dept. Agr. Bul.* 1291. 1925.

BETTS, H. S.: Aspen—American Woods. Forest Service, U.S. Department of Agriculture. 1945.

JOHNSON, R. P. A., JOSEPH KITTREDGE, and HENRY SCHMITZ: Aspen, Availability, Properties and Utilization. *Minn. Univ., Agr. Expt. Sta. Tech. Bul.* 70. 1930.

Lake States Forest Experiment Station: Aspen Reports 1–21, Forest Service, U.S. Department of Agriculture, 1947.

MEINECKE, E. P.: Quaking Aspen, A Study in Applied Pathology. *U.S. Dept. Agr. Tech. Bul.* 155. 1929.

WILLOW, BLACK WILLOW

Salix nigra Marsh., etc.

Plate VIII, Fig. 43; Plate LVII, Figs. 207 and 208

General Characteristics and Properties.—*Sapwood* whitish, thin or thick; *heartwood* light brown to pale reddish or grayish brown, frequently with darker streaks along the grain; *wood* without characteristic odor or taste, usually straight-grained, moderately light to light (sp. gr. approx. 0.34 green, 0.41 ovendry), moderately soft, very weak in bending, exceedingly weak in endwise compression, moderately high in shock resistance, works well with tools, glues well, low in nail-holding ability but does not split readily, stains and finishes well, shrinks considerably, very low in durability. *Growth rings* inconspicuous, narrow to wide. *Pores* numerous, small, the largest barely visible to the naked eye in the springwood, decreasing gradually in size through the summerwood (wood semi-ring to diffuse-porous), solitary and in multiples of 2–several. *Parenchyma* terminal, generally not visible at low magnifications. *Rays* very fine, scarcely visible with a hand lens.

Minute Anatomy.—*Vessels* 30–120 per square millimeter, the largest 90–160 microns in diameter; perforation plates simple; intervessel pits

Plate LVII

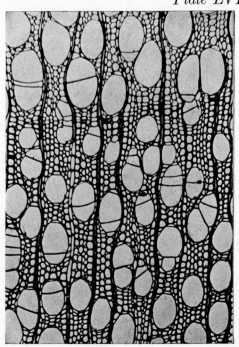 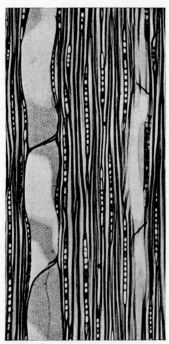

Fig. 207.—(*x*—75 ×) Fig. 208.—(*t*—75 ×)
Willow, Black Willow, *Salix nigra* Marsh.

orbicular to oval or angular through crowding, large (6–10 microns in diameter). *Parenchyma* terminal, forming a narrow, continuous or interrupted, 1–2 seriate line. *Fibers* thin- to moderately thick-walled, 16–32 microns in diameter. *Rays* unstoried, uniseriate, heterogeneous; upright cells in 1–several (mostly 1) marginal rows and not infrequently also in the body of the ray; pits leading to vessels restricted to the upright cells, fairly numerous and forming a more or less reticulate pattern.

Remarks.—The woods of *Salix* and *Populus* are very similar but can usually be separated through color; the willows exhibit a decided brown or reddish-brown cast in contrast to the grayish-white or light grayish-brown shades that characterize *Populus spp.* Accurate identification as to genus is assured by the fact that the rays are always heterogeneous in *Salix* and essentially homogeneous in *Populus*.

Uses.—*Artificial limbs* (because of its light weight, ability to dent without splintering and to hold its shape when dry); *boxes* and *crates; furniture* (core stock, turned pieces, table tops); *slack cooperage; woodenware* and *novelties;* frequently sold in admixture with, and used for the same purposes as, cottonwood lumber (see page 517); *charcoal,* resulting from destructive distillation is especially suitable for black powder manufacture.

Selected References

ANON.: The Southern Hardwoods. Southern Hardwood Producers, Inc., Memphis, Tenn. 1941.

BETTS, H. S.: Black Willow—American Woods. Forest Service, U.S. Department of Agriculture. 1945.

LAMB, G. N.: Willows: Their Growth, Use and Importance. *U.S. Dept. Agr. Bul.* 316 1915.

BLUE-BEECH, AMERICAN HORNBEAM

Carpinus caroliniana Walt.

Plate XII, Fig. 68; Plate XX, Fig. 116; Plate LVIII, Figs. 209 and 210

General Characteristics and Properties.—*Sapwood* nearly white, thick; *heartwood* pale yellowish or brownish white; *wood* without characteristic odor or taste, heavy (sp. gr. approx. 0.58 green, 0.72 ovendry), hard, moderately strong in bending, moderately weak in endwise compression, exceedingly high in shock resistance, shrinks considerably. *Growth rings* usually distinct (wood diffuse porous), delineated by a narrow, whitish band at the outer margin, sinuate (trunk of tree fluted). *Pores* small, indistinct without a hand lens, arranged for the most part in multiples of 2–several which are usually further aggregated into radial strings. *Parenchyma* distinct or indistinct with a hand lens, when visible appearing as fine light-colored lines spanning the intervals between the rays. *Rays* of two types, broad (aggregate) and narrow (simple); (*a*) aggregate rays visible to the naked eye (*x*), numerous, more or less irregularly distributed, separated by several–many narrow rays; (*b*) narrow rays indistinct without a hand lens.

Minute Anatomy.—*Vessels* 50–70 per square millimeter, the largest 60–100 microns in diameter; perforation plates simple or rarely scalariform with 3–6 thick bars; spiral thickening present; intervessel pits orbicular to oval or angular through crowding (Fig. 116, page 415), large (6–10 microns in diameter). *Parenchyma* metatracheal, metatracheal-diffuse, and terminal; metatracheal parenchyma very abundant, the lines uniseriate; metatracheal-diffuse and terminal parenchyma relatively

Plate LVIII

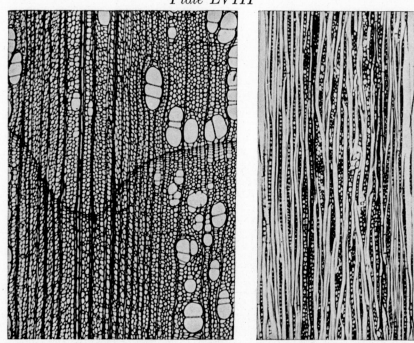

Fig. 209.—(*x*—75 ×)   Fig. 210.—(*t*—75 ×)
Blue-Beech, American Hornbeam, *Carpinus caroliniana* Walt.

sparse. *Fibers* thin- to moderately thick-walled, 12–20 microns in diameter. Narrow *rays* 1–4 (mostly 1–2)-seriate, homogeneous to heterogeneous; aggregate rays consisting (1) of units similar to the narrow rays and (2) of included fibers and vessels.

Uses.—Locally for *handles; vehicle parts; fuel wood.*

HOP-HORNBEAM

Ostrya virginiana (Mill.) K. Koch

Plate XII, Fig. 71; Plate LIX, Figs. 211 and 212

General Characteristics and Properties.—*Sapwood* whitish, wide; *heartwood* whitish to light brown tinged with red; *wood* without character-

Plate LIX

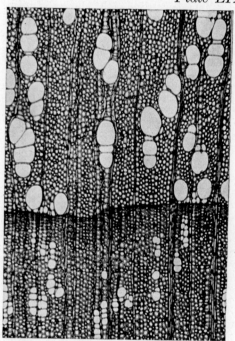 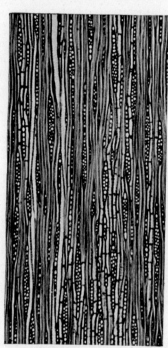

Fig. 211.—(*x*—75 ×)   Fig. 212.—(*t*—75 ×)

Hop-Hornbeam, *Ostrya virginiana* (Mill.) K. Koch.

istic odor or taste, very heavy (sp. gr. approx. 0.63 green, 0.76 ovendry), very hard, strong in bending and endwise compression, stiff, very high in shock resistance, shrinks considerably. *Growth rings* inconspicuous (wood diffuse porous), with ragged (erose) contours, the late summerwood often specked with white. *Pores* small, indistinct or barely visible to the naked eye, solitary and in multiples of 2–several which are more or less unevenly distributed throughout the growth ring and are often further aggregated into flamelike groups. *Zonate parenchyma* generally visible with a lens in the outer portion of the ring. *Rays* fine, indistinct to the naked eye, close and often seemingly occupying half of the area on the transverse surface of the wood.

Minute Anatomy.—*Vessels* 60–150 per square millimeter, the largest 60–160 microns in diameter; perforation plates simple or rarely scalariform with 3–6 bars, spiral thickening present; intervessel pits orbicular to oval or angular through crowding, large (6–10 microns in diameter). *Parenchyma* metatracheal-diffuse, metatracheal, and terminal; lines of zonate parenchyma more evident in the outer portion of the ring, uniseriate; terminal parenchyma sparse. *Fibers* medium thick-walled, 12–20 microns in diameter. *Rays* unstoried, 1–3-seriate, homogeneous to heterogeneous, the tallest less than 1000 microns in height along the grain.

Remarks.—Sometimes confused with birch from which it differs in possessing ragged growth rings which are often specked with white near the outer margin, vessels which exhibit more or less a tendency toward aggregation into flamelike groups, vessel segments with simple perforations and spiral thickening, and zonate parenchyma in the outer portion of the ring.

Uses.—Locally for *furniture; vehicles* (such parts as axles); *handles; levers; mallets; canes; woodenware* and *novelties; fuel wood.*

BIRCH

Yellow Birch (*Betula lutea* Michx. f.), Plate XIII, Fig. 78; Plate XIV, Fig. 79; Plate XXII, Fig. 126; Plate LX, Figs. 215 and 216

Sweet Birch, Black Birch, Cherry Birch (*Betula lenta* L.), Plate XIV, Fig. 80; Plate LX, Figs. 213 and 214

River Birch, Red Birch (*Betula nigra* L.), Plate LXI, Figs. 217 and 218

Paper Birch, White Birch (*Betula papyrifera* Marsh.), Plate XIV, Fig. 81; Plate LXI, Figs. 219 and 220

Gray Birch (*Betula populifolia* Marsh.)

General Characteristics and Properties.—*Sapwood* whitish, pale yellow, or light reddish brown; *heartwood* light to dark brown or reddish brown; *wood* without characteristic odor or taste, straight-grained, moderately heavy to very heavy (sp. gr. 0.45–0.60 green, 0.55–0.71 ovendry), moderately hard to hard, moderately strong to very strong in bending, moderately weak to strong in endwise compression, high to very high in shock resistance (of the three commercially important species, the wood of paper birch is the lightest and weakest,[1] yellow birch occupies the intermediate position, and black birch is the heaviest and strongest), turns well (especially paper birch), capable of finishing very smoothly, average in gluing, has tendency to split but possesses good nail-holding capacity, shrinks considerably but holds its shape moderately well, moderately durable to nondurable when in contact with the ground.

---

[1] Paper birch is subject to a defect known as "red heart," which affects 15 to 30 per cent of the trees in mature stands.

Growth rings frequently not very distinct without a lens (wood diffuse porous), delineated by a fine line of denser fibrous tissue at the outer margin and usually by smaller pores in the summerwood portion of the ring. *Pores* appearing as whitish dots to the naked eye, the larger obviously wider than the widest rays, nearly uniform in size and evenly distributed throughout the growth ring, solitary and in multiples of 2–several. *Parenchyma* not visible. *Rays* fine, generally not distinct to the naked eye but plainly visible with a hand lens, narrower than the largest pores.

Minute Anatomy.—*Vessels* 50–100 per square millimeter, the largest 60–160 microns in diameter; perforation plates scalariform; intervessel pits orbicular to broad-oval or angular through crowding (Fig. 126, page 429), minute (2–4 microns in diameter), the orifices frequently confluent. *Parenchyma* metatracheal-diffuse, paratracheal, and terminal. *Fibers* thin- to moderately thick-walled, 20–36 microns in diameter. *Rays* unstoried, 1–5-seriate, homogeneous.

Remarks.—The woods of the different species of *Betula* cannot be separated with certainty on the basis of either gross structure or minute anatomy; black birch and yellow birch are harder, heavier, and stronger than the other native species.

Uses.—*Veneer* (the largest and the best logs of yellow and black birch); *hardwood distillation; cooperage* (slack); *railroad ties.* Lumber used for *furniture,* (one of the principal furniture woods of the United States, for which purpose its good working and finishing qualities, hardness, pleasing figure, and attractive color recommend it very highly); *radio* and *phonograph cabinets; boxes, baskets,* and *crates; woodenware* and *novelties; toys; planing-mill products* (especially interior trim, flooring, sash, and doors); *shuttles, spools, bobbins,* and a variety of other turned articles; *butcher blocks; agricultural implements; refrigerators; musical* and *scientific instruments; toothpicks* and *shoe pegs* (paper birch).

Selected References

BETTS, H. S.: Birch—American Woods. Forest Service, U.S. Department of Agriculture. 1945.

DANA, S. T.: Paper Birch in the Northeast. *U.S. Dept. Agr. Cir.* 163. 1909.

HAUSBROUGH, J. R., A. M. WATERMAN, and R. F. LUXFORD: The Significance of the Discolorations in Aircraft Veneers: Yellow Birch. *Forest Prod. Lab., Mimeo* 1377. 1943.

MAXWELL, HU.: Uses of Commercial Woods of the United States: Beech, Birches and Maples. *U.S. Dept. Agr. Bul.* 12. 1913.

NEUBRECH, W. LEROY: American Hardwoods and Their Uses. *Trade Prom. Ser.,* No. 178, Bureau of Foreign and Domestic Commerce, U.S. Department of Commerce. 1938.

WAKEFIELD, W. E.: A Comparison of the Mechanical and Physical Properties of the Heartwood and Sapwood of Yellow Birch. *Forest Serv. Cir.* 51, Department of Mines and Resources, Ottawa. 1937.

Plate LX

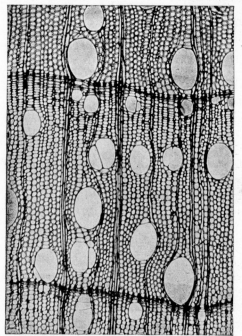

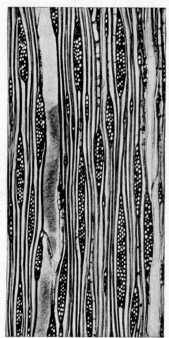

Fig. 213.—(*x*—75 ✕)

Fig. 214.—(*t*—75 ✕)

Sweet Birch, Black Birch, Cherry Birch, *Betula lenta* L.

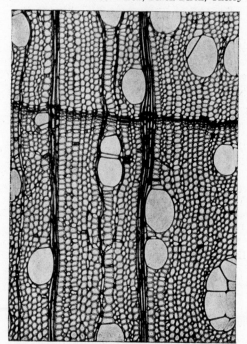

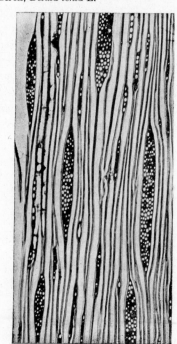

Fig. 215.—(*x*—75 ✕)

Fig. 216.—(*t*—75 ✕)

Yellow Birch, *Betula lutea* Michx. f.

Plate LXI

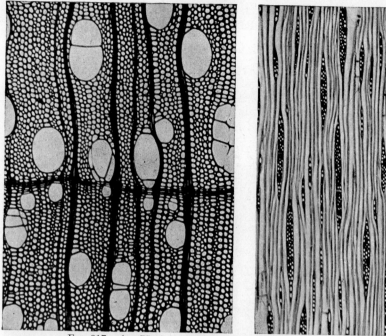

Fig. 217.—(x—75 ×)　　　　　　　Fig. 218.—(t—75 ×)
River Birch, Red Birch, *Betula nigra* L.

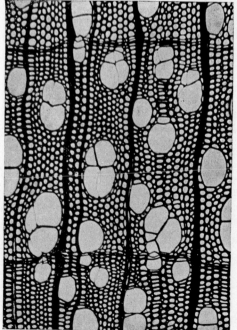

Fig. 219.—(x—75 ×)　　　　　　　Fig. 220.—(t—75 ×)
Paper Birch, White Birch, *Betula papyrifera* Marsh.

RED ALDER

Alnus rubra Bong.

Plate XII, Figs. 69 and 70; Plate XX, Fig. 115; Plate LXII, Figs. 221 and 222

General Characteristics and Properties.—*Wood* whitish when first sawed, aging to flesh color or light brown with a reddish tinge, subject to oxidative sap stain; *heartwood* indistinct; without characteristic odor or

Plate LXII

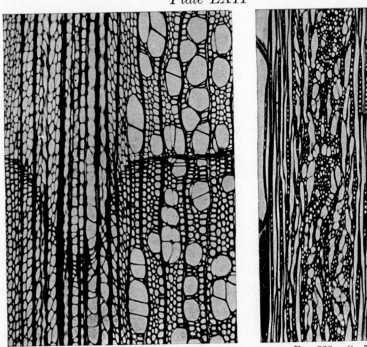

FIG. 221.—(*x*—75 ✕)   FIG. 222.—(*t*—75 ✕)
Red Alder, *Alnus rubra* Bong.

taste, straight-grained, moderately light (sp. gr. approx. 0.37 green, 0.43 ovendry), moderately weak to moderately strong in bending and endwise compression, moderately stiff and moderately low in shock resistance, shrinks moderately, easy to work, finishes smooth, glues and takes paint well, not durable when used under conditions favorable to decay. *Growth rings* distinct (wood diffuse porous), delineated by a whitish or brownish line at the outer margin. *Pores* small, indistinct without a hand lens, solitary and in multiples of 2–several. *Parenchyma* indistinct. *Rays* of two types, narrow (simple) and broad (aggregate); (*a*) narrow rays closely spaced, not visible without a hand lens; (*b*) aggregate rays at irregular and often at wide intervals, not sharply delineated and relatively inconspicuous to the naked eye (x), up to $\frac{4}{5}$ plus inches in height (t) along the grain.

Minute Anatomy.—*Vessels* 70–110 per square millimeter, the largest 70–100 microns in diameter; perforation plates scalariform with 15 plus thin bars; intervessel pits orbicular to oval (Fig. 115, page 415), quite widely spaced, fairly small (4–6 microns in diameter). *Parenchyma* paratracheal, metatracheal-diffuse, and occasionally terminal; (*a*) paratracheal parenchyma sparse, restricted to occasional cells (not forming a sheath); (*b*) metatracheal-diffuse parenchyma sparse to fairly abundant, the cells solitary or in short tangential rows of 2–several; (*c*) terminal parenchyma present or wanting, when present forming an interrupted uniseriate line. *Fibers* thin- to moderately thick-walled, 16–40 microns in diameter. *Rays* unstoried, homogeneous; (*a*) narrow rays uniseriate or rarely in part biseriate; (*b*) aggregate rays consisting of units similar to the narrow rays, and of included fibers and vessels.

Remarks.—Sometimes confused with birch (*Betula spp.*) but softer (readily dented with the thumbnail) and lighter, with aggregate rays (at least at wide intervals). Readily separated from cottonwood (*Populus spp.*) and willow (*Salix spp.*) through the presence of scalariform perforation plates with many bars (perforation plates simple in *Populus* and *Salix*), parenchyma in the body of the ring (parenchyma strictly terminal in *Populus* and *Salix*), and aggregate rays (at least at wide intervals).

Uses.—Although of little importance outside its natural range, red alder is the leading hardwood of the Pacific Northwest. The principal uses include *furniture* (mainly for turned and other exposed parts in stained and enameled furniture and in chairs for which it is especially suited because of its workability, its pleasing grain, the ease with which it takes glue, its finishing qualities, and its ability to take and hold nails and screws); *core stock* and *crossbands* in plywood, for which it is considered on a par with chestnut because of moderate shrinkage and good gluing qualities; *woodenware* and *novelties* (such as floor lamps, candlesticks, umbrella stands, ferneries, hatracks); *sash*, *doors*, and other *millwork; fixtures; handles; charcoal.*

Selected References

BETTS, H. S.: Red Alder—American Woods. Forest Service, U.S. Department of Agriculture. 1945.

JOHNSON, H. M., E. J. HANZLICK, and W. H. GIBBONS: Red Alder of the Pacific Northwest, Its Utilization, with Notes on Growth and Management. *U.S. Dept. Agr. Bul.* 1437. 1926.

NEUBRECH, W. LEROY: American Hardwoods and Their Uses. *Trade Prom Ser.,* No. 178, Bureau of Foreign and Domestic Commerce, U.S. Department of Commerce. 1938.

BEECH, AMERICAN BEECH

Fagus grandifolia Ehrh.

Plate XI, Fig. 66; Plate XII, Fig. 67; Plate XXI, Fig. 118; Plate LXIII, Figs. 223
and 224

General Characteristics and Properties.—*Sapwood* whitish; *heartwood*
whitish with a reddish tinge to reddish brown; *wood* without characteristic
odor or taste, straight- to interlocked-grained, heavy (sp. gr. approx.
0.56 green, 0.67 ovendry), hard, strong in bending (bends readily after
steaming) and endwise compression, high in shock resistance, difficult to
work with hand tools but machines satisfactorily, excellent for turning,
stays smooth when subjected to friction, high in nail- and screw-holding
ability but with a tendency to split along the rays, with unusually high
shrinkage, checks, splits, and warps in seasoning unless very carefully
dried, moderately durable to nondurable (lumbermen sometimes recognize
two grades according to the color of the heartwood, red and white beech;
the former is considered to be the more durable). *Growth rings* distinct
(wood diffuse porous), delineated by a dark line or band of denser summerwood. *Pores* small, indistinct without a hand lens, usually crowded
and largest in the springwood, decreasing in number and size through the
central portion of the ring, scattered and very small in the late summerwood. *Parenchyma* not visible with a hand lens or zonate in the late
summerwood, the lines then appearing very finely punctate. *Rays* of
two types, broad (oak-type) and narrow; (*a*) broad rays plainly visible
to the naked eye, separated by several narrow rays, appearing on the
tangential surface as short, rather widely spaced, staggered lines which
are visible without magnification; (*b*) narrow rays, fine, not visible without magnification.

Minute Anatomy.—*Vessels* 50–200 per square millimeter, the largest
60–90 microns in diameter; tyloses present in the heartwood, in uniseriate
longitudinal rows for the most part (the upper and lower walls in contact
and appearing as nearly horizontal transverse partitions arranged in a
ladderlike series); perforation plates simple or those in the smaller vessels
occasionally scalariform; intervessel pits oval to long-elliptical (Fig. 118,
page 423), with horizontal or nearly horizontal orifices, 6–20 microns in
diameter. *Parenchyma* abundant, metatracheal and metatracheal-diffuse, the lines of the former more evident toward the outer margin of the
ring. *Fibers* thick-walled, 16–22 microns in diameter. *Rays* unstoried,
homogeneous or with marginal upright cells; (*a*) broad (oak-type) rays
15–25 plus seriate, 1–several mm. in height along the grain; (*b*) narrow
rays much more numerous than the broad oak-type rays, 1–5-seriate, up
to 500 plus microns in height.

Remarks.—Comparable to the oaks (*Quercus spp.*) in possessing two types of rays, but diffuse porous.

Uses.—*Hardwood distillation; railroad ties* (treated with creosote by pressure method); *pulp* (by soda method); *slack cooperage* (largely for vegetable and fruit barrels); *veneer,* mainly for the manufacture of crates, baskets, and fruit containers and to some extent for furniture; *fuel wood* (ranks high in fuel value). Lumber used for *boxes* and *crates;*

Plate LXIII

 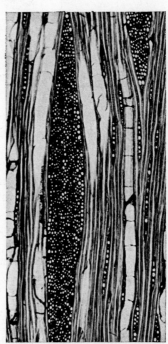

FIG. 223.—(*x*—75 ×)   FIG. 224.—(*t*—75 ×)
Beech, American Beech, *Fagus grandifolia* Ehrh.

furniture (especially for curved and turned parts of chairs); *handles* and *brush backs; woodenware* and *novelties* (including toys, spools, clothespins, and a variety of other small turned articles); *planing-mill products* (especially flooring); *dairy* and *poultry equipment; laundry appliances.*

Selected References

ANON.: The Southern Hardwoods. Southern Hardwood Producers, Inc., Memphis, Tenn. 1941.

BETTS, H. S.: American Beech—American Woods. Forest Service, U.S. Department of Agriculture. 1945.

HOYLE, R. J., H. L. HENDERSON, J. O. BLEW, and N. C. BROWN: Beech, Its Production, Uses, Seasoning and Treatment. *N. Y. State Col. Forestry, Syracuse Univ., Tech. Bul.* 51. 1940.

MAXWELL, HU.: Uses of Commercial Woods of the United States: Beech, Birches, and Maples. *U.S. Dept. Agr. Bul.* 12. 1913.

NEUBRECH, W. LEROY: American Hardwoods and Their Uses. *Trade Prom. Ser.*, No. 178, Bureau of Foreign and Domestic Commerce, U.S. Department of Commerce. 1938.

CHESTNUT, AMERICAN CHESTNUT

Castanea dentata (Marsh.) Borkh.

Plate X, Fig. 58; Plate LXIV, Figs. 225 and 226

General Characteristics and Properties.—*Sapwood* narrow, whitish to light brown; *heartwood* grayish brown to brown, turning darker with age; *wood* without characteristic odor, with mild astringent taste due to its tannin content, straight-grained, moderately light (sp. gr. approx. 0.40 green, 0.45 ovendry), moderately hard, moderately weak in bending and endwise compression, moderately low in shock resistance, works readily under tools, glues very well, splits frequently in nailing but has better than average nail-holding ability, seasons well and shows little tendency to warp, check, or honeycomb, shrinks moderately, stays in place well, very resistant to decay due to its tannin content (6 to 11 per cent, based on the ovendry weight of wood), frequently with pin (worm) holes (especially stock from blight-killed trees). *Growth rings* conspicuous except in very narrow ringed stock (wood ring porous). *Springwood-pores* very large, plainly visible to the naked eye, forming a broad, conspicuous band several pores in width; transition from spring- to summerwood abrupt; *summerwood pores* small, arranged in obliquely radial (flame-shaped) patches of light tissue which are less obvious in narrow rings. *Parenchyma* indistinct. *Rays* very fine, barely visible with a hand lens.

Minute Anatomy.—*Vessels* in the summerwood 80–130 per square millimeter; largest springwood vessels 240–360 microns in diameter; perforation plates simple, or those in the summerwood vessels occasionally scalariform; pits leading to contiguous tracheary cells orbicular to long-elliptical, with horizontal or nearly horizontal orifice, 8–18 microns in diameter. *Vasicentric tracheids* present, confined to the vicinity of the springwood vessels. *Parenchyma* paratracheal and metatracheal-diffuse; (*a*) paratracheal parenchyma sparse, restricted to occasional cells (not forming a sheath); (*b*) metatracheal-diffuse parenchyma abundant, especially in the summerwood. *Fibers* thin-walled, 16–34 microns in diameter. *Rays* unstoried, uniseriate or rarely in part biseriate, homogeneous.

Remarks.—Distinctive among North American woods. Occasionally confused with oak (produced by *Quercus spp.*) but lighter in weight and softer, without the broad rays that are a feature of that timber.

Plate LXIV

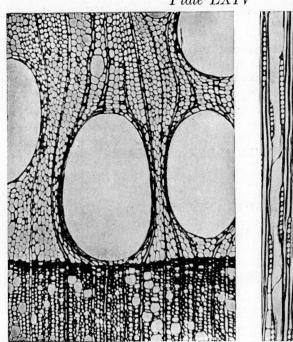 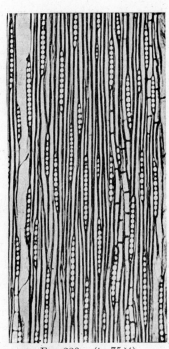

Fig. 225.—(*x*—75 ×)   Fig. 226.—(*t*—75 ×)
Chestnut, American Chestnut, *Castanea dentata* (Marsh.) Borkh.

Uses.—Most of the chestnut has been killed by the blight [*Endothia parasitica* (Murr.) A. & A.]; the uses listed below are indicative of the important rank formerly held and still held, for certain purposes, by this wood. *Tannin* (principal domestic source of tannin; obtained by soaking the wood chips in hot water and evaporating the resulting liquor to the desired concentration); *semichemical pulp* (manufactured from the extracted chips as well as from fresh wood), for fiberboard; *poles, fence posts*, and *railroad ties*, for which it is very suitable because of its natural durability combined with sufficient strength and hardness; *slack cooperage*. Lumber used for *furniture; caskets* and *coffins* (a leading wood because of its outstanding durability and good working qualities); *boxes* and *crates; millwork* (especially sash and doors); *plywood* (as a core stock and cross-bending material), for which its freedom from warping, low density, moderate shrinkage, and good gluing qualities recommend it very highly.

Selected References

ASHE, W. W.: Chestnut in Tennessee. *Tenn. Dept. Ed., Div. Geol. Bul.* 10, Nashville. 1912.

BETTS, H. S.: Chestnut—American Woods. Forest Service, U.S. Department of Agriculture. 1945.

MORBECK, G. C., R. P. A. JOHNSON, and C. V. SWEET: The Principal Uses of Chestnut. *Hardwood Rec.*, Vol. 49 (7); pp. 20–21, 24, 26–27. 1931.

NEUBRECH, W. LEROY: American Hardwoods and Their Uses. *Trade Prom. Ser.*, No. 178, Bureau of Foreign and Domestic Commerce, U.S. Department of Commerce. 1938.

GIANT EVERGREEN CHINKAPIN

Castanopsis chrysophylla (Hook.) DC.

Plate X, Fig. 57; Plate LXV, Figs. 227 and 228

General Characteristics and Properties.—*Sapwood* narrow, light brown with a pinkish tinge, hardly distinguishable from the heartwood; *heartwood* light brown tinged or striped with pink; *wood* without characteristic odor or taste, moderately heavy (sp. gr. approx. 0.42 green, 0.48 ovendry), fairly hard, moderately strong in bending and endwise compression, moderately limber, moderately high in shock resistance, average in working qualities, shrinks moderately, not durable under conditions favorable to decay. *Growth rings* conspicuous (wood ring porous). *Springwood pores* plainly visible to the naked eye, in a uniseriate (very rarely 2- or more-seriate) interrupted row; transition from spring- to summerwood abrupt; *summerwood pores* small, indistinct without a hand lens, arranged in obliquely radial (flame-shaped) patches of light tissue which are less obvious in narrow rings. *Parenchyma* indistinct. *Rays* very fine, barely visible with a hand lens.

Minute Anatomy.—*Vessels* in the summerwood 70–150 per square millimeter; largest springwood vessels 150–200 microns in diameter; perforation plates simple, or those in the smaller summerwood vessels occasionally scalariform; pits leading to contiguous tracheary cells orbicular to long-elliptical, 6–18 microns in diameter. *Vasicentric tracheids* present, confined to the vicinity of the springwood vessels. *Parenchyma* paratracheal, metatracheal-diffuse, and metatracheal; (*a*) paratracheal parenchyma sparse, restricted to occasional cells (not forming a sheath); (*b*) metatracheal-diffuse parenchyma abundant, the cells sometimes banded together in more or less interrupted, inconspicuous, 1–3 (mostly 1)-seriate lines of (*c*) metatracheal parenchyma.   *Fibers* thin-

Plate LXV

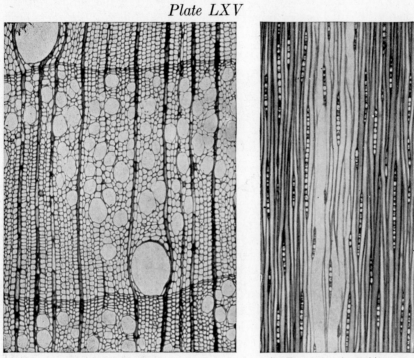

FIG. 227.—(*x*—75×)

FIG. 228.—(*t*—75×)

Giant Evergreen Chinkapin, *Castanopsis chrysophylla* (Hook.) DC.

walled, 12–30 microns in diameter.   *Rays* unstoried, uniseriate or rarely in part biseriate, homogeneous.

TAN-OAK

Lithocarpus densiflorus (Hook. & Arn.) Rehd.

Plate XI, Fig. 64; Plate LXVI, Figs. 229 and 230

General Characteristics and Properties.—*Sapwood* light reddish brown when first exposed, turning darker with age and then difficult to distinguish from the heartwood, wide; *heartwood* light brown tinged with red, aging to dark reddish brown; *wood* without characteristic odor or taste, heavy (sp. gr. approx. 0.58 green), hard, strong in bending and end-wise compression, high in shock resistance, shrinks considerably, not durable (because largely sapwood; heartwood is said to be very durable owing to its tannin content). *Growth rings* scarcely distinct or wanting, when visible, delineated by a faint narrow line of darker (denser) fibrous tissue at the outer margin. *Pores* barely visible to the naked eye,

Plate LXVI

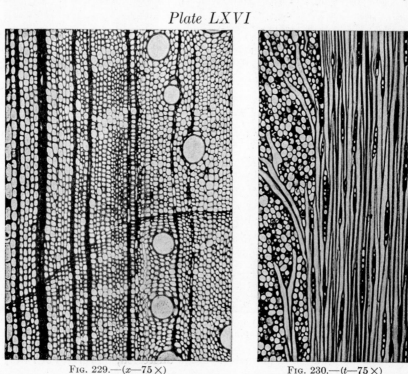

FIG. 229.—(*x*—75 ×)   FIG. 230.—(*t*—75 ×)
Tan-Oak, *Lithocarpus densiflora* (Hook. & Arn.) Rehd.

unevenly distributed, inserted in light-colored tissue in streamlike clusters which extend for some distance radially (across several–many rings when these are evident), those in the early springwood usually somewhat larger but the transition in pore size from spring- to summerwood gradual. *Parenchyma* visible with a hand lens, in tangential, rather wide, ragged lines which usually do not contrast sharply with the background of fibrous tissue and are hence poorly defined. *Rays* of two types (*x*), broad (aggregate and oak-type) and narrow; (*a*) broad rays present in some samples and wanting in others, when present, distinct and frequently conspicuous to the naked eye on the transverse section, separated by several–many narrow rays, of the same color as the background on the tangential surface and hence indistinct, forming a high fleck on the quarter; (*b*) narrow rays much more numerous than the broad rays, indistinct without magnification.

Minute Anatomy.—*Vessels* rather thick-walled, orbicular or oval for the most part, 7–15 per square millimeter, the largest 100–160 microns in diameter; perforation plates simple; pits leading to contiguous tracheary cells orbicular, 6–10 microns in diameter. *Vasicentric tracheids* present, forming a 1–several (mostly 1–2)-seriate sheath about the vessels which is rarely interrupted by parenchyma, passing over into wide-lumened fibers. *Parenchyma* paratracheal, metatracheal, and metatracheal-diffuse; (*a*) paratracheal parenchyma restricted to occasional cells contiguous to the vessels; (*b*) metatracheal parenchyma very abundant, conspicuous, in numerous, concentric, more or less continuous, 1–3 (mostly 1–2)-seriate, ragged lines; (*c*) metatracheal-diffuse parenchyma sparse, appearing as occasional cells in the tracts of fibrous tissue. *Fibers* thick-walled, frequently gelatinous, 12–26 microns in diameter. *Rays* unstoried, homogeneous or nearly so; (*a*) broad (aggregate and oak-type) rays several–many-seriate, up to 400 microns in width, many cells (into the hundreds) in height along the grain (*t*); aggregate rays composed of smaller rays separated by strands of fibrous tissue, otherwise comparable to the broad rays; (*b*) narrow rays very numerous, uniseriate, variable in height (1–12 plus cells) along the grain.

Uses.—Locally for *fuel wood;* occasionally for *furniture; mine timbers.* *Tannin* in commercial quantities is obtained from the bark; hence the common name of the tree, "tan-oak."

LIVE OAK

Quercus virginiana Mill.

Plate XI, Fig. 65; Plate LXVII, Figs. 231 and 232

General Characteristics and Properties.—*Sapwood* whitish to grayish brown; *heartwood* dull brown to gray-brown; *wood* without characteristic odor or taste, irregular grained, exceedingly heavy (sp. gr. approx. 0.81 green, 0.98 ovendry), exceedingly hard, very strong in bending, exceedingly strong in endwise compression, exceedingly stiff, high in shock resistance, shrinks considerably on drying. *Growth rings* scarcely distinct, delineated by a faint narrow line of darker (denser) fibrous tissue at the outer margin. *Pores* barely visible to the naked eye, unevenly distributed in streamlike clusters which extend for some distance radially (across several–many rings when these are evident), those in the early springwood usually somewhat larger but the transition in pore size from spring- to summerwood gradual. *Parenchyma* barely visible with a hand lens, in closely spaced, punctate lines which are poorly differentiated against the background of fibrous tissue. *Rays* of two types (*x*), broad (aggregate and oak-type) and narrow; (*a*) broad rays usually conspicuous

Plate LXVII

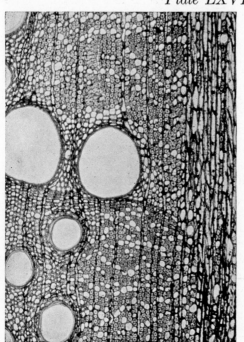 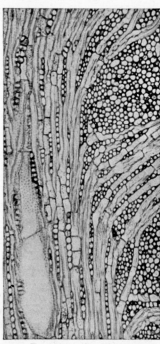

Fig. 231.—(*x*—75 ×)　　　　　　　Fig. 232.—(*t*—75 ×)
Live Oak, *Quercus virginiana* Mill.

to the naked eye on the transverse section, separated by several–many narrow rays, appearing on the tangential surface as rather widely spaced, staggered lines of varying length, forming a high fleck on the quarter; (*b*) narrow rays much more numerous than the broad rays, indistinct at low magnification.

Minute Anatomy.—*Vessels* rather thick-walled, orbicular or oval for the most part, 5–12 per square millimeter, the largest 200–280 microns in diameter; perforation plates simple; pits leading to contiguous tracheary cells orbicular to oval, 6–10 microns in diameter. *Vasicentric tracheids* present, forming a 1–several-seriate sheath about the vessels which is interrupted by parenchyma. *Parenchyma* paratracheal, metatracheal-diffuse, and metatracheal; (*a*) paratracheal parenchyma restricted to occasional cells contiguous to the vessels; (*b*) metatracheal-diffuse parenchyma abundant, scattered among the fibers as single cells or in small cells clusters, passing over into numerous, conspicuous, 1–2 (mostly 1)-seriate, ragged, anastomosing lines of (*c*) metatracheal parenchyma. *Fibers* thick-walled, sometimes gelatinous, 10–25 microns in diameter. *Rays* unstoried, homogeneous or nearly so; (*a*) broad (oak-type and aggregate) rays many-seriate, up to 600 microns in width through the central portion, many cells (into the hundreds) in height along the grain (*t*); aggregate rays composed of smaller rays separated by strands of fibrous tissue, otherwise comparable to the other broad rays; (*b*) narrow rays very numerous, 1–3 (mostly 1)-seriate, variable in height (1–20 plus cells) along the grain.

Uses.—Valued for shipbuilding before the advent of steel vessels; used locally for articles requiring exceptional strength and toughness.

RED OAK

Northern Red Oak (*Quercus borealis* Michx. f.), Plate LXVIII, Figs. 233 and 234

Black Oak (*Quercus velutina* Lam.), Plate V, Fig. 30; Plate LXVIII, Figs. 235 and 236.

Shumard Oak (*Quercus shumardi* Buckl.), Plate XX, Fig. 114

Scarlet Oak (*Quercus coccinea* Muenchh.) Plate VI, Fig. 31

Pin Oak (*Quercus palustris* Muenchh.)

Willow Oak (*Quercus phellos* L.)

Other Species of the Erythrobalanus Group

General Characteristics and Properties.—*Sapwood* whitish to grayish or pale reddish brown; *heartwood* pinkish to light reddish brown, the flesh-colored cast generally pronounced, occasionally light brown; *wood* without characteristic odor or taste, generally straight-grained, heavy to very heavy (sp. gr. 0.52–0.61 green, 0.62–0.76 ovendry), hard to very hard, strong in bending and endwise compression, stiff, high in shock resistance, machines well, finishes smooth, holds nails well but shows tendency to split along the rays, average in gluing, shrinks considerably, difficult to dry (tendency to checking, splitting, and casehardening), not durable when exposed to conditions favorable to decay. *Growth rings* very distinct (wood ring porous). *Springwood pores* large, distinctly visible to the naked eye, forming a conspicuous band 1–4 pores in width, with few or no tyloses in the heartwood; transition from spring- to summerwood gradual to more or less abrupt; *summerwood pores* abundant

WHITE OAK

White Oak (*Quercus alba* L.), Plate VI,
Fig. 34; Plate LXIX, Figs. 237 and 238
Bur Oak (*Quercus macrocarpa* Michx.)
Overcup Oak (*Quercus lyrata* Walt.)
Post Oak (*Quercus stellata* Wangenh.);
Plate VI, Fig. 33; Plate LXX, Figs. 241
and 242

Swamp Chestnut Oak, Basket Oak
(*Quercus prinus* L.)
Chestnut Oak, Rock Oak (*Quercus montana* Willd.), Plate LXIX, Figs. 239
and 240
Swamp White Oak (*Quercus bicolor* Willd.), Plate VI, Fig. 32
Other Species of the Leucobalanus
Group

General Characteristics and Properties.—*Sapwood* whitish to light brown, thin or thick; *heartwood* rich light brown to dark brown; *wood* without characteristic odor or taste, usually straight-grained, heavy to very heavy (sp. gr. 0.55–0.64 green, 0.66–0.79 ovendry), hard to very hard, strong in bending and endwise compression, moderately stiff, high in shock resistance, machines well, finishes smooth, holds nails well but shows a tendency to split along the rays, glues well, shrinks considerably, difficult to dry (tendency to checking, splitting, and casehardening), durable when exposed to conditions favorable to decay. *Growth rings* very distinct except in slow-grown stock (wood ring porous). *Springwood pores* large, distinctly visible to the naked eye, forming a conspicuous band 1–3 pores in width, often occluded with tyloses in the heartwood; transition from spring- to summerwood abrupt or somewhat gradual; *summerwood pores* numerous, small, not sharply defined with a hand lens, scattered in radially aligned, flame-shaped tracts of light-colored tissue, thin-walled. *Parenchyma* visible with a hand lens, (1) forming part of the conjunctive tissue between the springwood pores and the rays, (2) composing most of the tissue in the flame-shaped tracts in which the summerwood pores are inserted, (3) usually zonate in fine, more or less regular, tangential lines in the outer portion of the ring. *Rays* of two types (*x*), broad (oak-type) and narrow (simple); (*a*) broad rays very conspicuous to the naked eye, separated by several–many narrow rays, appearing on the tangential surface as rather widely spaced, staggered lines of varying length which frequently extend 1 inch or more along the grain, forming a handsome, high fleck on the quarter; (*b*) narrow rays much more numerous than the broad rays, indistinct without magnification.

Minute Anatomy.—*Vessels* in the summerwood 20–120 per square millimeter; largest springwood vessels 180–380 microns in diameter; perforation plates simple; pits leading to contiguous tracheary cells orbicular to oval, 6–10 microns in diameter. *Vasicentric tracheids* present, intermingled with parenchyma, (1) forming most of the conjunctive tissue between the springwood vessels and the rays and (2) composing part of the flame-shaped tracts in which the summerwood vessels are inserted. *Parenchyma* abundant, paratracheal, metatracheal-diffuse, and usually metatracheal; (*a*) paratracheal parenchyma intermingled with tracheids and distributed as described above; (*b*) metatracheal-diffuse parenchyma restricted to the fibrous tracts and toward the outer portion of the ring (particularly in wide rings) exhibiting more or less a tendency toward aggregation into concentric lines of

Plate LXX

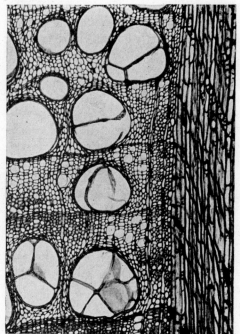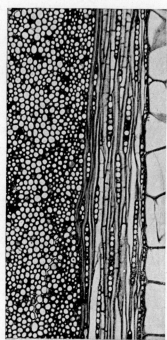

Fig. 241.—(*x*—75 ✕)   Fig. 242.—(*t*—75 ✕)

Post Oak, *Quercus stellata* Wangenh.

(*c*) metatracheal parenchyma. *Fibers* medium thick- to thick-walled, frequently gelatinous, 14–22 microns in diameter. *Rays* unstoried, homogeneous; (*a*) broad (compound) rays 12–30 plus seriate and 150–400 plus microns wide through the central portion, many cells (into the hundreds) in height along the grain (*t*); (*b*) narrow rays very numerous, uniseriate or occasionally in part biseriate through the central portion, very variable in height (1–20 plus cells) along the grain.

Remarks.—The woods of the various oaks belonging to the white oak group (*Leucobalanus*) cannot be identified with certainty.

For differences between white oak and red oak, see Remarks under Red Oak, page 543.

Uses.—*Railroad ties* (favorite tie wood because of its hardness, resiliency, and natural durability); *tight cooperage* (owing to its impermeability to liquids, strength, and durability); *slack cooperage; fence posts; mine timbers; poles; piling; export logs* and *timbers; veneer* (sliced), used largely in furniture and interior paneling; *firewood* (very high in fuel value). Lumber used for *flooring* (principal species, widely used because of its hardness, high resistance to abrasion, ability to finish smoothly, and attractive figure); *motor* and *nonmotor vehicles; planing-mill* products (sash, doors, trim, wainscoting, general millwork); *furniture* (especially desks and tables, chairs, frames for upholstered furniture); *cabinets; sewing machines; refrigerators; fixtures; railroad cars; boxes* and *crates* (good nail-holding ability, but heavy and tends to split in nailing), where strength is important; *ship-* and *boatbuilding; agricultural implements; caskets* and *coffins; handles.*

Selected References

ANON.: The Southern Hardwoods. Southern Hardwood Producers, Inc., Memphis, Tenn. 1941.

————: Identification of Oak Woods. *Forest Prod. Lab., Tech. Note* 125.

BETHEL, J. S.: Factors Influencing the Specific Gravity of Chestnut-oak Wood. *Jour. Forestry*, Vol. 41, pp. 599–601. 1943.

BETTS, H. S.: Oaks—American Woods. Forest Service, U.S. Department of Agriculture. 1945.

FOSTER, H. D., and W. W. ASHE: Chestnut Oak in the Southern Appalachians. *U.S. Forest Serv. Cir.* 135. 1908.

GREELEY, W. B., and W. W. ASHE: White Oak in the Southern Appalachians. *U.S. Forest Serv. Cir.* 105. 1907.

NEUBRECH, W. LeROY: American Hardwoods and Their Uses. *Trade Prom. Ser.*, No. 178, Bureau of Foreign and Domestic Commerce, U.S. Department of Commerce. 1938.

PAUL, B. H.: Variation in the Porosity of Twelve Species of Oak. *South. Lumberman*, Vol. 164 (2063), pp. 31–33. 1942.

WILLIAMS, SIMON: Secondary Vascular Tissues of the Oaks Indigenous to the United States—I. The Importance of Secondary Xylem in Delimiting Erythrobalanus and Leucobalanus. *Bul. Torrey Bot. Club*, Vol. 66, pp. 353–365. 1939; II. Types of Tyloses and Their Distribution in Erythrobalanus and Leucobalanus. *Bul. Torrey Bot. Club*, Vol. 69, pp. 1–10. 1942.

WHITE ELM, AMERICAN ELM

Ulmus americana L.

Plate VIII, Fig. 45; Plate LXXI, Figs. 243 and 244

General Characteristics and Properties.—*Sapwood* grayish white to light brown, thick; *heartwood* light brown to brown, frequently with a reddish tinge; *wood* without characteristic odor or taste, straight- or sometimes interlocked-grained, moderately heavy (sp. gr. approx. 0.46 green, 0.55 ovendry), moderately hard, moderately weak in endwise compression, with excellent bending qualities, high in shock resistance, tough, difficult to split, difficult to work with tools, average in nail-holding ability, difficult to season (because of its tendency to warp and twist); shrinks considerably, does not stay in place well, moderately resistant to decay. *Growth rings* distinct (wood ring porous), usually fairly wide. *Springwood pores* large, distinctly visible to the naked eye, arranged in a 1 (rarely 2–3)-seriate, more or less continuous row, those at the beginning of the ring approximately equal in size; transition from spring- to summerwood abrupt; *summerwood pores* small, numerous, arranged in more or less continuous, wavy, concentric bands. *Parenchyma* not visible. *Rays* not distinct to the naked eye.

Minute Anatomy.—*Vessels* in the summerwood 80–200 per square millimeter; largest springwood vessels 200–270 microns in diameter; perforation plates simple; spiral thickening present in the smaller vessels; intervessel pits orbicular or angular through crowding, 10–12 microns in diameter. *Vascular tracheids* present both in the springwood porous zone and in the wavy bands of summerwood vessels, grading into small vessels, with spiral thickening. *Parenchyma* paratracheal and meta-tracheal-diffuse; (*a*) paratracheal parenchyma abundant, associated with vascular tracheids, (1) contiguous to but never forming a continuous sheath about the large springwood pores, (2) marginal to and included in the clusters of smaller springwood vessels and vascular tracheids, and (3) marginal to and included in the wavy concentric bands of summerwood vessels and vascular tracheids; (*b*) metatracheal-diffuse parenchyma sparse, scattered in the fibrous tracts. *Fibers* medium thick- to thick-walled, frequently gelatinous, 14–26 microns in diameter. *Rays* unstoried, 1–7 (mostly 4–6)-seriate, essentially homogeneous.

Remarks.—American elm is sometimes confused with hard elm [*Ulmus spp.* (see p. 552)], slippery elm (*U. fulva* Michx.) and hackberry (*Celtis spp.*); for distinguishing characters, see Keys for Identification, pages 372 and 416, respectively.

Uses.—*Slack cooperage* for staves and hoops (although elm[1] is still considered superior to other native woods for slack staves, it ranks below red-gum, pine, ash, and tupelo gum in the quantity used; elm hoops have been largely displaced by metal hoops); *boxes* and *crates*, and other containers required to withstand rough handling, for which strength, toughness, and superior bending qualities make it very serviceable;

Plate LXXI

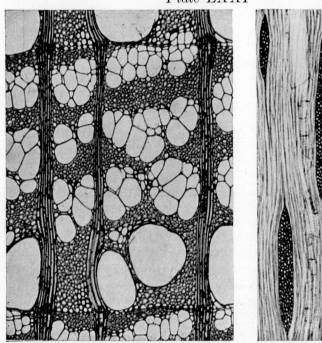

Fig. 243.—(*x*—75 ×)   Fig. 244.—(*t*—75 ×)

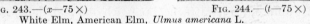

White Elm, American Elm, *Ulmus americana* L.

veneer for fruit and vegetable containers and round cheeseboxes; *furniture* (especially bent parts such as rockers and arms, also for upholstery frames and dinettes); *vehicles; dairy, poultry,* and *apiary supplies; interior trim; agricultural implements.*

Selected References

Anon.: The Southern Hardwoods.   Southern Hardwood Producers, Inc., Memphis, Tenn.   1941.

[1] In the trade, the term "elm" is applied indiscriminately to the timbers of American (white) elm, slippery (red) elm, and hard elm (see p. 552).   American elm outranks the other species in the quantity consumed for the uses here stated.

Betts, H. S.: American Woods. Forest Service, U.S. Department of Agriculture. 1945.

Brush, W. D.: Utilization of Elm. *U.S. Dept. Agr. Bul.* 683. 1918.

Neubrech, W. LeRoy: American Hardwoods and Their Uses. *Trade Prom. Ser.*, No. 178, Bureau of Foreign and Domestic Commerce, U.S. Department of Commerce. 1938.

RED ELM, SLIPPERY ELM

Ulmus fulva Michx.

Plate VIII, Fig. 48; Plate LXXII, Figs. 245 and 246

General Characteristics and Properties.—*Sapwood* grayish white to light brown, narrow, with a faint characteristic odor resembling that of

Plate LXXII

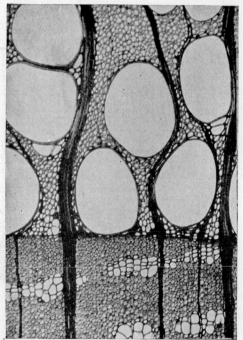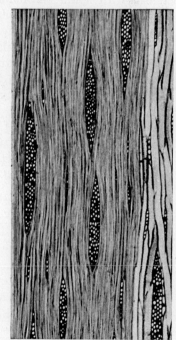

Fig. 245.—(x—75×)   Fig. 246.—(t—75×)
Red Elm, Slippery Elm, *Ulmus fulva* Michx.

the inner bark; *heartwood* brown to dark brown, frequently with shades of red, usually odorless; *wood* without characteristic taste, straight- or sometimes interlocked-grained, moderately heavy (sp. gr. approx. 0.48

green, 0.57 ovendry), moderately hard, strong in endwise compression, with excellent bending qualities, very high in shock resistance, difficult to season (because of tendency to warp and twist), shrinks considerably, moderately resistant to decay.   *Growth rings* distinct (wood ring porous). *Springwood pores* large, distinctly visible to the naked eye, forming a conspicuous band 2–4 pores in width; transition from spring- to summerwood abrupt; *summerwood pores* very small, numerous, arranged in more or less continuous, wavy, concentric bands.   *Parenchyma* not visible. *Rays* not distinct to the naked eye.

Minute Anatomy.—*Vessels* in the summerwood 100–200 per square millimeter; largest springwood vessels 200–290 microns in diameter; perforation plates simple; spiral thickening present in the smaller vessels; intervessel pits orbicular or angular through crowding, 8–12 microns in diameter.   *Vascular tracheids* present both in the springwood porous zone and in the wavy bands of summerwood vessels, grading into small vessels, with spiral thickening.   *Parenchyma* paratracheal and metatracheal-diffuse; (*a*) paratracheal parenchyma abundant, (1) associated with vascular tracheids and forming tracts of conjunctive tissue between the springwood vessels, (2) marginal to and occasionally included in the wavy concentric bands of summerwood vessels and vascular tracheids; (*b*) metatracheal-diffuse parenchyma sparse, scattered in the fibrous tracts.   *Fibers* medium thick- to thick-walled, frequently gelatinous, 16–24 microns in diameter.   *Rays* unstoried, 1–5 (mostly 3–4)-seriate, essentially homogeneous.

Remarks.—See Remarks under American Elm, page 549.

Uses.—Commonly marketed with American elm as "elm," or sometimes as "soft elm" and used for the same purposes.

Selected References

Betts, H. S.: Elm—American Woods.   Forest Service, U.S. Department of Agriculture.   1945.
Brush, W. D.: Utilization of Elm.   *U.S. Dept. Agr. Bul.* 683.   1918.

HARD ELM

Rock Elm, Cork Elm (*Ulmus thomasi* Sarg.) Plate VIII, Fig. 46; Plate LXXIII, Figs. 247 and 248
Winged Elm (*Ulmus alata* Michx.)
Cedar Elm (*Ulmus crassifolia* Nutt.)

General Characteristics and Properties.—*Sapwood* light brown to brown, narrow; *heartwood* light brown to brown, frequently with a reddish tinge; *wood* without characteristic odor or taste, straight- or sometimes interlocked-grained, heavy (sp. gr. approx. 0.57 green, 0.66 ovendry), hard, strong in bending and endwise compression, very high in shock resistance, difficult to work with tools, difficult to season (because of tendency to warp and twist), does not stay in place well, moderately resistant to decay. *Growth rings* fairly distinct (wood ring porous). *Springwood pores* variable in size; larger pores scarcely visible to the naked eye, spaced at more or less irregular intervals in an interrupted

Plate LXXIII

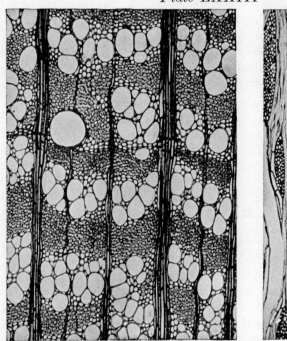 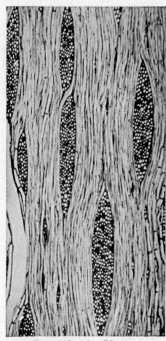

Fig. 247.—(*x*—75 ×)   Fig. 248.—(*t*—75 ×)
Rock Elm, Cork Elm, *Ulmus thomasi* Sarg.

row and separated by smaller pores; transition from spring- to summer-wood more or less gradual; *summerwood pores* small, numerous, arranged in more or less continuous, wavy, concentric bands. *Parenchyma* not visible. *Rays* not distinct to the naked eye.

Minute Anatomy.—*Vessels* in the summerwood 90–110 per square millimeter; largest springwood vessels 140–180 microns in diameter; perforation plates simple; spiral thickening present in the smaller vessels; intervessel pits orbicular or angular through crowding, 8–12 microns in diameter. *Vascular tracheids* present both in the springwood porous zone and in the wavy bands of summerwood vessels, grading into small vessels, with spiral thickening. *Parenchyma* paratracheal and meta-tracheal-diffuse; (*a*) paratracheal parenchyma abundant, associated with vascular tracheids, (1) contiguous to but never forming a continuous sheath about the larger springwood pores, (2) marginal to and included in the clusters of smaller springwood vessels and vascular tracheids, and (3) marginal to and included in the wavy concentric bands of summerwood vessels and vascular tracheids; (*b*) metatracheal-diffuse parenchyma sparse, scattered in the fibrous tracts. *Fibers* medium thick- to thick-walled, frequently gelatinous, 14–21 microns in diameter. *Rays* unstoried, 1–10 (mostly 4–6)-seriate, essentially homogeneous.

Remarks.—See Remarks under American Elm, page 549.[1]

Uses.—Hard elm is used for the manufacture of the same products as American and slippery elms; it is preferred, however, where hardness and ability to resist shock are of primary importance.

Selected References

Betts, H. S.: Elm—American Woods. Forest Service, U.S. Department of Agriculture. 1945.

Brush, W. D.: Utilization of Elm. *U.S. Dept. Agr. Bul.* 683. 1918.

HACKBERRY

Common Hackberry (*Celtis occidentalis* L.), Plate VIII, Fig. 47; Plate LXXIV, Figs. 249 and 250   **Sugar Hackberry** (*Celtis laevigata* Willd.)

General Characteristics and Properties.—*Sapwood* pale yellow to grayish or greenish yellow, frequently discolored with blue sap stain, wide; *heartwood*, when present, yellowish gray to light brown streaked with yellow; *wood* without characteristic odor or taste, straight- or sometimes interlocked-grained, moderately heavy (sp. gr. approx. 0.49 green, 0.56 ovendry), moderately hard, with good bending qualities, moderately weak in endwise compression, high in shock resistance, relatively free from warping, shapes poorly, planes and turns moderately well (superior to elm), average in nail-holding capacity (shows tendency to splitting,) glues extremely well, shrinks moderately, average in resistance to decay. *Growth rings* distinct (wood ring porous). *Springwood pores* large, distinctly visible to the naked eye, forming a conspicuous band 2–5 pores in width; transition from spring- to summerwood more or less abrupt;

[1] For the separation of the three hard elms, see the supplemental Key, footnote, p. 372.

summerwood pores small, numerous, arranged in more or less continuous, wavy, concentric bands. *Parenchyma* not visible. *Rays* distinctly visible to the naked eye.

Minute Anatomy.—*Vessels* in the summerwood 50–180 per square millimeter; largest springwood vessels 230–300 microns in diameter; perforation plates simple; spiral thickening present in the smaller vessels; intervessel pits orbicular or angular through crowding, 8–12 microns in

Plate LXXIV

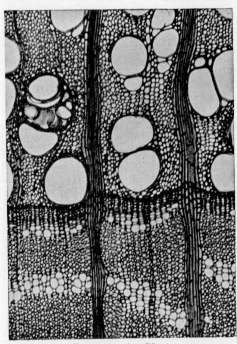 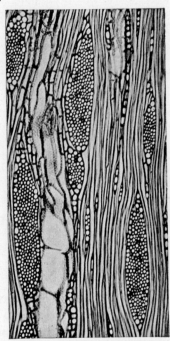

Fig. 249.—(*x*—75 ×)   Fig. 250.—(*t*—75 ×)

Common Hackberry, *Celtis occidentalis* L.

diameter. *Vascular tracheids* present both in the springwood porous zone and in the wavy bands of summerwood vessels, grading into small vessels, with spiral thickening. *Parenchyma* paratracheal and metatracheal-diffuse; (*a*) paratracheal parenchyma abundant, (1) associated with vascular tracheids and forming tracts of conjunctive tissue between the springwood vessels, (2) marginal to and occasionally included in the wavy concentric bands of summerwood vessels and vascular tracheids; (*b*) metatracheal-diffuse parenchyma very sparse, scattered in the fibrous tracts. *Fibers* moderately thick- to thick-walled, frequently gelatinous, 14–22 microns in diameter. *Rays* unstoried, 1–13 (mostly 5–8)-seriate, heterogeneous for the most part.

Remarks.—The woods of common hackberry and sugar hackberry are indistinguishable. Hackberry is sometimes confused with elm (*Ulmus spp.*) but has a wider sapwood, with a distinct yellowish tinge (whitish to light brown in elm), and wider rays.

Uses.—At many mills, not distinguished from and used for the same purposes as American and slippery elms, and white ash. The better grades are used principally for *furniture*, and to a lesser extent for *millwork*, and *sporting* and *athletic* goods; the low-grade lumber is made up largely into *boxes* and *crates*.

Selected References

ANON.: The Southern Hardwoods. Southern Hardwood Producers, Inc. Memphis, Tenn. 1941.

BETTS, H. S.: Hackberry—American Woods. Forest Service, U.S. Department of Agriculture. 1945.

COX, M. J.: The Comparative Anatomy of the Secondary Stem of Five American Species of Celtis. *Amer. Midland Nat.*, Vol. 25, pp. 348–357. 1941.

DAVIS, E. M.: Some Machining and Related Properties of Hackberry. *South. Lumberman*, Vol. 157(1985), pp. 140–142. 1938.

RED MULBERRY

Morus rubra L.

Plate XI, Fig. 61; Plate LXXV, Figs. 251 and 252

General Characteristics and Properties.—*Sapwood* yellowish, narrow; *heartwood* orange-yellow to golden-brown, turning russet-brown on exposure; *wood* without characteristic odor or taste, straight-grained, heavy (sp. gr. approx. 0.59 green), hard, very durable when exposed to conditions favorable to decay. *Growth rings* distinct (wood ring porous). *Springwood pores* large, plainly visible to the naked eye, forming a band 2–8 pores in width, occasionally with white deposits; transition from spring- to summerwood abrupt; *summerwood pores* small, arranged in nestlike groups which exhibit more or less of a tendency, especially in the late summerwood, toward aggregation into concentric, wavy, interrupted bands, sometimes solitary. *Parenchyma* not visible. *Rays* plainly visible to the naked eye, forming a pronounced fleck on the radial surface.

Minute Anatomy.—*Vessels* 15–90 per square millimeter, the largest 150–250 microns in diameter; perforation plates simple; spiral thickening present in the small vessels in the summerwood; intervessel pits orbicular to oval or angular through crowding, 8–10 microns in diameter; spring-wood vessels in the heartwood partly occluded with tyloses, sometimes with white deposits. *Parenchyma* paratracheal and metatracheal-diffuse; (*a*) paratracheal parenchyma (1) abundant in the porous springwood zone and composing part of the conjunctive tissue between the vessels and the rays, (2) less abundant elsewhere in the ring forming a 1–several

Plate LXXV

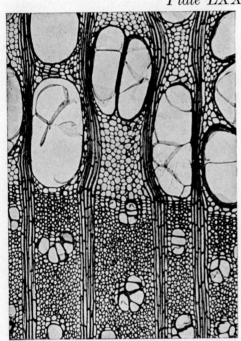 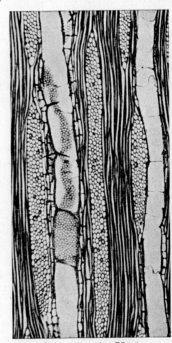

Fig. 251.—(*x*—75 ✕)   Fig. 252.—(*t*—75 ✕)

Red Mulberry, *Morus rubra* L.

(mostly 1)-seriate, often interrupted sheath about the vessels or vessel groups; (*b*) metatracheal-diffuse parenchyma sparse, confined to the fibrous tracts. *Fibers* thin- to thick-walled, frequently gelatinous, 18–26 microns in diameter. *Rays* unstoried, 1–8 (mostly 5–7)-seriate, homogeneous to heterogeneous.

Uses.—Locally for *fence posts; furniture; interior finish; caskets; agricultural implements; wagon stock; cooperage.*

Selected Reference

Tippo, O.: Comparative Anatomy of the Moraceae and Their Presumed Allies. *Bot Gaz.*, Vol. 100, pp. 1–99. 1938.

OSAGE-ORANGE

Maclura pomifera (Raf.) Schneid.

Plate IX, Fig. 49; Plate XX, Fig. 113; Plate LXXVI, Figs. 253 and 254

General Characteristics and Properties.—*Sapwood* light yellow, narrow; *heartwood* golden-yellow to bright orange, darkening upon exposure, often with reddish streaks along the grain; coloring matter readily soluble in tepid water; *wood* without characteristic odor or taste, straight-grained, exceedingly heavy (sp. gr. approx. 0.76 green, 0.84 oven-dry), very hard, very strong, very stiff, shrinks little, very durable when exposed to conditions favorable to decay. *Growth rings* distinct (wood ring porous). *Springwood pores* large, forming a band 2–3 pores in width, completely occluded with tyloses in the heartwood and the contours of the individual pores hence indistinct, the springwood zone appearing as a light-colored band (*x*) to the naked eye; transition from spring- to summerwood abrupt; *summerwood pores* small, arranged in nestlike groups which coalesce in the late summerwood forming interrupted concentric bands. *Parenchyma* not distinct as such. *Rays* barely visible to the naked eye.

Minute Anatomy.—*Vessels* 10–60 per square millimeter, the largest 150–250 microns in diameter; perforation plates simple; spiral thickening present in the small vessels in the summerwood; tyloses in the springwood vessels small, appearing cellular *en masse;* intervessel pits orbicular to oval or angular through crowding, 8–12 microns in diameter, the orifices frequently confluent (Fig. 113, page 415). *Parenchyma* abundant, paratracheal, paratracheal-confluent, and terminal; (*a*) paratracheal parenchyma (1) intermingled with some fusiform parenchyma cells (substitute fibers) and fibers and composing an appreciable portion of the conjunctive tissue between the vessels and the rays in the porous springwood zone, (2) forming an irregular, 1–several-seriate, continuous or interrupted sheath about the vessels or groups of vessels farther out in the ring, (3) toward the outer margin of the ring passing over into (*b*) paratracheal-confluent parenchyma and frequently serving as conjunctive tissue uniting proximate groups of vessels laterally (across the rays) or in the extreme outer portion of the ring forming interrupted tangential bands devoid of vessels; (*c*) terminal parenchyma abundant but not forming a distinct line, passing over into the paratracheal parenchyma of the succeeding ring. *Fusiform parenchyma cells* (substitute fibers) occasional, intermingled with parenchyma. *Fibers* moderately thick- to thick-walled, 10–16 microns in diameter. *Rays* unstoried, 1–6 (mostly 2–4)-seriate, homogeneous for the most part.

Remarks.—The wood of Osage-orange is frequently confused with that of black locust (*Robinia pseudoacacia* L.); for differences between these timbers, see Remarks under Black Locust, page 580.

Uses.—*Fence posts* (very durable); *insulator pins* (because of durability, strength, and minimal shrinking and swelling which tend to prevent

Plate LXXVI

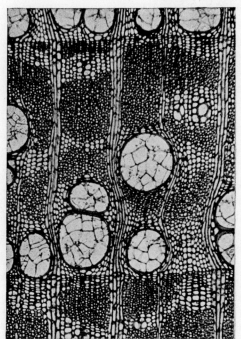 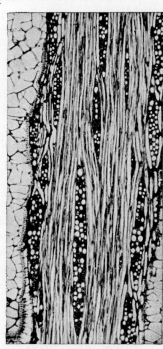

FIG. 253.—(*x*—75 ×)   FIG. 254.—(*t*—75 ×)

Osage-Orange, *Maclura pomifera* (Raf.) Schneid.

the pins from loosening in the crossarms); *nonmotor vehicle parts* (especially for hubs); *treenails; machinery parts; archery* (bows); *dyewood* (contains yellow, green, and brown coloring principles).

Selected References

BETTS, H. S.: Osage-orange—American Woods. Forest Service, U.S. Department of Agriculture, 1945.

KRESSMAN, F. W.: Osage Orange—Its Value as a Commercial Dyestuff. *Jour. Indus. and Engin. Chem.*, Vol. 6(6), pp. 462–464. 1914.

MAGNOLIA

Cucumber Magnolia, Cucumber-tree
(*Magnolia acuminata* L.), Plate XV,
Figs. 87; Plate XXI, Fig. 120; Plate
LXXVII, Figs. 255 and 256

Evergreen Magnolia, Southern Magnolia
(*Magnolia grandiflora* L.), Plate XV,
Fig. 88; Plate LXXVII, Figs. 257 and
258

General Characteristics and Properties.—*Sapwood* whitish, narrow or wide; *heartwood* yellow, greenish yellow to brown, or greenish black (the latter is said to be common in evergreen magnolia); *wood* without characteristic odor or taste, straight-grained, fairly heavy (sp. gr. 0.44–0.46 green, 0.52–0.53 ovendry), moderately hard to hard, moderately strong in bending, moderately weak to moderately strong in endwise compression, fairly stiff to stiff, moderately high to high in shock resistance, works moderately hard under tools but is capable of smooth finish, glues satisfactorily, takes and holds paint, stains and natural finishes well, average in nail-holding ability, shrinks considerably, stays in place well when properly seasoned, not durable when exposed to conditions favorable to decay. *Growth rings* distinct, delineated by a whitish line of terminal parenchyma. *Pores* small, indistinct without a hand lens, quite uniform in size, fairly evenly distributed throughout the ring (wood diffuse porous), solitary or in multiples of 2–several. *Parenchyma* terminal, the line plainly visible to the naked eye. *Rays* distinct to the naked eye (*x*), nearly uniform in width.

Minute Anatomy.—*Vessels* 60–120 per square millimeter, the largest 80–100 microns in diameter; perforation plates simple or occasionally scalariform in the first few annual rings in *Magnolia acuminata* L., mostly scalariform with 6–10 stout bars in *M. grandiflora* L.; spiral thickening present in the vessels of *M. grandiflora* L.; intervessel pitting scalariform (Fig. 120, page 423), the pits linear or rarely elliptical, 12–50 microns in diameter. Line of terminal *parenchyma* 1–several-seriate. *Fibers* thin- to moderately thick-walled, 28–40 microns in diameter. *Rays* 4–7 per millimeter (*x*), unstoried, 1–5 (mostly 1–2)-seriate, homogeneous to heterogeneous, where heterogeneous the upper and lower margins generally consisting of one row of upright cells; upright cells less than 60 microns in height along the grain.

Remarks.—Cucumber magnolia and evergreen magnolia cannot always be separated with certainty; the latter can frequently be distinguished by its darker (greenish-black) heartwood, by the presence of scalariform perforation plates in addition to those of the simple type in the mature wood, and by the spiral thickenings in the vessels; the rays of *M. grandiflora* L. are also wider, ranging from 1–5 cells in breadth. For separation of magnolia timbers from yellow-poplar, see Remarks under the latter, page 563.

Plate LXXVII

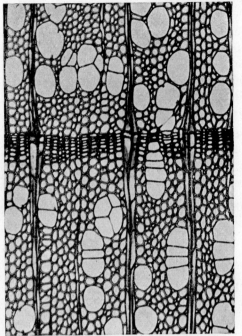

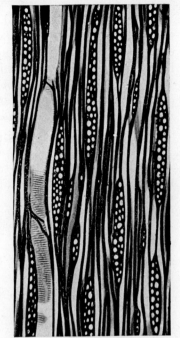

Fig. 255.—(x—75 ×)

Fig. 256.—(t—75 ×)

Cucumber Magnolia, Cucumber-Tree, *Magnolia acuminata* L.

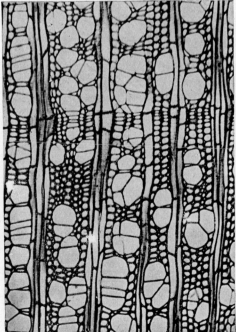

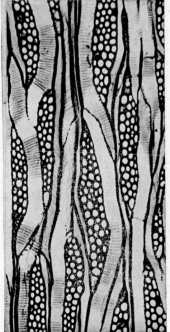

Fig. 257.—(x—75 ×)

Fig. 258.—(t—75 ×)

Evergreen Magnolia, Southern Magnolia, *Magnolia grandiflora* L.

Uses.—Frequently mixed with yellow-poplar and sold as such or under its own name (the dark-colored heartwood of evergreen magnolia commands a higher price; preferred for *furniture* and other uses where hardness is a factor). Other important uses for magnolia are for *fixtures; Venetian blinds* (growing in popularity with blind manufacturers, because of good finishing qualities and freedom from twisting and warping); *interior finish; siding; sash; doors; general millwork; boxes* and *crates.*

Selected References

ANON.: The Southern Hardwoods. Southern Hardwood Producers, Inc., Memphis, Tenn. 1941.

BETTS, H. S.: Magnolia—American Woods. Forest Service, U.S. Department of Agriculture. 1945.

NEUBRECH, W. LEROY: American Hardwoods and Their Uses. *Trade Prom. Ser.,* No. 178, Bureau of Foreign and Domestic Commerce, U.S. Department of Commerce. 1938.

YELLOW-POPLAR, TULIP-POPLAR, WHITEWOOD

Liriodendron tulipifera L.

Plate XV, Fig. 86; Plate XXII, Fig. 128; Plate LXXVIII, Figs. 259 and 260

General Characteristics and Properties.—*Sapwood* whitish, often variegated or striped, narrow; *heartwood* variable in color, ranging from clear yellow to tan or greenish brown, frequently marked with shades of purple, dark green, blue, and black (these colorations have no apparent effect on the physical properties of this wood, and affect its value only where a natural finish is desired);[1] *wood* without characteristic odor or taste, straight-grained, moderately light (sp. gr. approx. 0.38 green, 0.43 ovendry), moderately soft, moderately weak in bending and endwise compression, moderately stiff, moderately low in shock resistance, easy to work, glues satisfactorily, takes and holds paint and enamel exceptionally well, low in nail-holding ability but shows little tendency to split, shrinks considerably, seasons easily, stays in place well, not durable when exposed to conditions favorable to decay. *Growth rings* distinct, delineated by a whitish line of terminal parenchyma. Pores small, not visible without a lens, fairly uniformly distributed throughout the ring (wood diffuse porous), solitary and in multiples of 2–several. Parenchyma terminal, the line plainly visible to the naked eye. Rays distinct to the naked eye (*x*), nearly uniform in width.

[1] Areas of plain brown, untinged by yellow or green, however, indicate tissue affected by fungous growth.

Minute Anatomy.—*Vessels* 60–180 per square millimeter, the largest 80–130 microns in diameter; perforation plates scalariform with 2–10 thin bars; intervessel pits oval or oval-angular for the most part (Fig. 128, page 429), arranged in transverse rows (opposite pitting), 6–12 microns in diameter, rarely linear and then up to 20 microns in diameter. Line of terminal *parenchyma* 1–several-seriate. *Fibers* thin- to moderately thick-walled, 24–40 microns in diameter. *Rays* 4–7 per millimeter (x),

Plate LXXVIII

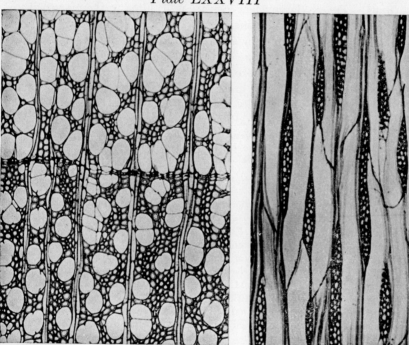

FIG. 259.—(x—75 ×) FIG. 260.—(t—75 ×)

Yellow-Poplar, Tulip-Poplar, *Liriodendron tulipifera* L.

unstoried or rarely somewhat storied, 1–5 (mostly 2–3)-seriate, homogeneous to heterogeneous, where heterogeneous the upper and lower margins generally consisting of one row of upright cells; upright cells less than 60 microns in height along the grain.

Remarks.—Yellow-poplar resembles magnolia but the figure of the flat-sawn stock is usually less prominent because the zones of terminal parenchyma are narrower and hence less accentuated. Accurate identification is assured with a compound microscope. In yellow-poplar the pits are oval or oval-angular and are arranged in transverse rows (see Fig. 128, p. 429); the intervessel pits of magnolia, in contrast, are predominately linear and extend nearly across the vessel wall (see Fig. 120, p. 423). The vessels of yellow-poplar are invariably devoid of spiral thickening; the same holds for the vessels of *Magnolia acuminata* L. but those of *M. grandiflora* L. occasionally possess spirals. The perforation plates of *M. acuminata* L. are simple in the mature wood, those of *M. grandiflora* L. mostly scalariform; the vessels of this last-named species also occasionally exhibit spiral thickening, a feature that is never present in yellow-poplar.

Uses.—*Veneer* (large, clear logs are well suited to the manufacture of rotary-cut veneer) used extensively for berry and fruit boxes, also in the form of plywood for interior finish, furniture, cabinetwork, and piano cases, and as corestock; *pulp* (by the soda process); *hat blocks*. Lumber used for *furniture*, cabinetwork, and *finish* that is to be painted or enameled; *boxes* and *crates* (lower grades); *millwork* (sash, doors, and blinds); *musical instruments* (especially radio and phonograph cabinets); *fixtures; miscellaneous uses*, such as kitchen utensils, toys, novelties, patterns, coffins and caskets, cigar boxes.

Selected References

ANON.: The Southern Hardwoods. Southern Hardwood Producers, Inc., Memphis, Tenn. 1941.

BETTS, H. S.: Yellow-poplar—American Woods. Forest Service, U.S. Department of Agriculture. 1945.

HEPTING, H., E. R. ROTH, and R. F. LUXFORD: The Significance of the Discolorations in Aircraft Veneers: Yellow Poplar. *Forest Prod. Lab., Mimeo.* 1375. 1942.

LUXFORD, R. F., and L. W. WOOD: Survey of Strength and Related Properties of Yellow Poplar. *Forest Prod. Lab., Rpt.* 1516. 1944.

McCARTHY, E. F.: Yellow Poplar: Characteristics, Growth and Management. *U.S. Dept. Agr. Tech. Bul.* 356. 1933.

NEUBRECH, W. LeRoy: American Hardwoods and Their Uses. *Trade Prom. Ser.*, No. 178, Bureau of Foreign and Domestic Commerce, U.S. Department of Commerce. 1938.

CALIFORNIA LAUREL, OREGON MYRTLE

Umbellularia californica (Hook. & Arn.) Nutt.

Plate XIII, Fig. 77; Plate LXXIX, Figs. 261 and 262

General Characteristics and Properties.—*Sapwood* whitish to light brown, thick; *heartwood* light rich brown to grayish brown, frequently with darker streaks of pigment figure; *wood* with a characteristic spicy odor (strong to very mild), without characteristic taste, straight- or sometimes interlocked-grained, heavy (sp. gr. approx. 0.51 green), moderately hard, subject to attack by powder-post beetles. *Growth rings* distinct, delineated by a darker band of denser summerwood. *Pores* small, barely visible to the naked eye, rather distant, evenly distributed throughout the growth ring (wood diffuse porous), solitary and in multiples of 2–several, encircled by a whitish sheath of *parenchyma* which is about as wide as the pore. *Rays* fine, not distinct to the naked eye, plainly visible with a hand lens.

Plate LXXIX

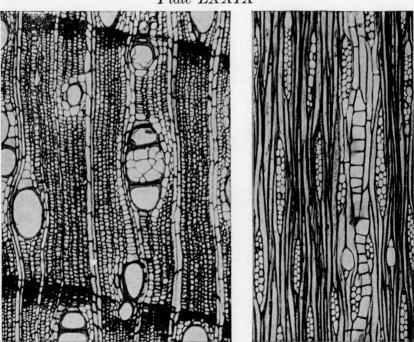

Fig. 261.—(x—75 ×)   Fig. 262.—(t—75 ×)
California Laurel, Oregon Myrtle, *Umbellularia california* (Hook. & Arn.) Nutt.

Minute Anatomy.—*Vessels* 8–20 per square millimeter, the largest 120–160 microns in diameter; perforation plates simple; spiral thickening occasional; intervessel pits orbicular to angular, 6–10 microns in diameter. *Parenchyma* paratracheal, abundant, forming a 1–3-seriate sheath. *Fibers* thin-walled, 20–35 microns in diameter, frequently gelatinous, in part septate. *Rays* unstoried, 1–4-seriate, typically heterogeneous, frequently with oil cells.

Remarks.—This wood darkens appreciably when soaked in water, a treatment that is often followed prior to its utilization.

Uses.—*Veneer,* used in the manufacture of furniture and for paneling (handsome burl stock is obtained from this species); *novelties* and *woodenware; turnery; cabinetwork; interior trim.* Used under the keel in launching ships; appears to resist crushing better and to have more "slip" than any other local species.

SASSAFRAS

Sassafras albidum (Nutt.) Nees

Plate X, Fig. 55; Plate LXXX, Figs. 263 and 264

General Characteristics and Properties.—*Sapwood* light yellow; *heartwood* dull grayish brown to orange-brown or dark brown; *wood* with

Plate LXXX

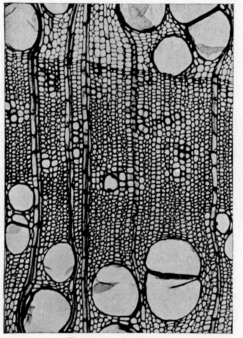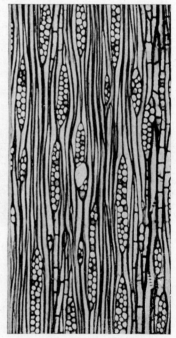

| Fig. 263.—(x—75 ×) | Fig. 264.—(t—75 ×) |

Sassafras, *Sassafras albidum* (Nutt.) Nees.

odor of sassafras on fresh-cut surface, with spicy taste, straight-grained, moderately heavy (sp. gr. approx. 0.42 green, 0.47 ovendry), moderately hard, moderately weak in bending and endwise compression, quite high in shock resistance, shrinks little, durable when exposed to conditions favorable to decay. *Growth rings* very distinct (wood ring porous). *Springwood pores* large, plainly visible to the naked eye, forming a band 3–8 pores in width; transition from spring- to summerwood abrupt; *summerwood pores* small, solitary, and in multiples of 2–3. *Parenchyma* visible with a hand lens, forming a narrow sheath around the summerwood pores and extending laterally from their flanks. *Rays* barely visible to the naked eye.

Minute Anatomy.—*Vessels* 8–20 per square millimeter, the largest 120–160 microns in diameter; perforation plates simple or occasionally scalariform in the summerwood vessels; intervessel pits orbicular to oval, generally not crowded, 6–10 microns in diameter. *Parenchyma* paratracheal, rarely paratracheal-confluent in the late summerwood, and metatracheal-diffuse; sheath of paratracheal parenchyma around the summerwood vessels 1–several-seriate, extending from the flanks (aliform); metatracheal-diffuse parenchyma very sparse. *Fibers* thin-walled, 20–35 microns in diameter. *Rays* unstoried, 1–4-seriate, homogeneous to heterogeneous, frequently containing oil cells (Text Fig. 47).

Remarks.—Frequently confused with black ash (*Fraxinus nigra* Marsh.), which it resembles in color, grain, and texture. Distinct from this species in possessing a characteristic odor on freshly exposed surfaces traceable to oil cells in the wood rays, and in the presence of aliform parenchyma extending from the flanks of the summerwood pores.

Uses.—Locally for *fence posts* and *general millwork; rails; foundation posts; wooden pails; small boat construction;* larger logs are occasionally sawed into lumber which is often sold as "black ash."

RED-GUM, AMERICAN SWEET GUM

Liquidambar styraciflua L.

Plate XII, Fig. 72; Plate XXII, Fig. 125; Plate LXXXI, Figs. 265 and 266

General Characteristics and Properties.—*Sapwood* (called "sap-gum" in the trade) white, frequently with a pinkish tinge, often discolored with blue sap stain; *heartwood* (called "red-gum" in the trade) carneous gray to varying shades of reddish brown, the darker grades frequently with darker streaks of pigment figure (called "figured red-gum" in the trade);[1] *wood* without characteristic odor or taste, frequently interlocked-grained,

[1] Dull yellowish to brown discolorations in red-gum indicate early stages of decay; the figure thus resulting should not be confused with that of figured red-gum.

moderately heavy (sp. gr. approx. 0.44 green, 0.53 ovendry), fairly hard, moderately strong in bending and endwise compression, moderately high in shock resistance, works moderately well with hand tools, machines satisfactorily, considerably above average in turning properties, veneers readily, average in ability to hold nails and screws and in resistance to nail splitting, glues satisfactorily under carefully controlled conditions, takes finishes (such as paint and stain) well, shrinks considerably, has a

Plate LXXXI

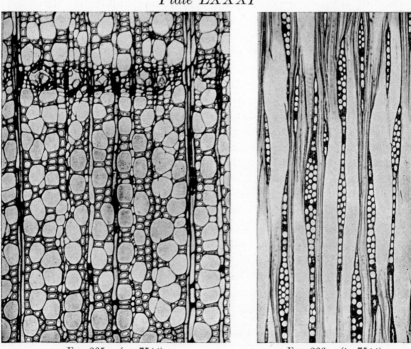

Fig. 265.—(x—75 ×)   Fig. 266.—(t—75 ×)

Red-Gum, American Sweet Gum, *Liquidambar styraciflua* L.

tendency to twist and warp and therefore considerable care is required in piling and seasoning, below average in ability to stay in place, moderately durable. *Growth rinqs* inconspicuous (wood diffuse porous). *Pores* small, not visible to the naked eye, quite uniform in size throughout the growth ring, numerous and frequently crowded, solitary, in multiples of 2–3 (mostly 2), or paired laterally (overlapping vessel segments). *Parenchyma* not visible. *Rays* not distinct to the naked eye, very close, seemingly occupying half the area on the transverse surface of the wood. Longitudinal wound (traumatic) *gum canals* sometimes present (Fig. 265, above), in tangential rows that usually appear at wide intervals, frequently occluded with white deposits.

Minute Anatomy.—*Vessels* 120–180 per square millimeter, the largest 60–95 microns in diameter; perforation plates exclusively scalariform, with many bars (15 plus); spiral thickening present, restricted to the tapering ends of the vessel segments; intervessel pits in transverse rows of 1–3 (Fig. 125, page 429), orbicular to oval or linear through fusion, 6–30 microns in diameter. *Parenchyma* paratracheal and metatracheal-diffuse, sparse. *Fiber tracheids* moderately thick-walled, 20–40 microns in diameter, with conspicuous bordered pits 7–9 microns in diameter. *Rays* 6–9 per millimeter (*k*), unstoried, of two types; (*a*) narrow rays uniseriate, homogeneous and consisting entirely of upright cells or heterogeneous with both upright and procumbent cells; (*b*) wider rays 2–3 (mostly 2)-seriate through the central portion which consists of procumbent cells, with uniseriate extensions (*t*) above and below consisting wholly or mainly of upright cells; several rays of the "*b*" type not infrequently confluent along the grain; upright cells in 1–5 plus rows (*r*), 30–100 microns in height along the grain. *Gum canals*, when present, arranged in a uniseriate tangential row (*x*), with angled orifice.

Remarks.—Unique among North American hardwoods. Red-gum, sometimes called "hazelwood" in the trade, is cut from the heartwood; the sapwood is marketed as "sap-gum" in the United States and as "hazel pine" in England. Figured red-gum (pigment figure) resembles Circassian walnut (*Juglans regia* L.) and is often marketed abroad as "satin walnut." The pigment figure of red-gum is best shown in flat-sawn timber and in rotary-cut veneer; a handsome ribbon stripe is obtained by quartering interlocked-grained stock.

Uses.—*Veneer*[1] used extensively in furniture, in panels, and in various cheap containers such as fruit baskets, boxes, crates, and cigar boxes; *slack cooperage; mine props; railroad ties; pulp* (alkaline process). Lumber used for *planing-mill products* (especially trim), *furniture, cabinetwork, boxes* and *crates* (lower grades); *turned articles.* A considerable quantity of red-gum lumber is normally shipped abroad, mainly to England, France, and Germany, where it is used in the manufacture of furniture, some of which is re-exported to the United States as "satin walnut" (see under Remarks).

Selected References

ANON.: Red and Sap Gum from Southern Hardwood Forests. *South. Hardwood Inform. Ser.*, No. 1. Southern Hardwood Producers, Inc., New Orleans. No date.

[1] Until a few years ago the most important veneer wood and today surpassed in quantity of output only by Douglas fir.

BETTS, H. S.: Sweetgum—American Woods.   Forest Service, U.S. Department of Agriculture.   1945.

CHITTENDEN, A. K., and W. K. HATT: The Red Gum.   *U.S. Dept. Agr. Bul.* 58 (rev.). 1906.

GUENTHER, E.: Styrax and Oil of Styrax.   *Soap Sanit. Chem.*, Vol. 19 (10), pp. 33–35, 73.   1943.

NEUBRECH, W. LeROY: American Hardwoods and Their Uses.   *Trade Prom. Ser.*, No. 178, Bureau of Foreign and Domestic Commerce, U.S. Department of Commerce.   1938.

SCHEFFER, TH. C., and J. R. HANSBROUGH: The Significance of Discoloration in Aircraft Veneers: Sweetgum.   *Forest Prod. Lab., Rpt.*, 1376.   1942.

TEESDALE, L. V.: The Control of Stain, Decay and Other Seasoning Defects in Red Gum.   *U.S. Dept. Agr. Cir.* 421.   1927.

SYCAMORE, BUTTONWOOD, AMERICAN PLANE-TREE

Platanus occidentalis L.

Plate XI, Figs. 62 and 63; Plate XXI, Fig. 117; Plate LXXXII, Figs. 267 and 268

General Characteristics and Properties.—*Sapwood* whitish to light yellowish or reddish brown; *heartwood* light to dark brown or reddish brown when distinguishable; *wood* without characteristic odor or taste, generally irregularly interlocked-grained, moderately heavy (sp. gr. approx. 0.46 green, 0.54 ovendry), moderately hard, moderately strong in bending and endwise compression, moderately stiff, moderately low in shock resistance, difficult to split (because of interlocked grain), turns well on a lathe, requires high-speed cotter head in surfacing (otherwise inclined to chip), intermediate in nail-holding ability, glues satisfactorily, shrinks considerably, inclined to warp in drying but dry quartersawn stock stays in place well, keeps its form well when bent after steaming, not durable when exposed to conditions favorable to decay. *Growth rings* distinct, delineated by a narrow band of lighter tissue at the outer margin. *Pores* small, indistinct, or barely visible to the naked eye, numerous and frequently crowded. *Parenchyma* not visible. *Rays* comparatively wide, conspicuous to the naked eye (*x*), nearly uniform in width, close, appearing as short, closely packed lines on the tangential surface (the pattern is characteristic), forming a high, reddish-brown or silvery fleck on the radial surface.

Minute Anatomy.—*Vessels* 100–140 per square millimeter, the largest 60–100 microns in diameter; perforation plates simple for the most part, occasionally scalariform with a few bars; intervessel pits oval to orbicular (Fig. 117, page 423), widely spaced, small (4–6 microns in diameter).

Parenchyma paratracheal and metatracheal-diffuse; (*a*) paratracheal parenchyma restricted to occasional cells, never forming a sheath; (*b*) metatracheal-diffuse parenchyma abundant, the cells scattered and zonate in short lines which exhibit no regularity. *Fibers* moderately thick-walled, 20–36 microns in diameter. *Rays* unstoried, 1–14 (mostly 3–14)-seriate, up to 3 plus mm. in height along the grain, homogeneous.

Plate LXXXII

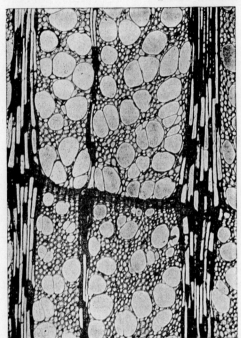

Fig. 267.—(*x*—75 ×)
Fig. 268.—(*t*—75 ×)

Sycamore, Buttonwood, American Plane-Tree, *Platanus occidentalis* L.

Remarks.—Distinct among North American woods because of its characteristic figure, either quartered or flat-sawn; the former is highly ornamental because of the large crowded rays.

Uses.—*Veneer*, for fruit and vegetable baskets, for cigar boxes, and occasionally for paneling (quartersawn); *slack cooperage* (especially sugar and flour barrels because it does not impart taste, odor, or stain). Lumber used for *boxes* and *crates* (especially for plug-tobacco boxes); *furniture* (largely concealed parts, such as drawer sides and bottoms, backs for cheaper chairs); *motor-vehicle parts; millwork* (interior trim and paneling; the beauty of quartersawn stock has not been sufficiently recognized); *laundry appliances.*

Selected References

ANON.: The Southern Hardwoods. Southern Hardwood Producers, Inc., Memphis, Tenn. 1941.

BETTS, H. S.: Sycamore—American Woods. Forest Service, U.S. Department of Agriculture. 1945.

BRUSH, W. D.: Utilization of Sycamore. *U.S. Dept. Agr. Bul.* 884. 1920.

NEUBRECH, W. LeROY: American Hardwoods and Their Uses. *Trade Prom. Ser.*, No. 178, Bureau of Foreign and Domestic Commerce, U.S. Department of Commerce. 1938.

BLACK CHERRY, CHERRY

Prunus serotina Ehrh.

Plate VII, Fig. 40; Plate XX, Fig. 109; Plate LXXXIII, Figs. 269 and 270

General Characteristics and Properties.—*Sapwood* whitish to light reddish brown, narrow; *heartwood* light to dark reddish brown, dull; *wood* without characteristic odor or taste, straight-grained, moderately heavy (sp. gr. approx. 0.47 green, 0.53 ovendry), moderately hard, strong in bending and endwise compression, high in shock resistance, works well with tools, finishes smoothly, glues satisfactorily, seasons well, moderately free from checking and warping, shrinks moderately, stays in place well after seasoning. *Growth rings* fairly distinct, delineated by a narrow, inconspicuous band of porous tissue in the early springwood. *Pores* small, indistinct to the naked eye, those at the beginning of the ring somewhat larger, closer, and aligned in a more or less definite uniseriate row (wood semi-ring porous), elsewhere in the ring quite uniform in size, fairly evenly distributed and arranged solitary, in multiples, and in nests which are frequently oblique to the rays. *Parenchyma* not visible. *Rays* plainly visible to the naked eye. Longitudinal traumatic lysigenous *gum canals* sometimes present.

Minute Anatomy.—*Vessels* 75–180 per square millimeter, the largest 70–90 microns in diameter; perforation plates simple; spiral thickening present (Fig. 109, page 415); intervessel pits broad-oval to orbicular or somewhat angular through crowding (Fig. 109, page 415), 7–10 microns in diameter; gummy infiltration occasionally present. *Parenchyma* very sparse, paratracheal, metatracheal-diffuse, and terminal. *Fibers* thin- to thick-walled, 20–24 microns in diameter. *Rays* unstoried, 1–6 (mostly 3–4)-seriate, homogeneous to heterogeneous.

Remarks.—One of the most handsome of our domestic woods because of its rich reddish-brown color and luster when properly finished. An excellent cabinet wood for the reasons mentioned above, coupled with low shrinkage and freedom from warping and checking.   Not used so extensively as formerly owing to its relative scarcity.

Uses.—*Printers' blocks* for mounting electrotypes (for which it is especially suited because of its strength, moderate hardness, moderate

Plate LXXXIII

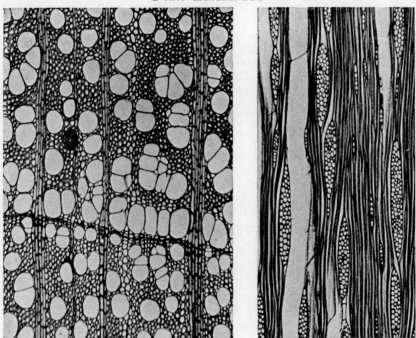

Fig. 269.—(*x*—75 ×)   Fig. 270.—(*t*—75 ×)
Black Cherry, Cherry, *Prunus serotina* Ehrh

shrinkage, and ability to stay in place); *furniture* (valued for its beautiful natural color and its good working and finishing qualities); *patterns; professional* and *scientific instruments; piano actions; cores* for high-class panels; *interior trim* (in buildings, cars, and boats); *handles; woodenware, novelties,* and *toys.*

Selected References

BETTS, H. S.: Black Cherry—American Woods.   Forest Service, U.S. Department of Agriculture.   1945.

COFFEE-TREE, KENTUCKY COFFEE-TREE

Gymnocladus dioicus (L.) K. Koch

Plate X, Fig. 60; Plate LXXXIV, Figs. 271 and 272

General Characteristics and Properties.—*Sapwood* yellowish white, narrow; *heartwood* light red to red or reddish brown; *wood* without

Plate LXXXIV

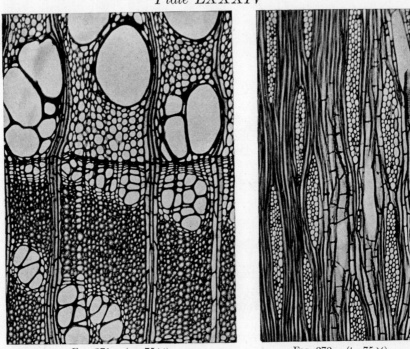

Fig. 271.—(x—75 ×)   Fig. 272.—(t—75 ×)
Coffee-Tree, Kentucky Coffee-Tree, *Gymnocladus dioicus* (L.) K. Koch

characteristic odor or taste, straight-grained, heavy (sp. gr. approx. 0.50 green), hard, moderately strong in bending and endwise compression, moderately durable when exposed to conditions favorable to decay. *Growth rings* conspicuous (wood ring porous). *Springwood pores* large, plainly visible to the naked eye, forming a band 3–6 pores in width, open, occasionally with deposits of reddish gum; transition from spring- to summerwood abrupt; *summerwood pores* small, visible with a hand lens, in the late summerwood in nestlike groups, which occasionally coalesce. *Parenchyma* not visible as such. *Rays* visible but not very conspicuous to the naked eye.

Minute Anatomy.—*Vessels* 8–60 per square millimeter, the largest 200–270 microns in diameter; perforation plates simple; spiral thickening present in the small vessels in the summerwood; intervessel pits orbicular to oval, vestured, 5–9 microns in diameter. *Parenchyma* paratracheal, paratracheal-confluent, and terminal; (*a*) paratracheal parenchyma fairly abundant, forming a 1–several (mostly 1)-seriate, occasionally interrupted sheath about the vessels or vessel groups, in the outer portion of the ring not infrequently extending tangentially as (*b*) paratracheal-confluent parachyma and joining proximate vessel groups; (*c*) terminal parenchyma abundant but not forming a distinct line, passing over into paratracheal-confluent parenchyma. *Fibers* thin- to thick-walled, 18–24 microns in diameter. *Rays* unstoried, 1–7 (mostly 3–5)-seriate, homogeneous, the tallest less than 1200 microns in height along the grain.

Remarks.—This wood is frequently confused with that of honey-locust (*Gleditsia triacanthos* L.), but can be readily distinguished with a hand lens. The vessels in the summerwood of coffee-tree are readily visible at low magnification (10×) and are arranged in nestlike groups which appear to be unaccompanied by parenchyma; in honey-locust, in contrast, the vessels toward the outer margin of the ring are barely visible with a hand lens, are solitary, in short radial rows or in small groups, and are embedded in short tangential bands of parenchyma. Honey-locust is also characterized by broader rays.

Uses.—Locally for *fence posts* and *rails; crossties; rough construction; furniture; cabinetwork; interior finish; fuel.*

HONEY-LOCUST

Gleditsia triacanthos L.

Plate X, Fig. 59; Plate LXXXV, Figs. 273 and 274

General Characteristics and Properties.—*Sapwood* yellowish, wide; *heartwood* light red to reddish brown; *wood* without characteristic odor or taste, very heavy (sp. gr. approx. 0.60 green, 0.67 ovendry), very hard, strong in bending, very strong in endwise compression, stiff, high in shock resistance, works hard with tools, holds nails well but exhibits a tendency to split, does not glue satisfactorily, shrinks little, durable when exposed to conditions favorable to decay. *Growth rings* conspicuous (wood ring porous). *Springwood pores* large, plainly visible to the naked eye, forming a band 3–5 pores in width, frequently with deposits of reddish-brown gum; transition from spring- to summerwood abrupt;

summerwood pores small, barely visible with a hand lens, solitary, in short radial rows, or in small groups, embedded in short, tangential bands of parenchyma in the late summerwood. *Parenchyma* as above, the whitish bands visible with a hand lens in the late summerwood. *Rays* conspicuous to the naked eye.

Minute Anatomy.—*Vessels* 5–30 per square millimeter, the largest 200–310 microns in diameter; perforation plates simple; spiral thickening

Plate LXXXV

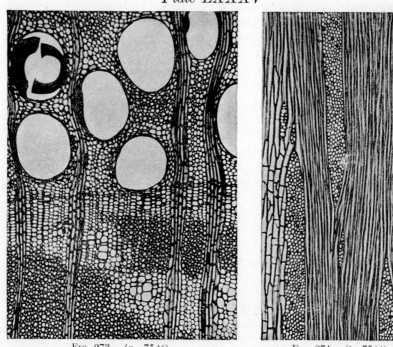

Fig. 273.—(*x*—75 ×)   Fig. 274.—(*t*—75 ×)
Honey-Locust, *Gleditsia triacanthos* L.

confined to the small vessels in the summerwood; intervessel pits orbicular to oval or somewhat angular through crowding, vestured, 5–10 microns in diameter, the apertures frequently confluent. *Parenchyma* abundant, paratracheal, paratracheal-confluent, and terminal; (*a*) paratracheal parenchyma (1) composing an appreciable portion of the conjunctive tissue between the vessels and the rays in the porous springwood zone, (2) forming fairly extensive tracts about the vessels farther out in the ring, (3) in the late summerwood extending from the flanks of the vessels and frequently uniting with parenchyma from proximate vessels and forming short, tangential, 1–8 plus seriate bands of (*b*) paratracheal-confluent parenchyma in which the vessels or vessel groups are included; (*c*) terminal parenchyma abundant but not forming a distinct line, passing over into the paratracheal parenchyma of the succeeding ring. *Fibers* moderately thick- to thick-walled, 18–24 microns in diameter. *Rays* unstoried, 1–14 (mostly 6–9)-seriate, essentially homogeneous, the tallest more than 1200 microns in height along the grain.

Remarks.—Honey-locust wood is frequently confused with that of coffee-tree [*Gymnocladus dioicus* (L.) K. Koch]; for differences between these timbers see Remarks under Coffee-tree, page 575.

Uses.—Locally for *fence posts* and *rails; general construction; furniture* (the wood possesses many desirable qualities such as attractive figure and color, strength, and hardness but is little used because of its scarcity); *interior trim; vehicles* (especially for wagon wheels).

YELLOWWOOD

Cladrastis lutea (Michx.) K. Koch

Plate VII, Fig. 39; Plate LXXXVI, Figs. 275 and 276

General Characteristics and Properties.—*Sapwood* narrow, nearly white; *heartwood* clear yellow, changing on exposure to light brown or yellow streaked with brown; *wood* without characteristic odor or taste, heavy (sp. gr. approx. 0.52 green), hard. *Growth rings* distinct but not prominent (wood semi-ring porous to diffuse porous), delineated by a whitish line of terminal parenchyma and also through a fairly abrupt difference in size between the pores of the late summerwood and those in the springwood of the succeeding ring. *Pores* scattered except in the early springwood where they are often arranged in a uniseriate, more or less continuous row, decreasing gradually in size toward the outer margin of the ring, showing as white specks to the naked eye, appearing thick-walled (because of encircling parenchyma) with a hand lens, solitary and in multiples of 2–several (sometimes in nests in the late summerwood); tyloses sparse; brownish gummy deposits fairly abundant. *Parenchyma* as above and terminal, the whitish line usually distinct with a hand lens. *Rays* visible to the naked eye.

Minute Anatomy.—*Vessels* 8–25 per square millimeter, the largest 150–220 microns in diameter; perforation plates simple; spiral thickening occasionally present in the small vessels in the summerwood, inconspicuous; intervessel pits mostly orbicular to angular, occasionally elliptical to linear, 6–18 microns in diameter, vestured. *Parenchyma* abundant, paratracheal, metatracheal-diffuse, and terminal; (*a*) paratracheal parenchyma forming an irregular, 1–several-seriate continuous sheath about the vessels or groups of vessels; (*b*) metatracheal-diffuse parenchyma sparse, restricted to occasional cells; (*c*) terminal parenchyma abundant, forming a distinct 1–several-seriate line. *Fibers* moderately thick- to thick-walled, frequently gelatinous (especially in

Plate LXXXVI

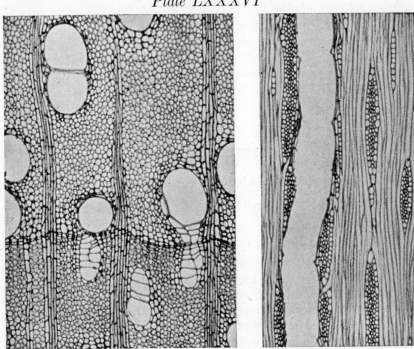

Fig. 275.—(*x*—75 ×)　　　　　　　　　Fig. 276.—(*t*—75 ×)
Yellowwood, *Cladrastis lutea* (Michx.) K. Koch.

the late summerwood), 12–36 microns in diameter. *Rays* unstoried, heterogeneous; (*a*) broader rays mostly 4–6 seriate, the upright cells frequently flanking the core of the rays as sheath cells, also in 1–several rows on the upper and lower margins of the rays; (*b*) narrow rays scarce, mostly 1–2-seriate; uniseriate rays consisting entirely of upright cells; biseriate rays with the upright cells confined to the upper and lower margins.

Uses.—*Veneer* (largely logs cut from trees used for ornamental plantings); *gunstocks* (occasionally); *fuel wood*.

BLACK LOCUST

Black Locust (*Robinia pseudoacacia* L.), Text Fig. 16, *E*; Plate IX, Fig. 50; Plate XX, Fig. 112; Plate LXXXVII, Fig. 277 and 278

Shipmast Locust (*Robinia pseudoacacia* var. *rectissima* Raber)

General Characteristics and Properties.—*Sapwood* yellowish, narrow; *heartwood* greenish yellow to dark yellowish, greenish, or golden-brown, (that of shipmast locust darker, ranging from deep yellow to golden- or rich reddish brown); *wood* without characteristic odor or taste, very heavy (sp. gr. approx. 0.66 green, 0.71 ovendry), very hard, exceedingly strong in bending, extremely strong in endwise compression, exceedingly stiff, very high in shock resistance, moderately low in shrinkage, turns well but difficult to work with hand tools, with high nail-holding ability, durable[1] [especially shipmast locust which is said to be at least twice as durable as the ordinary kind (see S. B. Detwiler, and Oran Raber, under Selected References)]. *Growth rings* distinct (wood ring porous). *Springwood pores* large, forming a band 2–3 pores in width, completely occluded with tyloses in the heartwood and the contours of the individual pores hence indistinct, the springwood zone appearing as a light-colored band (*x*) to the naked eye; transition from spring- to summerwood abrupt; *summerwood pores* small, arranged in nestlike groups which coalesce laterally in the late summerwood forming interrupted concentric bands. *Parenchyma* not distinct as such. *Rays* generally visible to the naked eye.

Minute Anatomy.—*Vessels* 5–35 per square millimeter, the largest 200–300 microns in diameter; perforation plates simple; spiral thickening present in the small vessels in the summerwood; tyloses in the springwood vessels small, appearing cellular *en masse;* intervessel pits orbicular to oval or angular through crowding (Fig. 112, page 415), vestured, 5–12 microns in diameter, the orifices frequently confluent. *Parenchyma* abundant, paratracheal, paratracheal-confluent, and terminal; (*a*) paratracheal parenchyma (1) intermingled with substitute fibers and some fibers and composing an appreciable portion of the conjunctive tissue between the vessels and the rays in the porous springwood zone, (2) forming an irregular, 1–several-seriate, continuous or interrupted sheath about the vessels or groups of vessels farther out in the ring, (3) toward the outer margin of the ring passing over into (*b*) paratracheal-confluent parenchyma and frequently serving as conjunctive tissue uniting proximate groups of vessels laterally (across the rays); (*c*) terminal parenchyma

---

[1] According to Th. C. Scheffer, H. G. Lachmund, and Henry Hopp (see Selected References), the superior decay resistance of black locust heartwood appears to be due to certain extractable chemical components found in the heartwood.

abundant but not forming a distinct line, passing over into the paratracheal parenchyma of the succeeding ring. *Fusiform parenchyma cells* (substitute fibers) present, intermingled with parenchyma. *Fibers* moderately thick- to thick-walled, occasionally gelatinous, 14–22 microns in diameter. *Rays* unstoried, 1–7 (mostly 3–5)-seriate, homogeneous to somewhat heterogeneous.

Plate LXXXVII

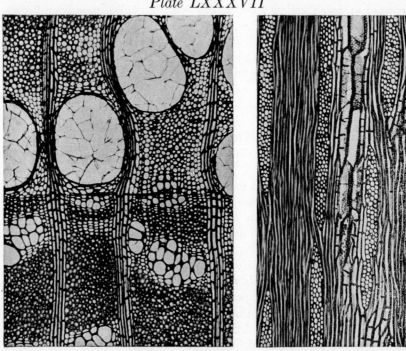

Fig. 277.—(*x*—75 ✕)   Fig. 278.—(*t*—75 ✕)
Black Locust, *Robinia pseudoacacia* L.

Remarks.—The wood of black locust is frequently confused with that of Osage-orange [*Maclura pomitera* (Raf.) Schneid.], but these woods can be distinguished by the following characters. The fresh-cut surface of Osage-orange is usually of a deeper shade of yellow or orange-brown, and the yellow coloring matter readily dissolves when shavings are placed in tepid water; very little coloring matter can be extracted by this method from black locust. Positive identification of black locust is ensured through the presence of vestured intervessel pits, a feature that is wanting in Osage-orange.

Uses.—*Fence posts, mine timbers, poles, railroad ties, stakes* (especially well suited for the above uses because of its durability, hardness, and strength); *insulator pins* (the principal product manufactured from black locust; well adapted for this purpose because of its strength, durability, and moderate shrinkage and swelling which tend to prevent the pins from loosening in the crossarms); *vehicle construction* (wagon hubs); *machine parts; woodenware* and *novelties; boxes* and *crates* (requiring exceptional strength); *planing-mill products; treenails; mine equipment.*

Selected References

BETTS, H. S.: Black Locust—American Woods. Forest Service, U.S. Department of Agriculture. 1945.

CUNO, J. B.: Utilization of Black Locust. *U.S. Dept. Agr. Cir.* 131. 1930.

DETWILER, S. B.: The History of Shipmast Locust. *Jour. Forestry,* Vol. 35, pp. 709–712. 1937.

HOPP, HENRY: Methods of Distinguishing between the Shipmast and Common Forms of Black Locust on Long Island, N.Y. *U.S. Dept. Agr. Tech. Bul.* 742. 1941.

RABER, ORAN: Shipmast Locust a Valuable Undescribed Variety of *Robinia pseudoacacia. U.S. Dept. Agr. Cir.* 379. 1936.

SCHEFFER, TH. C., H. G. LACHMUND, and HENRY HOPP: Relation between Hot-water Extractives and Decay Resistance of Black Locust Wood. *Jour. Agr. Res.,* Vol. 68, pp. 415–426. 1944.

HOLLY

Ilex opaca Ait.

Plate XV, Fig. 89; Plate XXI, Fig. 124; Plate LXXXVIII, Figs. 279 and 280

General Characteristics and Properties.—*Sapwood* white; *heartwood* ivory-white, frequently with bluish streaks or a bluish cast; *wood* without characteristic odor or taste, heavy (sp. gr. approx. 0.50 green, 0.61 ovendry), hard, moderately strong in bending, moderately weak in endwise compression, high in shock resistance, carves, turns, and works with tools well, shrinks considerably, requires considerable care in drying to avoid checking and warping, when properly seasoned stays in place well, not durable when exposed to conditions favoring decay. *Growth rings* barely distinct (wood diffuse porous), delineated by a faint line of denser fibrous tissue at the outer margin. *Pores* very small, barely visible with a hand lens, grouped in radial strings (pore clusters) which not infrequently extend across the rings and cross the ring boundaries. *Parenchyma* indistinct. *Rays* of two widths; (*a*) broader rays visible to the naked eye, wider than the largest pores; (*b*) narrow rays barely visible with a hand lens, several between the broad rays.

Minute Anatomy.—*Vessels* 100–180 per square millimeter, the largest 40–80 microns in diameter; perforation plates scalariform with many bars (15 plus); spiral thickening present; intervessel pits generally orbicular to oval and mostly opposite in a low spiral, 4–7 microns in diameter, occasionally linear and then up to 25 microns in diameter (Fig. 124, page 423).   *Parenchyma* paratracheal and metatracheal-diffuse; (*a*) paratracheal parenchyma very sparse, restricted to occasional cells;

Plate LXXXVIII

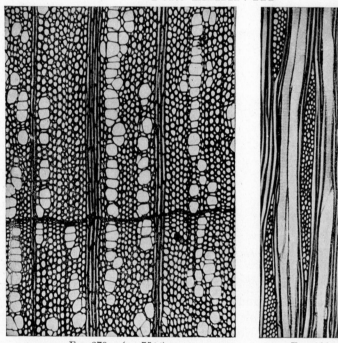

Fig. 279.—(*x*—75 ×)   Fig. 280.—(*t*—75 ×)
Holly, American Holly, *Ilex opaca* Ait.

(*b*) metatracheal-diffuse parenchyma sparse to fairly abundant, the cells scattered. *Fibers* thin- to moderately thick-walled, with spiral thickenings, 16–24 microns in diameter. *Rays* unstoried, heterogeneous; (*a*) broader rays 3–5 (mostly 5)-seriate, many cells in height, with 1–several (mostly 1) rows of upright cells on the upper and lower margins; (*b*) narrow rays uniseriate, few–many cells in height, consisting entirely of upright cells.

Remarks.—Distinct among North American woods because of its ivory-white heartwood, small pores in radial strings (pore clusters) which frequently extend across the rings and occasionally across the ring boundaries, latticed vessel perforations with many bars (15 plus), and spiral thickening in the vessel segments and fibers. The wood of blue-beech (*Carpinus caroliniana* Walt.) approaches holly in color but is quite distinct in its structural features (aggregate rays, vessel perforations simple or scalariform with 3–6 bars, and with spiral thickening confined to the vessels).

Uses.—*Furniture* (largely inlay work); *fixtures; brush backs; handles; turnery; novelties; engravings, scrollwork; carvings; scientific instruments;* (measuring scales and rules). Occasionally stained black to imitate ebony produced by *Diospyros* and *Maba spp.*, especially for piano keys.

Selected References

ANON.: The Southern Hardwoods. Southern Hardwood Producers Inc., Memphis, Tenn. 1941.

BETTS, H. S.: American Holly—American Woods. Forest Service, U.S. Dept. of Agriculture. 1945.

HARD MAPLE

Sugar Maple (*Acer saccharum* Marsh.), **Black Maple** (*Acer nigrum* Michx. f.)
Plate XVI, Figs. 93 and 94; Plate LXXXIX, Figs. 281 and 282

General Characteristics and Properties.—*Sapwood* white with a reddish tinge, narrow; *heartwood* uniform light reddish brown; *wood* without characteristic odor or taste, usually straight-grained (occasionally curly- or wavy-grained or with bird's-eye figure), heavy (sp. gr. 0.52 green, 0.62–0.68 ovendry), hard, very strong in bending, strong in endwise compression, stiff, high in shock resistance, works well with tools, turns well, stays smooth under abrasion, capable of taking a high polish, takes stain satisfactorily, high in nail-holding ability but splits readily along the rays, intermediate in gluing, dries fairly easily, shrinks moderately, below average in ability to stay in place, not durable when exposed to conditions favorable to decay. *Growth rings* usually fairly distinct, delineated by a narrow, darker line of denser fibrous tissue. *Pores* small, indistinct without a hand lens, quite uniform in size, evenly distributed throughout the growth ring (wood diffuse porous), solitary and occasionally in multiples of 2–several. *Parenchyma* not visible. *Rays* of two widths; (*a*) broader rays visible to the naked eye (*x*), fully as wide as the largest pores, separated by several narrow rays, forming a pronounced close ray fleck on the quarter surface, appearing on the tangential surface as short crowded lines which are visible without magnification; (*b*) narrow rays scarcely visible with a hand lens.

Minute Anatomy.—*Vessels* 40–80 per square millimeter, the largest 70–90 microns in diameter; perforation plates simple; spiral thickening present; intervessel pits orbicular or angular through crowding, 6–10 microns in diameter. *Parenchyma* sparse, restricted to occasional cells, terminal, paratracheal, and metatracheal-diffuse. *Fibers* thin- to moder-

Plate LXXXIX

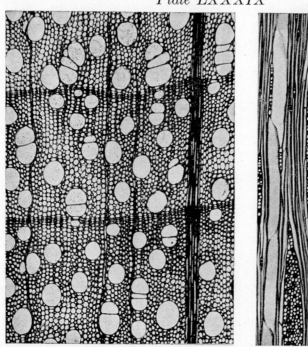 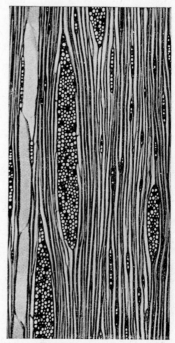

Fig. 281.—(*x*—75 ✕)   Fig. 282.— (*t*—75 ✕)
Sugar Maple, *Acer saccharum* Marsh.

ately thick-walled, 16–30 microns in diameter. *Rays* unstoried, essentially homogeneous; (*a*) broader rays 3–8 (mostly 5–7)-seriate, up to 800 plus microns in height along the grain; (*b*) narrow rays 1–3 (mostly 1)-seriate, much lower than the broader rays (majority less than 200 microns in height).

Remarks.—Sugar maple and black maple are sold indiscriminately as hard maple. Hard maple can be distinguished from the soft maples (*A. rubrum* L., *A. saccharinum* L.) and from Oregon maple (*A. macrophyllum* Pursh) in that the rays intergrade in size (*x*) in these last-named species and the widest rays are not so broad. Sometimes confused with dogwood (*Cornus spp.*); for distinguishing features, see Remarks under Dogwood, page 600.

Uses.—*Hardwood distillation* (standard wood along with beech and birch); *railroad ties* (very suitable as to hardness and resiliency but must be pressure-treated against decay); *veneer* (especially logs showing curly, wavy, and bird's-eye figures; such stock is used in the manufacture of furniture and musical instruments, and to some extent for interior finish); *shoe lasts; bowling pins; fuel wood.* Lumber used for *furniture* (one of the leading native woods because of its hardness, strength, and good working and finishing qualities combined with pleasing color and grain); *flooring* (long a favorite because of its uniform texture and hardness resulting in high resistance to abrasion, even under such severe conditions of use as in bowling alleys, and dance and factory floors); *boxes* and *crates; boot* and *shoe findings; motor vehicles; handles; woodenware* and *novelties; shuttles, spools, bobbins* and other turned products; *toys; butchers' blocks* and *skewers; general millwork* (such as sash and doors); *sporting* and *athletic goods* (bowling pins, billiard cues, croquet mallets and balls, dumbbells); *musical instruments* [especially piano frames and the backs (curly stock) of violins]; *refrigerators;* the standard wood in the United States for shear-test blocks.

Selected References

BENSON, A. O.: Woods and Mill Studies of the Manufacture of Birch, Beech and Maple Lumber in the Northeast. *Forest Prod. Lab., Mimeo.* 1217. 1939.

BETTS, H. S.: Maple—American Woods. Forest Service, U.S. Department of Agriculture. 1945.

MAXWELL, HU.: Uses of Commercial Woods of the United States: Beech, Birches, and Maples. *U.S. Dept. Agr., Bul.* 12. 1913.

NEUBRECH, W. LeROY: American Hardwoods and Their Uses. *Trade Prom. Ser.,* No. 178, Bureau of Foreign and Domestic Commerce, U.S. Department of Commerce. 1938.

PAUL, B. H., and N. A. NORTON: Judging the Quality of Sugar Maple. Reprinted from *Wood Prod.* March, 1936.

OREGON MAPLE, BIGLEAF MAPLE

Acer macrophyllum Pursh

Plate XVI, Fig. 92; Plate XC, Figs. 283 and 284

General Characteristics and Properties.—*Sapwood* reddish white, sometimes with a grayish cast; *heartwood* pinkish brown; *wood* without characteristic odor or taste, generally straight- but occasionally wavy-grained, moderately heavy (sp. gr. approx. 0.44 green, 0.51 ovendry), moderately hard, moderately strong in bending and endwise compression, moderately stiff, moderately low in shock resistance, turns and otherwise works moderately well with tools, polishes well, takes paints and stains readily, difficult to glue, shrinks moderately, not durable when exposed to conditions favorable to decay. *Growth rings* not very distinct, delineated by a narrow light line of fibrous tissue. *Pores* moderately

Plate XC

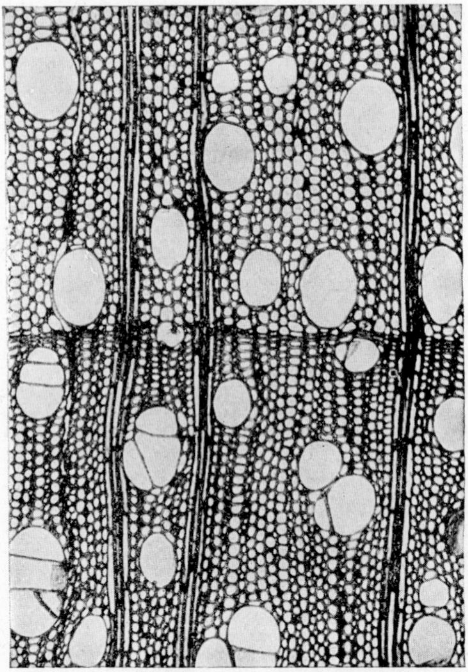

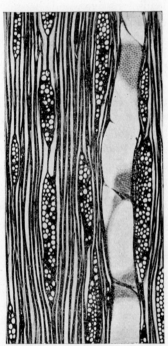

Fig. 283.—(*x*—75 ×)   Fig. 284.—(*t*—75 ×)
Oregon Maple, Bigleaf Maple, *Acer macrophyllum* Pursh.

small to medium-sized, indistinct without a hand lens, evenly distributed throughout the growth ring or somewhat more numerous in the early springwood, solitary and occasionally in multiples of 2–several. *Parenchyma* not visible. *Rays* visible to the naked eye, intergrading in width, the broadest about as wide as the largest pores, forming a pronounced close ray fleck on the quarter surface, appearing on the tangential surface as short crowded lines which are visible without magnification.

Minute Anatomy.—*Vessels* 30–80 per square millimeter, the largest 80–120 microns in diameter; perforation plates simple; spiral thickening present; intervessel pits orbicular or angled through crowding, 4–10 microns in diameter; gummy deposits not infrequent. *Parenchyma* sparse, terminal, paratracheal, and metatracheal-diffuse. *Fibers* thin-to moderately thick-walled, 16–30 microns in diameter. *Rays* unstoried, 1–5 (mostly 3–5)-seriate, essentially homogeneous.

Remarks.—Oregon maple differs from the soft maples in the color of the heartwood, which has a decidedly pinkish cast, and in possessing larger pores (60–120 microns in diameter in Oregon maple; 60–80 microns in the soft maples) and fewer uniseriate rays. For differences between Oregon maple and the hard maples, see Remarks under Hard Maple, page 584.

Uses.—*Veneer* (plain and figured); the plain veneer is largely made into backing and cross-banding in the furniture industry; the figured consists of burl, blister, curly, and quilted patterns[1] and is used for veneer faces and inlay work for expensive furniture; *furniture* including living-room, dining-room, and bedroom sets [finished as walnut or mahogany, enameled or natural (if of fancy veneer)], also overstuffed and upholstered articles and chairs; *handles, fixtures; woodenware* and *novelties.*

Selected References

BETTS, H. S.: Maple—American Woods. Forest Service, U.S. Department of Agriculture. 1945.

JOHNSON, H. M.: Utilization of Bigleaf Maple of the Pacific Northwest. *U.S. Dept. Agr. Cir.* 225. 1932.

SOFT MAPLE

Red Maple (*Acer rubrum* L.), Plate XV, Fig. 90

Silver Maple (*Acer saccharinum* L.), Plate XVI, Fig. 91; Plate XXI, Fig. 121; Plate XCI, Figs. 285 and 286

General Characteristics and Properties.—*Sapwood* white, wide; *heartwood* light brown, sometimes with a grayish or greenish tinge or with a faint purplish cast; *wood* without characteristic odor or taste, straight-grained (sometimes curly-grained), moderately heavy (sp. gr.

---

[1] Quilted maple (see frontispiece) was so named by P. J. Landry of the Kelso Veneer Company, Kelso, Wash., and is traceable to blisterlike elevations in the wood which form under the bark. The quilted structure does not extend around the trunk but is confined to the concave side of leaning trees and to the wider side of trunks with eccentric heartwood; it may continue lengthwise along the trunk from the root crown into the smaller limbs. Landry estimates that quilted maple will become a commercial rarity within a short time.

0.44–0.49 green, 0.51–0.55 ovendry), moderately hard to hard, moderately weak to strong in bending, moderately weak to moderately strong in endwise compression, limber to stiff, moderately high in shock resistance, works well under tools, glues satisfactorily but requires considerable care for best results, finishes smoothly, moderately low in shrinkage, stays in place well when dry, not durable when exposed to conditions favorable to decay. *Growth rings* not very distinct, delineated by a narrow, darker

Plate XCI

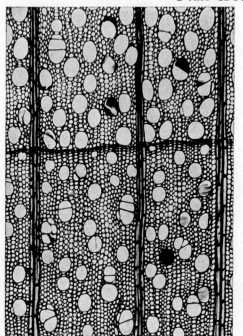 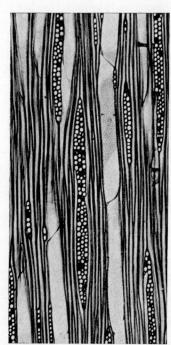

Fig. 285.—(*x*—75 ✕)   Fig. 286.—(*t*—75 ✕)
Silver Maple, *Acer saccharinum* L.

line of denser fibrous tissue. *Pores* small, indistinct without a hand lens, evenly distributed throughout the growth ring, solitary and occasionally in multiples of 2–several. *Parenchyma* not visible. *Rays* visible to the naked eye, intergrading in width, the broadest about as wide as the largest pores, forming a pronounced close ray fleck on the quarter surface, appearing on the tangential surface as short crowded lines which are visible without magnification.

Minute Anatomy.—*Vessels* 30–80 per square millimeter, the largest 60–80 microns in diameter; perforation plates simple; spiral thickening present; intervessel pits orbicular to broad-oval or somewhat angled through crowding (Fig. 121, page 423), 5–9 microns in diameter; gummy deposits not infrequent. *Parenchyma* sparse, restricted to occasional cells, terminal, paratracheal, and metatracheal-diffuse. *Fibers* thin- to moderately thick-walled, 16–30 microns in diameter. *Rays* unstoried, 1–5-seriate (uniseriate rays usually sparse), essentially homogeneous.

Remarks.—As the common name indicates, the wood of the soft maples is not so hard as that of hard maple produced by *A. saccharum* Marsh. and *A. nigrum* Michx. f. For differences between soft and hard maple, see Remarks under Hard Maple, page 584.

Uses.—Used largely for the same purposes as hard maple (except where strength and hardness are a primary requisite), principally for *furniture; boxes* and *crates; food containers* (especially butter tubs); *truck bodies; wall paneling; planing-mill products;* preferred to hard maple for *core stock.*

Selected References

Anon.: The Southern Hardwoods. Southern Hardwood Producers, Inc., Memphis, Tenn. 1941.

Betts, H. S.: Maple—American Woods. Forest Service, U.S. Department of Agriculture. 1945.

Maxwell, Hu.: Uses of Commercial Woods of the United States: Beech, Birches and Maples. *U.S. Dept. Agr. Bul.* 12. 1913.

BUCKEYE

Yellow Buckeye (*Aesculus octandra* Marsh.), Plate XIII, Fig. 73; Plate XXI, Fig. 122; Plate XCII, Figs. 287 and 288

Ohio Buckeye (*Aesculus glabra* Willd.)

General Characteristics and Properties.—*Sapwood* white to grayish white, gradually merging into the heartwood; *heartwood* creamy white to pale yellowish white, frequently with darker (grayish) streaks of oxidative sap stain; *wood* odorless or with a mild characteristic odor (especially when moist) resembling that of basswood (*Tilia spp.*), without characteristic taste, light (sp. gr. approx. 0.33 green, 0.38 ovendry), soft, weak in bending and endwise compression, low in shock resistance, works easily under hand tools, shrinks moderately but rates low in such machining properties as shaping, turning, and mortising, very low in durability. *Growth rings* not visible or barely distinct and delineated by a light-colored line, generally narrow. *Pores* numerous, minute, not visible without a hand lens, nearly constant in size and quite evenly distributed throughout the growth ring (wood diffuse porous), solitary and in multiples of 2–several. *Parenchyma* not visible or barely visible as a light line terminating the growth ring. *Rays* very fine, scarcely visible with a hand lens, close and seemingly forming half of the area on the transverse surface, storied or unstoried, in the first instance forming fine ripple marks on the tangential surface.

Plate XCII

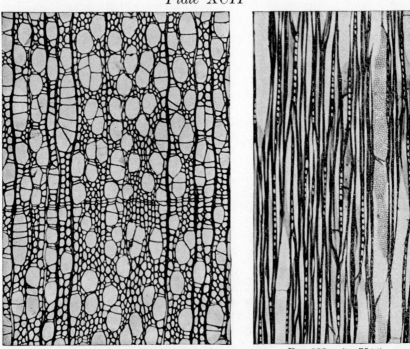

Fig. 287.—(*x*—75 ×)   Fig. 288.—(*t*—75 ×)

Yellow Buckeye, *Aesculus octandra* Marsh.

Minute Anatomy.—*Vessels* 120–200 per square millimeter, the largest 40–80 microns in diameter; vessel members storied with the other elements, or unstoried; perforation plates simple; spiral thickening present or wanting; when present, occasionally restricted to the vessels in the summerwood; intervessel pits orbicular to oval or angular through crowding (Fig. 122, page 423), 5–10 microns in diameter. *Parenchyma* terminal and paratracheal, the cambiform rows along the grain storied with the other elements, or unstoried; (*a*) terminal parenchyma in a more or less continuous, 1–several-seriate line; (*b*) paratracheal parenchyma sparse, restricted to occasional cells (not forming a sheath). *Fibers* thin-walled, 16–30 microns in diameter, the central portion conforming to the storied structure of the wood when this situation prevails. *Rays* storied with the other elements, or unstoried, uniseriate, homogeneous to heterogeneous.

Remarks.—Yellow buckeye can usually be distinguished from Ohio buckeye in that it possesses distinct ripple marks traceable to storied rays and longitudinal elements. Ripple marks are wanting or sporadic in Ohio buckeye since the elements are never regularly storied. Buckeye is sometimes confused with aspen (*Populus spp.*) which is also fine-textured. For means of separating these woods, see under **99** in the Key Based on Minute Features, page 426.

Uses.—*Boxes, crates,* and other shipping containers; *cigar* and *tobacco boxes; artificial limbs; woodenware* and *novelties; toys; furniture* (unexposed parts); *trunks* and *valises* (usually as plywood); excellent for *drawing boards; plaques* for pyrography.

Selected References

BETTS, H. S.: Buckeye—American Woods. Forest Service, U.S. Department of Agriculture. 1945.

CASCARA BUCKTHORN

Rhamnus purshiana DC.

Plate XV, Fig. 85; Plate XCIII, Figs. 289 and 290

General Characteristics and Properties.—*Sapwood* yellowish white; *heartwood* yellowish brown tinged with red; *wood* without characteristic odor or taste, hard (sp. gr. approx. 0.50 green, 0.55 ovendry), heavy, moderately weak in bending, moderately strong in endwise compression, not stiff, high in shock resistance, shrinks very little on drying. *Growth rings* fairly distinct, delineated by a difference in the size and number of the pores in the summerwood and in the springwood of succeeding rings. *Pores* small, indistinct without a hand lens, more numerous and somewhat larger in the springwood (wood diffuse porous) and sometimes forming a more or less continuous uniseriate row at the beginning of the ring, solitary and in multiples of 2–several. *Parenchyma* not visible. *Rays* visible to the naked eye.

Minute Anatomy.—*Vessels* 20–80 per square millimeter, the largest 60–80 microns in diameter; perforation plates simple; spiral thickening present; intervessel pits not crowded, orbicular to oval, 6–8 microns in diameter, occasionally oval-linear and then up to 12 microns in diameter. *Parenchyma* paratracheal and metatracheal-diffuse; (*a*) paratracheal parenchyma forming an interrupted uniseriate sheath around the vessels or groups of vessels; (*b*) metatracheal-diffuse parenchyma sparse, confined to occasional cells. *Fibers* thin-walled, 10–20 microns in diameter. *Rays* unstoried, 1–5 (mostly 3–4)-seriate, essentially homogeneous.

Uses.—*Posts, built-up turned articles,* and other local uses. The chief value of this species is in its bark; an extract prepared from it is widely

Plate XCIII

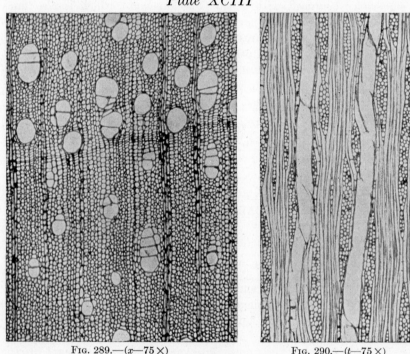

Fig. 289.—(*x*—75 ×)   Fig. 290.—(*t*—75 ×)
Cascara Buckthorn, *Rhamnus purshiana* DC.

used for laxative purposes in the United States and abroad. The finely ground wood also yields an extract up to 75 per cent of efficiency.

Selected References

ARNST, A.: Cascara—A Crop from West Coast Farms. *Jour. Forestry*, Vol. 43, pp. 805–811. 1945.

DAVIDSON, J.: The Cascara Tree in British Columbia. *Brit. Columbia Dept. Agr., Bul.* No. A 108 (rev. ed.). 1942.

STARKER, T. J., and A. R. WILCOX: Cascara. *Amer. Jour. Pharm.*, Vol. 103, Nos. 2 and 3. 1931.

WASSERMAN, B.: Cascara Segrada. *U.S. Bur. Foreign and Dom. Com., Indus. Ref. Serv.*, Vol. 3, Part 2, No. 46. 1945.

BASSWOOD

Basswood (*Tilia americana* L.), Plate XIV, Fig. 82; Plate XXI, Fig. 119 Etc.

White Basswood (*Tilia heterophylla* Vent.), Plate XCIV, Figs. 291 and 292

General Characteristics and Properties.—*Sapwood* whitish to creamy white or pale brown, merging more or less gradually into the darker heartwood; *heartwood* pale brown, sometimes with a reddish tinge; *wood* with a faint characteristic odor on fresh-cut surface (especially when wet), tasteless, straight-grained, light (sp. gr. approx. 0.32 green, 0.40 ovendry), soft, weak in endwise compression and moderately weak in bending, low in shock resistance, works exceptionally well (valued for hand carvings), finishes smoothly, takes and holds paints and lacquers very well, glues well, has poor nail-holding ability but does not split in nailing, shrinks considerably but holds its shape moderately well when thoroughly dry, seasons easily, free from most seasoning defects (such as checking and warping), very low in durability. *Growth rings* fairly distinct, delineated by a difference in size of the pores in the summerwood and in the springwood of the succeeding ring. *Pores* numerous, small, distinctly visible with a hand lens, quite evenly distributed (wood diffuse porous), solitary and in multiples or tangential groups of 2–several. *Parenchyma* not distinct or barely visible with a hand lens, zonate. *Rays* variable in width, the broader not distinct on the transverse surface without a hand lens, forming high, scattered ray flecks on the quarter surface.

Minute Anatomy.—*Vessels* 100–160 per square millimeter, the largest 60–160 microns in diameter; perforation plates simple; spiral thickening present; intervessel pits polygonal through crowding (Fig. 119, page 423), 5–8 microns in diameter, rarely orbicular to broad-oval. *Parenchyma* abundant, terminal and metatracheal, the lines of the latter numerous and uniseriate. *Fibers* thin-walled, 24–36 microns in diameter. *Rays* unstoried or rarely somewhat storied, of two widths; (*a*) broader rays 1–6-seriate, up to 1.2 plus mm. in height along the grain (*t*), essentially homogeneous; (*b*) narrow rays uniseriate for the most part, much lower than the broad rays (the majority less than 300 microns in height), the cells nearly uniform in size but higher than those in the broad rays.

Remarks.—Devoid of figure. Readily recognized by its faint but characteristic odor, the smoothness with which it cuts, the ease of indentation with the thumbnail, and its characteristic, high, widely spaced ray fleck. Sometimes confused with buckeye (*Aesculus spp.*) but distinct in color (without the yellowish cast of buckeye) and in possessing larger pores, zonate parenchyma, and wider rays (see description of buckeye, page 589).

Uses.—*Veneer* (cut almost entirely by the rotary method) used in the manufacture of *plywood*, for drawer panels, mirror backings, and other concealed parts of furniture (because of its freedom from checking and warping, the light color of the wood, and ease of gluing) and for trunk panels and valises (because it does not split readily under abrasion); as *core stock* (thick veneer) on which thin veneers of expensive cabinet woods are glued; as *veneer stock* for baskets. *Slack cooperage*, especially

Plate XCIV

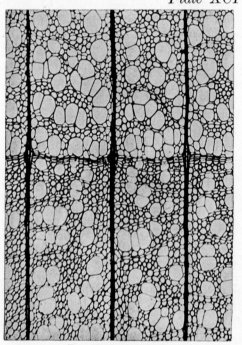 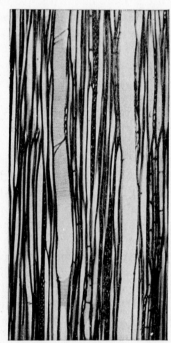

Fig. 291.—(*x*—75 ×)   Fig. 292.—(*t*—75 ×)

White Basswood, *Tilia heterophylla* Vent.

heading for flour barrels (because of its clear appearance, freedom from checking and warping, and the lack of taste and color pigments that might be transmitted to the flour). *Excelsior* (a good native wood for this purpose, because of light weight and color, straight grain, and ease with which it can be shaved into thin but tough and resilient strands but prone to develop a malodor if used under moist conditions; not used at present so extensively as formerly because of the steady demand for other purposes). *Lumber* used for *boxes* and *crates* (because of its lightness, light color, good nailing properties, and freedom from objectionable odor and taste); *dairy, poultry,* and *apiary supplies; furniture* (concealed parts); *core stock* for panels; *millwork* (especially sash and doors); *trunks* and *valises; woodenware* and *novelties; toys; caskets* and *coffins; laundry appliances; refrigerators; kitchen cabinets; handles; shade* and *map rollers; fixtures; Venetian-blind slats; piano keys* (lumber cut from frozen logs, carefully air-seasoned in diffused light to preserve color and selected for straightness of grain).

Selected References

BETTS, H. S.: American Basswood—American Woods. Forest Service, U.S. Department of Agriculture. 1945.

BRUSH, W. D.: Utilization of Basswood. *U.S. Dept. Agr. Bul.* 1007. 1922.

KUKACHKA, B. FRANCIS, and L. W. REES: Systematic Anatomy of the Woods of the Tiliaceae. *Minn. Univ. Agr. Expt. Sta., Tech. Bul.* 158. 1943.

McELHANNEY, T. A., *et al.*: Canadian Woods, Their Properties and Uses. *Canada.* Department of the Interior, Forest Service. 1935.

NEUBRECH, W. LeROY: American Hardwoods and Their Uses. *Trade Prom. Ser.*, No. 178, Bureau of Foreign and Domestic Commerce, U.S. Department of Commerce. 1938.

BLACK GUM, SWAMP TUPELO, AND TUPELO GUM

Black Gum, Black Tupelo, Pepperidge (*Nyssa sylvatica* Marsh.), Plate XIII, Fig. 75; Plate XXII, Fig. 127; Plate XCV, Figs. 295 and 296

Swamp Tupelo, Swamp Black Gum [*Nyssa sylvatica* var. biflora (Walt.) Sarg.]

Tupelo Gum, Water Gum (*Nyssa aquatica* L.) Plate XIII, Fig. 76; Plate XCV, Figs. 293 and 294

General Characteristics and Properties.—*Sapwood* white to grayish white, gradually merging into the darker heartwood; *heartwood* greenish or brownish gray; *wood* without characteristic odor or taste, usually interlocked-grained and hence showing a distinct ribbon figure when quartersawn (especially black gum), moderately heavy (sp. gr. approx. 0.46 green, 0.52–0.55 ovendry), moderately hard, moderately strong in bending and endwise compression, moderately high in shock resistance (occasional trees, and some butt logs of tupelo, produce wood exceptionally light in weight and low in strength properties), difficult to split, quite refractory under hand tools, below average to average in machining characteristics; below average in steam bending, finishes unusually well with enamels, paints, stains, and lacquers, intermediate in nail-holding ability, glues satisfactorily but may require special treatment for best results, shrinks considerably and tends to warp and twist (due to interlocked-grain), requires considerable care in drying (especially plain-sawn

Plate XCV

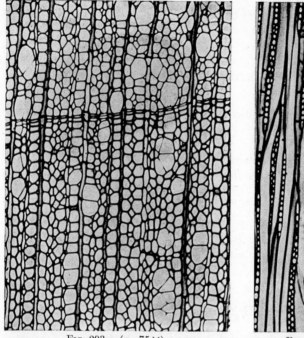

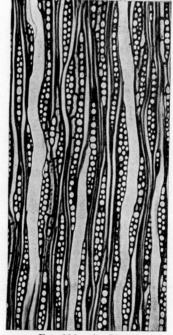

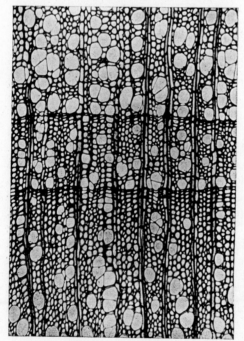

Fig. 293.—(x—75×)   Fig. 294.—(t—75×)

Tupelo Gum, Water Gum, *Nyssa aquatica* L.

Fig. 295.—(x—75×)   Fig. 296.—(t—75×)

Black Gum, Black Tupelo, Pepperidge, *Nyssa sylvatica* Marsh.

stock), low in ability to stay in place under conditions of actual use, not durable when exposed to conditions favorable to decay. *Growth rings* generally indistinct, even under a lens (wood diffuse porous). *Pores* small, not visible to the naked eye, quite uniform in size, numerous and fairly evenly distributed, solitary or occasionally in short radial groups and in multiples. *Parenchyma* not visible. *Rays* fine, not distinct on the transverse surface without a hand lens, very close and seemingly occupying one-half the area on the transverse surface of the wood.

Minute Anatomy.—*Vessels* 90–180 per square millimeter, the largest 60–90 microns in diameter; perforation plates exclusively scalariform with numerous thin bars; spiral thickening occasionally present, restricted to the tapering ends of the vessel segments; intervessel pits in transverse rows of 1–5 plus (opposite pitting—, Fig. 127, page 429), for the most part oval-rectangular and 5–12 microns in diameter, occasionally linear through fusion and then up to 20 microns in diameter. *Parenchyma* paratracheal and metatracheal-diffuse, the cells scattered. *Fibers* moderately thick- to thick-walled, 20–32 microns in diameter. *Rays* 8–13 per millimeter (*x*), unstoried, 1–4-seriate, heterogeneous; upright cells generally restricted to one row on the upper and lower margins, less than 60 microns in height along the grain.

Remarks.—Black gum, swamp tupelo, and tupelo gum are difficult to separate with certainty, even at high magnifications, but the last two woods are usually somewhat softer, lighter, and more porous, with more crowded, slightly larger vessels. The vessels are frequently greatly restricted in number in wood from the swollen butt log of tupelo gum; since the fibers are also thinner walled and radially aligned, the tissue, as viewed in the transverse section at high magnifications, strikingly resembles that of a coniferous wood.

Uses.[1]—*Veneer*, most of which is converted into fruit and berry boxes and similar containers; *plywood*, for panels (not too satisfactory as it tends to warp); *pulp* (alkaline process; these woods can also be pulped satisfactorily by the sulphite and semichemical processes); *cooperage* (mostly slack staves and heading); *railroad ties* (heartwood takes preservative readily and interlocked grain obviates use of antisplitting irons). *Lumber* used for *boxes* and *crates*, for which its light color and toughness recommend it very highly (such boxes are extensively used in the export trade because the wood shows stenciling well); *furniture*, especially in concealed parts (such as drawer sides and bottons); *refrigerators* and *kitchen cabinets; laundry appliances; dairy, poultry,* and *apiary*

---

[1] Until recently, black gum and the tupelos were sold in mixture under either common name; at present, there is a growing tendency to merchandise these woods under their own names, respectively.

supplies; factory floors and *platform planking* required to withstand heavy wear; *planing-mill products* (such as trim, molding, and built-in cabinets); *motor vehicles; cigar boxes* [as core stock covered with a veneer of Spanish cedar (*Cedrela spp.*) or with paper bearing the image (along the grain) of this species]; *woodenware, novelties,* and *fixtures; handles.*

Selected References

ANON.: Tupelo and Black Gum from Southern Hardwood Forests. *South. Hardwood Inform. Series* 4, Southern Hardwood Producers, Inc., Memphis, Tenn. No date.

BETTS, H. S.: Tupelo—American Woods. Forest Service, U.S. Department of Agriculture. 1945.

HOLROYD, H. B.: The Utilization of Tupelo. *U.S. Dept. Agr. Forest Serv. Cir.* 40. 1906.

NEUBRECH, W. LeRoy: American Hardwoods and Their Uses. *Trade Promotion Series*, No. 178, Bureau of Foreign and Domestic Commerce, U.S. Department of Commerce. 1938.

SMILEY, G. R.: Stacking, Seasoning and Treatment of Gum (*Nyssa*) Lumber for Railroads. *Proc. Amer. Wood Preservers' Assoc.*, Vol. 36, pp. 208–211. 1940.

SUDWORTH, G. B., and C. D. MELL: Distinguishing Characteristics of North American Gum Woods. *U.S. Dept. Agr. Forest Serv. Bul.* 103. 1911.

DOGWOOD, FLOWERING DOGWOOD

Dogwood (*Cornus florida* L.), Plate XVI, Fig. 95; Plate XCVI, Figs. 297 and 298

Pacific Dogwood (*Cornus nuttalli* Audub.), Plate XVI, Fig. 96; Plate XCVI, Figs. 299 and 300

General Characteristics and Properties.—*Sapwood* carneous to light pinkish brown, very wide; *heartwood*, when present, dark brown, frequently variegated; *wood* without characteristic odor or taste, heavy to very heavy (sp. gr. 0.58–0.64 green, 0.70–0.80 ovendry), hard to very hard, moderately strong to strong in bending, strong in endwise compression, very high in shock resistance, difficult to cut and work with tools, wears smooth with use, glues poorly, high in ability to hold nails, difficult to season, characterized by very great to extremely great shrinkage, low in ability to stay in place under conditions of actual use, not very resistant to decay (because the commercial run consists largely of sapwood). *Growth rings* distinct but not sharply delineated (wood diffuse porous). *Pores* small, not visible without a hand lens, solitary and in multiples of 2–several. *Parenchyma* not distinct or barely distinct with a hand lens, zonate. *Rays* of two widths; (*a*) broader rays visible to the naked eye but not sharply delineated against the background of pores and fibrous tissue; (*b*) narrow rays scarcely distinct with a lens.

Plate XCVI

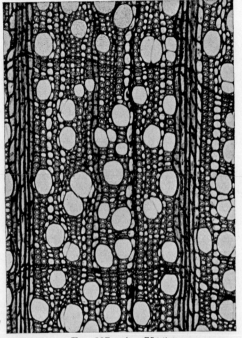

FIG. 297.—(x—75 ×)   FIG. 298.—(t—75 ×)

Dogwood, Flowering Dogwood, *Cornus florida* L.

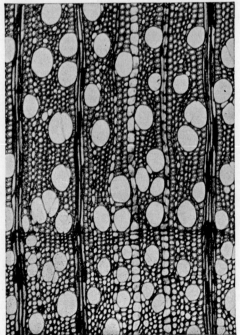

FIG. 299.—(x—75 ×)   FIG. 300.—(t—75 ×)

Pacific Dogwood, *Cornus nuttalli* Audub.

Minute Anatomy.—*Vessels* 40–110 per square millimeter, the largest 60–120 microns in diameter; perforation plates scalariform, with many (20 plus) fine bars; intervessel pits oval to linear (the scalariform pitting common), 8–20 plus microns in diameter. *Parenchyma* paratracheal, metatracheal, and metatracheal-diffuse; (*a*) paratracheal parenchyma restricted to occasional cells, never forming a sheath; (*b*) metatracheal and (*c*) metatracheal-diffuse parenchyma abundant, the former in broken tangential, mostly uniseriate lines which form no definite pattern. *Fibers* moderately thick- to thick-walled, 20–32 microns in diameter. *Rays* unstoried, heterogeneous; (*a*) broader rays 3–8-seriate and composed of horizontal cells through the central portion, with uniseriate margins of 1–5 plus (occasionally many) rows of upright cells; narrow rays 1–2-seriate, composed wholly or largely of upright cells.

Remarks.—Pacific dogwood resembles the eastern species very closely, and samples cannot always be identified with certainty. The broad rays in *C. florida* are 3–8-seriate through the central portion and up to 80 cells in height (*t*); the western species, in contrast, is featured by broad rays which are 3–5-seriate for the most part and seldom over 40 cells in height. Dogwood is sometimes confused with hard maple produced by *Acer saccharum* Marsh., and *A. nigrum* Michx. f., respectively. Dogwood usually has a decided flesh-colored cast (sapwood), the annual rings are less distinct than those of hard maple, and the wood rays do not stand out so sharply on the transverse surface. Positive identification of dogwood is assured through the presence of zonate parenchyma, scalariform plates with many bars, and linear intervessel pits.

Uses.—*Shuttles* for textile weaving (approx. 90 per cent of the "cut"); *spools; bobbin heads; small pulleys; mallet heads; golf-club heads* (occasionally); *turnpins* for shaping the ends of lead pipes; *jewelers' blocks; machinery bearings*. The major uses of this wood are contingent on its hardness and close texture which cause it to work and stay smooth under continuous wear.

Selected References

BETTS, H. S.: Flowering Dogwood—American Woods. Forest Service, U.S. Department of Agriculture. 1945.

CRUIKSHANK, J. W.: The Utilization of Dogwood in the Lower South. *Jour. Forestry*, Vol. 38, pp. 284–285. 1940.

CUNO, J. B.: Utilization of Dogwood and Persimmon. *U.S. Dept. Agr. Bul.* 1436. 1926.

SOURWOOD

Oxydendrum arboreum (L.) DC.

Plate XIV, Fig. 84; Plate XCVII, Figs. 301 and 302

General Characteristics and Properties.—*Sapwood* yellowish brown to light pinkish brown, wide (up to 80 plus growth rings); *heartwood* brown

Plate XCVII

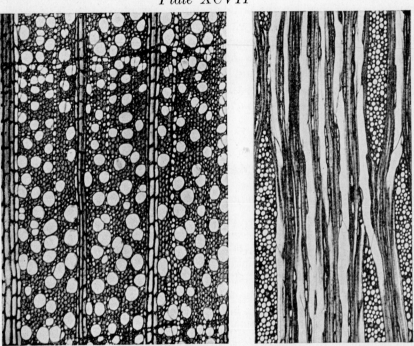

Fig. 301.—(*x*—75 ×)   Fig. 302.—(*t*—75 ×)
Sourwood, *Oxydendrum arboreum* (L.) DC.

tinged with red when first exposed, becoming duller with age; *wood* without characteristic odor or taste, heavy (sp. gr. approx. 0.50 green, 0.59 ovendry), hard, strong in bending, moderately strong in endwise compression, stiff, moderately hard in shock resistance, shrinks considerably. *Growth rings* distinct but not prominent (wood diffuse porous), delineated by a narrow band of denser fibrous tissue at the outer margin, narrow to medium wide. *Pores* numerous, very small (indistinct to the naked eye) and nearly uniform in size except in the late summerwood, solitary for the most part, quite evenly distributed throughout the growth ring. *Parenchyma* not distinct. *Rays* not distinct on the transverse surface without a hand lens, appearing to be quite uniform in size, nearly as wide as the largest pores.

Minute Anatomy.—*Vessels* 150–200 per square millimeter, the largest 40–65 microns in diameter; spiral thickening present, often inconspicuous; perforation plates simple, scalariform or occasionally reticulate (foraminate), the first type the most frequent; tyloses wanting; pits leading to contiguous tracheary cells orbicular to oval or rarely linear, 4–11 microns in diameter. *Parenchyma* sparse, metatracheal-diffuse and very rarely paratracheal, in the latter instance restricted to occasional cells. *Fiber tracheids* thick-walled, with bordered pits, 17–23 microns in diameter. *Rays* 3–5 per millimeter, unstoried, heterogeneous; (*a*) broader rays 5–7-seriate, many cells in height, the upright cells confined to 1–several rows on the upper and lower margins; (*b*) narrow rays uniseriate, 1–6 plus cells in height, consisting entirely of upright cells.

Uses.—Locally for *tool handles; bearings of machinery; sled runners.*

PACIFIC MADRONE, MADROÑA

Arbutus menziesi Pursh

Plate XIV, Fig. 83; Plate XCVIII, Figs. 303 and 304

General Characteristics and Properties.—*Sapwood* white or cream colored, frequently with a pinkish tinge; *heartwood* light reddish brown; *wood* without characteristic odor or taste, heavy (sp. gr. approx. 0.58 green, 0.69 ovendry), hard, moderately strong in bending and endwise compression, moderately high in shock resistance, somewhat below average in working properties, difficult to glue, shrinks excessively on drying and is difficult to season. *Growth rings* barely visible with a hand lens, delineated by a continuous, uniseriate row of pores in the early springwood. *Pores* numerous, minute (barely visible with a hand lens), nearly uniform in size except for a row of large pores in the early springwood (wood diffuse porous), arranged as described above in the early springwood, elsewhere solitary, in multiples, or in short radial rows and frequently further clustered or in bands, the zones of pores then usually alternating with bands of dense (darker) fibrous tissue. *Parenchyma* not evident. *Rays* barely to readily visible with a hand lens.

Minute Anatomy.—*Vessels* 150–250 per square millimeter, the largest 40–60 microns in diameter; perforation plates scalariform or occasionally reticulate (foraminate); spiral thickening present; intervessel pits orbicular, 3–5 microns in diameter. *Parenchyma* paratracheal, very sparse, restricted to occasional cells.   *Fiber tracheids* moderately thick- to thick-walled, (*a*) in the proximity of vessels with conspicuous bordered pits and frequently with spiral thickenings, (*b*) elsewhere with small, inconspicuous bordered pits and devoid of spiral thickening, frequently septate, 15–20 microns in diameter.   *Rays* unstoried, heterogeneous; (*a*) broader rays 3–5-seriate, low (usually under 25 cells in height), with 1–several

Plate *XCVIII*

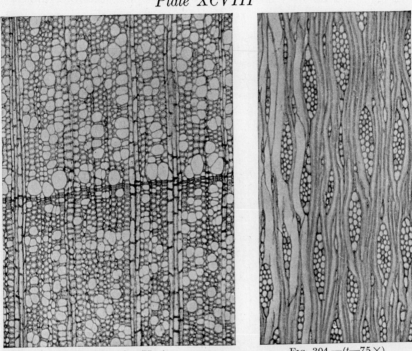

Fig. 303.—(*x*—75 ✕)

Fig. 304.—(*t*—75 ✕)

Pacific Madrone, Madroña, *Arbutus menziesi* Pursh.

(mostly 1) rows of upright cells on the upper and lower margins; (*b*) narrow rays 1–2-seriate, less than 15 cells in height; uniseriate rays of the *b* type consisting entirely of upright cells; biseriate rays of the *b* type consisting of horizontal cells through the central portion, with 1–several rows of marginal upright cells.

Uses.—Locally for *fuel;* as a substitute for dogwood (*Cornus florida* L. and *C. nuttalli* Audub.), for *shuttles;* as *rollers,* 6 to 8 inches in diameter, in shifting heavy cargoes aboard ships.   Formerly converted into *charcoal.*

PERSIMMON

Diospyros virginiana L.

Plate VII, Fig. 37; Plate XX, Fig. 110; Plate XCIX, Figs. 305 and 306

General Characteristics and Properties.—*Sapwood* white to creamy white when freshly cut, darkening on exposure to light yellowish brown or grayish brown, wide (practically all of the stock used for commercial

Plate XCIX

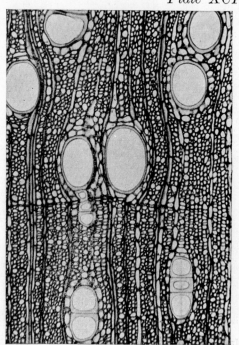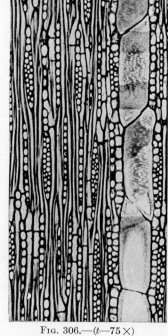

Fig. 305.—(*x*—75 ×)   Fig. 306.—(*t*—75 ×)

Persimmon, *Diospyros virginiana* L.

purposes is sapwood); *heartwood* usually very small, blackish brown to black, often streaked, irregular in outline (*x*); *wood* without characteristic odor or taste, very heavy (sp. gr. approx. 0.64 green, 0.78 ovendry), very hard, very strong in bending and endwise compression, high in shock resistance, difficult to work with tools, wears smooth with use, does not glue well, high in ability to hold nails, difficult to season, characterized by considerable shrinkage, high in ability to stay in place when properly used, not very resistant to decay (because it consists largely of sapwood). *Growth rings* distinct but not conspicuous (wood semi-ring porous).

Springwood pores visible to the naked eye, decreasing gradually or somewhat abruptly in size toward the outer margin of the ring, solitary and in multiples of 2–3. *Parenchyma* visible with a hand lens, appearing closely and evenly punctate, the lines quite distinct. *Rays* indistinct without a hand lens, storied with the longitudinal elements and forming ripple marks on the tangential surface.

Minute Anatomy.—*Vessels* 5–20 per square millimeter, the largest 120–200 microns in diameter; vessel members storied with the other elements; perforation plates simple; intervessel pits orbicular to broadoval (Fig. 110, page 415), minute (2–4 microns in diameter), the apertures of several frequently confluent. *Parenchyma* paratracheal, metatracheal and terminal, in cambiform rows along the grain which are storied with the other elements; (*a*) paratracheal parenchyma confined to the immediate vicinity of the vessels, the sheath narrow and mostly 1–2-seriate; (*b*) metatracheal parenchyma very abundant, the lines close, 1–2-seriate; (*c*) terminal parenchyma forming a 1–2-seriate line, the cells somewhat larger than those in the body of the ring. *Fibers* relatively thin- to thick-walled, 12–30 microns in diameter, the central portion conforming to the storied structure of the wood. *Rays* storied, 1–3-seriate, homogeneous to heterogeneous.

Remarks.—Characterized by unusually thick-walled vessels, minute intervessel pits the apertures of which are frequently confluent, close narrow lines of metatracheal parenchyma [cells appearing punctate (*x*) at low magnifications], and ripple marks (*t*) traceable to storied wood rays and longitudinal elements. Sometimes confused with hickory (produced by *Carya spp.*) but distinct in possessing minute intervessel pits (those of hickory 6–8 microns in diameter) and ripple marks (*t*).

Uses.—*Shuttles* for textile weaving; *spools; bobbins; golf-club heads* (all these uses are based on the inherent hardness, strength, and toughness of this wood, and its ability to stay smooth under friction); *boxes* and *crates; shoe lasts* (formerly widely used but now largely replaced by less expensive woods, such as maple); *handles.*

Selected References

BETTS, H. S.: Persimmon—American Woods. Forest Service, U.S. Department of Agriculture. 1945.

CUNO, J. B.: Utilization of Dogwood and Persimmon. *U.S. Dept. Agr. Bul.* 1436. 1926.

FLETCHER, W. F.: The Native Persimmon. *U.S. Dept. Agr., Bur. Plant Indus., Farmers' Bul.* 685. 1915.

WHITE ASH AND OREGON ASH

White Ash (*Fraxinus americana* L.), Plate IX, Fig. 53; Plate C, Figs. 307 and 308
Red Ash (*Fraxinus pennsylvanica* Marsh.)
Green Ash [*Fraxinus pennsylvanica* var. *lanceolata* (Borkh.) Sarg.]
Etc.

Oregon Ash (*Fraxinus oregona* Nutt.), Plate IX, Fig. 54; Plate C, Figs. 309 and 310

General Characteristics and Properties.—*Sapwood* nearly white, wide; *heartwood* grayish brown, light brown, or pale yellow streaked with brown; *wood* somewhat lustrous, without characteristic odor or taste, straight-grained, heavy (sp. gr. 0.50–0.55 green, 0.58–0.64 ovendry), hard, strong, stiff, high in shock resistance, with excellent bending qualities, wears smooth with use, works well (above average in most machining characteristics), better than average in nail- and screw-holding ability, intermediate in gluing, shrinks moderately but holds its shape well (even under the action of water), can be kiln-dried rapidly and satisfactorily, not durable under conditions favorable to decay, subject (sapwood) to attack by powder-post beetles. *Growth rings* distinct (wood ring porous). *Springwood pores* large, distinctly visible to the naked eye, forming a band 2–4 pores in width; transition from spring- to summerwood abrupt; *summerwood pores* small, barely visible to the naked eye, solitary and in multiples of 2–3. *Parenchyma* visible with a hand lens in the summerwood, forming a narrow sheath about the pores and frequently uniting them laterally toward the outer margin of the ring. *Rays* not distinct or barely visible to the naked eye.

Minute Anatomy.—*Vessels* 6–15 per square millimeter; largest springwood vessels 150–260 microns in diameter; perforation plates simple; intervessel pits orbicular to short-oval or occasionally somewhat angular through crowding, 3–5 microns in diameter. *Vasicentric tracheids* present, confined to the immediate vicinity of the springwood vessels. *Parenchyma* paratracheal, paratracheal-confluent in the late summerwood, and terminal. *Fibers* thin- to medium thick-walled, 12–22 microns in diameter. *Rays* unstoried, 1–3-seriate, homogeneous.

Remarks.—The woods of red ash (*F. pennsylvanica* Marsh.), green ash [*F. pennsylvanica* var. *lanceolata* (Borkh.) Sarg.], and Oregon ash (*F. oregona* Nutt.) are very similar to that of white ash (*F. americana* L.) and are not distinguished from it in the trade. For separation of white ash and Oregon ash from black ash, see Remarks under the latter, page 610.

Uses.—*Handles* for which it is second only to hickory in importance (the standard wood for shovel, spade, rake, and other long handles,

Plate C

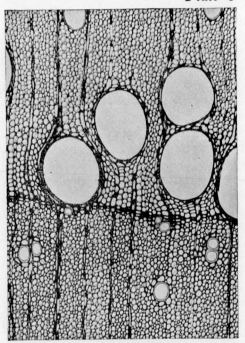

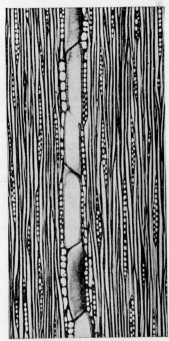

FIG. 307.—(*x*—75 ×)　　　　　FIG. 308.—(*t*—75 ×)

White Ash, *Fraxinus americana* L.

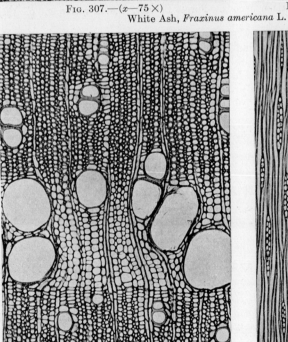

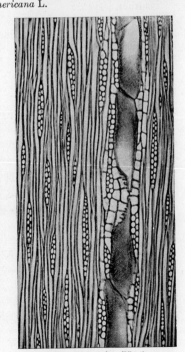

FIG. 309.—(*x*—75 ×)　　　　　FIG. 310.—(*t*—75 ×)

Oregon Ash, *Fraxinus oregona* Nutt.

because of its straightness of grain, stiffness, hardness, strength, moderate weight, good bending qualities, and capacity for wearing smooth in use); *furniture*, especially for bent parts and chair bottoms (it is especially well adapted for the latter use because it can be easily split into thin, but tough and elastic strips); *vehicle parts*, such as poles, shafts, trees, and braces for wagons, and bottom boards; formerly used for frames in automobiles and airplanes; *car construction; sporting* and *athletic goods* (practically all baseball bats and long oars, a considerable number of short oars and paddles, also tennis-racket frames, snowshoes, ski, polo, and hockey sticks, and other sporting goods); *boxes, baskets,* and *crates; refrigerators* and *kitchen cabinets; agricultural implements; planing-mill products* (such as trim, for which old-growth ash is preferred); *ship-* and *boatbuilding; dairy, poultry,* and *apiary supplies; wood pipe; toys; woodenware* and *novelties; sewing machines; cooperage,* principally for slack staves and headings, also for tight staves and headings for butter tubs, and oil and pork barrels (for which its freedom from odor and taste and its good working qualities recommend it very highly).

Selected References

ANON.: The Southern Hardwoods. Southern Hardwoods Producers, Inc., Memphis, Tenn. 1941.

BETTS, H. S.: Ash—American Woods. Forest Service, U.S. Department of Agriculture. 1945.

NEUBRECH, W. LeRoy: American Hardwoods and Their Uses. *Trade Prom. Ser.*, No. 178, Bureau of Foreign and Domestic Commerce, U.S. Department of Commerce. 1938.

PILLOW, M. Y.: Characteristics of Ash from Southern Bottomlands. *South. Lumberman*, Vol. 159 (2009), pp. 131–136. 1939.

STERRETT, W. D.: The Ashes: Their Characteristics and Management. *U.S. Dept. Agr. Bul.* 299. 1915.

———: Utilization of Ash. *U.S. Dept. Agr. Bul.* 523. 1917.

BROWN ASH, BLACK ASH

Fraxinus nigra Marsh.

Plate X, Fig. 56; Plate CI, Figs. 311 and 312

General Characteristics and Properties.—*Sapwood* whitish to light brown, narrow; *heartwood* grayish brown to brown [darker than that of the white ash (*F. americana* L.)], dull; *wood* without characteristic odor or taste, straight-grained, medium heavy (sp. gr. approx. 0.45 green, 0.53 ovendry), medium hard, moderately strong, moderately stiff, high in shock resistance, with excellent bending qualities (in general, black ash ranks below the other commercial ashes in strength properties), splits easily (especially through the springwood zone of the annual increments), average in workability, shrinks considerably, not durable under conditions favorable to decay, subject (sapwood) to attack by powder-post beetles. *Growth rings* distinct (wood ring porous), frequently narrow. *Springwood pores* large, distinctly visible to the naked eye, forming a band 2–4 pores

Plate CI

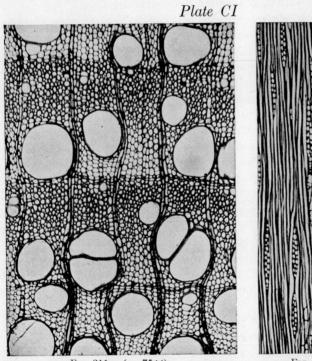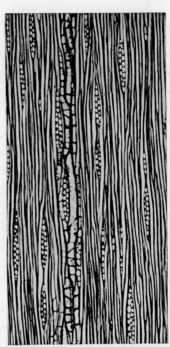

FIG. 311.—(x—75 ×) FIG. 312.—(t—75 ×)
Brown Ash, Black Ash, *Fraxinus nigra* Marsh.

in width; transition from spring- to summerwood abrupt; *summerwood pores* small, barely visible to the naked eye, solitary and in multiples of 2–3, rarely joined laterally by parenchyma in the late summerwood (usually connected by parenchyma in white ash). *Parenchyma* visible with a hand lens, forming a narrow sheath around the pores in the summerwood, rarely uniting them laterally as described above. *Rays* indistinct or barely visible to the naked eye.

Minute Anatomy.—*Vessels* 8–30 per square millimeter; largest springwood vessels 160–260 microns in diameter; perforation plates simple; intervessel pits orbicular to short-oval or occasionally somewhat angular through crowding, 3–6 microns in diameter. *Vasicentric tracheids* present, confined to the vicinity of the springwood vessels. *Parenchyma* paratracheal, rarely paratracheal-confluent in the late summerwood, and terminal; sheath of paratracheal parenchyma around the summerwood vessels uniseriate for the most part; terminal parenchyma fairly abundant, grading into the tissue of the succeeding ring, not forming a distinct line. *Fibers* thin- to fairly thick-walled, 12–22 microns in diameter. *Rays* unstoried, 1–3-seriate, homogeneous.

Remarks.—Black ash intergrades with white ash (various species) and is frequently confused with this timber. Black ash is generally lighter in weight and weaker, and the heartwood is usually of a more decided brown and less lustrous; hence the term "brown ash," which is sometimes used in the trade. The rings are generally narrower in black ash but, in contrast, the porous zone of springwood is usually wider (linear measurement, not in number of pores) and occupies more space in the ring. In black ash, the pores in the outer part of the ring are seldom united by paratracheal-confluent parenchyma, a feature that generally characterizes the white ashes and Oregon ash.

Uses.—The better grades of lumber are used for the same purposes as white ash. "Old-growth" black ash is utilized for *planing-mill* products (such as interior trim) and for *cabinetwork* (frequently preferred to white ash for these purposes because it exhibits a more handsome figure and retains its shape better); *basketmaking* because the wood splits readily through the springwood zone of the annual increments when logs are pounded. Stock for pack baskets, etc., is made in this way by local craftsmen on a number of the Indian reservations.

Selected References

See references under White Ash, page 608.

CATALPA

Northern Catalpa (*Catalpa speciosa* Ward.), Plate VIII, Fig. 44; Plate CII, Figs. 313 and 314

Southern Catalpa (*Catalpa bignonioides* Walt.)

General Characteristics and Properties.—*Sapwood* pale gray, narrow; *heartwood* grayish brown, occasionally with a lavender tinge; *wood* with a faint aromatic, noncharacteristic odor, without characteristic taste, straight-grained, moderately light (sp. gr. approx. 0.38 green, 0.42 ovendry), moderately soft, moderately weak in bending, weak in endwise compression, moderately high in shock resistance, shrinks very little, very durable. *Growth rings* distinct (wood ring porous), generally wide; individual rings often variable in width and the rings then sinuate in contour. *Springwood pores* large, distinctly visible to the naked eye, arranged in a band 3–5 plus pores in width, somewhat lighter in color than the denser summerwood; transition from spring- to summerwood abrupt, or more or

Plate CII

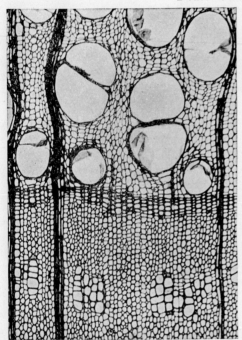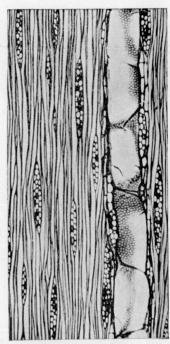

Fig. 313.—(*x*—75 ×)   Fig. 314.—(*t*—75 ×)

Northern Catalpa, *Catalpa speciosa* Ward.

less gradual; *summerwood pores* small, arranged in small groups which are further aggregated into interrupted or continuous concentric bands toward the outer margin of the ring. *Parenchyma* not distinct, or associated with pores and then distinct and zonate toward the outer margin of the ring. *Rays* usually indistinct to the naked eye, plainly visible with a hand lens.

Minute Anatomy.—*Vessels* 8–20 per square millimeter, the largest 160–210 microns in diameter; perforation plates simple; spiral thickening present in the small vessels in the summerwood; intervessel pits orbicular or nearly so, 6–8 microns in diameter. *Parenchyma* paratracheal and paratracheal-zonate, the zonate parenchyma more frequent near the outer margin of the ring and the outermost band not infrequently devoid of vessels. *Fibers* thin, 20–52 microns in diameter. *Rays* unstoried, 1–6 (mostly 2–3)-seriate, homogeneous to heterogeneous.

Uses.—Locally for *fence posts; rails; general construction work; interior finish; cabinetwork; fuel.*

GLOSSARY

aggregate ray: composite structure, consisting of a number of small rays, fibers, and sometimes also vessels, which to the unaided eye or at low magnification appears as a single broad ray.

alburnum: sapwood; the outer (younger) portion of a woody stem (or a log), usually distinguishable from the core (heartwood) by its lighter color; see *duramen*.

aliform parenchyma: type of paratracheal parenchyma that extends out from the flanks of a pore, forming an eyelet with it.

alternate pitting: type of pitting in which bordered pits are arranged in diagonal rows across the cell; when crowded, the pits become polygonal in surface view.

amorphous areas: portions of the cell walls of the higher plants in which the chain molecules of cellulose are not parallel; see *crystallites*.

Ångstrom unit: one hundred-millionth of a centimeter; 10^{-8} cm.

annual growth: layer of wood laid down during a given year; same as annual or seasonal increment; see *seasonal increment*.

annual increment: see *annual growth*.

annual ring: annual increment of wood as it appears on a transverse surface or in a transverse section; same as *growth ring*.

apical growing point: meristematic tissue at the apices of the tree, responsible for elongation of stems and roots.

aspirated bordered pit pair: a bordered pit pair in which the torus is no longer in the medial position.

bark: the tissues in the cylindrical axis of a tree outside of the cambium; bark is composed of inner living bark and outer dead brown bark.

bark pockets: small patches of bark embedded in wood.

bars: remnants of the perforation plate between the openings in scalariform perforations.

Bars of Sanio: same as *crassulae*.

bast fibers: fibers of the secondary phloem.

bird's-eye figure: figure on the plain-sawn and rotary-cut surface of wood exhibiting numerous rounded areas resembling a bird's-eye; caused by local fiber distortions; most common in hard maple.

biseriate ray: ray consisting of two rows of cells, as viewed in the tangential section.

black check: bark pockets containing a certain amount of resin; common in western hemlock; also called *black streak*.

black streak: black streaks in western hemlock [*Tsuga heterophylla* (Raf.) Sarg.] caused by the maggots of a fly.

blind pit: pit leading into an intercellular space between two cells, *i.e.*, a pit without a complementary pit in an adjacent cell.

blister figure: figure on smooth plain-sawn and rotary-cut surfaces that appears to consist of small, more or less widely spaced, elevated, or depressed areas of rounded contour.

bordered pit: pit with an overhanging margin, *i.e.*, a pit in which the cavity becomes abruptly constricted during the thickening of the secondary wall (see Text Fig. 15, B_2).

bound moisture: water in the wood that is found in the cell walls.

bowing: longitudinal warping, flatwise, from a straight line drawn end to end of the piece.

brashness: abnormal condition in wood that causes it to break suddenly and completely across the grain when the piece is bent only a small amount.

broken stripe: figure formed by tapering stripes, 1 foot or more in length, on the quartered surface of an interlocked grained wood.

burl: bulge or excrescence that forms on the trunk and branches of a tree.

cambial initial: individual cell in the cambium.

cambial ray: that portion of a ray included in the cambium.

cambial ray initial: cambial initial that gives rise to ray cells through repeated division; unless the ray consists of a single row of cells (*t*), cambial ray initials are grouped in ray areas; the cells are often isodiametric, as seen in a tangential section.

cambium: growing (generative) layer between the xylem and phloem; a lateral meristem responsible for formation of xylem and phloem.

casehardening: condition in wood that develops as a result of too rapid drying; characterized by a difference in the final set of dry wood, accompanied by stresses in lumber.

cell wall: the wall that encloses the cell contents; in a mature cell it is compound, *i.e.*, it consists of several layers.

cellulose: principal chemical constituent of the cell walls of the higher plants; complex carbohydrate whose empirical formula is $(C_6H_{10}O_5)n$; soluble in acids but resistant to alkalies.

checks: ruptures along the grain that develop during seasoning either because of a difference in radial and tangential shrinkage or because of uneven shrinkage of the tissue in adjacent portions of the wood.

chemical stain: stain that is caused by chemical changes in the materials present in the lumina of xylary cells.

closing membrane: in a bordered pit with a torus, the unthickened portion of the pit membrane around the torus.

coalescent pit apertures: slitlike inner pit apertures of several pits, united to form spiral grooves.

collapse: defect that sometimes develops *above the fiber saturation point* when very wet heartwood of certain species is dried; evidenced by abnormal and irregular shrinkage.

commercial veneers: veneers that are used for the central plies of plywood or in concealed parts of furniture; see *face veneers*.

companion cells: special type of parenchyma cells associated structurally and functionally with sieve tubes in all angiosperms; lacking in pteridophytes and gymnosperms.

compound middle lamella: a term of convenience for the compound layer between the secondary walls of contiguous cells; this layer consists of intercellular substance (the true middle lamella) and the primary walls on each side of it.

compound ray: obsolete term formerly applied to the unusually large wood ray (accompanied by small rays) that is found in certain species of *Quercus*, in *Fagus grandifolia* Ehrh., etc.

compression failures: localized buckling of fibers and other longitudinal elements produced by the compression of wood along the grain beyond its proportional limit; compression failures sometimes develop in standing trees.

compression wood: abnormal wood formed in the lower side of branches and that of leaning tree trunks of all coniferous species; see *tension wood.*

coniferous wood: wood produced by coniferous trees; same as *softwood* or *nonporous wood.*

cortex: that portion of the primary axis of a vascular plant that immediately surrounds the central cylinder (stele); on the outside, it is enveloped by a uniseriate layer—the epidermis (stems) or the exodermis (roots).

crassulae: thicker, generally arching portions of the intercellular layer above and below primary pit fields; formerly called *Bars of Sanio.*

crooking: longitudinal warping, edgewise, from a straight line drawn from end to end of the piece.

cross grain: in standing trees, grain in which the fiber alignment deviates from the vertical; in wooden members, grain in which the fiber alignment deviates from a direction parallel to the long axis of the piece.

cross section: section cut at right angles to the grain; same as *transverse section.*

crotch: segment of a stem that forks.

crystalliferous: bearing crystals.

crystallites: portions of the cell walls of the higher plants in which the chain molecules of cellulose are parallel; see *amorphous areas;* crystallites do not have sharp boundaries.

cupping: warping of the face of a plank or board so that it assumes a troughlike shape, the edges remaining approximately parallel to each other.

cupressoid pit pair: a pit pair of the type occurring between a ray parenchyma cell and a longitudinal tracheid in *Chamaecyparis, Libocedrus,* and *Juniperus* (see Text Fig. 34, *F*).

curly grain: grain that results from more or less abrupt and repeated right and left deviations from the vertical in fiber alignment; the radial split faces of such wood are corrugated, the split tangential faces smooth (see Text Fig. 57).

cutin: the layer of waxy, waterproofing material overlying the epidermis in plants.

defect: any abnormality or irregularity that lowers the commercial value of wood by decreasing its strength or affecting adversely its working or finishing qualities or its appearance.

deliquescent growth: growth in which the trunk divides rather abruptly into limbs.

density of wood: mass of wood per unit of volume.

dentate: toothed; with toothlike projections.

dermatogen: the region of incompletely differentiated tissue between the apical promeristem and the epidermis (stem) or exodermis (root) in the cylindrical axis of a vascular plant.

diagonal grain: type of cross grain resulting from failure to saw tangent to the growth increments.

diamonding: uneven shrinkage that causes "squares" to become diamond-shaped on drying; usually develops in pieces in which the growth increments extend diagonally, so that the faces of the piece are neither flat- nor edge-grained.

diffuse parenchyma: parenchyma the cells of which are scattered in the growth ring.

diffuse-porous wood: porous wood in which the pores exhibit little or no variation in size indicative of seasonal growth; see *ring-porous wood.*

diffuse-zonate parenchyma: parenchyma the cells of which exhibit more or less a tendency toward arrangement in concentric lines or bands in the growth ring.

discontinuous growth ring: growth ring formed on only one side of the stem.

double ring: growth ring that appears to consist of two rings, one of which is a false ring; see *false ring*.

duramen: heartwood; the dead inner core of a woody stem (or a log), generally distinguishable from the outer portion (sapwood) by its darker color; see *alburnum*.

earlywood: that portion of an annual increment which is produced at the beginning of the growing season (in the spring); springwood; see *latewood*.

edge-grained: said of wood so sawn that the radial face of the wood is exposed on the surface of boards; same as *quartersawn*.

encased knot: that portion of a branch which becomes embedded in the bole of a tree after the branch dies; also called *loose knot*.

end checks: seasoning checks that develop on the ends of a piece of wood.

endodermis: the innermost layer of cortex, one cell thick, without intercellular spaces and consisting of cells with suberized or cutinized walls.

enzymes: complex, naturally occurring organic substances of unknown chemical composition that accelerate (catalyze) specific transformations in plants and animals.

epidermis: the outermost, generally uniseriate, layer of primary tissue that is continuous over the younger portions of the aerial part of a plant except where interrupted by stomatal openings; in woody plants, the epidermis ceases to function after a periderm forms beneath it, and is subsequently cast.

epithelial: of the nature of, or pertaining to, epithelium; see *epithelium*.

epithelium: excreting parenchymatous tissue surrounding the cavity of resin and gum canals.

erose: with jagged margin as if gnawed.

excurrent growth: growth in which the axis is prolonged, forming an undivided main trunk, as in pine.

extended pit aperture: inner aperture of a pit that crosses the boundary of the pit annulus, as seen in surface view; see *included pit aperture*.

face veneer: veneer that is used for exposed surfaces in plywood.

false heartwood: pathological heartwood formed in species that do not possess normal heartwood (on the basis of color).

false ring: band of what appears to be summerwood followed outwardly by tissue resembling springwood, which in turn is followed by true summerwood, wholly included within the boundaries of a true ring; see *double ring*.

feather crotch: figure with a design resembling a cluster of feathers, found in crotch veneer.

fiber: an elongated cell with pointed ends and a thick or not infrequently a thin wall; includes (1) *fiber tracheids* with bordered pits and (2) *libriform fibers* with simple pits.

fiber saturation point: point when all water is evaporated from the cell cavities, but the cell walls are still fully saturated with moisture.

fibrils: threadlike components of cell walls requiring special chemical treatment for their demonstration; fibrils are composed of chain molecules of cellulose extending through regions of parallelism (crystallites) and regions of nonparallelism (amorphous regions).

figure: in a broad sense, any design or distinctive markings on the longitudinal surfaces of wood; in a restricted sense, such decorative designs in wood as are prized in the furniture and cabinetmaking industries.

flat-sawn: said of wood so sawed that the tangential face of the wood is exposed on the surfaces of boards; same as *plain-sawn*.

floccosoids: white spots that frequently are present in the wood of western hemlock [*Tsuga heterophylla* (Raf.) Sarg.].

free moisture: water in wood that is found in cell cavities, either in liquid form or as a gas.

frost cracks: radial, longitudinal splits near the base of a tree, formed during extremely cold weather.

frost ring: brownish line extending circumferentially within a growth ring, consisting of collapsed cells and abnormal zones of parenchyma cells; traceable to injury of the cambium or of young, unlignified wood cells by either early or late frost.

fusiform cambial initial: cambial initial that, through repeated division, gives rise to a radially directed row of longitudinal elements of xylem and phloem; such a cell is fusiform in shape; same as longitudinal cambial initial; see *cambial ray initial*.

fusiform parenchyma cell: parenchymatous cell that arises from a longitudinal cambial initial without subdivision, *i.e.*, it has the shape of a short fiber.

fusiform ray: spindle-shaped ray, as viewed in a tangential section of wood, containing a resin canal.

gelatinous fiber: fiber the inner wall of which is more or less gelatinous, or jellylike.

grain of wood: arrangement and direction of alignment of wood elements when considered *en masse*.

growth ring: ring of wood on a transverse surface or in a transverse section, resulting from periodic growth; if but one growth ring is formed during a year it is called an *annual ring*.

grub holes: oval, circular, or irregular holes (⅜ to 1 inch in diameter) in wood, caused by larvae and adult insects.

half-bordered pit pair: a pit pair one pit of which is simple and the other bordered; same as *semibordered pit pair*.

hardwood: wood produced by broad-leaved trees such as oak, elm, and ash; same as *porous wood*.

heart shake: separation of wood across the ring and generally following the rays; also called *heart check* and *rift crack*.

heartwood: dead inner core of a woody stem (or a log), generally distinguishable from the outer portion (sapwood) by its darker color; see *sapwood*.

hemicellulose: group of carbohydrates found in the cell wall in more or less intimate association with cellulose; sometimes defined as those less resistant substances in the cell wall which though insoluble in hot water can be removed with either hot or cold dilute alkalies or readily hydrolyzed into sugars and constituent acids by means of hot dilute acids.

herringbone figure: figure that results when two quartersawn pieces are matched so that the rays meet at an angle.

heterogeneous ray: in the *hardwoods*, a ray consisting of two kinds of cells, *procumbent* and *upright;* in the *softwoods*, a ray consisting of *ray parenchyma* and *ray tracheids*.

heterotropic cell-wall layers: the layers that are different in structure and in properties in different directions.

holocellulose: lignin-free carbohydrate fraction of wood freed of its extraneous materials.

homogeneous ray: a ray consisting entirely of one kind of cell.

honeycombing: internal splitting in wood that develops in drying; caused by internal stresses or by closing of surface checks.

hypodermis: the tissue immediately underlying the epidermis, especially if this is different structurally from tissues deeper in the plant.

incipient decay: initial stage of decay.

included pit aperture: inner aperture of a pit that is included within the boundary of the pit annulus; see *extended pit aperture*.

included sapwood: streaks or irregularly shaped areas of light-colored wood with the general appearance of normal sapwood, found embedded in the darker colored heartwood; common in western red cedar.

inner pit aperture: opening of the pit canal into the cell lumen.

intercellular substance: strongly lignified layer that cements the walls of contiguous cells together; the *true middle lamella*.

intergrown knot: that portion of a branch which is embedded in the tree trunk while this branch is alive; also called *tight knot*.

interlocked grain: grain in which the direction of the fiber alignment alternates at intervals, resulting in ribbon figure when wood is quartersawn.

intervessel pit: bordered pit in a vessel wall complementary to a similar pit in the wall of a contiguous vessel.

isotropic cell-wall layer: the layer that has the same structure and properties in all directions.

kiln brown stain: chemical stain, that develops during kiln drying; see *chemical stain* and *yard brown stain*.

knot: branch base that is embedded in the wood of a tree trunk or of a larger branch.

latewood: that portion of an annual increment which is produced during the latter part of the growing season (during the summer); summerwood; see *earlywood*.

latticed perforation plate: perforation plate with multiple perforations elongated and parallel, with barlike remnants of the plate between the openings; see *scalariform perforation plate*.

lignification: physicochemical process whereby cell walls are rendered harder, presumably by infiltration of certain substances known under the general term of "lignin"; the final phase in the ontogeny of a woody cell.

lignin: one of the principal constituents of woody cell walls whose exact chemical composition is still unknown; soluble in alkalies but resistant to acids.

linear pit: a pit with a greatly elongated, usually transversely oriented orifice.

longitudinal parenchyma: parenchyma extending along the grain, *i.e.*, in the same direction as the vessels and fibers, in contrast to ray parenchyma; usually designated as *parenchyma*.

longitudinal resin canal: resin canal extending with the grain, appearing as an opening or fleck on the transverse surface with the naked eye or hand lens.

longitudinal strand parenchyma: cells of longitudinal parenchyma arranged in a row along the grain; such a row is formed through further (postcambial) division of a single longitudinal cell cut off from a fusiform initial in the cambium.

loose knot: that portion of any branch which is incorporated into the bole of a tree after the death of that branch.

loosened grain: loosened small portions of the wood on the flat-grained surfaces of boards, usually of the tops and edges of the growth increments.

lumen: the cavity of a cell (pl. *lumina*).

marginal cell: cell on the upper or the lower margin of a wood ray, as viewed in the tangential or radial section.

marine borers: mollusks and crustaceans that attack submerged wood in salt and brackish water.

meristem: tissue consisting of living, thin-walled cells that are capable of repeated division.

metatracheal parenchyma: parenchyma in the body of the ring the cells of which are relatively abundant and are loosely grouped into lines or bands; in hardwoods, mostly independent of the vessels.

metatracheal-diffuse parenchyma: parenchyma the cells of which (as seen in a cross section) are widely distributed between the fibrous elements; also called *diffuse parenchyma*.

metaxylem: the primary xylem formed after the differentiation of the protoxylem; primary xylem consists of protoxylem and metaxylem.

micelles: discrete ultramicroscopic particles in the cell walls of the higher plants as postulated by Nägeli.

microscopic checks: minute checks in wood between the fibrils in the secondary walls that cannot be detected without a compound microscope.

middle lamella: see *true middle lamella* and *compound middle lamella*.

mineral stain: olive and greenish-black streaks believed to designate areas of abnormal concentration of mineral matter; common in hard maple, hickory, and basswood; also called *mineral streak*.

mineral streak: see *mineral stain*.

moisture content of wood: the weight of the moisture in wood, expressed as a percentage of its ovendry weight.

monopodial growth: same as *excurrent growth*.

moonshine crotch: swirling figure found in crotch veneer.

multiple perforation: two or more openings in a perforation plate.

multiple ring: growth ring that contains within its boundaries several false rings; see *false ring*.

multiseriate ray: ray consisting of several to many rows of cells, as viewed in the tangential section.

nonporous wood: wood devoid of pores (vessels); same as *softwood* or *coniferous wood*.

ontogeny: the life history or development of an individual organism or of a part thereof; see *phylogeny*.

opposite pitting: type of pitting in which bordered pits are arranged in transverse rows extending across the cell; when crowded, the outlines of the pits become rectangular in surface view.

orifice: mouth or opening, as of a tube or pit; opening; hole.

outer pit aperture: opening of the pit canal into the pit chamber.

ovendry weight: weight of wood obtained by drying it at 100°C. until it has ceased to lose weight, indicating that all the moisture has been driven off.

oxidative stain: nonpathological stain in sapwood caused by chemical changes in the materials contained in the cells of the wood.

paratracheal parenchyma: parenchyma the cells of which are obviously associated with the pores (vessels).

paratracheal-confluent parenchyma: a form of paratracheal parenchyma that extends out laterally from the pores, joining two or more of them together.

paratracheal-zonate parenchyma: same as *paratracheal-confluent parenchyma*.

parenchyma: tissue consisting of short, relatively thin-walled cells, generally with simple pits; concerned primarily with storage and distribution of carbohydrates; used specifically as a synonym for *longitudinal parenchyma* which occurs in strands along the grain; may be visible with a hand lens on the transverse surface of wood as dots, as sheaths about pores, or as broken or continuous lines or bands.

peckiness: rot common to southern cypress and incense cedar; characterized by finger-sized pockets of decay running with the grain; also called *pecky* or *pocket dry rot.*

perforation: the openings (or openings) between two vessel members.

perforation plate: term of convenience for the portion of the wall involved in the coalescence of two vessel members to form a plate that is perforated.

perforation rim: marginal portion of a perforation plate remaining after it has become perforate.

periblem: the region of incompletely differentiated tissue between the apical promeristem and the cortex in the cylindrical axis of a vascular plant.

pericycle: outermost layer of the stele consisting normally of parenchyma but sometimes also of fibers.

periderm: a protective layer that forms in the epidermis, just beneath it, or in deeper lying tissues, after which the epidermis ceases to function.

phellem: outermost layer of periderm, composed of cork cells formed to the outside by the phellogen; see *phellogen.*

phelloderm: innermost layer of periderm composed of cells formed to the inside by the phellogen; see *phellogen.*

phellogen: median layer of periderm from which the phellem and the phelloderm originate by cell division; cork cambium; see *phellem* and *phelloderm.*

phloem: inner bark; principal tissue concerned with the distribution of elaborated foodstuffs, characterized by the presence of sieve tubes.

phloem ray: that portion of a ray included in the phloem.

phylogeny: the evolution of a race or group of organisms; see *ontogeny.*

piciform pit pair: a pit pair of the type occurring between a ray parenchyma cell and a longitudinal tracheid in *Picea, Larix,* and *Pseudotsuga* (see Text Fig. 34, *D*).

pigment figure: figure in wood occasioned by irregular infiltration, resulting in dark lines, bands, zones, streaks, etc.

pinholes: small, round holes ($\frac{1}{100}$ to $\frac{1}{4}$ inch in diameter) in wood that result from the mining of ambrosia beetles and timber worms.

pinoid pit pair: a pit pair of the type occurring between a ray parenchyma cell and a longitudinal tracheid in hard pines other than red pine (see Text Fig. 34, *B* and *C*).

pit: recess in the secondary wall of a cell, with its external closing membrane (middle lamella).

pit annulus: narrowed thickened rim on the margin of the pit membrane.

pit aperture: opening of a pit into a cell lumen or into a pit chamber; see *inner* and *outer pit aperture.*

pit canal: passage from the cell lumen to the chamber in bordered pits.

pit cavity: entire space within a pit from the membrane (middle lamella) to the lumen.

pit chamber: in a bordered pit, the space between the pit membrane (middle lamella) and the overhanging border.

pit field: areas on the radial walls of longitudinal coniferous tracheids bounded above and below by crassulae, containing one or more pits or devoid of pits (see Text Fig. 30, *C*).

pit membrane: that portion of the compound middle lamella which closes a pit cavity externally.

pit orifice: opening or mouth of a pit; same as *pit aperture.*

pit pair: term used to designate the two complementary pits on the walls of contiguous cells (see Text Fig. 17, *A, B, C,* and *D*); formerly interpreted as a single pit.

pitch pocket: lens-shaped opening in the grain at the common boundary of two growth increments, or sometimes within a growth increment, empty, or containing solid or liquid resin; found in certain coniferous woods.

pitch streaks: localized accumulation of resin, which permeates the cells, forming resin-soaked patches or streaks in coniferous woods.

pith: primary tissue in the form of a central parenchymatous cylinder found in stems and sometimes in roots.

pith flecks: small areas of wound tissue darker or lighter than the surrounding tissue, produced in wood through injury to the cambium by the larvae of flies of the genus *Agromyza* and subsequent occlusion of the resulting tunnels with parenchymatous cells.

plain-sawn: said of wood so sawn that the tangential face of the wood is exposed on the surface of boards; same as *flat-sawn*.

plasmodesma: extremely fine strands of protoplasm extending through the cell wall, connecting the protoplasts of adjacent young cells.

plerome: the region of incompletely differentiated tissue between the apical promeristem and the mature stele in the cylindrical axis of a vascular plant.

pore: cross section of a vessel; a vessel as it appears on a transverse surface or in a transverse section of wood.

pore chain: several to many pores arranged in a radial line or series, the adjacent pores retaining their separate identities.

pore cluster: nested pores or an irregular aggregation of pores.

pore multiple: group of two or more pores contiguous radially and flattened along the lines of contact so as to appear as subdivisions of a single pore.

porous wood: wood containing pores (vessels); same as *hardwood, i.e.,* wood produced by broad-leaved trees.

powder-post damage: small holes ($\frac{1}{16}$ to $\frac{1}{2}$ inch in diameter) filled with dry, pulverized wood, resulting from the work of beetles (largely *Lyctus*) in seasoned and unseasoned wood.

primary growth: elongation of the main and secondary axes, in both stems and roots, traceable to the activities of apical growing points.

primary phloem: first-formed phloem derived from an apical meristem.

primary pit field: an area on the cell wall in which the wall is thinner and within the boundary of which one or more pits usually develop; the true middle lamella is thinner in a pit field.

primary tissue: tissue arising from the activities of apical growing points.

primary wall: initial layer of the cell wall; formed during or following cell division and later modified during the postcambial differentiation of the cell; see also *compound middle lamella*.

primary xylem: first-formed xylem which originates from an apical meristem.

procambium: tissue differentiating to the rear of the plerome that is the precursor of the primary vascular tissue around the pith; the procambium may be a continuous layer or may consist of longitudinal strands.

procumbent ray cell: narrow cell elongated in the direction of the ray, of the type that composes *homogeneous rays* and the body of *heterogeneous rays*.

promeristem: meristem in a region of a growing plant body in which the formation of new organs or parts of organs is in progress.

prosenchyma: cells whose functions are mainly conductive and mechanical, generally equipped with bordered pits; see *parenchyma*.

protophloem: first-formed primary phloem.

protoxylem: first-formed primary xylem, with tracheary elements characterized by annular or spiral thickenings.

punctate: dotted with minute spots or depressions.

quartersawn: said of wood so sawn that the radial face of the wood is exposed on the surface of boards.

quarter section: section cut along the grain parallel to the wood rays.

quarter surface: surface that is exposed when a log is cut along the grain in a radial direction (parallel to the wood rays).

quilted figure: blisterlike figure found sometimes in Oregon maple (*Acer macrophyllum* Pursh).

(r): symbol indicating a radial section or surface; see *radial section*.

radial section: section cut along the grain parallel to the wood rays and usually at right angles to the growth rings; see under *tangential section*.

raised grain: roughened condition of the surface of dressed lumber on which the hard summerwood is raised above the softer springwood but is not torn loose from it.

ramiform pits: pits of the type formed by the coalescence of the narrow canals of simple pits as they approach the lumen of the cell; common in stone cells and thick-walled tyloses.

ray: ribbon-shaped strand of tissue extending in a radial direction across the grain, so oriented that the face of the ribbon is exposed as a fleck on the quarter surface; see *wood ray*.

ray crossing: quadrangle formed by the vertical walls of a longitudinal tracheid and the horizontal walls of a ray cell, as viewed in the radial section; a term of convenience used in the description of coniferous woods.

ray fleck: portion of a ray as it appears on the quarter surface.

ray parenchyma: parenchyma included in rays, in contrast to *longitudinal parenchyma* which extends along the grain; see *ray tracheid*.

ray tracheid: cell with bordered pits and devoid of living contents, found in the wood rays of certain *softwoods*.

reaction wood: abnormal wood found in leaning trunks and limbs, both in hardwoods and softwoods; see *compression wood* and *tension wood*.

resin canal: tubular, intercellular space sheathed by secreting cells (epithelium), bearing resin in the sapwood.

resinous tracheid: tracheid containing lumps or amorphous deposits of reddish-brown or black resinous materials.

ribbon figure: figure consisting of changeable (with light) darker and lighter bands, obtained by quartersawing or slicing interlocked grained wood; also called *stripe*.

rift crack: see *heart shake*.

ring-porous wood: porous wood in which the pores formed at the beginning of the growing season (in the springwood) are much larger than those farther out in the ring, particularly if the transition from one to the other type is more or less abrupt; see *diffuse-porous wood*.

ring shake: rupture in wood that occurs between increments or less frequently within an annual growth layer; sometimes called *wind shake*.

ripple marks: striations across the grain on the tangential surface of a wood, occasioned by storied rays or by these and other storied elements.

roe figure: figure formed by short stripes (less than 1 foot in length) on the quartered surface of an interlocked grained wood.

rotary-cut veneer: veneer obtained by rotating a log against a cutting knife in such a way that a continuous sheet of veneer is unrolled spirally from the log.

sap stains: stains in the sapwood caused by wood-staining fungi or by the oxidation of compounds present in the lumina of living cells.

sapwood: outer (younger) portion of a woody stem (or a log), usually distinguishable from the core (heartwood) by its lighter color; see *heartwood*.

scalariform perforation plate: perforation plate with multiple elongated and parallel perforations, with barlike remnants of the plate between the openings; see *latticed perforation plate*.

scalariform pitting: type of pitting in which bordered linear pits are arranged in a ladderlike series.

seasonal increment: layer of wood laid down during a given year; see *annual growth*.

secondary growth: growth traceable to the activities of a lateral cambium; also called *secondary thickening*.

secondary periderms: periderms that form subsequently under the first periderm in trees, resulting in rough bark; see *periderm*.

secondary phloem: part of phloem (inner bark) produced by the cambium.

secondary wall: last-formed (innermost) layer of the cell wall; it varies considerably in thickness, and in its physical and chemical properties; it is stratified and usually pitted.

secondary xylem: wood produced by cambium.

semibordered pit pair: see *half-bordered pit pair*.

semi-diffuse porous wood: wood intermediate between diffuse-porous and ring-porous wood; see *semi-ring porous wood*.

semi-ring porous wood: same as *semi-diffuse porous wood*.

septate fiber: fiber provided with cross walls (septa).

shake: rupture of cells or between cells resulting in the formation of an opening in the grain of the wood; the opening may develop at the common boundary of two rings or within a growth ring.

sieve pitting: sievelike clustered pits in the ends of the narrow tubular processes between disjunctive cells.

sieve plates: thin areas in sieve tubes provided with small openings through which the protoplasts of two adjacent sieve-tube elements are connected.

sieve tube: composite structure found in the phloem of all vascular plants; it is composed of a longitudinal series of sieve-tube elements whose protoplasts are connected by strands of protoplasm extending through small openings in sieve plates.

sieve-tube element: one of the cellular units composing a sieve tube.

silver grain: quartersawn wood with conspicuous, lustrous rays.

simple perforation plate: perforation plate with one rounded opening.

simple pit: pit without a conspicuously overhanging margin (Text Fig. 15, *A2*); see *bordered pit*.

simple ray: small wood ray of the type that accompanies *compound* (oak-type), or *aggregate* rays, as in oak and alder; see *compound ray* and *aggregate ray*.

sliding growth: growth in plants whereby cells in contact enlarge as they mature or undergo rearrangement with respect to one another.

softwood: wood produced by coniferous trees; same as *nonporous wood*.

specific gravity of wood: weight of an ovendry block of wood divided by the weight of an equal volume of water; the specific gravity of wood may be taken under varying conditions of volume (see page 62) and is expressed decimally.

spiral grain: grain in which the fibers are aligned spirally in the standing tree.

spiral thickening: ridgelike thickening on the inner face of the secondary wall, in the form of a spiral.

springwood: that portion of an annual increment or annual ring produced at the beginning of the growing season (in the spring); the inner portion of a growth ring; see *summerwood.*

star shake: heart shake that radiates from the pith.

stele: central core of the cylindrical axis of a vascular plant arising from the further differentiation of the plerome; it consists of pith, primary xylem, cambium, primary phloem, and pericycle.

storied rays: rays arranged in tiers or in echelon, as viewed on a tangential surface or in a tangential section; see *ripple marks.*

straight grain: grain in which the direction of the fiber alignment is straight or nearly so; grain in which the fiber alignment is vertical or nearly so in the standing tree.

strand parenchyma: see *longitudinal strand parenchyma.*

strand tracheids: tracheids in coniferous wood that arise from the further division of a cell which otherwise would have developed into a longitudinal tracheid; differing from the latter in being shorter and having one or both end walls at right angles to the longitudinal walls.

stump wood: bell-shaped base of the tree just above the roots.

substitute fiber: fibrous parenchymatous cell in wood; fibrous cell in wood that remains living while it is a part of the sapwood.

summerwood: that portion of an annual increment or annual ring produced during the latter part of the growing season (during the summer); the outer portion of a growth ring; see *springwood.*

surface checks: seasoning checks that develop on the surface and extend into the wood for varying distances.

swirl crotch: figure obtained from that section of the tree where the typical crotch figure fades into that of normal stem wood.

(*t*): symbol indicating a tangential section or surface; see *tangential section.*

tangential section: section cut along the grain at right angles to the wood rays; see *radial section.*

taxodioid pit pair: a pit pair of the type occurring between a ray parenchyma cell and a longitudinal tracheid in *Sequoia, Taxodium,* and *Abies* (see Text Fig. 34, *E*).

tension wood: abnormal wood formed on the upper side of inclined tree trunks and branches in hardwoods.

terminal parenchyma: parenchyma the cells of which are restricted to the outer face of the annual increment (growth ring); parenchyma terminating annual growth.

texture of wood: expression that refers to the size and the proportional amounts of woody elements; in coniferous woods, the average tangential diameter of the tracheids is the best indicator of texture; in the hardwoods, the tangential diameters and number of vessels and rays.

tight knot: that portion of a branch which is embedded in the tree trunk while the branch is alive; also called *intergrown knot.*

torus: central thickened portion of the pit membrane of a bordered pit.

trabecula: cylindrical, barlike structure extending across the lumen of a tracheid from one tangential wall to the other; trabeculae usually occur in series.

tracheid: fibrous lignified cell with bordered pits and imperforate ends; in coniferous wood, the tracheids are very long (up to 7 plus mm.) and are equipped with large, prominent bordered pits on their radial walls; tracheids in hardwoods are shorter fibrous cells (seldom over 1.5 mm.), are as long as the vessel segments with which they are associated, and possess small bordered pits; see *vascular tracheids* and *vasicentric tracheids*.

transverse resin canals: resin canals extending across the grain that are included in fusiform wood rays.

transverse section: section cut at right angles to the grain; see *cross section*.

traumatic resin canal: resin canal supposedly arising as a result of injury.

true middle lamella: intercellular substance; strongly lignified layer that cements the cell walls of contiguous cells together.

twisting: warping in which one corner of a piece of wood twists out of the plane of the other three.

tyloses: saclike or cystlike structures that sometimes develop in a vessel and rarely in a fiber through the proliferation of the protoplast (living contents) of a parenchymatous cell through a pit pair, the pit membrane forming the wall of the cyst (sing. *tylosis*).

tylosoids: structures in resin canals resembling tyloses in hardwoods; they arise through the proliferation of thin-walled epithelial cells (sing. *tylosoid*).

uniseriate ray: ray consisting of one row of cells, as viewed in the tangential section.

upright ray cell: short, high cell (at least twice the height of an ordinary ray cell), occurring on the margins and frequently in addition on the flanks and in the body of a heterogeneous ray; see *procumbent ray cell*.

vascular plant: plant possessing specialized conducting tissue consisting of xylem and phloem.

vascular tissue: specialized conducting tissue consisting of xylem and phloem.

vascular tracheids: specialized cells in certain hardwoods, similar in shape, size, and arrangement to the small vessel segments but differing from them in being imperforate at the ends; see *vasicentric tracheids*.

vasicentric parenchyma: type of paratracheal parenchyma present in sufficient amount to form a narrow or broad aureole several to many cells in thickness encircling the pore.

vasicentric tracheids: short, irregularly shaped fibrous cells with conspicuous bordered pits; vasicentric tracheids abound in the proximity of the large springwood vessels of certain ring-porous hardwoods; they differ from vascular tracheids not only in shape but in arrangement (they are not arranged in definite longitudinal rows like vascular tracheids); see *vascular tracheids*.

veneer: thin sheet of wood sliced, sawed, or rotary-cut from a log or a flitch.

vessel: composite, and hence articulated, tubelike structure found in porous wood, arising through the fusion of the cells in a longitudinal row through the partial or complete disappearance of the cross walls; see *simple perforation plate* and *scalariform perforation plate*.

vessel member: one of the cellular units entering into the structure of a vessel; also known as a *vessel segment*.

vestured pit: bordered pit with its cavity wholly or partly lined with projections from the overhanging secondary wall.

warping: any distortion in a piece of wood from its true plane that may occur in seasoning.

wavy grain: grain due to undulations in the direction of fiber alignment; when a wavy grained wood is split radially, the exposed surfaces are wavy.

wind shake: see *ring shake*.

windowlike pit pair: a half-bordered pit pair between a ray parenchyma cell and a longitudinal tracheid in certain soft pines, with very wide pit apertures spanned by a thin compound pit membrane which frequently arches into the lumen of the longitudinal tracheid.

wood: xylary portion of fibrovascular tissue.

wood ray: that portion of a ray included in the wood; see *ray*.

wound heartwood: patches of dead sapwood that develop in the vicinity of wounds, *i.e.*, sapwood in which the parenchyma is no longer living; wound heartwood is similar to normal heartwood except in location.

(x): symbol indicating a transverse section or surface made by cutting across the grain at right angles.

xylary ray: that portion of a ray included in the xylem; wood ray; see *ray*.

xylem: principal strengthening and water-conducting tissue of the stems, roots, and leaves of vascular plants, characterized by the presence of tracheary elements; the woody portion of vascular tissue.

yard brown stain: chemical stain that develops during air seasoning or in storage; see *chemical stain* and *kiln brown stain*.

zonate: arranged in concentric lines or bands, as viewed in the transverse section; said of banded *pores* or *parenchyma*.

INDEX

Figures in **boldface** type refer to pages dealing with Descriptions of Woods by Species.

A